The Authors

THELMA G. JAMES is professor of English in the College of Liberal Arts at Wayne State University, Detroit. She is a specialist in folklore and a former president of the American Folklore Society. For many years she has taught courses in "The English Bible as Literature" and in "World Literature," has contributed articles to many journals and reviews, and has lectured widely. She was co-author, with Northcott and Shattuck, of *World Neighbors.*

WALTER R. NORTHCOTT is head of the English Department at Cody High School in Detroit. He has been co-editor of several literature anthologies.

MARQUIS E. SHATTUCK is a former president of the National Council of Teachers of English and a former assistant superintendent of schools in Detroit. A successful textbook author and editor, he has contributed many articles on literature and the teaching of English to leading periodicals.

FREDERICK S. KILEY, assistant professor of English at Trenton State College in New Jersey, formerly taught in the Killingly, Connecticut, public schools. He has contributed book reviews and criticism to *College English* and other journals, and is a columnist for *The English Journal.*

Literature

edited by

THELMA G. JAMES
WALTER R. NORTHCOTT
MARQUIS E. SHATTUCK
FREDERICK S. KILEY

of the World

WEBSTER DIVISION, McGRAW-HILL BOOK COMPANY

ST. LOUIS   NEW YORK   SAN FRANCISCO   DALLAS   TORONTO   LONDON

The editors wish to thank the following for permission to reprint material included in this anthology:

Stewart Alsop and Ralph E. Lapp for "The Strange Death of Louis Slotin," copyright 1954, by Stewart Alsop and Ralph E. Lapp.

G. S. Amundsen for "How I Became an Explorer" from *My Life As an Explorer*, by Roald Amundsen.

Van Wyck Brooks for selections from his article, "Helen Keller," which originally appeared in *Harper's Magazine*.

Brandt & Brandt for "By the Waters of Babylon" from *Selected Works of Stephen Vincent Benét*, Holt, Rinehart and Winston, Inc. Copyright 1937 by Stephen Vincent Benét. Reprinted by permission of Brandt & Brandt.

Whit Burnett and *Story Magazine* for "Indian Business" by Eric Howard from *Story in America, 1933–1934*.

The Clarendon Press, Oxford, for Arthur Waley's translation of "Pretext" by Yakamochi, from *Japanese Poetry* by Arthur Waley.

Thomas Y. Crowell Company for Chapter XXI from *My Heart Lies South* by Elizabeth Borton de Treviño. Copyright 1953, Elizabeth Borton de Treviño.

Crown Publishers, Inc., for "Funeral of a Whale" by J. Benibengor Blay from *An African Treasury* by Langston Hughes. Copyright 1960 by Langston Hughes. By permission of Crown Publishers, Inc.

The Curtis Publishing Company for "Stopover In Querétaro" by Jerrold Beim. Reprinted by permission of Constance Smith Associates.

Joan Dash for her "You Say 'Tomahto' and We Ask For 'Sneakers'" from *The Guardian Weekly*.

Bertha Klausner and Robert Payne for translations of two Chinese poems from *The White Pony*, ed. Robert Payne, the John Day Company.

The John Day Company for Lin Yutang's translation of "The Tiger," © 1948, 1951, 1952 by Lin Yutang. Reprinted from *Famous Chinese Short Stories* by Lin Yutang.

The Devin-Adair Company, Inc., for "The End of a Good Man" from *The Man Who Invented Sin* by Sean O'Faolain, published by and copyright 1948 by The Devin-Adair Company, Inc.

George Dillon for his translation of "The Albatross" from *Flowers of Evil*, translated by Edna St. Vincent Millay and George Dillon, Harper & Brothers.

Dodd, Mead & Company for "Street Cries" by Sarojini Naidu from *The Sceptred Flute* by Sarojini Naidu.

Doubleday & Company, Inc. for "Four Years in a Shed" from *Madame Curie* by Eve Curie. Copyright 1937 by Doubleday & Company, Inc.; for "The

Knives" by Valentine Kataev, translated by Basil Creighton, from *Tellers of Tales* by W. Somerset Maugham. Copyright 1939 by Doubleday & Company, Inc.; for "The Silver Mine" from *The Girl from the Marsh Croft* by Selma Lagerlöf. Copyright 1910 by Doubleday & Company, Inc.; for "Friends in San Rosario" from *Roads of Destiny* by O. Henry. All reprinted by permission of Doubleday & Company, Inc.

E. P. Dutton & Co., Inc., for "The Nefarious War" from *The Works of Li Po* translated by Shigeyoshi Obata. Copyright, 1922, renewal, 1950, by E. P. Dutton & Co., Inc. By permission of the publishers.

Faber & Faber, Ltd., for permission to reprint in Canada "The Unknown Citizen" from *The Collected Poetry of W. H. Auden*.

Farrar, Straus & Cudahy, Inc., for "The Petition." Reprinted from *Don Camillo and His Flock* by Giovanni Guareschi. Copyright © 1952 by Giovanni Guareschi; for "The Snake and the Crocodile." Reprinted from *The Dark Child* by Camara Laye. Copyright © 1944 by Camara Laye. Both reprinted by permission of Farrar, Straus & Cudahy, Inc.

Angel Flores for his translation of "The Sorrel Colt" from *Spanish Stories*, published by Bantam Books, Inc.; and for Claire Noyes's translation of "Who Knows?" from *19th Century French Tales*, published by Anchor Books, Doubleday & Company, Inc.

Editions Gallimard, Paris: for permission to use a selection from Marguerite Yourcenar's *Présentation critique de Constantin Cavafy* as basis of the translation of "Waiting for the Barbarians."

Grove Press, Inc., and George Allen & Unwin, Ltd., London, for permission to use Arthur Waley's translation of "The Dwarf Trees" as the basis for the adaptation printed in this volume. Mr. Waley's version appears in *The Nō Plays of Japan*, published by the Grove Press, Inc.

Harcourt, Brace & World, Inc., for "Leeuwenhoek" from *Microbe Hunters*, copyright, 1926, 1953, by Paul de Kruif; for "Shooting an Elephant" from *Shooting an Elephant* by George Orwell, copyright, 1945, 1946, 1949, 1950, by Sonia Brownell Orwell; for "Jazz Fantasia" from *Smoke and Steel* by Carl Sandburg, copyright, 1920, by Harcourt, Brace & World, Inc., renewed, 1948, by Carl Sandburg. All reprinted by permission of Harcourt, Brace & World, Inc.

Harper & Brothers for "Shark Close-Ups" and "Epilogue" from *The Silent World* by Captain J.-Y. Cousteau with Frédéric Dumas. Copyright 1953 by Harper & Brothers; and for selections from *The Savage My Kinsman* by Elisabeth Elliot. Copyright

1961, by Elisabeth Elliot. All reprinted by permission of Harper & Brothers.

William Heinemann, Ltd., for permission to reprint in Canada: "Street Cries" from *The Sceptred Flute* by Sarojini Naidu.

Professor Harold G. Henderson for permission to reprint eleven haiku from *An Introduction to Haiku*, published by Doubleday & Company, Inc.

Thor Heyerdahl for his article, "Kon-Tiki," which originally appeared in *Natural History Magazine*. Reprinted by permission of the author.

Holiday House, Inc., for sections from "The Runaway General, Gilbert du Motier, Marquis de Lafayette" from *Teenagers Who Made History* by Russell Freedman, through arrangement with Holiday House, Inc.

Holt, Rinehart and Winston, Inc., for "Fire and Ice" and "Stopping by Woods on a Snowy Evening" from *You Come Too* by Robert Frost. Copyright 1923 by Holt, Rinehart and Winston, Inc. Copyright renewed 1951 by Robert Frost; and for seven lines from "Two Tramps in Mud Time," a much longer poem, from *Complete Poems of Robert Frost*. Copyright 1936 by Robert Frost. All reprinted by permission of Holt, Rinehart and Winston, Inc.

Sr. Francisco H.-Pinzón Jiménez for permission to translate "Yellow Spring" by Juan Ramón Jiménez.

Eugene M. Kayden for his translation of Pasternak's "Hamlet." All rights reserved.

Alfred A. Knopf, Inc., for "Christmas in a Concentration Camp" from *Child of Our Time* by Michel Del Castillo. Copyright 1958 by Peter Green; for "The Guest" from *Exile and the Kingdom* by Albert Camus. Copyright 1957, 1958 by Alfred A. Knopf, Inc.; and for "The Hussar" by Hebel, from *German Stories and Tales*, edited by Robert Pick. Copyright 1954 by Alfred A. Knopf, Inc. All reprinted by permission of Alfred A. Knopf, Inc.

Little, Brown and Company for "The Wonderful Cabbages of Mutahwie Ben Ali Ben Sassie El Nasee" from *Point Four Assignment* by Russell G. Davis and Brent K. Ashabranner. Copyright 1959 by Russell G. Davis and Brent K. Ashabranner. By permission of Little, Brown and Company.

Little, Brown and Company, and the *Atlantic Monthly Press* for passages from *Christopher Columbus, Mariner* by Samuel Eliot Morison. Copyright 1942, 1955 by Samuel Eliot Morison; and for "Saudin's Visit to America" from *Land Below the Wind* by Agnes Newton Keith. Copyright 1939 by Agnes Newton Keith. Both reprinted by permission of Little, Brown and Company, and the *Atlantic Monthly Press*.

MacGibbon & Kee for permission to reprint in Canada "Eraser's Dilemma" from *Ways of Sunlight* by Samuel Selvon.

The Macmillan Company, New York, for "The Man He Killed" from *The Collected Poems of Thomas Hardy*. Copyright 1925 by The Macmillan Company; for "The Monkey" from *A Treasury of Russian Verse*, ed., Avrahm Yarmolinsky. Copyright 1949 by The Macmillan Company; for "The Home" from *Collected Poems and Plays of Rabindranath Tagore*. Copyright 1915, 1941, by The Macmillan Company; for "My Lord, the Baby" from *The Hungry Stones and Other Stories* by Rabindranath Tagore, translated by C. F. Andrews. Copyright 1916 by The Macmillan Company; for "An Irish Airman Foresees His Death" from *The Collected Poems of W. B. Yeats*. Copyright 1919 by The Macmillan Company. Copyright 1946 by Bertha Georgie Yeats; for "For Anne Gregory" from *The Collected Poems of W. B. Yeats*. Copyright 1933 by The Macmillan Company. Copyright 1961 by Bertha Georgie Yeats; for "Imitated from the Japanese" from *The Collected Poems of W. B. Yeats*. Copyright 1933 by The Macmillan Company. Copyright 1961 by Bertha Georgie Yeats; and for "My Fiftieth Year" ("Vacillation, IV") from *The Collected Poems of W. B. Yeats*. Copyright 1940 by Bertha Georgie Yeats. All reprinted by permission of The Macmillan Company.

Macmillan & Co., Ltd., London, The Macmillan Co. of Canada, Limited, and the Trustees of the Hardy Estate, to reprint in Canada "The Man He Killed" from *The Collected Poems of Thomas Hardy*.

Macmillan & Co., Ltd., London, The Macmillan Co. of Canada, Limited, and the Trustees of the Tagore Estate for permission to reprint in Canada "The Home" from *Collected Poems and Plays of Rabindranath Tagore;* and for "My Lord, the Baby" from *The Hungry Stones and Other Stories*.

The Macmillan Co. of Canada Limited, A. P. Watt and Son, and Mrs. W. B. Yeats for permission to reprint in Canada "An Irish Airman Foresees His Death," "For Anne Gregory," "Imitated from the Japanese," and "My Fiftieth Year" ("Vacillation, IV") from *The Collected Poems of W. B. Yeats*.

McGraw-Hill Book Company, Inc., for a selection from *The Odyssey of Homer, Translated into English Verse by Herbert Bates*. Copyright, 1929, by the McGraw-Hill Book Company, Inc. Copyright renewed 1957 by Chaloner Bates.

The Honorable Luis Muñoz Marin for his "Pamphlet." Printed by permission of the author.

Harold Matson Company for "The Snob" by Morley Callaghan. Copyright 1934 by Morley Callaghan.

W. Somerset Maugham for permission to reprint in Canada Basil Creighton's translation of "The Knives" by Valentine Kataev, from *Tellers of Tales*.

John Murray (Publishers), Ltd., London, and the Trustees of the Estate of Sir Arthur Conan Doyle for permission to reprint in Canada "The Adventure of the Bruce-Partington Plans" from *His Last Bow* by Sir Arthur Conan Doyle.

Natural History Magazine for the Foreword to Thor Heyerdahl's article, "Kon-Tiki," by the editors of *Natural History Magazine*.

New Directions and Professor Francisco García Lorca for "Rider's Song," "The Balcony," and "Gypsy Funeral" from *The Selected Poems of Federico García Lorca*. Spanish texts: Copyright 1955 by New Directions; "Taking Leave of a Friend," "The River-Merchant's Wife," "Ballad of the Mulberry Road," and "Song of the Bowmen of Shu" translated by Ezra Pound from *Personae: The Collected Poems of Ezra Pound*. Copyright 1926 1954, by Ezra Pound; for "The Use of Force" from *Make Light of It* by William Carlos Williams. Copyright © 1961 by New Directions; and for "The Wizard" by A. S. Yakolev from *New Russian Stories*, translated and edited by B. G. Guerney. All rights reserved. All reprinted by permission of New Directions, Publishers.

W. W. Norton & Company, Inc., and Insel-Verlag for permission to print translations of "Autumn" and "Solemn Hour" from *Das Buch Der Bilder* by Rainer Maria Rilke.

Harold Ober Associates, Incorporated, for "The Enemy" by Pearl Buck, originally published in *Harper's Magazine*. Copyright, © 1942, by Pearl S. Buck. Reprinted by permission of Harold Ober Associates, Incorporated.

Oxford University Press, London, for "A Conversation Among Wealthy People" from *The Death of Ivan Ilych* by Leo Tolstoy, translated by Alymer Maude. Reprinted by permission of the publisher.

G. P. Putnam's Sons for Chapter 18, "The Dream Comes True." Reprinted by permission of G. P. Putnam's Sons from *Tiger of the Snows* by Tenzing Norgay & James Ramsey Ullman. Copyright © 1955 by Tenzing Norgay & James Ramsey Ullman.

Random House, Inc., for "The Unknown Citizen" by W. H. Auden. Copyright 1940 by W. H. Auden, reprinted from *The Collected Poetry of W. H. Auden;* and for "Barua a Soldani." Copyright © 1960 by Isak Dinesen, reprinted from *Shadows on the Grass*, by Isak Dinesen. All reprinted by permission of Random House, Inc.

William H. and Mary M. Roberts, and the New American Library of World Literature, Inc., for permission to reprint selections from William H. and Mary M. Roberts' translation of *Platero and I* by Juan Ramón Jiménez.

John D. Rockefeller, 4th, for his "Students of Japan: An Intimate Glimpse" from *The New York Times Magazine*. Reprinted by permission of the author.

Nicholas G. Rutgers for "His Mother's People" from *Faery Lands of the South Seas* by Charles B. Nordhoff and James N. Hall.

The Ryerson Press, Toronto, for "Indian Reservation: Caughnawaga." Reprinted from *The Rocking Chair and Other Poems* by A. M. Klein; and for "Bangkok." Reprinted from *Events and Signals* by F. R. Scott. Both by permission of The Ryerson Press, Toronto.

St Martin's Press, Inc., for "Eraser's Dilemma" from *Ways of Sunlight* by Samuel Selvon. Reprinted by permission of St Martin's Press, Inc.

Charles Scribner's Sons for "The Beggar" from *Stories of Russian Life* by Anton Chekov, translated by Marian Fell. Copyright 1914 Charles Scribner's Sons; renewal copyright 1942 Olivia Fell Vans Agnew; for the selection from *Green Hills of Africa*, pp. 217–222, by Ernest Hemingway. Copyright 1935 Charles Scribner's Sons; for "Richard Cory" from *The Children of the Night* by Edwin Arlington Robinson; and for the Foreword from *A Book Lover's Holidays in the Open*, pp. vii–x, by Theodore Roosevelt. Copyright 1916 Charles Scribner's Sons; renewal copyright 1944 Edith K. Carow Roosevelt. All reprinted by permission of Charles Scribner's Sons.

Martin Secker & Warburg, Ltd., for permission to reprint in Canada "Shooting an Elephant" by George Orwell.

Simon and Schuster, Inc., for Indro Montanelli's "His Excellency" from *Modern Italian Short Stories*, edited by Marc Slonim. Copyright 1954 by Marc Slonim; and for "The Monster" from *Of Men and Music* by Deems Taylor. Copyright 1937 by Deems Taylor.

The Society of Authors as the Literary Representative of the Estate of the late W. W. Jacobs, for "The Monkey's Paw" by W. W. Jacobs.

The Society of Authors for permission to reprint in Canada George Bernard Shaw's *Arms and the Man*.

Jaime Torres Bodet for permission to print a translation of his poem "The Window."

Verlag Ullstein GMBH for "Duel with Guynemer" from *Ace of the Black Cross* by Ernst Udet. By permission of Verlag Ullstein GMBH, Frankfurt/M–Berlin, © 1935 by Deutscher Verlag, Berlin.

The Viking Press, Inc., for "The Sleeper of the Valley" by Rimbaud, from *The Poets of Modern France*, translated by Ludwig Lewisohn. Copyright 1918 by B. W. Huebsch, 1946 by Ludwig Lewisohn and for "The Oyster" from *Mooltiki* by Rumer Godden, Copyright 1941 by Rumer Godden. Originally published in *The New Yorker* Magazine. Both by permission of The Viking Press, Inc.

Ives Washburn, Inc., for "Language of Oxen" from *No Garlic in the Soup* by Leonard Wibberley.

Mary Yost Associates for "The Adventure of the Bruce-Partington Plans" from *His Last Bow* by Sir Arthur Conan Doyle. Reprinted by permission of the Estate of Sir Arthur Conan Doyle.

Marguerite Yourcenar and Grace Frick for permission to reprint Miss Frick's English version of Miss Yourcenar's French translation of C. P. Cavafy's "Waiting for the Barbarians."

The translations of the following selections were prepared especially for this anthology, and are copyright © 1963 by the McGraw-Hill Book Company, Inc.: Cervantes, selections from *Adventures of Don Quixote*; Seami Motokiyo, *The Dwarf Trees*, based on the translation by Arthur Waley; Heine, "Pine Tree and Palm Tree"; Juan Ramón Jiménez, "Yellow Spring"; Federico García Lorca, "Rider's Song," "The Balcony," and "Gypsy Funeral"; Victor Hugo, "June Nights"; Simonides, "Inscription for the Grave of a Dog"; La Fontaine, "The Fox and the Crow"; Villon, "Ballad of the Hanged Men," revised from the translation by Andrew Lang; "The Inscription at Thermopylae"; Saadi, "Advice"; "Life Is a Dream" from Calderón de la Barca, *La Vida Es Sueño;* Lope de Vega, "Tomorrow," revised from the translation by Longfellow; Saadi, "The Legend of the King and the Peasant," revised from the translation by James Ross; Rainer Maria Rilke, "The Solemn Hour" and "Autumn"; Jaime Torres Bodet, "The Window."

Credits for photographs, by page numbers: The Bettmann Archive, 12, 35, 91, 109, 141, 154, 162, 257, 342, 459, 482; Sheldon A. Brody, 399; Continental Distributing, Inc., 65; Ewing Galloway, 81 and 349; French Government Tourist Office, 362; Philip Gendreau, N.Y., 16, 21, 264, 299, 381, 408; Rapho-Guillumette Pictures, 424 (Marc and Eveyne Bernheim) and 431 (Ylla); National Gallery of Art, Washington, D.C., 126 (Chester Dale Collection); New York Public Library Theater Collection, 448; Northern Pacific Railroad, 50; Pan American World Airways, 377; Sovfoto, 388; Spanish National Tourist Agency, 452; Swedish National Travel Office, 27; United Nations, 355, 415, 443; U.P.I., 147, 272, 308, 321, 326; World Wide Photos, 86.

Preface

This is a completely new anthology reflecting the best literature of both the Western and non-Western worlds. The book supplies students and teachers with material for a wide-ranging study of styles, periods, ideas, and cultures. Together with many landmarks of world literature, we have included a high proportion of selections here first presented in a textbook. Many of these selections are not, in fact, easily available for classroom study in any other form. Although the classical ages of Greece, Rome, China, Spain, Japan, and other civilizations are amply represented, the table of contents, in which approximately half of the selections date from the twentieth century, truly represents the times we live in.

Particular care has been taken to provide modern, readable translations. We feel strongly that the use of antiquated translations remains one of the greatest stumbling blocks to the enjoyment of literature from other cultures. Many of the translations were prepared especially for this volume.

Most of the selections are printed in their complete and original forms. The few excerpts from longer works, such as the passages from *Don Quixote*, the *Odyssey*, and Hemingway's *Green Hills of Africa*, can be read independently. The book avoids "snippets," that is, masterpieces presented in brief cuttings which are difficult to enjoy apart from their contexts.

The selections have been grouped in nine teaching units, according to literary type and according to theme.

There are two units on the short story:

Stories and Tales from the Past and *Stories of the Twentieth Century*. The former displays the range of the story from works close to legends and folktales ("The Tiger," "The Silver Mine," "The Father," and "The Hussar") to the more realistic and complex work of the nineteenth-century masters Maupassant and Chekhov. The second unit brings together seven examples of the contemporary short story.

Biography and Autobiography is an attempt to show something of the great range in point of view open to the biographer. For example, we deliberately chose Deems Taylor's acid sketch of Wagner, "The Monster," so that it might be compared with the more judicious and scholarly writing in such a piece as Morison's "Christopher Columbus, Mariner." Del Castillo's "Christmas in a Concentration Camp" is an example of a common type of literature often neglected in textbooks—the lightly fictionalized autobiography.

The fourth unit, *Drama*, contains two complete plays, Shaw's *Arms and the Man* and Seami Motokiyo's nōh play, *The Dwarf Trees*. These contrasting works give the student an opportunity to compare the dramatic conventions of the Western and the Eastern stage.

The selection of *Poetry* spans a wide range of authors, periods, and styles. To point out how poets in all ages have concerned themselves with the same major subjects, the poems are arranged in thematic groups: love, nature, war, death, and several others.

Of the remaining four units, three examine themes which play a large role in the world's literature: *Adventure*, from Homer to the atomic age; *Meetings of Cultures*, in which conflicts are sometimes resolved and sometimes not; and *No Man Is an Island*, examining the concept of the brotherhood of man. *People and Places* is a series of glimpses at ways of life in many parts of the world.

There are general introductions to each of the units as well as introductory notes to each selection—notes which we hope will whet the reader's interest and give him any information he may need for enjoyment of the piece. The questions "For Discussion" emphasize literary analysis through close reading.

We kept in mind these questions as we selected the readings to be included in this anthology: Does the selection, in content or form or in both, offer some feature worth studying and worth teaching? Does the selection provide a window on literature as well as a window on the modern world? Will the reading be accessible even to those who are still being introduced to serious writing?

From our own experience as teachers, we have chosen readings which have a direct appeal to students, selections that reflect the questions with which students are concerned, and which introduce them to the great issues to which writers of all ages have addressed themselves.

Naturally, not each selection struck the same sparks of enthusiasm from each editor. It would be a bland book indeed in which each selection was of equal interest to every reader. We preferred to make a book compounded of individual enthusiasms and one which did not turn away from the realities of life as reflected in the work of good authors. This book, we said, must have a character of its own. We hope that the tastes and enthusiasms of our readers will correspond with ours.

In order to present a page which is inviting to the eye, we have avoided heavily footnoting the selections. References which might become problems for most readers are explained in footnotes, but we expect the reader occasionally to refer to his dictionary. A pronouncing glossary of all foreign names and phrases is included at the end of the book.

Our thanks are due to many who have read the selections and contributed suggestions. Miss Betty Binns designed the book. Mr. Thomas E. Kennelly, High School Principal, American School, Chicago, helped to shape the book from its inception, and has reviewed portions of the manuscript at several stages.

The book provides readings for classes in modern literature, world literature, humanities, and general introductions to literature.

It is the hope of the editors of this book of readings by distinguished writers from many lands that they have provided teachers and students with a rich supply of materials for classes in modern literature, world literature, humanities, and general introductions to literature.

THELMA G. JAMES
WALTER R. NORTHCOTT
MARQUIS E. SHATTUCK
FREDERICK S. KILEY

Contents

UNIT 1: Stories and Tales from the Past

UNIT 2: Stories of the Twentieth Century

UNIT 3: Biography and Autobiography

UNIT 4: *Drama*

UNIT 5: *Poetry*

UNIT 8: *People and Places*

UNIT 9: *No Man Is an Island*

HENRI DE TOULOUSE-LAUTREC

The Procession of the Rajah

(Collection of Mr. and Mrs. André Meyer)

UNIT I: STORIES AND TALES FROM THE PAST

Every man is a storyteller.

The father at the dinner table gives an enthusiastic account of something that happened during his day's work. In doing so, he reenacts a ritual that took place around the campfire after the hunt hundreds of centuries ago. A mother describes her first dance. Her daughter listens and begs for details, delighted by the image of her mother as a girl. A boy describes a two-alarm fire. A child bursts into the kitchen, impatient to tell that he has just learned to roller-skate. All are engaged in the art of story-telling, though they are not aware of the intricate process involved in organizing the chaos of their experience into a meaningful narrative pattern.

The father wants his family to understand how important he is at the office. He selects details that convey this impression. The mother talks about herself as a means of instructing her daughter. She gives greater emphasis to the parts of her story that serve as a lesson. The boy wants his listeners to share in the excitement of the fire. He dwells on the noise, the action, the destruction, the heroism of the firemen. The child sees only victory in his accomplishment. He forgets to mention how many times he tumbled.

Storytelling springs from a basic need in man: the need to express the mysteries of existence. Man wants to find the significance of his activities and to put order into his surroundings. Before written language was invented, men chipped pictures into the walls of caves to relate life's excitement, grief, nobility, and comedy.

Today, we can still read stories that amused Egyptians in 6000 B.C. The fables told by the Greek slave Aesop are familiar to all of us. Christ used stories to make his sermons clear. Ovid's tales of pagan gods and goddesses continue to enjoy popularity among modern readers. Chaucer's *Canterbury Tales* make the medieval Englishman forever modern. And as our lives become more and more complicated in a technological civilization, new stories appear, dramatizing our confusion and helping us find the values we must live by.

The story was not invented by literary men. Rather, serious writers recognized how basic the story was to a human exchange of ideas. They took up the story as a form through which they might reach a wide audience. Grad-ually, short-story writers became interested in the nature of the form itself. Edgar Allan Poe was one of the first writers who discussed the short story as an independent type of literature. He defined it as a work of fiction that could be read at one sitting and that contained elements all of which contributed toward a single effect.

Poe's own classic stories, such as "The Pit and the Pendulum" and "The Cask of Amontillado," are filled with strange characters in bizarre and ghostly predicaments. Later, Anton Chekhov, the Russian playwright and story writer, developed the short story into a more realistic presentation of character. Chekhov's people are usually ordinary men in commonplace situations. No two approaches to the form of the short story could be more different than those of Poe and Chekhov. Yet both are great story writers. The same reader may find both equally entertaining, for the short story does not have to follow any single set of literary principles. More important are the author's insight into life, his dramatic sense of selection, and the way in which he handles language.

The variety of the fiction in this book indicates the great range of the short story. Here are tragedy, comedy, irony, and pathos—all reflecting insight into the puzzle of human experience. Like the small boy telling about a two-alarm fire, Tagore, Chekhov, Maupassant, Li Fu Yen, and Cervantes—all of whom are represented in these stories and tales from the past—have organized their visions of reality into a narrative design.

The writers of the stories in this first section were born on four continents and wrote in nine languages. By their art they reveal something of men in all countries and in all centuries. This timelessness is the quality that makes the difference between the dinner-table anecdote and great storytelling.

Who Knows?

GUY DE MAUPASSANT

This tale by the great nineteenth-century French storyteller, Maupassant, may remind the reader of the work of Edgar Allan Poe. Like Poe's "Cask of Amontillado" and "Tell-Tale Heart," this story explores a haunted mind. Through the atmosphere of hallucination, and through the revealing voice of the speaker, Maupassant probes into the mysterious machinery of a troubled man. Two stories travel side by side in the narrative of "Who Knows?" One is the story that the speaker tells; the other is the one he tries to hide, even from himself. By the time the reader has finished the story, he knows more about the speaker than the speaker knows about himself. This ironic approach gives the weird story a double significance. To the speaker the events represent the unfathomable mystery that has victimized him; to the reader they symbolize the pit of despair that the speaker has dug for himself.

THANK GOD! At last I shall write what happened! But can I? Do I dare? It is so fantastic, so inexplicable, so incomprehensible, so mad!

If I were not sure of what I saw, sure that there was no flaw in my reasoning, no error in my conclusions, no gap in the inflexible sequence of my observations, I should believe myself simply subject to hallucinations, the victim of a strange vision. After all, who knows?

Today I am in a sanatorium,[1] but I entered voluntarily, out of prudence, or was it fear?

One man alone knows my story, the house doctor. Now I shall set it all down, I don't know quite why. Perhaps to unburden myself of the thing inside me that haunts me like some dreadful nightmare. Anyhow, here it is.

I have always been a recluse, a dreamer, a kind of philosopher, detached and kindly, satisfied with little, harboring no bitterness against men and no grudge against heaven. I have always lived alone, because a kind of uneasiness seizes me in the presence of others. How can I explain it? I cannot. It's not that I shun society. I enjoy chatting or dining with my friends but when I feel them near me for any length of

---

[1] *sanatorium* Here, an establishment for treating nervous or mental diseases.

3

GUY DE MAUPASSANT (*1850–1893*) *is one of the master craftsmen of the short story. Born in Normandy, he did much of his work in Paris and enjoyed great popular success during his lifetime. He worked intensely and produced a great deal (including much work of inferior quality) to earn money to support elaborate tastes. For his subjects he often chose people who seem to linger on the fringes of society and sanity, people who possessed the appeal of oddity.*

The swift, concise narrative, the realistic details, the quick revelation of the mind that hides behind the words the mouth speaks—all indicate the accomplished craftsmanship in Maupassant's work. Disciplined by limited newspaper space and by the necessity to arouse and sustain a casual reader's interest, he refined the art of storytelling and was widely imitated by later writers. Toward the end of his short life, he became preoccupied with morbid states of mind. The stories written during this period reflect his gloomy speculations about the twisted patterns that disturbed human beings make of their lives.

During his short career Maupassant produced over three hundred short stories and six novels. His two most famous stories, each of which has been reprinted hundreds of times, are "A Piece of String" and "The Necklace."

---

a fainting spell? Of course, probably only a fainting spell.

I am so fond of being alone that I cannot even endure the nearness of others sleeping under my roof; I cannot live in Paris because living there is for me a constant agony. I die inside, and for me it is both physical and nervous torture to sense this huge swarming crowd, breathing around me even in their sleep. Ah! The sleep of others is even more painful to me than their speech. And I can never rest, when I know or feel that there are other beings, on the other side of the wall, who suffer this nightly suspension of consciousness.

Why am I this way? Who knows? Perhaps the reason is quite simple: I tire very quickly of anything outside myself. There are many people like me.

There are two kinds of people. Those who need others, who are distracted, amused, soothed by company, while loneliness assails, exhausts, and destroys them, as would the ascent of a terrible glacier or the crossing of the desert. And those who, on the contrary, are worried, bored, irritated, and cramped, by contact with others, while solitude gives them peace and rest in the freedom and fantasy of their thoughts.

It is, in fact, a recognized psychological phenomenon. The former are meant to live the life of the extrovert; the latter, that of the introvert. In my own case, my attention to outward things is brief and quickly exhausted, and, when it reaches its limits, I am conscious of an unbearable physical and mental discomfort.

The result has been that I am, or rather was, very much attached to inanimate objects, which take on for me the importance of human beings, and that my house has, or rather had, become a world in which I lived a lonely but active life, surrounded by things, furniture, and ornaments that I knew and loved like friends. I had gradually filled my life with them, and embellished it with them, and felt content and satisfied, happy as in the arms of a loving woman whose

time, even the most intimate, I get bored, tired, unnerved, and feel a growing, obsessive desire to have them leave me to myself, to be alone.

This desire is more than a need, it is an irresistible necessity. And if I were to be forced to remain with people, if I had to give lengthy attention to their conversation, something would happen. What? Ah! Who knows? Possibly only familiar caress has become a calm and gentle need.

I had had this house built in a beautiful garden that separated it from the roads, not far from a town, where I could enjoy the social amenities, of which I felt the need from time to time. All my servants slept in a building at the far end of a walled kitchen garden. In the silence of my house, hidden as it was and buried under the foliage of tall trees, the enveloping darkness of the nights was so restful and welcome that I always put off going to bed for several hours, so that I might enjoy it longer.

That evening *Sigurd* [2] had been given at the local theater. It was the first time I had heard this beautiful fairy play with music and I had thoroughly enjoyed it.

I was returning home on foot, at a lively pace, with scraps of melody running in my head, and entrancing scenes still vivid in my mind. It was dark, pitch black; I could hardly see the road, and several times I nearly fell headlong into the ditch. From the tollhouse to my place is a little more than half a mile or about twenty minutes' slow walking. It was one o'clock in the morning, one or one-thirty; the sky suddenly cleared a little before me and the crescent moon appeared, the melancholy crescent of the waning moon. The moon in its first quarter, when it rises at four or five in the evening, is bright, with cheerful, silvery light, but in the last quarter, when it rises after midnight, it is a dull copper color, and ominous—a real witches' Sabbath [3] moon. All night walkers must have noted this. The first quarter's crescent, even when slender as a thread, sheds a faint but cheerful gleam, which lifts the heart, and throws clearly defined shadows on the ground; the last quarter's crescent sheds a feeble, fitful light that casts almost no shadow.

The dark silhouette of my garden loomed

[2] *Sigurd* A play based on the legend of Siegfried.
[3] *witches' Sabbath* A midnight meeting of witches and magicians held at Halloween and at other times, such as Walpurgis Night.

ahead and for some reason I felt rather hesitant at the idea of going in. I slackened my pace. The night was very mild. The great mass of trees looked like a tomb, in which my house lay buried.

I opened my garden gate and went down the long driveway leading to the house. The rows of sycamores, arched overhead, made a lofty tunnel that flowed by dense clusters of green and wound around the lawn on which flower beds in the lightening darkness formed oval patches of no particular color.

Nearing the house, I felt curiously uneasy. I paused. There was not a sound, not a breath of air stirring in the leaves. "What's wrong with me?" I thought. For ten years I had been coming home like this without ever feeling nervous. I was not afraid. I have never been afraid of the dark. The sight of a man, a burglar or a thief, would merely have thrown me into a rage, and I would have jumped on him without a moment's hesitation. Besides, I was armed. I had my revolver. But I did not put my hand on it, because I wanted to resist the fear stirring within me.

What was it? A foreboding? The mysterious premonition that grips a man's mind at the approach of the supernatural? Perhaps. Who knows?

As I went on, I felt shivers running down my spine, and when I was close to the wall of my great shuttered house, I felt that I must wait a few minutes before opening the door and entering. So I sat down on a garden seat under the drawing-room windows. I stayed there, trembling, leaning my head against the wall, staring into the blackness of the foliage. During those first moments I noticed nothing unusual around me. I was aware of a buzzing in my ears, but I often hear that. I sometimes think I can hear trains passing, bells ringing, or crowds tramping.

But soon the humming became more distinct, more definite, more recognizable. I had been wrong. It was not the usual throbbing of my arteries that caused these noises in my ears, but a definite, though confused, noise that was coming, no doubt about it, from inside my house.

I could hear it through the wall, a continuous noise, no, more a rustling than a noise, a faint stirring of things, as of many objects being moved about, as if someone were shifting all my furniture and dragging it about.

Naturally, for some time I thought I must be mistaken. But, having put my ear against a shutter to hear the strange noises in my house more clearly, I was quite firmly convinced that something abnormal and inexplicable was going on inside. I was not afraid, but, I was—how shall I say?—bewildered and astonished. I did not cock my revolver, suspecting—and how right I was!—that it would be of no use. I waited.

I waited a long while, unable to come to a decision, with my mind perfectly clear but deeply disturbed. I waited motionless, listening to the growing noise, which kept gaining in intensity until it finally rose to an impatient, angry rumble.

Then, suddenly, ashamed of my cowardice, I seized my bunch of keys, chose the one I needed, thrust it into the lock, turned it twice, and, pushing in the door with all my strength, I sent it crashing against the wall inside.

The bang echoed like a gunshot, and the crash was answered by a fearful uproar from cellar to attic. It was so sudden, so terrifying, so deafening that I stepped back several paces, and, although I realized it was useless, I drew my revolver from its holster.

I still waited, but not for long. I could now distinguish an extraordinary sound of tramping, not of human feet or shoes, but of crutches, wooden stumps, iron stumps that rang out like cymbals.

Suddenly, on the threshold of the front door I saw an armchair, my big reading chair, come strutting out. It moved off into the garden. It was followed by others from the drawing room; next came the low sofas crawling along like crocodiles on their stumpy legs, then all the rest of my chairs, leaping like goats, and the little footstools hopping along like rabbits.

Imagine my feelings! I slipped into a flower bed where I crouched, my eyes glued on this exodus of my furniture. It all came out, one piece after another, quickly or slowly, according to shape and weight. My piano, a concert grand, galloped past like a runaway horse, with a faint jangle of music still inside it; the smaller objects, brushes, cut glass, goblets, slid over the gravel like ants, gleaming like glowworms in the moonlight. The carpets and hangings crawled away, with all the oozing elasticity of devil fish.[4] Then I saw my desk appear, a rare eighteenth-century collector's item, containing all my letters and the whole painful record of my heart's spent passion. And in it were also my photographs.

Suddenly I was no longer afraid, I threw myself upon it, I grappled it as one grapples with a thief in flight, but it pursued its irresistible course, and in spite of my utmost efforts, I could not even slow it up. As I wrestled like a madman with this terrible force, I fell to the ground in the struggle. Then it rolled me over and over, dragging me through the gravel, and the other furniture close on its heels had already begun to tread on me, trampling and bruising my legs, then, when I let go, the others swept over my body like a cavalry charge over an unhorsed soldier.

At last, mad with terror, I managed to drag myself out of the main path and I hid again in the trees, watching the disappearance of the smallest, tiniest, humblest pieces I had ever owned.

Presently I heard, in the distance, inside my house, now as sonorous as it was empty, a terrific din of doors being shut. They banged from attic to basement, until at last the hall door, which I myself had left open in my mad flight, slammed shut with a final bang.

I fled at a run toward the town and did not recover my composure until I got to the streets

4 *devil fish*   A kind of octopus.

and met some people coming home late. I rang
the bell of a hotel where I was known. I had
dusted off my clothes, and I explained that I
had lost my keys, including the key of the
kitchen garden where my servants slept in a
separate house, behind the garden wall that
protected my fruit and vegetables from thieves.

I buried myself in the bed they gave me, but I
couldn't sleep, so I waited for daylight, listening
to the violent beating of my heart. I had given
orders for my servants to be informed at dawn,
and my valet knocked at my door at seven in
the morning.

He looked upset.

"A terrible thing happened last night, sir," he
said.

"What?"

"All your furniture has been stolen, sir, everything, down to the smallest things."

This news cheered me. Why? Who knows? I
was calm, sure that I could conceal my feelings
and never tell anyone what I had seen. I would
hide it, bury it in my mind like some ghastly
secret. I answered:

"Then they are the same people who stole
my keys. The police must be informed immediately. I'm getting up and will be with you
in a few moments."

The inquiry lasted five months. Not even
the smallest of my ornaments or the slightest
trace of the thieves was ever found. Good God!
If I had told what I knew—if I had told—they
would have put away, not the thieves, but me,
the man who could have seen such a thing!

Of course, I knew how to keep my mouth
shut. But I did not furnish my house again. It
was no good. It would only have happened
again. I never wanted to go back to it again. I
never did. In fact, I never saw it again.

I went to a hotel in Paris and consulted doctors about my state of nerves, which had been
worrying me since that dreadful night.

They prescribed travel and I took their advice. I began with a trip to Italy. The sun did
me good. For six months I wandered from
Genoa to Venice, from Venice to Florence,
from Florence to Rome, from Rome to Naples.
Next I toured Sicily, that land of such wonderful scenery and monuments, relics left by the
Greeks and Normans. I crossed to Africa and
traveled at my leisure through the great desert,
so yellow and calm, where still camels, gazelles,
and nomadic Arabs roam, where, in the clear,
dry air no obsession can persist by night or day.

I returned to France via Marseilles, and in
spite of the gaiety of Provence [5] the diminished
intensity of the sunlight depressed me. On my
return to the continent, I had the odd feeling of
a patient who thinks he is cured but who is
warned by a dull pain that the source of illness
has not been eradicated.

I went back to Paris, but after a month I was
bored. It was autumn, and I wanted to tour
Normandy,[6] which was new ground to me,
before winter set in.

I began with Rouen,[7] of course, and for a
week I wandered about, intrigued, delighted,
and thrilled in this medieval town, the amazing
museum of rare Gothic monuments.

Then, one afternoon, about four o'clock, as
I was walking down an extraordinary street,
along which flowed an inky black stream, my
attention, previously centered on the strange
and ancient appearance of the houses, was
caught suddenly by a row of secondhand furniture shops.

They had, indeed, chosen the right spot, these
seedy junk dealers in this fantastic alley of
houses overlooking this sinister stream, under
pointed roofs of tile or slate on which the
weather vanes of a vanished age still creaked.
Stacked in the rear of the dark shops could be
seen carved chests, china from Rouen, Nevers,
and Moustiers, statues, some painted, others
carved in wood, crucifixes, Madonnas, saints,
church ornaments, vestments, copes,[8] even
chalices and an old gilded wooden tabernacle

---

[5] *Provence* A section in the South of France.

[6] *Normandy* A section in the North of France.

[7] *Rouen* The principal city of Normandy.

[8] *cope* An embroidered cape worn by priests during
certain ceremonies.

now vacated by God. What extraordinary store-rooms in these great, lofty houses, packed from cellar to attic with all sorts of objects whose usefulness was really at an end, and that had out-lived their natural owners, their century, their period, their fashion, to be bought as curios by later generations.

My passion for antiques revived in this collector's paradise. I went from shop to shop, crossing in two strides the bridge made of four rotten planks thrown over the stinking flow of the stream. Then—God have mercy!—I felt my heart in my throat! I saw one of my finest wardrobes[9] at the edge of a vault crammed with junk and that looked like the entrance to the catacombs of some cemetery of old furniture. I drew near, trembling all over, trembling to such an extent that I did not dare touch it. I put out my hand, then I hesitated. But it *was* mine—a unique Louis XIII,[10] unmistakable to anyone who had ever seen it. Suddenly, peering farther along toward the darker interior of this gallery, I noticed three of my petit-point[11] chairs, and, farther off, my two Henry II tables, which were so rare that people came from Paris to see them.

Imagine, just imagine my state of mind!

Then I went forward, dazed and gripped by emotion, but I persisted, for I am no coward. I went on as a knight of the Dark Ages would have penetrated a magic circle. As I advanced, I found all my belongings, my tapestries, my weapons, everything, except the desk containing my letters, which I could not discover anywhere.

And so I continued, descending to dark corridors to climb up again to the upper stories. I was alone. I called but there was no answer. I was alone; there was no one in this huge, winding labyrinth of a building.

Night came on and I had to sit down in the

dark on one of my own chairs, for I wouldn't go away. From time to time I called out, "Hello! Anybody there?"

I must have been there for more than an hour when I heard footsteps, light, slow steps; I could not tell where they were coming from. I nearly ran away, but, pulling myself together, I called out again and saw a light in the next room.

"Who's there?" said a voice.

I answered, "A customer."

The answer came: "It's rather late; we're closed."

I retorted, "I've been waiting for more than an hour."

"You could have come back tomorrow."

"No. Tomorrow, I am leaving Rouen."

I did not dare go to him and he did not come to me. All this time I saw the reflection of his candle shining on a tapestry in which two angels were hovering over the dead on a battlefield. That, too, belonged to me. I said:

"Well! Are you coming?"

He replied, "I'm waiting for you."

I got up and went toward him.

In the center of a large room stood a very short man, very short and very fat, phenomenally, hideously fat.

He had a sparse beard, straggling, ill-kept, dirty yellow beard, and not a hair on his head, not one! As he held his candle raised at arm's length in order to see me, the dome of his bald head looked like a miniature moon shining in this huge room stacked with old furniture. His face was wrinkled and bloated, his eyes mere slits.

I bargained for three of my chairs, paid a large sum for them, then and there, giving him merely the number of my suite at the hotel. They were to be delivered the next day before 9 A.M.

Then I left. He saw me to the door quite politely.

I went straight to the police station, where I told the inspector of the theft of my furniture and the discovery I had just made.

---

[9] *wardrobe*   A portable closet for clothes.

[10] *Louis XIII*   A piece of furniture dating from the reign of King Louis XIII.

[11] *petit-point*   Hand embroidery used in upholstering.

He got in touch immediately by telegraph with the magistrate who had first investigated the theft at my home, and asked me to wait for the answer. An hour later it was received and completely confirmed my story.

"I'll have him arrested and questioned at once," he said, "for he might become suspicious and move your belongings. You had best have your dinner and come back in two hours. I'll have him here and interrogate him in your presence."

"Fine! And thank you very much."

I had dinner at my hotel, and my appetite was better than I should have thought possible. I was rather pleased. My man was caught.

Two hours later I was back at the police station, where the officer was waiting for me.

"Well, sir," he said, seeing me approach. "We didn't find your man. My men couldn't lay their hands on him."

I felt faint.

"But—you have found the house?" I asked.

"Of course. It will be watched until he comes back. But he has disappeared."

"Disappeared?"

"Yes. He usually spends the evening with his neighbor, a queer old hag, a widow called Madame Bidoin, a second-hand dealer like himself. She hasn't seen him this evening and couldn't help us. We shall have to wait until tomorrow."

I left. The streets of Rouen now seemed sinister and threatening, with the disturbing effect of a haunted house.

I slept badly, plagued by nightmares whenever I dozed.

Since I did not want to seem too worried or impatient, I waited until ten o'clock the next morning before going back to the police.

The dealer had not returned. His shop was still closed.

The inspector said, "I have taken the necessary steps. The prosecutor has been informed. We'll go together to the shop, have it opened, and you can show me what belongs to you."

We took a cab. Officers were stationed, along with a locksmith, in front of the shop door, which had been opened.

When I entered, I saw that my wardrobe, my chairs, my tables, and all my household effects were gone. And the night before I had not been able to take a single step without bumping into one of my possessions! The superintendent, surprised, looked at me, with suspicion at first.

"Well, sir," I said, "the disappearance of my furniture coincides strangely with the disappearance of the dealer."

He smiled.

"That's true. You were wrong to buy and pay for your own belongings, yesterday. It tipped him off."

I replied, "What I can't understand is that all the space occupied by my things is now filled with other pieces."

"Oh," said the superintendent, "he had all night, and accomplices, no doubt. This building must communicate with the neighboring houses. Don't fear, sir, I'll see to this business myself. The thief will not escape us for long, we've got his hideout."

My heart was pounding so violently I thought it would burst.

I stayed on for two weeks in Rouen. The man never came back. Unbelievable! God knows nobody could outwit or trap a man like that!

Then on the following morning I received this strange letter from my gardener, who had been acting as caretaker for my house, which had remained unoccupied since the robbery.

Dear Sir:

I beg to inform you that last night something happened, which we can't explain, nor the police either. All the furniture has come back; all of it, even the smallest bits. The house is now just as it was the night of the robbery. It's enough to make you doubt your sanity! It all happened the night of Friday and in the early hours of Saturday. The paths are cut up as if everything had been dragged from the garden gate to the

door. It was just the same the day it all dis-
appeared.

I await your return and remain, -
                    Your respectful servant,
                            Philippe Raudin

No, no, never! I will not return there!

I took the letter to the chief inspector in Rouen.

"Now that's a very clever way of making restitution. Let's play possum. We'll catch our man one of these days."

But they didn't catch him. No! They never caught him, and now I am as terrified of him as if a wild animal were loose on my track.

Disappeared, escaped, this monster with the bald head like a full moon! They'll never catch him. He'll never go back to his shop. Why should he? I am the only one who can find him and I refuse to.

I won't, I won't!

And if he does go back, if he returns to his shop, who can prove that my furniture was ever there? There is only my word against his, and I have a feeling it is becoming suspect.

No! My life was getting impossible. And I couldn't keep the secret of what I had seen. I could not go on living normally with the fear that this horror might begin again.

I went and consulted the doctor who is director of this sanatorium and told him the the whole story.

After questioning me thoroughly, he said:

"My dear sir, would you be willing to stay here a while?"

"Of course, Doctor."

"You have means?"

"Yes, Doctor."

"Would you like a private apartment?"

"Yes, Doctor."

"Would you like your friends to come and see you?"

"No, no. No one. The man from Rouen might venture to pursue me here to get even with me."

And I have been alone, completely alone here for three months now. My mind is almost at ease. I am afraid of only one thing—supposing the antiquary [12] went mad—and was sent to this asylum—Even prisons aren't safe!

[*translated by* CLAIRE NOYES]

For Discussion

1. Characterize the speaker. When he says he is "sure" of what he saw, and "sure" that there is no gap in his reasoning, whom does he seem to be trying to convince? When he asks the question, "Why am I this way?" does the statement, "I tire quickly of anything outside myself," answer it? How many instances can you find where the speaker's comments divulge aspects of himself that he does not recognize or that he does not want to reveal?

2. Does the weird, galloping escape of the furniture suggest what has happened inside the man? Why does he say that he will not furnish his house again because the furniture will only make another escape? How does the dark, empty house reflect the man who cannot bear other people near him?

3. Why does the speaker fear that the man from Rouen will pursue him to the sanatorium? Can you explain why all the furniture returns to the house after he buys some of it back from the dealer? Why does he fear this person? The speaker ends his story by saying, "Even prisons aren't safe!" What meaning can you find in this statement?

4. What seems to be the cause of the speaker's trouble? Has he committed a crime, offended anyone? Will he ever be "cured"? Does he improve in the course of the story? Does he grow worse? Does this suggest that he need go no further than himself to find the source of his problem? But where does he always seek the cause?

---

[12] *antiquary* The antique dealer.

The Beggar

ANTON CHEKHOV

One of the great themes of fiction is the fact that life is not always what it appears to be on the surface. In "The Beggar" Chekhov presents a humorous example of the way in which reality can turn out to be illusion.

"KIND SIR, have pity; turn your attention to a poor, hungry man! For three days I have had nothing to eat; I haven't five kopecks[1] for a lodging. I swear it before God. For eight years I was a village schoolteacher and then I lost my place through intrigues. I fell a victim to calumny. It is a year now since I have had any work—"

The lawyer Skvortsoff looked at the ragged, fawn-colored overcoat of the applicant, at his dull, drunken eyes, at the red spot on either cheek, and it seemed to him as if he had seen this man somewhere before.

"I have now had an offer of a position in the province of Kaluga," the beggar went on, "but I haven't the money to get there. Help me kindly; I am ashamed to ask, but—I am obliged to by circumstances."

Skvortsoff's eyes fell on the man's overshoes, one of which was high and the other low, and he suddenly remembered something.

"Look here, it seems to me I met you day before yesterday in Sadovaya Street," he said, "but you told me then that you were a student who had been expelled, and not a village schoolteacher. Do you remember?"

"No-no, that can't be so," mumbled the beggar, taken aback. "I am a village schoolteacher, and if you like I can show you my papers."

"Never mind lying! You called yourself a student and even told me what you had been expelled for. Don't you remember?"

Skvortsoff flushed and turned away from the ragged creature with an expression of disgust.

"This is dishonesty, my dear sir!" he cried angrily. "This is swindling! I shall send the police for you! Even if you are poor and hungry, that does not give you any right to lie brazenly and shamelessly!"

The poor man caught hold of the door handle and looked furtively round the entrance hall, like a detected thief.

"I—I am not lying—" he muttered. "I can show you my papers."

"Who would believe you?" Skvortsoff continued indignantly. "Don't you know that it's a low, dirty trick to exploit the sympathy which society feels for village schoolteachers and students? It's revolting."

Skvortsoff lost his temper and began to scold the beggar unmercifully. The impudent lying

---

[1] *kopeck* A Russian coin of little value: one hundred kopecks equal one ruble.

ANTON CHEKHOV (*1860–1907*) *was born
of peasant parents in southern Russia.
His family later moved to Moscow,
where Anton entered the university to
study medicine. After graduating as a
physician, he continued to write, for
although he had been trained as a
scientist, he was an artist by temperament. The characters in his fiction are
not heroic or tragic. They are government clerks, impoverished aristocrats,
cab drivers, lawyers, peasants, and
soldiers. These people dramatize the
inner truths about humanity that lie
hidden behind the routine of their drab
existence.*

*His influence upon the theater was great.
Four plays are his masterpieces:* The
Cherry Orchard, The Three Sisters,
The Seagull, *and* Uncle Vanya.

---

of the ragamuffin offended what he, Skvortsoff,
most prized in himself: his kindness, his tender
heart, his compassion for all unhappy things.
That lie, an attempt to take advantage of the
pity of its "subject," seemed to him to profane
the charity which he liked to extend to the
poor out of the purity of his heart. At first the
ragged man continued to protest innocence, but
soon he grew silent and hung his head in confusion.

"Sir!" he said, laying his hand on his heart,
"the fact is I—was lying! I am neither a student
nor a schoolteacher. All that was a fiction.
Formerly I sang in a Russian choir and was sent
away for drunkenness. But what else can I do? I
can't get along without lying. No one will give
me anything when I tell the truth. With truth
a man would starve to death or die of cold for
lack of a lodging. You reason justly, I understand you, but—what can I do?"

"What can you do? You ask what you can
do?" cried Skvortsoff, coming close to him.
"Work! That's what you can do! You must
work!"

"Work—yes, I know that myself; but where
can I find work?"

"Rot! You're young and healthy and strong;
you could always find work if you only wanted
to, but you're lazy and spoiled and drunken!
You smell like a barroom. You're rotten and
false to the core, and all you can do is to lie.
When you consent to lower yourself to work,
you want a job in an office or in a choir or in
a billiard parlor—any employment for which
you can get money without doing anything!
How would you like to try your hand at
manual labor? No, you'd never be a porter or
a factory hand; you're a man of pretentions,
you are!"

"You judge harshly," cried the beggar with a
bitter laugh.

"Where can I find manual labor? It's too late
for me to be a clerk because in trade one has to
begin as a boy; no one would ever take me for a
porter because they couldn't order me about; no
factory would have me because for that one has
to know a trade, and I know none."

"Nonsense! You always find some excuse!
How would you like to chop wood for me?"

"I wouldn't refuse to do that, but in these
days even skilled woodcutters find themselves
sitting without bread."

"Huh! You loafers all talk that way. As soon
as an offer is made you, you refuse it! Will you
come and chop wood for me?"

"Yes, sir; I will."

"Very well; we'll soon find out. Splendid—
we'll see—"

Skvortsoff hastened along, rubbing his hands, not without a feeling of malice, and called his cook out of the kitchen.

"Here, Olga," he said, "take this gentleman into the woodshed and let him chop wood."

The tattered scarecrow shrugged his shoulders as if in perplexity, and went irresolutely after the cook. It was obvious from his gait that he had not consented to go and chop wood because he was hungry and wanted work, but simply from pride and shame, because he had been trapped by his own words. It was obvious, too, that his strength had been undermined by vodka and that he was unhealthy and did not feel the slightest inclination for toil.

Skvortsoff hurried into the dining room. From its windows one could see the woodshed and everything that went on in the yard. Standing at the window, Skvortsoff saw the cook and the beggar come out into the yard by the back door and make their way across the dirty snow to the shed. Olga glared wrathfully at her companion, shoved him aside with her elbow, unlocked the shed, and angrily banged the door.

"We probably interrupted the woman over her coffee," thought Skvortsoff. "What an ill-tempered creature!"

Next he saw the false teacher, false student seat himself on a log and become lost in thought with his red cheeks resting on his fists. The woman flung down an ax at his feet, spat angrily, and judging from the expression of her lips, began to scold him. The beggar irresolutely pulled a log of wood toward him, set it up between his feet, and tapped it feebly with the ax. The log wavered and fell down. The beggar again pulled it to him, blew on his freezing hands, and tapped it with his ax cautiously, as if afraid of hitting his overshoe or of cutting off his finger. The stick of wood again fell to the ground.

Skvortsoff's anger had vanished and he now began to feel a little sorry and ashamed of himself for having set a spoiled, drunken, perchance sick man to work at menial labor in the cold.

"Well, never mind," he thought, going into his study from the dining room. "I did it for his own good."

An hour later Olga came in and announced that the wood had all been chopped.

"Good! Give him half a ruble," [2] said Skvortsoff. "If he wants to he can come back and cut wood on the first day of each month. We can always find work for him."

On the first of the month the beggar made his appearance again and earned half a ruble, although he could barely stand on his legs. From that day on he often appeared in the yard and every time work was found for him. Now he would shovel snow, now put the woodshed in order, now beat the dust out of rugs and mattresses. Every time he received from twenty to forty kopecks, and once, even a pair of old trousers were sent out to him.

When Skvortsoff moved into another house he hired him to help in the packing and hauling of the furniture. This time the poor fellow was sober, gloomy, and silent. He hardly touched the furniture, and walked behind the wagons hanging his head, not even making a pretense of appearing busy. He only shivered in the cold and became embarrassed when the carters jeered at him for his idleness, his feebleness, and his tattered, fancy overcoat. After the moving was over Skvortsoff sent for him.

"Well, I see that my words have taken effect," he said, handing him a ruble. "Here's for your pains. I see you are sober and have no objection to work. What is your name?"

"Lushkoff."

"Well, Lushkoff, I can now offer you some other, cleaner employment. Can you write?"

"I can."

"Then take this letter to a friend of mine tomorrow and you will be given some copying to do. Work hard, don't drink, and remember what I have said to you. Good-by!"

Pleased at having put a man on the right path, Skvortsoff tapped Lushkoff kindly on the shoulder and even gave him his hand at parting.

[2] *ruble* The basic unit of Russian money.

Lushkoff took the letter, and from that day forth came no more to the yard for work.

Two years went by. Then one evening, as Skvortsoff was standing by the ticket window of a theater paying for his seat, he noticed a little man beside him with a coat collar of curly fur and a worn sealskin cap. This little individual timidly asked the ticket seller for a seat in the gallery and paid for it in copper coins.

"Lushkoff, is that you?" cried Skvortsoff, recognizing in the little man his former wood-chopper. "How are you? What are you doing? How is everything with you?"

"All right. I work for the government now and get thirty-five rubles a month."

"Thank Heaven! That's fine! I am delighted for your sake. I am very, very glad, Lushkoff. You see, you are my godson, in a sense. I gave you a push along the right path, you know. Do you remember what a scolding I gave you, eh? I nearly had you sinking into the ground at my feet that day. Thank you, old man, for not forgetting my words."

"Thank you, too," said Lushkoff. "If I hadn't come to you then I might still have been calling myself a teacher or a student to this day. Yes, by flying to your protection I dragged myself out of a pit."

"I am very glad, indeed."

"Thank you for your kind words and deeds. You talked splendidly to me then. I am very grateful to you and to your cook. God bless that good and noble woman! You spoke finely then, and I shall be indebted to you to my dying day; but, strictly speaking, it was your cook, Olga, who saved me."

"How is that?"

"Like this. When I used to come to your house to chop wood she used to begin: 'Oh, you sot, you! Oh, you miserable creature! There's nothing for you but ruin.' And then she would sit down opposite me and grow sad, look into my face and weep. 'Oh, you unlucky man! There is no pleasure for you in this world and there will be none in the world to come. You drunkard! You will burn in hell. Oh, you un-happy one!' And so she would carry on, you know, in that strain. I can't tell you how much misery she suffered, how many tears she shed for my sake. But the chief thing was—she used to chop the wood for me. Do you know, sir, that I did not chop one single stick of wood for you? She did it all. Why this saved me, why I changed, why I stopped drinking at the sight of her I cannot explain. I only know that, owing to her words and noble deeds a change took place in my heart; she set me right and I shall never forget it. However, it is time to go now; there goes the bell."

Lushkoff bowed and entered the theater.

For Discussion

1. What is the difference between what Lushkoff really is and what he appears to be? Is there a similar difference in Skvortsoff and Olga?

2. Does Skvortsoff genuinely want to reform Lushkoff? Or does he merely wish to flatter his own vanity by creating Lushkoff in his own image?

3. Is Skvortsoff a villain? Does your attitude toward Skvortsoff change during the story? Does it change toward Lushkoff and Olga?

4. Compare the first description of Olga by Skvortsoff with the last description of her by Lushkoff. What is the significance of this difference?

5. Judging from your own experience of life, are there more Skvortsoffs in the world, or more Olgas?

6. Is money the only thing Lushkoff begs for?

7. Why does Lushkoff say that he owes a deeper gratitude to Olga?

8. Good literature is often said to be "universal" in its appeal, that is to say, that it has meaning for all people in all ages. This story was written in Russia in the days of the Czars. What has it to do with modern readers? Could it have happened in an American city today?

The Tiger

LI FU YEN

Li Fu Yen wrote this classic tale during one of the richest periods of Chinese literature, the T'ang dynasty (618–906 A.D.). There are only two stories in this anthology which are older—the selection from Homer's Odyssey *and the Biblical parable of the Good Samaritan. "The Tiger" is here retold in a version by the modern Chinese scholar and writer Lin Yutang.*

This tale, based on weird, fantastic happenings, is typical of much Oriental literature. Chinese, Japanese, and Indian stories and plays are filled with ghosts, reincarnations of spirits, and transformations in which gods turn into men, and men into birds and beasts. Eastern tales usually move from one magical or bloody event to the next; they seldom depend upon the kind of neat plot structure we have come to look for in Western fiction. And, as in "The Tiger," the separation between the world of nature and the world of man is not too distinct.

CHANG FENG was traveling in Fukien. He was a northerner, and the luxuriant subtropical vegetation was new and interesting to him. Among other things, he had heard of tigers in the south. One day he was stopping with his servant at an inn in Hengshan, a small town near Foochow, lying on the watershed of the high mountain ranges which divide Fukien from Chekiang. Having deposited his luggage, he went out to take in his first impressions of the land, its people and the women's costumes. Walking alone with a cane in his hand, he went on and on, attracted by the refreshing green of the country after rain, and the bracing winds which came over the mountain. He felt strangely excited. Before him lay a landscape which was a riotous display of colors. It was autumn and the hillsides literally glowed with the gold and red of maple forests. A beautiful white temple stood halfway up the mountain above a thickly wooded slope. The golden sunset transformed the mountainside and the fields into a landscape of brilliant pastels, blue and purple and green, changing in hue every moment, mingling with the dazzling red and gold. It was like a magic land.

Suddenly he felt a fainting sensation: stars danced before his eyes and his head reeled. He thought it was due to the altitude, the over-exertion, and the sudden change of climate, or perhaps he was affected by the strange light. Just a few steps before him he saw a pasture land covered with velvety lawn, lying just where the wooded slope began. He took off his gown and put it with his walking stick against a tree, and lay down to take a rest. He felt a little better. As he looked up at the blue sky, he thought how beautiful and peaceful nature was. Men fought for money and position and fame; they lied and cheated and killed for gain; but here was peace—in nature. As he rolled in the grass, he felt happy and relaxed. The smell of the sod and a gentle breeze soon caressed him into sleep.

When he woke up, he felt hungry and remembered it was evening. As he rolled his hands over his stomach, he touched a coating of soft fur. Quickly he sat up, and he saw his body covered with beautiful black stripes, and as he stretched his arms, he felt a delightful new strength in them, sinewy and full of power. He yawned and was surprised at his own powerful roar. Looking down his own face, he saw the tips of long white whiskers. Lo, he had been transformed into a tiger!

Now, that is delightful, he thought to himself. I am no longer a man, but a tiger. It is not bad for a change.

Wanting to try his new strength, he ran into the woods and bounced from rock to rock, delighting in his new strength. He went up to the monastery, and pawed at the gate, seeking admittance.

"It is a tiger!" he heard a monk inside shouting. "I smell it. Do not open!"

Now that is uncomfortable, he thought to himself. I only intended to have a simple supper and discuss Buddhist philosophy with him. But of course I am a tiger now, and perhaps I do smell.

He had an instinct that he should go down the hill to the village and seek for food. As he hid behind a hedge on a country path, he saw a beautiful girl passing by, and he thought to himself, I have been told that Foochow girls are famous for their white complexion and small stature. Indeed it is true.

As he made a move to go up to the girl, she screamed and ran for her life.

What kind of a life is this, when everybody takes you for an enemy? he wondered. I will not eat her, she is so beautiful. I will take a pig, if I can find one.

At the thought of a nice, fat pig, or a small juicy lamb, his mouth watered, and he felt ashamed of himself. But there was this infernal hunger gnawing at his stomach, and he knew he had to eat something or die. He searched the village for a pig or calf, or even a chicken, but they were all under good shelters. All doors were shut against him, and as he crouched in a dark alley, waiting for a stray animal, he heard people talking inside their houses about a tiger in the village.

Unable to satisfy his hunger, he went back to the mountain, and lay in wait for some wayfarer in the night. All night he waited, but nothing came his way. For a while, he must have fallen asleep.

Toward dawn, he woke up. Soon travelers began to pass along the mountain road. He saw a man coming up from the city who stopped several passengers to ask whether they had seen Cheng Chiu, a bureau chief of Foochow, who was expected to return to his office today. He was evidently a clerk from the bureau who had been sent to welcome the chief.

Something told the tiger that he must eat Cheng Chiu. Just why he must eat that person he could not tell, but the feeling was very definite that Cheng Chiu was destined to be his first victim.

"He was getting up from the inn when I left. I think he is coming behind us," he heard a man reply to the clerk's question.

"Is he traveling alone, or is he accompanied by others? Tell me his dress so that I can recognize him, for I do not want to make a mistake when I go up to greet him."

"There are three of them traveling together. The one dressed in a dark green is Cheng."

As the tiger listened to the conversation from his hiding place, it seemed as if it were taking place expressly for his benefit. He had never seen or heard of Cheng Chiu in his life. He crouched in a thicket and waited for his victim.

Soon he saw Cheng Chiu coming up the road with his secretaries, along with a group of other travelers. Cheng looked fat and juicy and delicious. When Cheng Chiu came within pouncing distance, the tiger, Chang, rushed out, felled him to the ground, and carried him up the mountain. The travelers were so frightened they all ran away. Chang's hunger was satisfied, and he only felt as if he had had a bigger breakfast than usual. He finished up the gentleman and left only the hair and bones.

Satisfied with his meal, he lay down to take a nap. When he woke up, he thought he must have been mad to eat a human being who had done him no harm. His head cleared and he decided it was not such a pleasant life, prowling night after night for food. He remembered the night before, when the instinct of hunger drove him to

the village and up the mountain, and he could do nothing to stop himself.

"Why do I not go back to that lawn and see if I can become a human being again?"

He found the spot where his clothing and walking stick were still lying by the tree. He lay down again, with the wish that he might wake up to be a man once more. He rolled over on the grass, and in a few seconds found that he had been restored to his human shape.

Greatly delighted, but puzzled by the strange experience, he put on his gown, took up his cane, and started back to the town. When he reached the inn, he found he had been away exactly twenty-four hours.

"Where have you been, Master?" asked his servant, "I have been out looking for you all day." The innkeeper also came up to speak to him, evidently relieved to see him return.

"We have been worried about you," said the innkeeper. "There was a tiger abroad. He was seen by a girl in the village last night, and this morning Cheng Chiu, a bureau chief who was returning to his office, was eaten by him."

Chang Feng made up a story that he had spent the night discussing Buddhist philosophy up in the temple.

"You are lucky!" cried the innkeeper, shaking his head. "It was in that neighborhood that Cheng Chiu was killed by the tiger."

"No, the tiger will not eat me," Chang Feng replied.

"Why not?"

"He cannot," said Chang Feng enigmatically.

Chang Feng kept the secret to himself, for he could not afford to tell anybody that he had eaten a man. It would be embarrassing, to say the least.

He went back to his home in Honan, and a few years went by. One day he was stopping at a city on the Huai River. His friends gave him a dinner and much wine was consumed, as was usual on such occasions. Between the courses and the sipping of wine, the guests were each asked to tell a strange experience, and if in the opinion of the company the story was not strange enough, the teller of the story was to be fined a cup of wine.

Chang Feng began to tell his own story, and it happened that one of the guests was the son of Cheng Chiu, the man he had eaten. As he proceeded with his story, the young man's face grew angrier and angrier.

"So it was you who killed my father!" the young man shouted at him, his eyes distended and the veins standing up on his temples.

Chang Feng hastily stood up and apologized. He knew he had got into a very serious situation. "I am sorry. I did not know it was your father."

The young man suddenly whipped out a knife and threw it at him. Luckily it missed and fell with a clang on the floor. The young man made a rush at him, and would have fallen on him, but the guests, greatly disturbed by the sudden turn of events, held him back.

"I will kill you to avenge my father's death. I will follow you to the ends of the earth!" the young man shouted.

The friends persuaded Chang Feng to leave the house at once and hide himself for a while, while they tried to calm Cheng Chiu's son. It was conceded by everybody that to avenge one's father's death was a noble and laudable undertaking, but after all, Cheng Feng had eaten Cheng Chiu when he was a tiger, and no one wanted to see more blood shed. It was a novel situation and posed a complicated moral problem as to whether revenge under such circumstances was justified. The youth still swore murder to appease his father's spirit.

In the end, the friends spoke to the commander of the region who ordered the young man to cross the Huai River and never return to the northern bank, while Chang Feng changed his name and went to the northwest to keep as far away from his sworn enemy as possible.

When the young man returned to his home, his friends said to him, "We entirely sympathize with your determination to avenge your father. That is a son's duty, of course. However, Chang Feng ate your father when he was a tiger and not responsible for his action. He did not know your father and had no purpose in killing him. That was a strange and special case, but it was not intentional murder, and if you kill him, you will be tried for murder yourself."

The son respected this advice and did not pursue Chang Feng any more.

For Discussion

1. The interest in this story does not depend upon its narrative excitement. Can you explain why? Why do you think many savage details are omitted from the description of Chang Feng's career as a tiger?

2. What is the first feeling Chang Feng has when he awakens from his enchanted sleep? What were his last thoughts just before he fell asleep? Is there a connection between the two?

3. Does Chang Feng as a tiger eat Cheng Chiu out of malice? What are his feelings just before he takes a nap after his meal? What are his first thoughts when he awakens? The author observes that Chang Feng thought he must have been mad to eat a human being who had done him no harm. Does this mean that eating Cheng Chiu would have been justified if he had done Chang Feng harm?

4. It has often been said that vengeance destroys the avenger as completely as its destroys his victim. Does the story suggest this? What is the difference between the urge of Cheng Chiu's son to kill Chang Feng and Chang Feng's urge to eat Cheng Chiu?

5. This story shows that both men and animals kill, but for different reasons. What seems to be the major separation between nature and the world of man? What are the similarities between the two?

6. What reasons do the friends of Cheng Chiu's son give to persuade him not to take revenge on Chang Feng? Is this concept of intent similar to the one our law courts hold today?

A Father

BJÖRNSTERNE BJÖRNSON

The man who gives his devotion entirely to one object sometimes finds that he has nothing left when that object has been removed. Some men blind themselves to the rest of the world in the pursuit of money or ambition. At times selfishness appears in the guise of love. The brief story, "A Father," dramatizes this theme as it tells the chronicle of a proud father and his son. At the end of the story we see a man whose tragic loss leads to a discovery of himself; his grief becomes a rebirth.

THE MAN whose story is here to be told was the wealthiest and most influential person in his parish; his name was Thord Overaas. He appeared in the priest's study one day, tall and earnest.

"I have a new son," said he, "and I wish to present him for baptism."

"What shall his name be?"

"Finn—after my father."

"And the sponsors?"

They were mentioned and proved to be the richest men and women of Thord's relations in the parish.

"Is there anything else?" inquired the priest, and looked up.

The peasant hesitated a little.

"I should like very much to have him baptized by himself," said he, finally, "and not with other children."

"That is to say on a weekday?" [1]

"Next Saturday at twelve o'clock noon."

"Is there anything else?" inquired the priest.

"There is nothing else," and the peasant twirled his cap as though he were about to go.

Then the priest rose. "There is yet this, however," said he, and walking toward Thord, he took him by the hand and looked gravely into his eyes: "God grant that the child may become a blessing to you!"

One day sixteen years later, Thord stood once more in the priest's study.

"Really, you carry your age astonishingly well, Thord," said the priest; for he saw no change whatever in the man.

---

[1] *a weekday* Ordinarily the baptism would have taken place on a Sunday.

BJÖRNSTERNE BJÖRNSON (*1832–1910*) *was
one of Norway's greatest writers. He
won the Nobel Prize in literature in
1903. He wrote in almost every form—
poems, plays, novels, stories, and essays.
In the Norwegian theater, his plays are
ranked second only to the work of
the great Henrik Ibsen. One of
Björnson's poems has become the
national anthem of Norway, and much
of his work portrays life among the
Norwegian peasants.*

"That is because I have no troubles," replied Thord.

To this the priest said nothing, but after a while he asked: "What is your pleasure this evening?"

"I have come this evening about that son of mine who is to be confirmed tomorrow."

"He is a bright boy."

"I did not wish to pay the priest until I heard what number the boy would have when he takes his place in church tomorrow."

"He will stand number one—in front of all the others."

"Now I have heard; and here are ten dollars for the priest."

"Is there anything else I can do for you?" inquired the priest, fixing his eyes on Thord.

"There is nothing else."

Thord went out.

Eight years more rolled by, and then one day a noise was heard outside the priest's study, for many men were approaching, and at their head was Thord, who entered first.

The priest looked up and recognized him.

"You come well attended this evening, Thord," said he.

"I am here to request that the banns may be published for my son; he is about to marry Karen Storliden, daughter of Gudmund, who stands here beside me."

"Why, that is the richest girl in the parish."

"So they say," replied the peasant, stroking back his hair with one hand.

The priest sat a while as if in deep thought, then entered the names in his book, without making any comments, and the men wrote their signatures underneath. Thord laid three dollars on the table.

"One is all I am to have," said the priest.

"I know that very well, but he is my only child. I want to do it handsomely."

The priest took the money.

"This is now the third time, Thord, that you have come here on your son's account."

"But now I am through with him," said Thord, and folding up his pocketbook he said farewell and walked away.

The men slowly followed him.

Two weeks later, the father and son were rowing across the lake, one calm, still day, to Storliden to make arrangements for the wedding.

"This board is not secure," said the son, and stood up to straighten the seat on which he was sitting.

At the same moment the board he was standing on slipped from under him; he threw out his arms, uttered a shriek, and fell overboard.

"Take hold of the oar!" shouted the father, springing to his feet and holding out the oar.

But when the son had made a couple of efforts he grew stiff.

"Wait a moment!" cried the father, and began to row toward his son. Then the son rolled over on his back, gave his father one long look, and sank.

Thord could scarcely believe it; he held the boat still, and stared at the spot where his son had gone down, as though he must surely come to the surface again. There rose some bubbles, then some more, and finally one large one that burst; and the lake lay there as smooth and bright as a mirror again.

For three days and three nights people saw the father rowing round and round the spot, without taking either food or sleep; he was dragging the lake for the body of his son. And toward the morning of the third day he found it,

"... the lake lay there as smooth and bright as a mirror again."

A fiord in Norway

and carried it in his arms up over the hills to his farm.

It might have been about a year from that day, when the priest, late one autumn evening, heard some one in the passage outside the door, carefully trying to find the latch. The priest opened the door, and in walked a tall, thin man, with bowed form and white hair. The priest looked long at him before he recognized him. It was Thord.

"Are you out walking so late?" said the priest, and stood still in front of him.

"Ah, yes! it is late," said Thord, and took a seat.

The priest sat down also, as though waiting. A long, long silence followed. At last Thord said: "I have something with me that I should like to give to the poor; I want it to be invested as a legacy in my son's name."

He rose, laid some money on the table, and sat down again. The priest counted it.

"It is a great deal of money," said he.

"It is half the price of my farm. I sold it to-day."

The priest sat long in silence. At last he said, but gently: "What do you propose to do now, Thord?"

"Something better."

They sat there for a while, Thord with downcast eyes, the priest with his eyes fixed on Thord. Presently the priest said slowly and softly: "I think your son has at last brought you a true blessing."

"Yes, I think so myself," said Thord, looking up, while two big tears coursed slowly down his cheeks.

[*translated by* R. B. ANDERSON]

For Discussion

1. "A Father" only once, in the drowning scene, gives a detailed picture of the active relationship between the father and son. Is it difficult for the reader to guess what this relationship might have been like? Would you say that the father's attitude was fair to his son?

2. In the baptism, confirmation, and publishing of the marriage banns of his son, Thord Overaas insists upon making special demands or giving more than the regular tithe. What is the significance of these demands and this generosity?

3. A parable is a short form of fiction which builds to a moral or spiritual truth. Some famous parables are "The Prodigal Son" and "The Good Samaritan." By comparison, is "A Father" a parable? What is the moral?

4. What seems to be the author's purpose in writing this story? Is it merely amusing, or does it have a deeper significance that the narrative events dramatize?

5. What does Thord Overaas mean by "Something better," when the priest asks him what he proposes to do? Why, in a story that has avoided detail, do we suddenly see two tears running down Thord's cheeks in the last sentence?

6. The full effect of the story will be lost if the reader does not come to see that Thord is overly proud and that he wants his son to receive special consideration. Yet Björnson never makes a direct statement concerning the father's character. By what details in the story does he establish Thord's pride?

The Silver Mine

SELMA LAGERLÖF

*Selma Lagerlöf's "The Silver Mine" resembles Björnson's "A Father"
in that, although they are by modern Scandinavian authors, they
both take on the simple tones of the folk tale, fable, or parable.
Most good fiction avoids pointing directly to a single moral: it presents
material dramatically, letting the reader discover meanings within it.
Björnson and Lagerlöf, however, in returning to the older form of
the fable or parable also return to giving their stories a definite moral.
Both tales study selfishness. In "A Father" a man allows his selfish
instincts to govern his life. "The Silver Mine" presents the opposite:
a community conquers its greed with the help of one man's wisdom.*

KING GUSTAF III was traveling through Dalecarlia. He was pressed for time, and all the way he wanted to drive like lightning. Although they drove with such speed that the horses were extended like stretched rubber bands and the coach cleared the turns on two wheels, the King poked his head out of the window and shouted to the driver, "Why don't you go ahead? Do you think you are driving over eggs?"

Since they had to drive over poor country roads at such a mad pace, it would have been almost a miracle had the harness and wagon held together! And they didn't, either; for at the foot of a steep hill the pole broke—and there the King sat! The courtiers sprang from the coach and scolded the driver, but this did not lessen the damage done. There was no possibility of continuing until the coach was mended.

When the courtiers looked around to try to find something with which the King could amuse himself while he waited, they noticed a church spire looming high above the trees in a grove a short distance ahead. They intimated to the King that he might step into one of the coaches in which the attendants were riding and drive up to the church. It was a Sunday, and the King might attend services to pass the time until the royal coach was ready.

The King accepted the proposal and drove toward the church. He had been traveling for hours through dark forest regions; but here it looked more cheerful, with fairly large meadows and villages, and with the Dal River gliding on light and pretty, between thick rows of alder bushes.

But the King had ill luck to this extent: the bell ringer took up the recessional chant just as the King was stepping from the coach and the people were coming out from the service. But when they came walking past him the King remained standing, with one foot in the wagon and the other on the footstep. He did not move from the spot—only stared at them. They were the finest lot of folk he had ever seen. All the men were above the average height, with intelligent and earnest faces, and the women were dignified and stately, with an air of Sabbath peace about them.

The whole of the preceding day the King had talked only of the desolate tracts he was passing through, and had said to his courtiers again and again, "Now I am certainly driving through the very poorest part of my kingdom!" But now, when he saw the people, garbed in the picturesque dress of this section of the country, he forgot to think of their poverty; instead his heart warmed, and he remarked to himself, "The King of Sweden is not so badly off as his enemies think. So long as my subjects look like this, I shall probably be able to defend both my faith and my country."

He commanded the courtiers to make known to the people that the stranger who was standing among them was their King and that they should gather around him, so he could talk to them.

And then the King made a speech to the people. He spoke from the high steps outside the vestry, and the narrow step upon which he stood is there even today.

The King gave an account of the sad plight in which the kingdom was placed. He said that the Swedes were threatened with war by both Russians and Danes. Under ordinary circumstances it would not be such a serious matter; but now the army was filled with traitors, and he did not dare depend upon it. Therefore there was no other course for him to take than to go himself into the country settlements and ask his subjects if they would be loyal to their King and help him with men and money, so he could save the Fatherland.

The peasants stood quietly while the King was speaking to them, and when he had finished they gave no sign either of approval or of disapproval.

The King himself thought that he had spoken well. The tears had sprung to his eyes several times while he was speaking. But when the peasants stood there all the while, troubled and undecided, and could not make up their minds to answer him, the King frowned and looked displeased.

The peasants understood that it was becoming monotonous for the King to wait, and finally one of them stepped out from the crowd.

"Now, you must know, King Gustaf, that we were not expecting a royal visit in the parish today," said the peasant, "and therefore we are not prepared to answer you at once. I advise you to go into the vestry and speak with our pastor, while we discuss among ourselves this matter which you have laid before us."

The King understood that a more satisfactory answer was not to be had immediately, so he felt that it would be best for him to follow the peasant's advice.

When he came into the vestry, he found no one there but a man who looked like a peasant. He was tall and rugged, with big hands, toughened by labor, and he wore neither cassock [1] nor collar, but leather breeches and a long white homespun coat, like all the other men.

He rose and bowed to the King when the latter entered.

"I thought I should find the parson in here," said the King.

The man grew somewhat red in the face. He thought it annoying to mention the fact that he was the parson of this parish, when he saw that the King had mistaken him for a peasant. "Yes," said he, "the parson is usually on hand in here."

The King dropped into a large armchair which stood in the vestry at that time and which stands there today, looking exactly like itself,

[1] *cassock* A priest's robe.

SELMA LAGERLÖF (*1858–1940*) *was the
first woman member of the Swedish
Academy. She was also the first woman
to win the Nobel Prize in literature
(1909). Many of her novels and stories
have been translated into English.*

with this difference: the congregation has had a gilded crown attached to the back of it.

"Have you a good parson in this parish?" asked the King, who wanted to appear interested in the welfare of the peasants.

When the King questioned him in this manner, the parson felt that he couldn't possibly tell who he was. "It's better to let him go on believing that I'm only a peasant," he thought, and replied that the parson was good enough. He preached a pure and clear gospel and tried to live as he taught.

The King thought that this was a good commendation, but he had a sharp ear and marked a certain doubt in the tone. "You sound as if you were not quite satisfied with the parson," said the King.

"He's a bit arbitrary," said the man, thinking that, if the King should find out later who he was, he would not think that the parson had been standing here and blowing his own horn; therefore he wished to come out with a little faultfinding also. "There are some, no doubt, who say the parson wants to be the only one to counsel and rule in this parish," he continued.

"Then, at all events, he has led and managed in the best possible way," said the King. He didn't like it that the peasant complained of one who was placed above him. "To me it appears as though good habits and old-time simplicity were the rule here."

"The people are good enough," said the curate, "but then they live in poverty and isolation. Human beings here would certainly be no better than others if this world's temptations came closer to them."

"But there's no fear of anything of the sort happening," said the King, with a shrug.

He said nothing further, but began thrumming on the table with his fingers. He thought he had exchanged a sufficient number of gracious words with this peasant and wondered when the others would be ready with their answer.

"These peasants are not very eager to help their King," thought he. "If I only had my coach, I would drive away from them and their palaver!"

The pastor sat there troubled, debating with himself as to how he should decide an important matter which he must settle. He was beginning to feel happy because he had not told the King who he was. Now he felt that he could speak with him about matters which otherwise he could not have placed before him.

After a while the parson broke the silence and asked the King if it was an actual fact that enemies were upon them and that the kingdom was in danger.

The King thought this man ought to have sense enough not to trouble him further. He simply glared at him and said nothing.

"I ask because I was standing in here and could not hear very well," said the parson. "But if this is really the case, I want to say to you that the pastor of this congregation might perhaps be able to procure for the King as much money as he will need."

"I thought that you said just now that everyone here was poor," said the King, thinking that the man did not know what he was talking about.

"Yes, that's true," replied the rector, "and the parson has no more than any of the others. But if the King would condescend to listen to me for a moment, I will explain how the pastor happens to have the power to help him."

"You may speak," said the King. "You seem to find it easier to get the words past your lips than your friends and neighbors out there, who never will be ready with what they have to tell me."

"It is not so easy to reply to the King! I'm

afraid that, in the end, it will be the parson who must undertake this on behalf of the others."

The King crossed his legs, folded his arms, and let his head sink down upon his breast. "You may begin now," he said in the tone of one already asleep.

"Once upon a time there were five men from this parish who were out on a moose hunt," began the clergyman. "One of them was the parson of whom we are speaking. Two of the others were soldiers, named Olaf and Eric Svärd; the fourth man was the innkeeper in this settlement, and the fifth was a peasant named Israel Per Persson."

"Don't go to the trouble of mentioning so many names," muttered the King, letting his head droop to one side.

"Those men were good hunters," continued the parson, "who usually had luck with them, but that day they had wandered long and far without getting anything. Finally they gave up the hunt altogether and sat down on the ground to talk. They said there was not a spot in the whole forest fit for cultivation; all of it was only mountain and swampland. 'Our Lord has not done right by us in giving us such a poor land to live in,' said one. 'In other localities people can get riches for themselves in abundance, but here, with all our toil and drudgery we can scarcely get our daily bread.'"

The pastor paused a moment, as if uncertain that the King heard him, but the latter moved his little finger to show that he was awake.

"Just as the hunters were discussing this matter, the parson saw something that glittered at the base of the mountain, where he had kicked away a moss tuft. 'This is a queer mountain,' he thought, as he kicked off another moss tuft. He picked up a sliver of stone that came with the moss and which shone exactly like the other. 'It can't be possible that this stuff is lead,' said he.

"Then the others sprang up and scraped away the turf with the butt end of their rifles. When they did this, they saw plainly that a broad vein of ore followed the mountain.

"'What do you think this might be?' asked the parson.

"The men chipped off bits of stone and bit into them. 'It must be lead, or zinc at least,' said they.

"'And the whole mountain is full of it,' added the innkeeper."

When the parson had got thus far in his narrative, the King's head was seen to straighten up a little and one eye opened. "Do you know if any of these persons knew anything about ore and minerals?" he asked.

"They did not," replied the parson.

Then the King's head sank and both eyes closed.

"The clergyman and his companions were very happy," continued the speaker, without letting himself be disturbed by the King's indifference; "they fancied that now they had found that which would give them and their descendants wealth. 'I'll never have to do any more work,' said one. 'Now I can afford to do nothing at all the whole week through, and on Sundays I shall drive to church in a golden chariot!' They were otherwise sensible men, but the great find had gone to their heads and they talked like children. Still they had enough presence of mind to put back the moss tufts and conceal the vein of ore. Then they carefully noted the place where it was, and went home. Before they parted company, they agreed that the parson should travel to Falun and ask the mining expert what kind of ore this was. He was to return as soon as possible, and until then they promised one another on oath not to reveal to a soul where the ore was to be found."

The King's head was raised again a trifle, but he did not interrupt the speaker with a word. It appeared as though he was beginning to believe that the man actually had something of importance he wished to say to him, since he didn't allow himself to be disturbed by his indifference.

"Then the parson departed with a few samples of ore in his pocket. He was just as happy in the thought of becoming rich as were the others. He was thinking of rebuilding the parsonage, which at present was no better than a peasant's cottage, and then he would marry a dean's [2] daughter whom he liked. He had thought that he might have to wait for her many years. He was poor and obscure and knew that it would be a long while before he should get any post that would enable him to marry.

"The parson drove over to Falun in two days, and there he had to wait another whole day because the mining expert was away. Finally he ran across him and showed him the bits of ore. The mining expert took them in his hand. He looked at them first, then at the parson. The parson related how he had found them in a mountain at home in his parish, and wondered if it might not be lead.

" 'No, it's not lead,' said the mining expert.

" 'Perhaps it is zinc, then?' asked the parson.

" 'Nor is it zinc,' said the mineralogist.

"The parson thought that all the hope within him sank. He had not been so depressed in many a long day.

" 'Have you many stones like this in your parish?' asked the mineralogist.

" 'We have a whole mountainful,' said the parson.

"Then the mineralogist came up closer, slapped the parson on the shoulder, and said, 'Let us see that you make such good use of this that it will prove a blessing both to yourselves and to the country, for this is silver.'

" 'Indeed?' said the parson, feeling his way. 'So it is silver!'

"The mineralogist began telling him how he should go to work to get legal rights to the mine and gave him many valuable suggestions, but the parson stood there dazed and did not listen to what the mineralogist was saying. He was thinking how wonderful it was that at home in his poor parish stood a whole mountain of silver ore, waiting for him."

The King raised his head so suddenly that the parson stopped short in his narrative. "It turned out, of course, that, when he got home and began working the mine, he saw that the mineralogist had only been fooling him," exclaimed the King.

"Oh, no, the mineralogist had not fooled him," said the parson.

"You may continue," said the King as he settled himself more comfortably in the chair to listen.

"When the parson was at home again and was driving through the parish," continued the clergyman, "he thought that first of all he should inform his partners of the value of their find. And as he drove alongside the innkeeper Sten Stensson's place, he intended to drive up to the house to tell him they had found silver. But when he stopped outside the gate, he noticed that a broad path of evergreen was strewn all the way up to the doorstep.

" 'Who has died in this place?' asked the parson of a boy who stood leaning against the fence.

" 'The innkeeper himself,' answered the boy. Then he let the clergyman know that the innkeeper had drunk himself full every day for a week. 'Oh, so much brandy, so much brandy, has been drunk here!'

" 'How can that be?' asked the parson. 'The innkeeper used never to drink himself full.'

" 'Oh,' said the boy, 'he drank because he said he had found a mine. He was very rich. He should never have to do anything now but drink, he said. Last night he drove off, full as he was, and the wagon turned over and he was killed.'

"When the parson heard this he drove homeward, distressed over what he had heard. He had come back so happy, rejoicing because he could tell the great news.

"When the parson had driven a few paces,

---

[2] *dean* A high-ranking authority in the church of Sweden.

he saw Israel Per Persson walking along. He looked about as usual, and the parson thought it was well that fortune had not gone to his head too. Him he would cheer at once with the good news that he was a rich man.

" 'Good day!' said Per Persson. 'Do you come from Falun now?'

" 'I do,' said the parson. 'And now I must tell you that it has turned out even better than we had imagined. The mineralogist said it was silver ore that we had found.'

"That instant Per Persson looked as though the ground had opened under him. 'What are you saying, what are you saying? Is it silver?'

" 'Yes,' answered the parson. 'We'll all be rich men now, all of us, and can live like gentlemen.'

" 'Oh, is it silver?' said Per Persson, looking more and more mournful.

" 'Why, of course it is silver,' replied the parson. 'You mustn't think that I want to deceive you. You mustn't be afraid to be happy.'

" 'Happy!' said Per Persson. 'Should I be happy? I believed it was only glitter that we had found, so I thought it would be better to take the certain for the uncertain; I have sold my share in the mine to Olaf Svärd for a hundred dollars.' He was desperate and, when the parson drove away from him, he stood on the highway and wept.

"When the clergyman got back to his home, he sent a servant to Olaf Svärd and his brother to tell them that it was silver they had found. He thought that he had had quite enough of driving around and spreading the good news.

"But in the evening, when the parson sat alone, his joy asserted itself again. He went out in the darkness and stood on a hillock upon which he contemplated building the new parsonage. It should be imposing, of course, as fine as a bishop's palace. He stood there long that night, nor did he content himself with rebuilding the parsonage! It occurred to him that, since there were such riches to be found in the parish, throngs of people would pour in and, finally, a whole city would be built around the mine. And then he would have to erect a new church in place of the old one. Toward this object a large portion of his wealth would probably go. And he was not content with this, either, but fancied that, when his church was ready, the King and many bishops would come to the dedication. Then the King would be pleased with the church; but he would remark that there was no place where a king might put up, and then he would have to erect a castle in the new city."

Just then one of the King's courtiers opened the door of the vestry and announced that the big royal coach was mended.

At the first moment the King was ready to withdraw, but on second thought he changed his mind. "You may tell your story to the end," he said to the parson. "But you can hurry it a bit. We know all about how the man thought and dreamed. We want to know about how he acted."

"But while the parson was still lost in his dreams," continued the clergyman, "word came to him that Israel Per Persson had killed himself. He had not been able to bear the disappointment of having sold his share in the mine. He had thought, no doubt, that he could not endure to go about every day seeing another enjoying the wealth that might have been his."

The King straightened up a little. He kept both eyes open. "Upon my word," he said, "if I had been that parson, I should have had enough of the mine!"

"The King is a rich man," said the parson. "He has quite enough at all events. It is not the same thing with a poor curate who possesses nothing. The unhappy wretch thought instead, when he saw that God's blessing was not with his enterprise, 'I will dream no more of bringing glory and profit to myself with these riches, but I can't let the silver lie buried in the earth! I must take it out, for the benefit of the poor and needy. I will work the mine, to put the whole parish on its feet.'

"So one day the parson went out to see Olaf Svärd, to ask him and his brother as to what should be done immediately with the silver mountain. When he came in the vicinity of the barracks he met a cart surrounded by armed peasants, and in the cart sat a man with his hands tied behind him and a rope around his ankles.

"When the parson passed by, the cart stopped and he had time to regard the prisoner, whose head was tied up so it was not easy to see who he was. But the parson thought he recognized Olaf Svärd. He heard the prisoner beg those who guarded him to let him speak a few words with the parson.

"The parson drew nearer, and the prisoner turned toward him. 'You will soon be the only one who knows where the silver mine is,' said Olaf.

"'What are you saying, Olaf?' asked the parson.

"'Well, you see, parson, since we have learned that it was a silver mine we had found, my brother and I could no longer be as good friends as before. We were continually quarreling. Last night we got into a controversy over which one of us five it was who first discovered the mine. It ended in strife between us, and we came to blows. I have killed my brother and he has left me with a souvenir across the forehead to remember him by. I must hang now, and then you will be the only one who knows about the mine; therefore I wish to ask something of you.'

"'Speak out!' said the parson. 'I'll do what I can for you.'

"'You know that I am leaving several little children behind me,' began the soldier, but the parson interrupted him.

"'As regards this, you can rest easy. That which comes to your share in the mine they shall have, exactly as if you yourself were living.'

"'No,' said Olaf Svärd, 'it was another thing I wanted to ask of you. Don't let them have any part of that which comes from the mine!'

"The parson staggered back a step. He stood there dumb and could not answer.

" 'If you do not promise me this, I cannot die in peace,' said the prisoner.

" 'Yes,' said the parson slowly and painfully. 'I promise you what you ask of me.'

"Thereupon the murderer was taken away, and the parson stood on the highway thinking how he should keep the promise he had given him. On the way home he thought of the wealth which he had been so happy over. What if it really were true that the people in this community could not stand riches? Already four were ruined who hitherto had been dignified and excellent men. He seemed to see the whole community before him, and he pictured to himself how this silver mine would destroy one after another. Was it befitting that he, who had been appointed to watch over these poor human beings' souls, should let loose upon them that which would be their destruction?"

All of a sudden the King sat bolt upright in his chair. "I declare!" said he, "you'll make me understand that a parson in this isolated settlement must be every inch a man."

"Nor was it enough with what had already happened," continued the parson, "for as soon as the news about the mine spread among the parishioners they stopped working and went about in idleness, waiting for the time when great riches should pour in on them. All the ne'er-do-wells there were in this section streamed in, and drunkenness and fighting were what the parson heard talked of continually. A lot of people did nothing but tramp round in the forest searching for the mine, and the parson marked that as soon as he left the house people followed him stealthily to find out if he wasn't going to the silver mountain and to steal the secret from him.

"When matters were come to this pass, the parson called the peasants together to vote. To start with he reminded them of all the misfortunes which the discovery of the mountain had brought upon them, and he asked them if they were going to let themselves be ruined or if they would save themselves. Then he told them that they must not expect him, who was their spiritual adviser, to help on their destruction. Now he had declared not to reveal to anyone where the silver mine was, and never would he himself take riches from it. And then he asked the peasants how they would have it henceforth. If they wished to continue their search for the mine and wait upon riches, then he would go so far away that no word of their misery could reach him; but if they would give up thinking about the silver mine and be as heretofore, he would remain with them. 'Whichever way you may choose,' said the parson, 'remember this, that from me no one shall ever know anything about the silver mountain.' "

"Well," said the King, "how did they decide?"

"They did as their pastor wished," said the parson. "They understood that he meant well by them when he wanted to remain poor for their sakes. And they commissioned him to go to the forest and conceal the vein of ore with evergreen and stone, so that no one would be able to find it—neither they nor their posterity."

"And ever since the parson has been living here just as poor as the rest?"

"Yes," answered the curate, "he has lived here just as poor as the rest."

"He has married, of course, and built a new parsonage?" said the King.

"No, he couldn't afford to marry and he lives in the old cabin."

"It's a pretty story that you have told me," said the King. After a few seconds he resumed, "Was it of the silver mountain that you were thinking when you said that the parson here would be able to procure for me as much money as I need?"

"Yes," said the other.

"But I can't put the thumbscrews on him," said the King. "Or how would you advise that I get such a man to show me the mountain—a man who has renounced his sweetheart and the allurements of life?"

"Oh, that's a different matter," said the parson. "But if it's the Fatherland that is in need of the fortune, he will probably give in."

"Will you answer for that?" asked the King.

"Yes, that I will answer for," said the clergyman.

"Doesn't he care, then, what becomes of his parishioners?"

"That can rest in God's hands."

The King rose from the chair and walked over to the window. He stood for a moment and looked upon the group of people outside. The longer he looked, the clearer his large eyes shone; and his figure seemed to grow. "You may greet the pastor of this congregation, and say that for Sweden's King there is no sight more beautiful than to see a people such as this!"

Then the King turned from the window and looked at the clergyman. He began to smile. "Is it true that the pastor of this parish is so poor that he removes his black clothes as soon as the service is over and dresses himself like a peasant?" asked the King.

"Yes, so poor is he," said the curate, and a crimson flush leaped into his roughhewn face.

The King went back to the window. One could see that he was in his best mood. All that was noble and great within him had been quickened into life. "You must let that mine lie in peace," said the King. "Inasmuch as you have labored and starved a lifetime to make these people such as you would have them, you may keep it as it is."

"But if the kingdom is in danger," said the parson.

"The kingdom is better served with men than with money," remarked the King. When he had said this, he bade the clergyman farewell and went out from the vestry.

Without stood the group of people, as quiet and taciturn as they were when he went in. As the King came down the steps, a peasant stepped up to him.

"Have you had a talk with our pastor?" said the peasant.

"Yes," said the King. "I have."

"Then of course you have our answer?" said the peasant. "We asked you to go in and talk with our parson, that he might give you an answer from us."

"I have the answer," said the King.

For Discussion

1. Why is King Gustaf a perfect listener to the parson's story? What is his state of mind when he stops at the village? Is he in an ideal mood to listen? Does he change during the story?

2. Why is it necessary for the parson to keep his identity a secret throughout the story? How does King Gustaf discover this? What method of storytelling does the parson use to maneuver the King into making a decision he might not have made if the silver mine had been offered to him right at the beginning? In what way is the parson's story like a sermon? How does he inspire King Gustaf to say, "Upon my word, if I had been that parson, I should have had enough of the mine"?

3. How does the combination, two soldiers, an innkeeper, a parson, and a peasant, represent society?

How does the fate of each suggest his nature: Eric's by violence; Olaf's by hanging; Sten Stensson's by gluttony; Israel Per Persson's by suicide after he had sold his share to Olaf Svärd?

4. In "The Silver Mine," is the parson too perfect? Geoffrey Chaucer in the "Prologue" to the *Canterbury Tales* describes a parson:

> A holy-minded man of good renown
> There was, and poor, the Parson to a town,
> Yet he was rich in holy thought and work.

Does this typify the parson of the story? Does he make himself the conscience of his parish? Are the peasants of his parish wholly dependent upon him to make all their moral decisions? Are they like children?

The Hussar

JOHANN PETER HEBEL

Men often try to repay evil with evil, to demand "an eye for an eye."
Such a concept of justice has caused discord among men and nations
throughout history. Hatred becomes a chain from man to man,
nation to nation. Neither has found it easy to follow Christ's
admonition to "turn the other cheek." Occasionally a man of great
restraint and compassion manages to break this chain of vengeance.
Johann Peter Hebel (1760–1826), poet and storyteller, was born in
Switzerland but spent most of his life in Germany.

WHEN, AT the beginning of the French Revolution, the Prussians made war against the French and rode through the province of Champagne, no one imagined that the wind would change and that before long, in the year of 1806, the French would come to Prussia and return the uninvited visit. For not every Prussian behaved as befits an honorable soldier in an enemy country.

Thus, then, a Prussian hussar, who was an evil person, invaded the house of a peaceable man, took from him all his money and much else of value, and finally even his pretty bed with the brand-new bedspread, and mistreated husband and wife. Their boy, eight years old, begged him on his knees at least to give back the bed to his parents. The hussar pushed him away harshly. Their daughter ran after him, caught hold of his cape, and implored him for mercy. But he seized her and threw her into the well in the courtyard, and got away with his loot.

Years afterward, he retired, settled in the city of Neisse in Silesia, and thought little of the crime he had once committed, believing that the grass had grown over it long ago.

But what happened in the year of 1806? The French marched into Neisse, and one evening a young sergeant was quartered at the home of a good woman who attended him well. The sergeant was honorable, behaved decently, and seemed cheerful.

The next morning the sergeant did not come down to breakfast. The woman thought: "He's still asleep," and put his coffee in the oven to keep warm. After a while, when he still didn't come, she went up to his room to see whether he was all right, and softly pushed open the door.

There was the young man, awake and sitting up in bed, with his hands folded, and sighing as if he'd met with some great misfortune, or as if he had become homesick or some such thing. He did not notice that someone was in the room.

31

The woman went quietly to him and asked: "What has happened to you, sergeant, and why are you so sad?"

The young man looked at her with a tearful expression and said that the spread of the bed in which he'd spent the night had belonged to his parents in Champagne; they'd lost everything in the pillage fourteen years before and had become paupers, and all that was coming back to him now, and his heart was full of sorrow. For the sergeant was the son of the man who had been robbed in Champagne, and he still recognized the spread and the red initials that his mother had sewed on it.

The good woman was frightened and said she'd bought the bed-cover from a hussar who still lived in Neisse, and that she should not be blamed.

The Frenchman got up and had himself taken to the home of the hussar, and recognized the man.

"Do you recall," he said to the hussar, "how fourteen years ago you took away from an innocent man in Champagne all his possessions, even his bed, and took no pity when an eight-year-old boy begged for mercy? And do you still remember my sister?"

At first the old wretch tried to make excuses, saying that in wartime, as everyone knows, not all things go as they should, and what one fellow leaves, another takes, so one might as well do the taking oneself. But when he saw that the sergeant really was the boy whose parents he had plundered and mistreated, and as he remembered the sister, the hussar's voice failed, in remorse and terror, and he fell on his shaking knees before the Frenchman unable to utter anything but "Forgive me." "But," he thought to himself, "this won't help much."

The gentle reader may think, gleefully: "Now the Frenchman will hack the hussar to pieces." But that would not tally with the truth. For when a man's heart is stirred and almost breaking in pain, he cannot take revenge. For vengeance is too small and contemptible, and he thinks: "We are in the hands of God," and he can't bring himself to repay evil with evil. Thus thought the Frenchman, too, and he said: "That you mistreated me, I forgive you. That you mistreated my parents and made them paupers, my parents will have to forgive you. That you threw my sister into the well, where she perished—may God forgive you that." With these words he went away without doing the hussar the slightest harm, and he became well again in his heart.

But the hussar felt afterward as though he'd stood before the Last Judgment and had been found wanting. He did not have one peaceful hour from that day on, and a quarter of a year later, it is said, he died.

[translated by PAUL PRATT]

For Discussion

1. Compare the son of the violated family to the son of Cheng Chiu in "The Tiger" (page 15). Do both sons have equal provocation for revenge? Which of the two achieves a better justice? Why?

2. In the great imaginative description of hell in Dante's *Inferno*, each sinner receives eternally a punishment which is appropriate to his sin. What is the hussar's punishment in this story? Who delivers it? Is it appropriate to his crime?

3. Do you agree with the hussar's claim that during wartime ordinary decency is suspended? What comment does the son's action make upon this statement?

4. Which of the two men seems more exactly to fit the image of the conquering soldier? Which of the two men possesses the greater strength?

5. When the author, Johann Peter Hebel, writes, "For vengeance is too small and contemptible," what does he mean? If the son had hacked the hussar to pieces, would he have satisfied the demands of justice, or would he only have added another evil to the evil already committed?

My Lord, the Baby

RABINDRANATH TAGORE

Tyranny takes many shapes. There is a tyranny of kings and dictators. There is a tyranny of strong minority groups, and the French Revolution showed the tyranny of the mob. The tyrant's methods make him the principal victim of his own destructive actions, and every step he takes to insure total power becomes a step closer to his doom.

Another form of tyranny is the inflexible demand that a human being often puts upon himself, his love, or his capabilities. Such tyranny, like its larger political counterparts, can be dangerous and cruel. Tagore's Raicharan, in the story that follows, is a man whose loyalty, love, and capacity for devotion seem limitless. Still, his relationship with his master's child and with his own son becomes a tyrannical self-sacrifice which makes him lose what he desires most.

RAICHARAN WAS TWELVE years old when he came as a servant to his master's house. He belonged to the same caste as his master, and was given his master's little son to nurse. As time went on the boy left Raicharan's arms to go to school. From school he went on to college, and after college he entered the judicial service. Always, until he married, Raicharan was his sole attendant.

But, when a mistress came into the house, Raicharan found two masters instead of one. All his former influence passed to the new mistress. This was compensated for by a fresh arrival. Anukul had a son born to him, and Raicharan by his unsparing attentions soon got a complete hold over the child. He used to toss him up in his arms, call to him in absurd baby language, put his face close to the baby's and draw it away again with a grin.

Presently the child was able to crawl and cross the doorway. When Raicharan went to catch him, he would scream with mischievous laughter and make for safety. Raicharan was amazed at the profound skill and exact judgment the baby showed when pursued. He would say to his mistress with a look of awe and mystery: "Your son will be a judge some day."

New wonders came in their turn. When the baby began to toddle, that was to Raicharan an epoch in human history. When he called his

RABINDRANATH TAGORE (*1861–1941*) *won
the Nobel Prize in literature in 1913.
Born in Calcutta, India, and educated
in Europe, he became a poet, composer,
educator, story writer, dramatist, and
painter. He also championed social
equality for his countrymen, and helped
to establish a university in Bengal. He
was knighted by King George V in
1915, when India was still a British
colony, but he later renounced his title
as a protest against the British government. His life spanned a period
of great and violent change in Hindu
life and culture, and his work helped
to shape the course of events that led to
India's eventual independence.*

*In his stories and fables, Tagore exercises
a detachment and irony that combine
with a deep sympathy for the weakness
and lack of awareness in his characters.
He loved his country and its people.
In spite of Indian reluctance to abandon
tradition in order to confront the
necessities of change, he wrote with a
gentleness that shows no trace of the
shrill bitterness of the social reformer.
He published his first story, "The
Beggar Woman," when he was sixteen,
and he continued to write stories until
his death. In these stories he attempted
to dramatize the dominant ideas of the
India of his time and to reveal the
special beauty of the Indian landscape.*

---

father Ba-ba and his mother Ma-ma and Raicharan Chan-na, then Raicharan's ecstasy knew no
bounds. He went out to tell the news to all the
world.

After a while Raicharan was asked to show
his ingenuity in other ways. He had, for instance, to play the part of a horse, holding the
reins between his teeth and prancing with his
feet. He had also to wrestle with his little charge,

and if he could not, by a wrestler's trick, fall
on his back defeated at the end, a great outcry
was certain.

About this time Anukul was transferred to
a district on the banks of the Padma. On his
way through Calcutta he bought his son a little
go-cart. He bought him also a yellow satin
waistcoat, a gold-laced cap, and some gold
bracelets and anklets. Raicharan was wont to
take these out, and put them on his little charge
with ceremonial pride, whenever they went for
a walk.

Then came the rainy season, and day after
day the rain poured down in torrents. The
hungry river, like an enormous serpent, swallowed down terraces, villages, cornfields, and
covered with its flood the tall grasses on the
sandbanks. From time to time there was a deep
thud, as the river-banks crumbled. The unceasing roar of the main current could be heard
from far away. Masses of foam, carried swiftly
past, proved to the eye the swiftness of the
stream.

One afternoon the rain cleared. It was cloudy,
but cool and bright. Raicharan's little despot
did not want to stay in on such a fine afternoon.
His lordship climbed into the go-cart. Raicharan,
between the shafts, dragged him slowly along
till he reached the rice-fields on the banks of
the river. There was no one in the fields, and
no boat on the stream. Across the water, on the
farther side, the clouds were rifted in the west.
The silent ceremonial of the setting sun was
revealed in all its glowing splendor. In the midst
of that stillness the child, all of a sudden, pointed
with his finger in front of him and cried:
"Chan-na! Pitty fow."

Close by on a mud-flat stood a large *Kadamba*
tree in full flower. My lord, the baby, looked
at it with greedy eyes, and Raicharan knew his
meaning. Only a short time before he had made,
out of these very flower balls, a small go-cart;
and the child had been so entirely happy dragging it about with a string, that for the whole
day Raicharan was not made to put on the

Rabindranath Tagore

reins at all. He was promoted from a horse into a groom.

But Raicharan had no wish that evening to go splashing knee-deep through the mud to reach the flowers. So he quickly pointed his finger in the opposite direction, calling out: "Oh, look, baby, look! Look at the bird." And with all sorts of curious noises he pushed the go-cart rapidly away from the tree.

But a child, destined to be a judge, cannot be put off so easily. And besides, there was at the time nothing to attract his eyes. And you cannot keep up for ever the pretense of an imaginary bird.

The little Master's mind was made up, and Raicharan was at his wits' end. "Very well, baby," he said at last, "you sit still in the cart, and I'll go and get you the pretty flower. Only mind you don't go near the water."

As he said this, he made his legs bare to the knee, and waded through the oozing mud toward the tree.

The moment Raicharan had gone, his little Master went off at racing speed to the forbidden water. The baby saw the river rushing by, splashing and gurgling as it went. It seemed as though the disobedient wavelets themselves were running away from some greater Raicharan with the laughter of a thousand children. At the sight of their mischief, the heart of the human child grew excited and restless. He got down stealthily from the go-cart and toddled off toward the river. On his way he picked up a small stick, and leant over the bank of the stream pretending to fish. The mischievous fairies of the river with their mysterious voices seemed inviting him into their play-house.

Raicharan had plucked a handful of flowers from the tree, and was carrying them back in the end of his cloth, with his face wreathed in smiles. But when he reached the go-cart, there was no one there. He looked on all sides and there was no one there. He looked back at the cart and there was no one there.

In that first terrible moment his blood froze within him. Before his eyes the whole universe swam round like a dark mist. From the depth of his broken heart he gave one piercing cry: "Master, Master, little Master."

But no voice answered "Chan-na." No child laughed mischievously back; no scream of baby delight welcomed his return. Only the river ran on, with its splashing, gurgling noise as before— as though it knew nothing at all, and had no time to attend to such a tiny human event as the death of a child.

As the evening passed by Raicharan's mistress became very anxious. She sent men out on all sides to search. They went with lanterns in their hands, and reached at last the banks of the Padma. There they found Raicharan rushing up and down the fields, like a stormy wind, shouting the cry of despair: "Master, Master, little Master!"

When they got Raicharan home at last, he fell prostrate at his mistress's feet. They shook him, and questioned him, and asked him repeatedly where he had left the child; but all he could say was, that he knew nothing.

Though everyone held the opinion that the Padma had swallowed the child, there was a lurking doubt left in the mind. For a band of gypsies had been noticed outside the village that afternoon, and some suspicion rested on them. The mother went so far in her wild grief as to think it possible that Raicharan himself had stolen the child. She called him aside with piteous entreaty and said: "Raicharan, give me back my baby. Oh! give me back my child. Take from me any money you ask, but give me back my child!"

Anukul tried to reason his wife out of this wholly unjust suspicion: "Why on earth," he said, "should he commit such a crime as that?"

The mother only replied: "The baby had gold ornaments on his body. Who knows?"

It was impossible to reason with her after that.

Raicharan went back to his own village. Up to this time he had had no son, and there was no hope that any child would now be born to him. But it came about before the end of a year that his wife gave birth to a son and died.

An overwhelming resentment at first grew up in Raicharan's heart at the sight of this new baby. At the back of his mind was resentful suspicion that it had come as a usurper in place of the little Master. He also thought it would be a grave offense to be happy with a son of his own after what had happened to his master's little child. Indeed, if it had not been for a widowed sister, who mothered the new baby, it would not have lived long.

But a change gradually came over Raicharan's mind. A wonderful thing happened. This new baby in turn began to crawl about, and cross the doorway with mischief in its face. It also showed an amusing cleverness in making its escape to safety. Its voice, its sounds of laughter and tears, its gestures, were those of the little Master. On some days, when Raicharan listened to its crying, his heart suddenly began thumping wildly against his ribs, and it seemed to him that his former little Master was crying somewhere in the unknown land of death because he had lost his Chan-na.

Phailna (for that was the name Raicharan's sister gave to the new baby) soon began to talk. It learnt to say Ba-ba and Ma-ma with a baby accent. When Raicharan heard those familiar sounds the mystery suddenly became clear. The little Master could not cast off the spell of his Chan-na, and therefore he had been reborn in his own house.

The arguments in favor of this were, to Raicharan, altogether beyond dispute:

   (i.) The new baby was born soon after his little Master's death.

   (ii.) His wife could never have accumulated such merit as to give birth to a son in middle age.

   (iii.) The new baby walked wth a toddle and called out Ba-ba and Ma-ma. There was no sign lacking which marked out the future judge.

Then suddenly Raicharan remembered that terrible accusation of the mother. "Ah," he said to himself with amazement, "the mother's heart was right. She knew I had stolen her child." When once he had come to this conclusion, he was filled with remorse for his past neglect. He now gave himself over, body and soul, to the new baby, and became its devoted attendant. He began to bring it up, as if it were the son of a rich man. He bought a go-cart, a yellow satin waistcoat, and a gold-embroidered cap. He melted down the ornaments of his dead wife, and made gold bangles and anklets. He refused to let the little child play with anyone of the neighborhood, and became himself its sole companion day and night. As the baby grew up to boyhood, he was so petted and spoilt and clad in such finery that the village children would call him "Your Lordship," and jeer at him; and older people regarded Raicharan as unaccountably crazy about the child.

At last the time came for the boy to go to school. Raicharan sold his small piece of land,

and went to Calcutta. There he got employment with great difficulty as a servant, and sent Phailna to school. He spared no pains to give him the best education, the best clothes, the best food. Meanwhile he lived himself on a mere handful of rice, and would say in secret: "Ah! my little Master, my dear little Master, you loved me so much that you came back to my house. You shall never suffer from any neglect of mine."

Twelve years passed away in this manner. The boy was able to read and write well. He was bright and healthy, and good-looking. He paid a great deal of attention to his personal appearance, and was specially careful in parting his hair. He was inclined to extravagance and finery, and spent money freely. He could never quite look on Raicharan as a father, because, though fatherly in affection, he had the manner of a servant. A further fault was this, that Raicharan kept secret from everyone that he himself was the father of the child.

The students of the hostel, where Phailna was a boarder, were greatly amused by Raicharan's country manners, and I have to confess that behind his father's back Phailna joined in their fun. But, in the bottom of their hearts, all the students loved the innocent and tender-hearted old man, and Phailna was very fond of him also. But, as I have said before, he loved him with a kind of condescension.

Raicharan grew older and older, and his employer was continually finding fault with him for his incompetent work. He had been starving himself for the boy's sake. So he had grown physically weak, and no longer up to his work. He would forget things, and his mind became dull and stupid. But his employer expected a full servant's work out of him, and would not brook excuses. The money that Raicharan had brought with him from the sale of his land was exhausted. The boy was continually grumbling about his clothes, and asking for more money.

Raicharan made up his mind. He gave up the situation where he was working as a servant, and left some money with Phailna and said: "I have some business to do at home in my village, and shall be back soon."

He went off at once to Baraset where Anukul was magistrate. Anukul's wife was still broken down with grief. She had had no other child.

One day Anukul was resting after a long and weary day in court. His wife was buying, at an exorbitant price, an herb from a mendicant quack,[1] which was said to insure the birth of a child. A voice of greeting was heard in the courtyard. Anukul went out to see who was there. It was Raicharan. Anukul's heart was softened when he saw his old servant. He asked him many questions, and offered to take him back into service.

Raicharan smiled faintly, and said in reply: "I want to make obeisance[2] to my mistress."

Anukul went with Raicharan into the house, where the mistress did not receive him as warmly as his old master. Raicharan took no notice of this, but folded his hands, and said: "It was not the river that stole your baby. It was I."

Anukul exclaimed: "Great God! Eh! What! Where is he?"

Raicharan replied: "He is with me. I will bring him the day after tomorrow."

It was Sunday. There was no magistrate's court sitting. Both husband and wife were looking expectantly along the road, waiting from early morning for Raicharan's appearance. At ten o'clock he came, leading Phailna by the hand.

Anukul's wife, without question, took the boy into her lap, and was wild with excitement, sometimes laughing, sometimes weeping, touching him, kissing his hair and his forehead, and gazing into his face with hungry, eager eyes. The boy was very good-looking and dressed like a gentleman's son. The heart of Anukul brimmed over with a sudden rush of affection.

[1] *mendicant quack* A beggar who makes his living by selling herbs and worthless medicines.
[2] *make obeisance* To bow, as a sign of respect.

Nevertheless the magistrate in him asked: "Have you any proofs?"

Raicharan said: "How could there be any proof of such a deed? God alone knows that I stole your boy, and no one else in the world."

When Anukul saw how eagerly his wife was clinging to the boy, he realized the futility of asking for proofs. It would be wiser to believe. And then—where could an old man like Raicharan get such a boy from? And why should his faithful servant deceive him for nothing?

"But," he added severely, "Raicharan, you must not stay here."

"Where shall I go, Master?" said Raicharan, in a choking voice, folding his hands; "I am old. Who will take an old man as a servant?"

The mistress said: "Let him stay. My child will be pleased. I forgive him."

But Anukul's magisterial conscience would not allow him. "No," he said, "he cannot be forgiven for what he has done."

Raicharan bowed to the ground, and clasped Anukul's feet. "Master," he cried, "let me stay. It was not I who did it. It was God."

Anukul's conscience was worse stricken than ever, when Raicharan tried to put the blame on God's shoulders.

"No," he said, "I could not allow it. I cannot trust you any more. You have done an act of treachery."

Raicharan rose to his feet and said: "It was not I who did it."

"Who was it then?" asked Anukul.

Raicharan replied: "It was my fate."

But no educated man could take this for an excuse. Anukul remained obdurate.

When Phailna saw that he was the wealthy magistrate's son, and not Raicharan's, he was angry at first, thinking that he had been cheated all this time of his birthright. But seeing Raicharan in distress, he generously said to his father: "Father, forgive him. Even if you don't let him live with us, let him have a small monthly pension."

After hearing this, Raicharan did not utter another word. He looked for the last time on the face of his son; he made obeisance to his old master and mistress. Then he went out, and was mingled with the numberless people of the world.

At the end of the month Anukul sent him some money to his village. But the money came back. There was no one there of the name of Raicharan.

For Discussion

1. Who is responsible for Raicharan's grief? Do you agree with him when he says, "It was my fate"? Why does Raicharan recreate his own son in the image of his master's drowned little boy?

2. Are Raicharan's three reasons for believing his son to be a reincarnation of the lost baby logical?

3. What is Phailna's attitude toward his father? Is there any justice in such an attitude? Who is responsible for it? Why do other children call Phailna, "Your lordship"? Why does Raicharan tell Anukul that Phailna is his lost son?

4. Has Raicharan really come to believe that Phailna is Anukul's lost son? Why doesn't Phailna protest? Has Raicharan ever been a real father to Phailna?

5. Compare the attitude of Raicharan with that of Thord Overaas in "A Father" (page 19). What motives do the two fathers have in common? Does Tagore seem to disapprove of Raicharan's actions as strongly as Björnson disapproves of Thord Overaas's?

6. Edgar Allan Poe said that in a true short story all the elements should contribute towards making a single effect. Consider the implications of Poe's statement, and then apply it to "My Lord, the Baby." Does the story make a "single effect"? If so, what is that effect? Do you think Poe would have considered "My Lord, the Baby" a true short story? What term other than "short story" might be used to describe it?

The Monkey's Paw

W. W. JACOBS

One of the classic themes of literature is the attempt of man to outwit or change his fate. Oedipus, in the Greek legend, ran away from his home in Corinth, attempting to avoid a prophecy that he would kill his own father. Unknown to him, the man he thought was his father had adopted him when he was a baby. Along the road he met and killed a stranger, but the "stranger," Laius, turned out to be his real father. In trying to escape from his destiny, Oedipus rushed headlong into it. Jonah, in the Old Testament, disobeyed God and ran away, only to find himself trapped inside the whale. He was hastened on to Nineveh where he was faced with the very duty he had tried to avoid.

"The Monkey's Paw" is a story in which gentle people tamper curiously with fate's secrets and turn the happiness of their quiet lives into a nightmare. They find that when they disturb the balance of destiny, they must pay a severe price for every gift they receive. The story asks: Is man's ignorance of the future a curse, or is it really a blessing?

WITHOUT, the night was cold and wet, but in the small parlor of Lakesnam Villa the blinds were drawn and the fire burned brightly. Father and son were at chess, the former, who possessed ideas about the game involving radical changes, putting his king into such sharp and unnecessary perils that it even provoked comment from the white-haired old lady knitting placidly by the fire.

"Hark at the wind," said Mr. White, who, having seen a fatal mistake after it was too late, was amiably desirous of preventing his son from seeing it.

"I'm listening," said the latter, grimly surveying the board as he stretched out his hand. "Check."

"I should hardly think that he'd come tonight," said his father, with his hand poised over the board.

"Mate," replied the son.

W. W. JACOBS (*1863–1943*) *was a popular English writer. "The Monkey's Paw" is by far his most widely reprinted work. It has been dramatized by L. N. Parker.*

"That's the worst of living so far out," bawled Mr. White, with sudden and unlooked-for violence; "of all the beastly, slushy, out-of-the-way places to live in, this is the worst. Pathway's a bog, and the road's a torrent. I don't know what people are thinking about. I suppose because only two houses on the road are let, they think it doesn't matter."

"Never mind, dear," said his wife soothingly; "perhaps you'll win the next one."

Mr. White looked up sharply, just in time to intercept a knowing glance between mother and son. The words died away on his lips, and he hid a guilty grin in his thin gray beard.

"There he is," said Herbert White, as the gate banged to loudly and heavy footsteps came toward the door.

The old man rose with hospitable haste, and opening the door, was heard condoling with the new arrival. The new arrival also condoled with himself, so that Mrs. White said, "Tut, tut!" and coughed gently as her husband entered the room, followed by a tall burly man, beady of eye and rubicund [1] of visage.

"Sergeant-Major Morris," he said, introducing him.

The sergeant-major shook hands, and taking the proffered seat by the fire, watched contentedly while his host got out whisky and tumblers and stood a small copper kettle on the fire.

At the third glass his eyes got brighter, and he began to talk, the little family circle regarding with eager interest this visitor from distant parts, as he squared his broad shoulders in the chair and spoke of strange scenes and doughty deeds, of wars and plagues and strange peoples.

"Twenty-one years of it," said Mr. White, nodding at his wife and son. "When he went away he was a slip of a youth in the warehouse. Now look at him."

"He don't look to have taken much harm," said Mrs. White politely.

"I'd like to go to India myself," said the old man, "just to look round a bit, you know."

"Better where you are," said the sergeant-major, shaking his head. He put down the empty glass and, sighing softly, shook it again.

"I should like to see those old temples and fakirs and jugglers," said the old man. "What was that you started telling me the other day about a monkey's paw or something, Morris?"

"Nothing," said the soldier hastily. "Leastways, nothing worth hearing."

"Monkey's paw?" said Mrs. White curiously.

"Well, it's just a bit of what you might call magic, perhaps," said the sergeant-major off-handedly.

His three listeners leaned forward eagerly. The visitor absent-mindedly put his empty glass to his lips and then set it down again. His host filled it for him.

"To look at," said the sergeant-major fumbling in his pocket, "it's just an ordinary little paw, dried to a mummy."

He took something out of his pocket and proffered it. Mrs. White drew back with a grimace, but her son, taking it, examined it curiously.

"And what is there special about it?" inquired Mr. White, as he took it from his son and, having examined it, placed it upon the table.

"It had a spell put on it by an old fakir," said the sergeant-major, "a very holy man. He wanted to show that fate ruled people's lives, and that those who interfered with it did so to their sorrow. He put a spell on it so that three separate men could each have three wishes from it."

His manner was so impressive that his hearers were conscious that their light laughter jarred somewhat.

"Well, why don't you have three, sir?" said Herbert White cleverly.

[1] *rubicund* Red, ruddy.

The soldier regarded him in the way that middle age is wont to regard presumptuous youth. "I have," he said quietly, and his blotchy face whitened.

"And did you really have the three wishes granted?" asked Mrs. White.

"I did," said the sergeant-major, and his glass tapped against his strong teeth.

"And has anybody else wished?" inquired the old lady.

"The first man had his three wishes, yes," was the reply. "I don't know what the first two were, but the third was for death. That's how I got the paw."

His tones were so grave that a hush fell upon the group.

"If you've had your three wishes, it's no good to you now, then, Morris," said the old man at last. "What do you keep it for?"

The soldier shook his head. "Fancy, I suppose," he said slowly. "I did have some idea of selling it, but I don't think I will. It has caused enough mischief already. Besides, people won't buy. They think it's a fairy tale, some of them, and those who do think anything of it want to try it first and pay me afterward."

"If you could have another three wishes," said the old man, eyeing him keenly, "would you have them?"

"I don't know," said the other. "I don't know."

He took the paw, and dangling it between his front finger and thumb, suddenly threw it upon the fire. White, with a slight cry, stooped down and snatched it off.

"Better let it burn," said the soldier solemnly.

"If you don't want it, Morris," said the old man, "give it to me."

"I won't," said his friend doggedly. "I threw it on the fire. If you keep it, don't blame me for what happens. Pitch it on the fire again, like a sensible man."

The other shook his head and examined his new possession closely. "How do you do it?" he inquired.

"Hold it up in your right hand and wish aloud," said the sergeant-major, "but I warn you of the consequences."

"Sounds like the *Arabian Nights*," said Mrs. White, as she rose and began to set the supper. "Don't you think you might wish for four pairs of hands for me?"

Her husband drew the talisman [2] from his pocket and then all three burst into laughter as the sergeant-major, with a look of alarm on his face, caught him by the arm.

"If you must wish," he said gruffly, "wish for something sensible."

Mr. White dropped it back into his pocket, and placing chairs, motioned his friend to the table. In the business of supper the talisman was partly forgotten, and afterward the three sat listening in an enthralled fashion to a second installment of the soldier's adventures in India.

"If the tale about the monkey paw is not more truthful than those he has been telling us," said Herbert, as the door closed behind their guest, just in time for him to catch the last train, "we shan't make much out of it."

"Did you give him anything for it, father?" inquired Mrs. White, regarding her husband closely.

"A trifle," said he, coloring slightly. "He didn't want it, but I made him take it. And he pressed me again to throw it away."

"Likely," said Herbert, with pretended horror. "Why, we're going to be rich, and famous, and happy. Wish to be an emperor, father, to begin with; then you can't be henpecked."

He darted round the table, pursued by the maligned Mrs. White armed with an antimacassar.

Mr. White took the paw from his pocket and eyed it dubiously. "I don't know what to wish for, and that's a fact," he said slowly. "It seems to me I've got all I want."

"If you only cleared the house, you'd be quite

[2] *talisman* A charm or a magical object carried to ward off evil.

happy, wouldn't you?" said Herbert, with his hand on his shoulder. "Well, wish for two hundred pounds, then; that'll just do it."

His father, smiling shamefacedly at his own credulity, held up the talisman, as his son, with a solemn face somewhat marred by a wink at his mother, sat down at the piano and struck a few impressive chords.

"I wish for two hundred pounds," said the old man distinctly.

A fine crash from the piano greeted the words, interrupted by a shuddering cry from the old man. His wife and son ran toward him.

"It moved," he cried, with a glance of disgust at the object as it lay on the floor. "As I wished it twisted in my hands like a snake."

"Well, I don't see the money," said his son, as he picked it up and placed it on the table, "and I bet I never shall."

"It must have been your fancy, father," said his wife, regarding him anxiously.

He shook his head. "Never mind, though; there's no harm done, but it gave me a shock all the same."

They sat down by the fire again while the two men finished their pipes. Outside, the wind was higher than ever, and the old man started nervously at the sound of a door banging upstairs. A silence unusual and depressing settled upon all three, which lasted until the old couple rose to retire for the night.

"I expect you'll find the cash tied up in a big bag in the middle of your bed," said Herbert, as he bade them good night, "and something horrible squatting up on top of the wardrobe watching you as you pocket your ill-gotten gains."

II

In the brightness of the wintry sun next morning as it streamed over the breakfast table Herbert laughed at his fears. There was an air of prosaic wholesomeness about the room which it had lacked on the previous night, and the dirty,

shriveled little paw was pitched on the sideboard with a carelessness which betokened no great belief in its virtues.

"I suppose all old soldiers are the same," said Mrs. White. "The idea of our listening to such nonsense! How could wishes be granted in these days? And if they could, how could two hundred pounds hurt you, father?"

"Might drop on his head from the sky," said the frivolous Herbert.

"Morris said the things happened so naturally," said his father, "that you might if you so wished attribute it to coincidence."

"Well, don't break into the money before I come back," said Herbert, as he rose from the table. "I'm afraid it'll turn you into a mean, avaricious man, and we shall have to disown you."

His mother laughed, and following him to the door, watched him down the road, and returning to the breakfast table, was very happy at the expense of her husband's credulity. All of which did not prevent her from scurrying to the door at the postman's knock, nor prevent her from referring somewhat shortly to retired sergeant-majors of bibulous habits when she found that the post brought a tailor's bill.

"Herbert will have some more of his funny remarks, I expect, when he comes home," she said, as they sat at dinner.

"I dare say," said Mr. White, pouring himself out some beer; "but for all that, the thing moved in my hand; that I'll swear to."

"You thought it did," said the old lady soothingly.

"I say it did," replied the other. "There was no thought about it; I had just—What's the matter?"

His wife made no reply. She was watching the mysterious movements of a man outside, who, peering in an undecided fashion at the house, appeared to be trying to make up his mind to enter. In mental connection with the two hundred pounds, she noticed that the stranger was well dressed and wore a silk hat of glossy newness. Three times he paused at the gate, and then walked on again. The fourth time he stood with his hand upon it, and then with sudden resolution flung it open and walked up the path. Mrs. White at the same moment placed her hands behind her, and hurriedly unfastening the strings of her apron, put that useful article of apparel beneath the cushion of her chair.

She brought the stranger, who seemed ill at ease, into the room. He gazed furtively at Mrs. White, and listened in a preoccupied fashion as the old lady apologized for the appearance of the room, and her husband's coat, a garment which he usually reserved for the garden. She then waited as patiently as her sex would permit for him to broach his business, but he was at first strangely silent.

"I—was asked to call," he said at last, and stooped and picked a piece of cotton from his trousers. "I come from Maw and Meggins."

The old lady started. "Is anything the matter?" she asked breathlessly. "Has anything happened to Herbert? What is it? What is it?"

Her husband interposed. "There, there, mother," he said hastily. "Sit down, and don't jump to conclusions. You've not brought bad news, I'm sure, sir," and he eyed the other wistfully.

"I'm sorry——" began the visitor.

"Is he hurt?" demanded the mother.

The visitor bowed in assent. "Badly hurt," he said quietly, "but he is not in any pain."

"Oh, thank God!" said the old woman, clasping her hands. "Thank God for that! Thank——"

She broke off suddenly as the sinister meaning of the assurance dawned upon her and she saw the awful confirmation of her fears in the other's averted face. She caught her breath, and turning to her slower-witted husband, laid her trembling old hand upon his. There was a long silence.

"He was caught in the machinery," said the visitor at length, in a low voice.

"Caught in the machinery," repeated Mr. White, in a dazed fashion, "yes."

He sat staring blankly out at the window, and taking his wife's hand between his own, pressed it as he had been wont to do in their old courting days nearly forty years before.

"He was the only one left to us," he said, turning gently to the visitor. "It is hard."

The other coughed, and rising, walked slowly to the window. "The firm wished me to convey their sincere sympathy with you in your great loss," he said, without looking round. "I beg that you will understand I am only their servant and merely obeying orders."

There was no reply; the old woman's face was white, her eyes staring, and her breath inaudible; on the husband's face was a look such as his friend the sergeant might have carried into his first action.

"I was to say that Maw and Meggins disclaim all responsibility," continued the other. "They admit no liability at all, but in consideration of your son's services they wish to present you with a certain sum as compensation."

Mr. White dropped his wife's hand, and rising to his feet, gazed with a look of horror at his visitor. His dry lips shaped the words, "How much?"

"Two hundred pounds," was the answer.

Unconscious of his wife's shriek, the old man smiled faintly, put out his hands like a sightless man, and dropped, a senseless heap, to the floor.

III

In the huge new cemetery, some two miles distant, the old people buried their dead, and came back to a house steeped in shadow and silence. It was all over so quickly that at first they could hardly realize it, and remained in a state of expectation as though of something else to happen—something else which was to lighten this load, too heavy for old hearts to bear. But the days passed, and expectation gave place to resignation—the hopeless resignation of the old, sometimes miscalled apathy. Sometimes they hardly exchanged a word, for now they had nothing to talk about, and their days were long to weariness.

It was about a week after that that the old

man, waking suddenly in the night, stretched out his hand and found himself alone. The room was in darkness, and the sound of subdued weeping came from the window. He raised himself in bed and listened.

"Come back," he said tenderly. "You will be cold."

"It is colder for my son," said the old woman, and wept afresh.

The sound of her sobs died away on his ears. The bed was warm, and his eyes heavy with sleep. He dozed fitfully, and then slept until a sudden wild cry from his wife awoke him with a start.

"The monkey's paw!" she cried wildly. "The monkey's paw!"

He started up in alarm. "Where? Where is it? What's the matter?"

She came stumbling across the room toward him. "I want it," she said quietly. "You've not destroyed it?"

"It's in the parlor, on the bracket," he replied, marveling. "Why?"

She cried and laughed together, and bending over, kissed his cheek.

"I only just thought of it," she said hysterically. "Why didn't I think of it before? Why didn't you think of it?"

"Think of what?" he questioned.

"The other two wishes," she replied rapidly. "We've only had one."

"Was not that enough?" he demanded fiercely.

"No," she cried triumphantly; "we'll have one more. Go down and get it quickly, and wish our boy alive again."

The man sat up in bed and flung the bedclothes from his quaking limbs. "Good God, you are mad!" he cried, aghast.

"Get it," she panted; "get it quickly, and wish —Oh, my boy, my boy!"

Her husband struck a match and lit the candle. "Get back to bed," he said unsteadily. "You don't know what you are saying."

"We had the first wish granted," said the old woman feverishly; "why not the second?"

"A coincidence," stammered the old man.

"Go and get it and wish," cried the old woman, and dragged him toward the door.

He went down in the darkness, and felt his way to the parlor, and then to the mantelpiece. The talisman was in its place, and a horrible fear that the unspoken wish might bring his mutilated son before him ere he could escape from the room seized upon him, and he caught his breath as he found that he had lost the direction of the door. His brow cold with sweat, he felt his way round the table, and groped along the wall until he found himself in the small passage with the unwholesome thing in his hand.

Even his wife's face seemed changed as he entered the room. It was white and expectant, and to his fears seemed to have an unnatural look upon it. He was afraid of her.

"Wish!" she cried, in a strong voice.

"It is foolish and wicked," he faltered.

"Wish!" repeated his wife.

He raised his hand. "I wish my son alive again."

The talisman fell to the floor, and he regarded it shudderingly. Then he sank trembling into a chair as the old woman, with burning eyes, walked to the window and raised the blind.

He sat until he was chilled with the cold, glancing occasionally at the figure of the old woman peering through the window. The candle end, which had burnt below the rim of the china candlestick, was throwing pulsating shadows on the ceiling and walls, until, with a flicker larger than the rest, it expired. The old man, with an unspeakable sense of relief at the failure of the talisman, crept back to his bed, and a minute or two afterward the old woman came silently and apathetically beside him.

Neither spoke, but both lay silently listening to the ticking of the clock. A stair creaked, and a squeaky mouse scurried noisily through the wall. The darkness was oppressive, and after lying for some time screwing up his courage, the husband took the box of matches, and striking one, went downstairs for a candle.

At the foot of the stairs the match went out,

and he paused to strike another, and at the same moment a knock, so quiet and stealthy as to be scarcely audible, sounded on the front door.

The matches fell from his hand. He stood motionless, his breath suspended until the knock was repeated. Then he turned and fled swiftly back to his room, and closed the door behind him. A third knock sounded through the house.

"*What's that?*" cried the old woman, starting up.

"A rat," said the old man, in shaking tones—"a rat. It passed me on the stairs."

His wife sat up in bed listening. A loud knock resounded through the house.

"It's Herbert!" she screamed. "It's Herbert!"

She ran to the door, but her husband was before her, and catching her by the arm, held her tightly.

"What are you going to do?" he whispered hoarsely.

"It's my boy; it's Herbert!" she cried, struggling mechanically. "I forgot it was two miles away. What are you holding me for? Let go. I must open the door."

"For God's sake don't let it in," cried the old man, trembling.

"You're afraid of your own son," she cried, struggling. "Let me go. I'm coming, Herbert; I'm coming."

There was another knock, and another. The old woman with a sudden wrench broke free and ran from the room. Her husband followed to the landing, and called after her appealingly as she hurried downstairs. He heard the chain rattle back and the bottom bolt drawn slowly and stiffly from the socket. Then the old woman's voice, strained and panting.

"The bolt," she cried loudly. "Come down. I can't reach it."

But her husband was on his hands and knees groping wildly on the floor in search of the paw. If he could only find it before the thing outside got in. A perfect fusillade of knocks reverberated through the house, and he heard the scraping of a chair as his wife put it down in the passage against the door. He heard the creaking of the bolt as it came slowly back, and at the same moment he found the monkey's paw, and frantically breathed his third and last wish.

The knocking ceased suddenly, although the echoes of it were still in the house. He heard the chair drawn back and the door opened. A cold wind rushed up the staircase, and a long loud wail of disappointment and misery from his wife gave him courage to run down to her side, and then to the gate beyond. The street lamp flickering opposite shone on a quiet and deserted road.

For Discussion

1. What does the opening scene of the story reveal about the White family? What do Mr. White's chess tactics suggest about his personality that prepares us for his role as the one to test the powers of the monkey's paw?

2. Why does Sergeant-Major Morris keep his three wishes a secret? Do you think they were similar to the three wishes that Mr. and Mrs. White made?

3. What happens to Mrs. White during the course of the story? In what way does she change? In what way does Mr. White change? Compare the way they both feel toward the monkey's paw after the fulfillment of the first wish.

4. Can the reader be sure that the monkey's paw brought about the final two wishes? What evidence is there that the son actually arose from the grave? What evidence is there that he returned to the grave? Do you think that the appearance of the son after his death existed only in Mr. and Mrs. White's imagination?

5. If you had a monkey's paw with similar powers, could you contrive a wish to outwit fate? What might it be?

Friends in San Rosario

O. HENRY

*O. Henry's story about life in a frontier town in the American West
is a variation on the tale of the city mouse and the country mouse.
There are many versions of this fable, ancient and modern. Usually,
when these two forces come together, the folk wisdom of the
countryside nips annoyingly at the heels of polished city efficiency.
O. Henry complicates the plot by adding the element of friendship.*

THE WEST-BOUND stopped at San Rosario on time at 8:20 A.M. A man with a thick black-leather wallet under his arm left the train and walked rapidly up the main street of the town. There were other passengers who also got off at San Rosario, but they either slouched limberly over to the railroad eating-house or the Silver Dollar saloon, or joined the groups of idlers about the station.

Indecision had no part in the movements of the man with the wallet. He was short in stature, but strongly built, with very light, closely trimmed hair, smooth, determined face, and aggressive, gold-rimmed nose glasses. He was well dressed in the prevailing Eastern style. His air denoted a quiet but conscious reserve force, if not actual authority.

After walking a distance of three squares he came to the center of the town's business area. Here another street of importance crossed the main one, forming the hub of San Rosario's life and commerce. Upon one corner stood the postoffice. Upon another Rubensky's Clothing Emporium. The other two diagonally opposing corners were occupied by the town's two banks,

the First National and the Stockmen's National. Into the First National Bank of San Rosario the newcomer walked, never slowing his brisk step until he stood at the cashier's window. The bank opened for business at nine, and the working force was already assembled, each member preparing his department for the day's business. The cashier was examining the mail when he noticed the stranger standing at his window.

"Bank doesn't open 'til nine," he remarked, curtly, but without feeling. He had had to make that statement so often to early birds since San Rosario adopted city banking hours.

"I am well aware of that," said the other man, in cool, brittle tones. "Will you kindly receive my card?"

The cashier drew the small, spotless parallelogram inside the bars of his wicket, and read:

J. F. C. NETTLEWICK
National Bank Examiner

"Oh—er—will you walk around inside, Mr.—er—Nettlewick. Your first visit—didn't know your business, of course. Walk right around, please."

The examiner was quickly inside the sacred precincts of the bank, where he was ponderously introduced to each employee in turn by Mr. Edlinger, the cashier—a middle-aged gentleman of deliberation, discretion, and method.

"I was kind of expecting Sam Turner round again, pretty soon," said Mr. Edlinger. "Sam's been examining us now for about four years. I guess you'll find us all right, though, considering the tightness in business. Not overly much money on hand, but able to stand the storms, sir, stand the storms."

"Mr. Turner and I have been ordered by the Comptroller to exchange districts," said the examiner, in his decisive, formal tones. "He is covering my old territory in southern Illinois and Indiana. I will take the cash first, please."

Perry Dorsey, the teller, was already arranging the cash on the counter for the examiner's inspection. He knew it was right to a cent, and he had nothing to fear, but he was nervous and flustered. So was every man in the bank. There was something so icy and swift, so impersonal and uncompromising about this man that his very presence seemed an accusation. He looked to be a man who would never make nor overlook an error.

Mr. Nettlewick first seized the currency, and with a rapid, almost juggling motion, counted it by packages. Then he spun the sponge cup toward him and verified the count by bills. His thin, white fingers flew like some expert musician's upon the keys of a piano. He dumped the gold upon the counter with a crash, and the coins whined and sang as they skimmed across the marble slab from the tips of his nimble digits. The air was full of fractional currency when he came to the halves and quarters. He counted the last nickel and dime. He had the scales brought, and he weighed every sack of silver in the vault. He questioned Dorsey concerning each of the cash memoranda—certain checks, charge slips, etc., carried over from the previous day's work—with unimpeachable courtesy, yet with something so mysteriously momentous in his frigid manner, that the teller was reduced to pink cheeks and a stammering tongue.

This newly imported examiner was so different from Sam Turner. It had been Sam's way to enter the bank with a shout, pass the cigars, and tell the latest stories he had picked up on his rounds. His customary greeting to Dorsey had been, "Hello, Perry! Haven't skipped out with the boodle yet, I see." Turner's way of counting the cash had been different too. He would finger the packages of bills in a tired kind of way, and then go into the vault and kick over a few sacks of silver, and the thing was done. Halves and quarters and dimes? Not for Sam Turner. "No chicken feed for me," he would say when they were set before him. "I'm not in the agricultural department." But, then, Turner was a Texan, an old friend of the bank's president, and had known Dorsey since he was a baby.

While the examiner was counting the cash, Major Thomas B. Kingman—known to everyone as "Major Tom"—the president of the First National, drove up to the side door with his old dun horse and buggy, and came inside. He saw the examiner busy with the money, and, going into the little "pony corral," as he called it, in which his desk was railed off, he began to look over his letters.

Earlier, a little incident had occurred that even the sharp eyes of the examiner had failed to notice. When he had begun his work at the cash counter, Mr. Edlinger had winked significantly at Roy Wilson, the youthful bank messenger, and nodded his head slightly toward the front door. Roy understood, got his hat and walked leisurely out, with his collector's book under his arm. Once outside, he made a bee-line for the Stockmen's National. That bank was also getting ready to open. No customers had, as yet, presented themselves.

"Say, you people!" cried Roy, with the familiarity of youth and long acquaintance, "you want to get a move on you. There's a new bank examiner over at the First, and he's a stem-winder.[1] He's counting nickels on Perry, and he's

[1] *stem-winder* Slang: a very meticulous person.

O. HENRY *(1862–1910) is the pen name of William Sydney Porter. He was born in Greensboro, North Carolina. When he was young, he traveled to Texas and spent several years working on a ranch. Later, he held a position as bank teller, but the charge that he had embezzled funds frightened him into escaping to South America. In 1898 he faced trial, pleading innocent. The court sentenced him to a five-year term in the penitentiary at Columbus, Ohio. In the surprise tradition of his later fiction, this seeming end to a man's career strangely turned out to be a beginning. He spent his time in prison writing stories which he sent to popular magazines. To conceal his real identity, he used the name O. Henry.*

In 1902, after his release from prison, he went to New York. He had little trouble in finding a market for his stories, and he began to write in earnest. To hold his reader's attention and to portray the whimsical fate that he felt prevailed in human experience, O. Henry often used the "surprise ending." His attitude toward life was more sentimental than it was profound, and his characters possess a simplicity that often makes them appear childlike.

---

got the whole outfit bluffed. Mr. Edlinger gave me the tip to let you know."

Mr. Buckley, president of the Stockmen's National—a stout, elderly man, looking like a farmer dressed for Sunday—heard Roy from his private office at the rear and called him.

"Has Major Kingman come down to the bank yet?" he asked of the boy.

"Yes, sir, he was just driving up as I left," said Roy.

"I want you to take him a note. Put it into his own hands as soon as you get back."

Mr. Buckley sat down and began to write.

Roy returned and handed to Major Kingman the envelope containing the note. The major read it, folded it, and slipped it into his vest pocket. He leaned back in his chair for a few moments as if he were meditating deeply, and then rose and went into the vault. He came out with the bulky, old-fashioned leather note case stamped on the back in gilt letters, "Bills Discounted." In this were the notes due the bank with their attached securities, and the major, in his rough way, dumped the lot upon his desk and began to sort them over.

By this time Nettlewick had finished his count of the cash. His pencil fluttered like a swallow over the sheet of paper on which he had set his figures. He opened his black wallet, which seemed to be also a kind of secret memorandum book, made a few rapid figures in it, wheeled and transfixed Dorsey with the glare of his spectacles. That look seemed to say: "You're safe this time, but—"

"Cash all correct," snapped the examiner. He made a dash for the individual bookkeeper, and, for a few minutes there was a fluttering of ledger leaves and a sailing of balance sheets through the air.

"How often do you balance your passbooks?" he demanded, suddenly.

"Er—once a month," faltered the individual bookkeeper, wondering how many years they would give him.

"All right," said the examiner, turning and charging upon the general bookkeeper, who had the statements of his foreign banks and their reconcilement memoranda ready. Everything there was found to be all right. Then the stub book of the certificates of deposit. Flutter-flutter—zip—zip—check! All right. List of overdrafts, please. Thanks. H'm-m. Unsigned bills of the bank next. All right.

Then came the cashier's turn, and easy-going Mr. Edlinger rubbed his nose and polished his glasses nervously under the quick fire of questions concerning the circulation, undivided profits, bank real estate, and stock ownership.

Presently, Nettlewick was aware of a big man towering above him at his elbow—a man sixty years of age, rugged and hale, with a rough, grizzled beard, a mass of gray hair, and a pair of penetrating blue eyes that confronted the formidable glasses of the examiner without a flicker.

"Er—Major Kingman, our president—er—Mr. Nettlewick," said the cashier.

Two men of very different types shook hands. One was a finished product of the world of straight lines, conventional methods, and formal affairs. The other was something freer, wider, and nearer to nature. Tom Kingman had not been cut to any pattern. He had been mule-driver, cowboy, ranger, soldier, sheriff, prospector and cattleman. Now, when he was bank president, his old comrades from the prairies, of the saddle, tent, and trail, found no change in him. He had made his fortune when Texas cattle were at the high tide of value, and had organized the First National Bank of San Rosario. In spite of his largeness of heart and sometimes unwise generosity toward his old friends, the bank had prospered, for Major Tom Kingman knew men as well as he knew cattle. Of late years the cattle business had known a depression, and the major's bank was one of the few whose losses had not been great.

"And now," said the examiner, briskly, pulling out his watch, "the last thing is the loans. We will take them up now, if you please."

He had gone through the First National at almost record-breaking speed—but thoroughly, as he did everything. The running order of the bank was smooth and clean, and that had facilitated his work. There was but one other bank in the town. He received from the Government a fee of twenty-five dollars for each bank that he examined. He should be able to go over those loans and discounts in half an hour. If so, he could examine the other bank immediately afterward, and catch the 11:45, the only other train that day in the direction he was working. Otherwise, he would have to spend the night and Sunday in this uninteresting Western town.

That was why Mr. Nettlewick was rushing matters.

"Come with me, sir," said Major Kingman, in his deep voice, that united the Southern drawl with the rhythmic twang of the West. "We will go over them together. Nobody in the bank knows those notes as I do. Some of 'em are a little wobbly on their legs, and some are mavericks without extra many brands on their backs, but they'll most all pay out at the round-up."

The two sat down at the president's desk. First, the examiner went through the notes at lightning speed, and added up their total, finding it to agree with the amount of loans carried on the book of daily balances. Next, he took up the larger loans, inquiring scrupulously into the condition of their endorsers or securities. The new examiner's mind seemed to course and turn and make unexpected dashes hither and thither like a bloodhound seeking a new trail. Finally he pushed aside all the notes except a few, which he arranged in a neat pile before him, and began a dry, formal little speech.

"I find, sir, the condition of your bank to be very good, considering the poor crops and the depression in the cattle interests of your state. The clerical work seems to be done accurately and punctually. Your past-due paper is moderate in amount, and promises only a small loss. I would recommend the calling in of your large loans, and the making of only sixty and ninety day or call loans until general business revives. And now, there is one thing more, and I will have finished with the bank. Here are six notes aggregating something like $40,000.00. They are secured, according to their faces, by various stocks, bonds, shares, etc., to the value of $70,000.00. Those securities are missing from the notes to which they should be attached. I suppose you have them in the safer vault. You will permit me to examine them."

Major Tom's light-blue eyes turned unflinchingly toward the examiner.

"No, sir," he said, in a low but steady tone: "those securities are neither in the safe nor the vault. I have taken them. You may hold me personally responsible for their absence."

Nettlewick felt a slight thrill. He had not expected this. He had struck a momentous trail when the hunt was drawing to a close.

"Ah!" said the examiner. He waited a moment, and then continued: "May I ask you to explain more definitely?"

"The securities were taken by me," repeated the major. "It was not for my own use, but to save an old friend in trouble. Come in here, sir, and we'll talk it over."

He led the examiner into the bank's private office at the rear, and closed the door. There was a desk, and a table, and half-a-dozen leather covered chairs. On the wall was the mounted head of a Texas steer with horns five feet from tip to tip. Opposite hung the major's old cavalry saber that he had carried at Shiloh and Fort Pillow.

Placing a chair for Nettlewick, the major seated himself by the window, from which he could see the post-office and the carved lime-

". . . or joined the group of idlers about the station."

A frontier town in the 1870s

stone front of the Stockmen's National. He did not speak at once, and Nettlewick felt, perhaps, that the ice should be broken by something so near its own temperature as the voice of official warning.

"Your statement," he began, "since you have failed to modify it, amounts, as you must know, to a very serious thing. You are aware, also, of what my duty must compel me to do. I shall have to go before the United States Commissioner and make—"

"I know, I know," said Major Tom, with a wave of his hand. "You don't suppose I'd run a bank without being posted on national banking laws and the revised statutes! Do your duty. I'm not asking any favors. But I spoke of my friend. I did want you to hear me tell you about Bob."

Nettlewick settled himself in his chair. There would be no leaving San Rosario for him that day. He would have to telegraph the Comptroller of the Currency; he would have to swear out a warrant before the United States Commissioner for the arrest of Major Kingman; perhaps he would be ordered to close the bank on account of the loss of the securities. It was not the first crime the examiner had unearthed. Once or twice the terrible upheaval of human emotions that his investigations had loosed had almost caused a ripple in his official calm. He had seen bank men kneel and plead and cry like women for a chance—an hour's time—the overlooking of a single error. One cashier had shot himself at his desk before him. None of them had taken it with the dignity and coolness of this stern old Westerner. Nettlewick felt he owed it to him at least to listen if he wished to talk. With his elbow on the arm of his chair, and his square chin resting upon the fingers of his right hand, the bank examiner waited to hear the confession of the president of the First National Bank of San Rosario.

"When a man's your friend," began Major Tom, somewhat didactically, "for forty years, and tried by water, fire, earth, and cyclones, when you can do him a little favor you feel like doing it."

("Embezzle for him $70,000.00 worth of securities," thought the examiner.)

"We were cowboys together, Bob and I," continued the major, speaking slowly, and deliberately, and musingly, as if his thoughts were rather with the past than the critical present, "and we prospected together for gold and silver over Arizona, New Mexico, and a good part of California. We were both in the war of 'sixtyone, but in different commands. We've fought Indians and horse thieves side by side; we've starved for weeks in a cabin in the Arizona mountains, buried twenty feet deep in snow; we've ridden herd together when the wind blew so hard the lightning couldn't strike—well, Bob and I have been through some rough spells since the first time we met in the branding camp of the old Anchor-Bar ranch. And during that time we've found it necessary more than once to help each other out of tight places. In those days it was expected of a man to stick to his friend, and he didn't ask any credit for it. Probably the next day you'd need him to get at your back and help stand off a band of Apaches, or put a tourniquet on your leg above a rattlesnake bite and ride for whisky. So, after all, it was give and take, and if you didn't stand square with your pardner, why, you might be shy one when you needed him. But Bob was a man who was willing to go further than that. He never played a limit.

"Twenty years ago I was sheriff of this county and I made Bob my chief deputy. That was before the boom in cattle when we both made our stake. I was sheriff and collector, and it was a big thing for me then. I was married, and we had a boy and a girl—a four and a six year old. There was a comfortable house next to the courthouse, furnished by the county, rent free, and I was saving some money. Bob did most of the office work. Both of us had seen rough times and plenty of rustling and danger, and I tell you it was great to hear the rain and the sleet dashing against the windows of nights and be warm and safe and comfortable, and know you could get up in the morning and be

shaved and have folks call you 'mister.' And then, I had the finest wife and kids that ever struck the range, and my old friend with me enjoying the first fruits of prosperity and white shirts, and I guess I was happy. Yes, I was happy about that time."

The major sighed and glanced casually out of the window. The bank examiner changed his positon, and leaned his chin upon his other hand.

"One winter," continued the major, "the money for the county taxes came pouring in so fast that I didn't have time to take the stuff to the bank for a week. I just shoved the checks into a cigar box and the money into a sack, and locked them in the big safe that belonged in the sheriff's office.

"I had been overworked that week, and was about sick, anyway. My nerves were out of order, and my sleep at night didn't seem to rest me. The doctor had some scientific name for it, and I was taking medicine. And so, added to the rest, I went to bed at night with that money on my mind. Not that there was much need of being worried, for the safe was a good one, and nobody but Bob and I knew the combination. On Friday night there was about $6,500.00 cash in the bag. On Saturday morning I went to the office as usual. The safe was locked, and Bob was writing at his desk. I opened the safe, and the money was gone. I called Bob, and roused everybody in the courthouse to announce the robbery. It struck me that Bob took it pretty quiet, considering how much it reflected upon both him and me.

"Two days went by and we never got a clue. It couldn't have been burglars, for the safe had been opened by the combination in the proper way. People must have begun to talk, for one afternoon in comes Alice—that's my wife—and the boy and girl, and Alice stamps her foot and her eyes flash, and she cries out, 'The lying wretches—Tom, Tom!' and I catch her in a faint, and bring her 'round little by little, and she lays her head down and cries and cries for the first time since she took Tom Kingman's name and fortunes. And Jack and Zilla—the youngsters—they were always wild as tigers' cubs to rush at Bob and climb all over him whenever they were allowed to come to the courthouse—they stood and kicked their little shoes, and herded together like scared partridges. They were having their first trip down into the shadows of life. Bob was working at his desk, and he got up and went out without a word. The grand jury was in session then, and the next morning Bob went before them and confessed that he had stolen the money. He said he lost it in a poker game. In fifteen minutes they had found a true bill and sent me the warrant to arrest the man with whom I'd been closer than a thousand brothers for many a year.

"I did it, and then I said to Bob, pointing: 'There's my house, and here's my office, and up there's Maine, and out that way is California, and over there is Florida—and that's your range 'til court meets. You're in my charge, and I take the responsibility. You be here when you're wanted.'

"'Thanks, Tom,' he said, kind of carelessly; 'I was sort of hoping you wouldn't lock me up. Court meets next Monday, so, if you don't object, I'll just loaf around the office until then. I've got one favor to ask, if it isn't too much. If you'd let the kids come out in the yard once in a while and have a romp I'd like it.'

"'Why not?' I answered him. 'They're welcome, and so are you. And come to my house the same as ever.' You see, Mr. Nettlewick, you can't make a friend of a thief, but neither can you make a thief of a friend, all at once."

The examiner made no answer. At that moment was heard the shrill whistle of a locomotive pulling into the depot. That was the train on the little, narrow-gauge road that struck into San Rosario from the south. The major cocked his ear and listened for a moment, and looked at his watch. The narrow-gauge was in on time —10:35. The major continued:

"So Bob hung around the office, reading the papers and smoking. I put another deputy to work in his place, and, after a while, the first excitement of the case wore off.

"One day when we were alone in the office Bob came over to where I was sitting. He was looking sort of grim and blue—the same look he used to get when he'd been watching for Indians all night or herd-riding.

"'Tom,' says he, 'it's harder than standing off redskins; it's harder than lying in the lava desert forty miles from water; but I'm going to stick it out to the end. You know that's been my style. But if you'd tip me the smallest kind of sign—if you'd just say, "Bob I understand," why, it would make it lots easier.'

"I was surprised. 'I don't know what you mean, Bob,' I said. 'Of course, you know I'd do anything under the sun to help you that I could. But you've got me guessing.'

"'All right, Tom,' was all he said, and he went back to his newspaper and lit another cigar.

"It was the night before the court met when I found out what he meant. I went to bed that night with the same old, light-headed, nervous feeling come back upon me. I dropped off to sleep about midnight. When I woke I was standing half-dressed in one of the courthouse corridors. Bob was holding one of my arms, our family doctor the other and Alice was shaking me and half crying. She had sent for the doctor without my knowing it, and when he came they had found me out of bed and missing, and had begun a search.

"'Sleep-walking,' said the doctor.

"All of us went back to the house, and the doctor told us some remarkable stories about the strange things people had done while in that condition. I was feeling rather chilly after my trip out, and, as my wife was out of the room at the time, I pulled open the door of an old wardrobe that stood in the room and dragged out a big quilt I had seen in there. With it tumbled out the bag of money for stealing which Bob was to be tried—and convicted—in the morning.

"'How the jumping rattlesnakes did that get

there?' I yelled, and all hands must have seen how surprised I was. Bob knew in a flash.

" 'You darned old snoozer,' he said, with the old-time look on his face, 'I saw you put it there. I watched you open the safe and take it out, and I followed you. I looked through the window and saw you hide it in that wardrobe.'

" 'Then, you blankety-blank, flop-eared, sheep-headed coyote, what did you say you took it for?'

" 'Because,' said Bob, simply, 'I didn't know you were asleep.'

"I saw him glance toward the door of the room where Jack and Zilla were, and I knew then what it meant to be a man's friend from Bob's point of view."

Major Tom paused, and again directed his glance out of the window. He saw someone in the Stockmen's National Bank reach and draw a yellow shade down the whole length of its plate-glass, big front window, although the position of the sun did not seem to warrant such a defensive movement against its rays.

Nettlewick sat up straight in his chair. He had listened patiently, but without consuming interest, to the major's story. It had impressed him as irrelevant to the situation, and it could certainly have no effect upon the consequences. Those Western people, he thought, had an exaggerated sentimentality. They were not businesslike. They needed to be protected from their friends. Evidently the major had concluded. And what he had said amounted to nothing.

"May I ask," said the examiner, "if you have anything further to say that bears directly upon the question of those abstracted securities?"

"Abstracted securities, sir!" Major Tom turned suddenly in his chair, his blue eyes flashing upon the examiner. "What do you mean, sir?"

He drew from his coat pocket a batch of folded papers held together by a rubber band, tossed them into Nettlewick's hands, and rose to his feet.

"You'll find those securities there, sir, every stock, bond, and share of 'em. I took them from the notes while you were counting the cash. Examine and compare them for yourself."

The major led the way back into the banking room. The examiner, astounded, perplexed, nettled, at sea, followed. He felt that he had been made the victim of something that was not exactly a hoax, but that left him in the shoes of one who had been played upon, used, and then discarded, without even an inkling of the game. Perhaps, also, his official position had been irreverently juggled with. But there was nothing he could take hold of. An official report of the matter would be an absurdity. And, somehow, he felt that he would never know anything more about the matter than he did then.

Frigidly, mechanically, Nettlewick examined the securities, found them to tally with the notes, gathered his black wallet, and rose to depart.

"I will say," he protested, turning the indignant glare of his glasses upon Major Kingman, "that your statements—your misleading statements, which you have not condescended to explain—do not appear to be quite the thing, regarded either as business or humor. I do not understand such motives or actions."

Major Tom looked down at him serenely and not unkindly.

"Son," he said, "there are plenty of things in the chaparral, and on the prairies, and up the canyons that you don't understand. But I want to thank you for listening to a garrulous old man's prosy story. We old Texans love to talk about our adventures and our old comrades, and the homefolks have long ago learned to run when we begin with 'Once upon a time,' so we have to spin our yarns to the stranger within our gates."

The major smiled, but the examiner only bowed coldly, and abruptly quitted the bank. They saw him travel diagonally across the street in a straight line and enter the Stockmen's National Bank.

Major Tom sat down at his desk and drew from his vest pocket the note Roy had given him. He had read it once, but hurriedly, and now, with something like a twinkle in his eyes, he read it again. These were the words he read:

DEAR TOM:

I hear there's one of Uncle Sam's greyhounds going through you, and that means that we'll catch him inside a couple of hours, maybe. Now, I want you to do something for me. We've got just $2,200.00 in the bank, and the law requires that we have $20,000.00. I let Ross and Fisher have $18,000.00 late yesterday afternoon to buy up that Gibson bunch of cattle. They'll realize $40,000 in less than thirty days on the transaction, but that won't make my cash on hand look any prettier to that bank examiner. Now, I can't show him those notes, for they're just plain notes of hand without any security in sight, but you know very well that Pink Ross and Jim Fisher are two of the finest men God ever made, and they'll do the square thing. You remember Jim Fisher—he was the one who shot that faro dealer in El Paso. I wired Sam Bradshaw's bank to send me $20,000.00, and it will get in on the narrow-gauge at 10:35. You can't let a bank examiner in to count $2,200 and close your doors. Tom, you hold that examiner. Hold him. Hold him if you have to rope him and sit on his head. Watch our front window after the narrow gauge gets in, and when we've got the cash inside we'll pull down the shade for a signal. Don't turn him loose till then. I'm counting on you, Tom.

> Your old Pard,
> BOB BUCKLEY,
> Prest. Stockmen's National

The major began to tear the note into small pieces and throw them into his waste basket. He gave a satisfied little chuckle as he did so.

"Confounded old reckless cowpuncher!" he growled, contentedly, "that pays him some on account for what he tried to do for me in the sheriff's office twenty years ago."

For Discussion

1. An author's selection of detail often reveals his attitude toward a character or an event. Through the details that characterize J. F. C. Nettlewick, what can you say about O. Henry's attitude toward him? By the same method, what can you say of O. Henry's opinion of Major Tom Kingman? Do the names Nettlewick and Kingman suggest anything about the men?

2. In this story O. Henry examines honesty from different angles. In what way is Major Kingman honest? In what way is he dishonest? In what way is J. F. C. Nettlewick honest? In what way is he dishonest? Which type of honesty does O. Henry tend to champion?

3. Major Tom Kingman's account of his relationship with Buckley creates a story within a story. What does the inner story of Bob's loyalty have to do with the larger frame of Major Kingman's delay of J. F. C. Nettlewick? Does Nettlewick understand the significance of Major Kingman's story?

4. O. Henry was famous, as was Maupassant, for his "surprise endings." Is the ending of this story really a surprise, or has O. Henry created an expectancy by dropping certain clues along the way? What, if any, are these clues?

5. Find evidence of the pioneer spirit in Major Tom Kingman and Bob Buckley. What is their background? What is their attitude toward inflexible rules and authority? What does O. Henry suggest about the future of the pioneer spirit when he makes Kingman and Buckley bankers?

Adventures of Don Quixote

MIGUEL DE CERVANTES

Only a gigantic imagination could have created Don Quixote, for the fabulous old knight is a symbol of the imagination itself. A man alone who sets out to right the wrongs of the world, he is at once noble and sad. Tall and gaunt, his piercing eyes find romantic drama in a row of windmills, a barber's basin, a flock of sheep, a country inn. This wandering reformer travels the Spanish countryside amazing onlookers with the extravagant manner in which he confronts everyday sights and circumstances. At his side the rosy and plump Sancho Panza rides, puzzled by the contradiction between what he sees and what Don Quixote tells him he has seen. His eyes verify one truth, but the romantic dreams of Don Quixote verify another. The following three episodes from the great novel typify their adventures.

Don Quixote's vision is so noble and lofty that he is blind to the common reality around him. Sancho indeed sees things as they are, but he cannot envision the poetry and the ideals without which our lives would be incomplete. Both visions are needed—the real and the ideal. Cervantes' stroke of genius was not so much in creating either Don Quixote or Sancho but in bringing them together.

DON QUIXOTE AND SANCHO SET OUT ON THEIR ADVENTURES

DON QUIXOTE persuaded a laborer, a neighbor of his named Sancho Panza, to join him on his adventures. This Sancho was a good man but not very bright. Don Quixote talked to him so much and made him so many promises that finally poor Sancho agreed to go along and serve him as squire. Don Quixote said that Sancho should be glad of the chance to serve him because upon one of their adventures they might easily conquer some island; and if that should happen, he would leave Sancho there as governor. In the light of this promise, and others like it, Sancho deserted his wife and children and became his neighbor's squire.

Statues are usually erected to the memory of great statesmen, saints, and warriors. But today in Spain there are large bronze monuments to two unforgettable characters who lived only in the pages of a book: Don Quixote and Sancho Panza. Both they and their creator, MIGUEL DE CERVANTES (*1547– 1616*), *are among the national heroes of Spain.*

But the story of Cervantes' life is a sad one. As a young man, he was a valiant soldier who fought against the Moors at the battle Lepanto. On his way back to Spain he was captured by Barbary pirates and held for ransom in Algeria for five years. Finally his family and friends raised some money, the pirates released him, and he returned to Spain. There he faced a life of dismal poverty, for he could no longer serve as a soldier. For years he earned a meager living writing plays and stories that had no particular success.

Toward the end of his life, Cervantes began the huge novel that was to make his name famous through the centuries to come. Don Quixote *is considered one of the supreme masterpieces of world literature, and one of the two or three greatest novels ever written. Cervantes died before his great novel could bring him fame or fortune.*

Next, Don Quixote set about raising money. Some things he sold, others he pawned—always making a bad bargain—until at last he had the sum he needed. Then he equipped himself with a shield, which he borrowed from a friend, and patched up his broken helmet as well as he could. Sancho, his squire, was informed of the day and hour on which they would set out so that he might prepare provisions for the journey. Don Quixote told him not to forget to bring saddlebags. Sancho agreed and added that he was going to bring along a very fine donkey, because he was not used to traveling on foot. The mention of the donkey made Don Quixote pause for a moment: he could not remember having heard of any instance in which a knight had been accompanied by a squire who rode on a donkey. But, in spite of this, he decided to let Sancho bring it and determined to provide him with a more noble mount as soon as he had a chance. After all, he was sure to meet with some discourteous knight whose horse he could take. He provided himself with shirts and everything else he could get his hands on. And when all these arrangements had been made, they set out upon their adventures: Sancho without saying goodbye to his wife and children, Don Quixote without bidding farewell to his housekeeper and niece. They left the town one evening without anyone seeing them, and rode so far in the night that by morning they felt sure no one could ever find them.

Sancho Panzo sat upon his donkey like a patriarch; he had his saddlebags, his leather bottle, and great hopes of becoming governor of the island his master had promised him.

"Your Honor, knight errant," said Sancho, "don't forget about that island you've promised me. I shall be a good governor, even if it is a very large island!"

Don Quixote replied: "Sancho Panza, my friend, you should know that the knights errant of old always appointed their squires to be governors of the islands or kingdoms they conquered. For my part, I shall honor this tradition. In fact, I shall improve upon it: some of those knights made their squires wait until they were very old. Then, after many hard days and worse nights of service, they would give them the title of Count, or perhaps at the most Marquis, of some unimportant valley or province. But if you live—and if I live!—it may very well happen that we shall not have to wait six days until I conquer a kingdom of such importance that it has other kingdoms beneath it. And you shall be crowned the king of one of them. Do not say impossible! For such surprising and unbelievable adventures befall a knight errant that I may easily give you more than I promise!"

"In that case," answered Sancho Panza, "if I were to become King—through the miracle of which Your Honor speaks—then my wife would be Queen and my children Princes."

"Do you doubt it?" asked Don Quixote.

"Yes, I do doubt it," said Sancho. "I believe that even if God rained crowns on the Earth, none of them would fit my wife's head. She would be a poor queen, sir. Yet I believe that with God's help she might make a good countess."

"Leave it to Heaven, Sancho," answered Don Quixote. "God will know what is best for her. As for yourself, do not humble yourself to accept less than the governorship of a province."

"No, sir, I shall not," answered Sancho, "not with a master like yourself. I know you will give me whatever is good for me, and as much as I can handle."

THE ADVENTURE OF THE WINDMILLS

JUST THEN, as they rode across the plain, there appeared thirty or forty windmills. As soon as Don Quixote spied them, he said to his squire:

"Fortune has guided us better than we could have hoped for. Look there, friend Sancho Panza, and you will see more than thirty horrid giants! I shall do battle with them and kill them all. What we take from them will be the beginnings of our fortunes: for it is a good and holy fight in which I shall wipe from the face of the earth these evil creatures!"

"What giants?" asked Sancho Panza.

"Those giants right there!" answered his master. "The ones with the long arms. Some giants are said to have arms several miles long."

"But Your Honor," said Sancho, "what you are looking at are not giants. They are windmills, and what look like arms are merely sails which turn in the wind."

"It is obvious that you know nothing about adventures," said Don Quixote. "If you are afraid, then fly and say your prayers. In the meantime I shall engage these giants in fierce and unequal battle."

Having said this, he dug his spurs into the sides of his horse Rosinante and dashed off, paying no attention to Sancho, who kept shouting that the figures he was about to attack were windmills and not giants. But Don Quixote was so certain that they were giants that he did not hear Sancho's cries, nor, when he came near them, did he notice the true nature of his enemies. He cried out to them in a loud voice:

"Do not run away from me, you cowards, you hateful creatures! It is one lone knight who attacks you!"

Just then a small breeze came across the plain and caused the sails to start turning. When Don Quixote saw this he cried:

"Though you have more arms than the famous giant Briareus, you shall soon pay for your evil deeds!"

Saying this, he dedicated himself to his lady, Dulcinea del Toboso,[1] that she might aid him in battle. Then he put up his shield, settled his lance in place, and set off on Rosinante at full gallop. He attacked the first windmill he came to, thrusting his lance into one of its sails. But the wind turned the sail with such strength that it shattered his lance and lifted both horse and rider into the air, tossing Don Quixote across the fields.

As fast as his donkey could trot, Sancho Panza came to the aid of his injured master. But when he arrived at Don Quixote's side, he found that the knight could not get up: such was the shock Rosinante had given him when they fell.

"God help us!" cried Sancho. "Didn't I tell Your Honor to be careful about what you were doing? Didn't I tell you they were windmills?

---

[1] *Dulcinea del Toboso* This lady existed only in Don Quixote's imagination. He knew that the ancient knights all had beautiful ladies to whom they dedicated their noble deeds.

And how could anyone miss it unless he had windmills in his head!"

"Be quiet, friend Sancho," replied Don Quixote. "The affairs of war are subject to change. Moreover, I believe—and it is a fact—that the evil magician Frestón—the same one who has robbed me of my house and all my books—has in fact changed those giants into windmills! He wants to rob me of the glory of conquering them. Yes, he hates me! But in the end, in the end, the power of his evil acts shall fall before the goodness of my sword!"

"God's will be done," said Sancho, and helped his master to get up and climb up on Rosinante, whose back was almost broken.

THE ADVENTURE OF THE ENCHANTED HELMET

TURNING to the right, they set off on another road. They had not traveled far before Don Quixote spied a man on horseback. On his head, this man had something that shone like gold.

As soon as Don Quixote caught a glimpse of him, he turned to Sancho Panza and said: "It is my opinion, Sancho, that all the old sayings have a good deal of truth in them. After all, they are drawn from Experience, which is the Mother of Science. I am thinking in particular of the saying that *When one door shuts, another door opens.* Look: here is another adventure—and a better one. Unless I am deceived, there comes towards us now a man wearing upon his head the Helmet of Mambrino. As you know, I have sworn an oath about this very helmet."

"Look carefully before you speak, sir, and move carefully before you act," said Sancho. "If I were free to speak my mind, I could give you several reasons why you are mistaken."

"How can I be mistaken, faithless traitor?" cried Don Quixote. "Tell me, do you or do you not see that knight who is riding towards us on a light gray horse? Is he not wearing upon his head a helmet of gold?"

"What I see," said Sancho, "or perhaps I should say what I *perceive*—is a man riding a grey donkey just like mine. And he has something shining on his head."

"Well! It is the Helmet of Mambrino!" said Don Quixote. "Stand to one side and let me handle him alone. I shall save time by refusing to speak a single word—yet I shall bring this adventure to its end. And I shall soon have the helmet I have so long desired."

Now, the truth of the matter about the helmet, the horse, and the horseman, was this: There were two villages nearby. One of them was so small that it could afford neither a druggist's nor a barber shop. The other village, not far away, had both. The barber from the larger town took care of the smaller one, too. It happened that day that there was a sick man who had to be bled, and someone else who needed a shave. And so the barber was riding over to take care of them, and he was bringing along with him his brass bowl.

Now, just as the barber was riding along, it began to rain. He did not want to get his hat wet (it was probably a new one), and so he put the bowl over his head. Since the brass was polished, it could be seen from half a mile away. He was, as Sancho said, riding a gray donkey. And that is how Don Quixote came to believe that the barber was a knight on a gray horse and that he wore a golden helmet. Don Quixote found it easy to adapt everything he saw to his own fancies about chivalry.

When Don Quixote saw the poor rider approach, he did not bother to speak to him, but he spurred Rosinante into a full gallop. He lowered his lance, meaning to spear the poor barber on it. Without slowing down, he shouted out:

"Defend yourself, base creature! Or surrender freely the helmet which is rightly mine!"

The barber, who had no idea what was going on, saw this phantom descending upon him. All he could do to avoid the lance was to let himself fall down off his donkey. As soon as he touched the ground, he got up and ran across the fields like the wind. The brass bowl was left lying on the ground.

Don Quixote was overjoyed to see the bowl, and said that the pagan had acted wisely. He ordered Sancho to pick up the helmet.

"Lord!" said Sancho, holding it in his hands, "What a fine brass bowl! This is worth a *real* if it's worth a penny."

He handed it to his master, who put it on his head and kept turning it around and around, looking for the vizor. But there was no vizor.

"The pagan for whom this helmet was made had an enormous head," said Don Quixote. "The worst of it is that part of it is missing."

When Sancho heard the brass bowl referred to as a helmet, he had to laugh. But he remembered how angry his master could get, and so he stopped.

"Why are you laughing, Sancho?" asked Don Quixote.

"I am laughing," Sancho said, "to think how big the head of the pagan who owned it must have been. In fact, it's exactly like the kind of bowl a barber uses."

"Sancho, do you know what I think?" said Don Quixote. "I think this famous and enchanted helmet has fallen into the hands of someone who did not know what it was. This person, when he saw it was made of pure gold, took part of it and melted it down for money. He turned the rest of it into what—as you say—looks like a barber's bowl. Never mind. The fact that it has undergone a transformation does not bother me, for I know what it really is. As soon as I arrive at a town where there is a blacksmith, I shall have it repaired. It shall be as fine a helmet as the one that Vulcan, god of blacksmiths, gave to Mars, the god of War. In the meantime, I shall wear it as well as I can, for something is better than nothing. Moreover, it will protect my head from stones."

For Discussion

Don Quixote and Sancho Set Out on Their Adventures

1. How does Don Quixote tempt Sancho Panza to leave his wife and children to become a knight's squire? Does this indicate that for all his matter-of-fact qualities Sancho, like Don Quixote, has illusions? Explain.

2. When Don Quixote speaks of the way of the "knights errant of old," what do we learn about his sense of reality? What happens to men who try to live in the past? How does Don Quixote resemble the type of man who sees only what he wants to see? What does Don Quixote want to see?

The Adventure of the Windmills

1. There is a familiar saying, "He is tilting at windmills." The saying has its source in this episode from *Don Quixote*. What does it mean? Is it an unnatural human impulse to "tilt at windmills"?

2. If you had the power of judgment over Don Quixote, would you confine him to a sanatorium for treatment? How do you think he would interpret his sudden confinement?

The Adventure of the Enchanted Helmet

1. What is the difference between the way Sancho sees the barber's bowl and the way Don Quixote sees it? Name the chief value placed on it by each. What does the way each man sees the bowl reflect about his own personality?

2. Is Don Quixote's statement, "Moreover, it will protect my head from stones," a concession to reality? Does he make any concessions to reality in the episode of the windmills? Does this statement suggest that a small change has taken place in Don Quixote between the two episodes?

3. In this instance, can you interpret Don Quixote's victory as a defeat? How will strangers react to a man wearing a barber's bowl for a helmet?

UNIT 2: STORIES OF THE TWENTIETH CENTURY

The modern short story has

roots in folk tales and legends. The previous unit included a fine example of
such an early tale in Li Fu Yen's "The Tiger." A similar example will be found
on page 465 in the Persian story "The Legend of the King and the Peasant."
In these ancient stories the characters are not highly developed, the action is
simple, and the purpose of the tale is to point out a definite moral. With
increased realism in fiction, the nature of the short tale changed.

The nineteenth-century masters of the short story, such as Maupassant, Chekhov, Gogol, Hawthorne, Kipling, and James, turned the simple tale into a form which could be used for a complex examination of life. The modern short story seldom points out a definite moral. It usually presents an action dramatically and leaves the reader to draw whatever meaning he can from the action. The modern writer is more concerned with asking questions about life than with giving final answers. In this search for truth, modern fiction has largely abandoned fantasy (though fantasy still flourishes in books of science fiction) to examine the complications of society and human characters.

Thus the best modern fiction tries to give the reader a sharp focus on reality. In earlier centuries brief tales were mostly concerned with imaginary happenings, with ghosts and fairies and lengendary heroes. Modern fiction is based on realism: the reader participates in a world that really exists. The modern story does not just "tell about" an event; it tries to create the event on the page so that the reader can live it.

Compare Indro Montanelli's "His Excellency" with Hebel's "The Hussar." Both are stories of war. Montanelli tells us what it was really like to have been imprisoned by the Germans during the Second World War. We come to feel that we have known the principal character and that we have watched him living out his last days. In reading Hebel's story, on the other hand, we have the feeling of being at a greater distance from the events. The characters behave believably, but beyond that the reader does not come to know much about them. Montanelli brings us up close to his people and lets us share their experience.

All the stories in this group convey a sense of reality. In Morley Callaghan's "The Snob" the reader suffers embarrassment along with the young hero. In "The Use of Force" William Carlos Williams brings the reader into a kitchen as he pays a physician's call; the dialogue is so brilliantly accurate that the reader seems to hear it rather than read it. Valentine Kataev transports us to a Russian amusement park; Benito Lynch to a farm on the Argentine pampas; Sean O'Faolain to the world of pigeon racing in Dublin; Albert Camus to the deserts of North Africa.

Reading the stories, we believe that they could really have taken place. In the case of "His Excellency" and "The Use of Force" we may almost be certain that the stories correspond closely to events which *did* take place. In both stories this feeling of truth is heightened by the fact that the writers have made themselves characters in their own stories. As with Michel del Castillo's "Christmas in a Concentration Camp" (page 145), the reader becomes aware that the line between fiction and nonfiction is not always easy to define. Defining it, in fact, does not matter. What matters is that the artist has given his experience a general meaning, one which will apply to all men. The writing of a good short story is so vivid and accurate that the reader can share in the reality of the experience.

Drawing the meaning from a story is often a challenge to the reader's skill. Each detail is important, and what is left unsaid can be as revealing as what is said. Modern writers demand close attention of their readers and often place great importance upon the smallest detail.

For those who wish further to examine the form of the modern short story, there are several first-rate examples included in later units of this book. Excellent twentieth-century stories include Yakolev's "The Wizard," Rumer Godden's "The Oyster," Giovanni Guareschi's "The Petition," and Pearl Buck's "The Enemy."

Looked at together, the short stories in this unit and throughout *Literature of the World* give the reader ample opportunity to study the possibilities writers have found in the versatile form of the short story.

His Excellency

INDRO MONTANELLI

*The violence of wartime ravages landscapes and makes jagged ruins of
cities and towns. Likewise, it uproots men from the normal courses
of their lives and gives them opportunities to test themselves under
the pressures of imminent death. Just such a chance—for heroism or for
cowardice—is given to the central character of "His Excellency."
This story takes place against the background of the last days of the
Second World War. During the war, the Nazis and the Italians had
fought side by side. Now, under the leadership of Badoglio, who is
mentioned in the story, the Italian army joined the British and Americans
and turned against the Germans. The characters in "His Excellency"
are Italian prisoners of war who have been captured by the Nazis.*

THERE IT IS, lined up with the other sixty-four
coffins from the Fossoli concentration camp,
and the crowd has sprinkled it, like the others,
with flowers. Among all these people gathered
here in the silence of the Milan cathedral, surely
I am not the only one to know. Yet there has
been no protest. Truly, men are as lenient to
the dead as they are harsh with the living. The
coffin will now pass like the others between the
reverent throngs, like the others it will be buried
and, on June 22 of each year, will receive its
quota of rhetoric spilled over the common
grave. Fair enough. . . . Who are we to judge?

His Excellency, General Della Rovere, army
corps commander, intimate friend of Badoglio's [1]

---

[1] *Badoglio* In 1943, after the fall of Mussolini, Field
Marshal Pietro Badoglio became Premier of Italy.
General Alexander was the British commander.

and "technical adviser" to General Alexander,
was locked up by the Germans in the San
Vittore prison of Milan in the spring of 1944
when the Allied armies were still fighting their
slow way up the Italian peninsula. He had been
captured near Genoa while trying to land at
night from an Allied submarine to take command of the resistance movement in the north.
A soldier to his finger tips, he had impressed
even Franz, the German warder, who would
stand at attention when addressing him and had
gone so far as to have a cot placed in his cell. So
the Italian guard, Ceraso, informed me as he
passed my spy hole with a rose in a glass, picked
expressly for His Excellency. Later Ceraso returned to say that the General wished to see
me, and, letting me out, escorted me to his cell.

"Cavalry officer" was written all over those
arched legs, that slight build, and aristocratic

INDRO MONTANELLI (*1909–   *) *is a*
popular Italian novelist and story writer.
"His Excellency" has been made into a
widely acclaimed movie, General Della
Rovere.

---

profile. Tight-corseted, he wore a monocle and
false teeth, and the thought struck me of how
convincing, after all, is our racial destiny. What
else could a man like that become if not a general? With steely grace he could give an order
and make it sound like a plea, and even now,
weeks after his capture, his cheeks were clean-
shaven, his trousers miraculously pressed, while
one could almost detect on his polished shoes a
pair of invisible spurs.

"Montanelli, I presume?" he said with a slight
drawl, polishing his monocle without giving me
his hand. "I already knew of your presence here
before landing. Badoglio in person had informed
me. His Majesty's Government [2] is following
your case with the utmost sympathy. Let it be
understood, however, that the day you face the
firing squad you will have done no more than
your duty. Please stand at ease." Only at these
last words did I realize that I was standing heels
joined, thumbs touching the seams of my trousers just as the drill book says. "We are all on
temporary duty here, right?" he continued,
cleaning the nail of one little finger with the
nail of the other. "An officer is at all times
merely on temporary duty, he is a *novio de la
muerte*, as the Spaniards say, a bridegroom of
death." He smiled at me, paced leisurely up and
down the cell flexing his slim, arched legs; then,
stopping again before me, cleaned and replaced
his monocle. "We two are very near our wedding day," he continued. "My sentence has already been pronounced. And yours?"

"Not yet, sir," I answered almost mortified.

"It will be," he went on. "You will have the
honor of being shot in the chest, I hear. Splendid. There is no better proof of your conduct
under interrogation. The Germans are rough in
obtaining confessions but chivalrous toward
those who abstain. Good. Your orders are to
continue. In case of torture, if you feel you
must utter a name—I cast no doubt on your
spiritual endurance, but there is a limit to the
physical—utter mine. I have nothing to lose.
Actually, I had nothing to hide even from my
old friend, Marshal Kesselring,[3] when he questioned me. I did, however, explain that I hardly
expected the British submarine captain to be
such a fool as to answer the decoy signals of a
German patrol boat. 'You trust the English?'
Kesselring smiled. 'Why not? We even trusted
the Germans once,' I smiled back. 'Sorry!' he
said, 'I have no choice but to shoot you.' 'No
hard feelings,' I concluded. But to come back to
your case: when you are up for questioning
again, stick to your line. After all, we have such
a simple duty left: to die like gentlemen. What
is your indictment?"

I explained my case fully. His Excellency
listened with his eyes to the ground like a confessor, nodding approbation from time to time.

"A clear case," he concluded. "Captured in
the performance of duty. It's a soldier's death.
They absolutely *must* shoot you in the chest.
It's strictly regulations. Let me know how things
develop. You can go now."

That was the first day in all the six months
since my arrest that I did not think of my wife
locked in her cell in another wing of the building. Toward evening I begged Ceraso to sign
me up for the barber the next day and in the
meanwhile to bring me a comb. And that night,
braving the cold, I took my trousers off before
lying on my plank and hung them on the window bars hoping they would regain their shape.

On the following days, through my spy hole,
I was able to observe His Excellency in his cell

---

[2] *His Majesty's Government* Victor Emmanuel III
was king of Italy in 1944.

[3] *Marshal Kesselring* The German commander.

Vittorio de Sica in the title role of the movie General Della Rovere

just across from mine. One by one, all the prisoners were called to report to him, and all came. In theory, our wing, the dreaded Fifth, was for "solitaries" and so it had been up till that time, but the prestige of His Excellency was obviously so great that the Italian warders felt they could stretch a point. On entering, his guests would stand at attention, even the Communists, and bow stiffly. Later, on leaving, they would walk with a prouder carriage. Number 215, who so often sobbed for his wife and children, after talking with the General fell silent, and even when caught smoking by Franz took his lashes without a whimper. Ceraso told me that almost all, after their talk, had asked, like me, for the barber, a comb, and a little soap. Even the warders now wore their caps straight and tried to speak correct Italian. The wing had never been so quiet, and when Müller came on inspection he praised the new discipline.

For the first time he omitted calling us "anti-Fascist dogs" and "dirty Badoglian traitors," confining himself to an allusion to the "felonious King," at which we all looked at the ceiling pretending not to hear, while His Excellency, who was standing a little forward as befitted his rank, turned deliberately on his heels and re-entered his cell. Müller snorted, but said nothing.

One morning Colonel P. and Colonel F. were taken. Asked if they had a last wish, they mentioned the General, who received them on his threshold, and that was the only time I ever saw him shake hands. Then, caressing with a slow gesture his silvery hair and adjusting his monocle, he smiled and said something to the two officers—something cordial and tender, I am sure. Suddenly, snapping to attention and fixing them coldly in the eyes, he gave them the military salute. P. and F. were pale as chalk, but smiling, and never had they looked so much like colonels as when they moved off, erect, with firm step, between the S.S. men.[4] We heard later that they had both cried, "Long live the King" as they fell.

That same afternoon I was taken down for questioning, and Müller warned me that this was my last chance and that if I did not speak up, etc. . . . But I hardly heard, nor, though I kept my eyes glued to his, saw him. All I could see were the two pale faces of P. and F. and the marblelike face of His Excellency, and all I could hear was his drawling soft voice . . . "*novio de la muerte* . . . performance of duty . . . death on the field. . . ." Müller gave me up without torture after two hours. Even if he had tortured me, I believe I would not have uttered a word, not even the name of His Excellency, in front of whose cell, on my return, I begged Ceraso to let me stop.

Della Rovere was sitting on the edge of his cot. Putting down his book, he stared at me at length while I stood at attention. Then he said slowly: "Yes, indeed. I expected as much of you," and dismissed me with a gesture. But on the threshold he called me back. "Just a second!" and he rose to his feet. "There is a thing I still wish to say. A—uhm—difficult thing. I am, I wish to say, extremely satisfied with your conduct, Captain Montanelli. And I wish this good warder to listen well, for he will be our only surviving witness. Very, very satisfied. . . . A jolly good show, sir!" And that night, for the first time, I felt alone in the world, joyously alone with my beautiful bride, Death, forgetful of my wife and my mother, and for once my Country seemed to me a real and an important thing.

I never saw him again, but after the liberation I gathered the details of his end from one of the survivors of Fossoli.

His Excellency appeared very put out when suddenly, together with a crowd of other San Vittore inmates, he was packed into a boxcar train and shipped to the Fossoli concentration camp. During the journey he sat on the kit packs which his fellow prisoners had laid down as a seat for him and refused to rise even when Schultze came in for inspection. Schultze struck him, shrieking: "*Du bist ein Schwein, Bertoni!*" [5] But the General found it superfluous to explain that he was not Bertoni, but Della Rovere, a corps commander, friend of Badoglio's and technical adviser to Alexander. Without a twitch he picked up his monocle, luckily unbroken, replaced it, and remained seated. Schultze went out cursing.

At Fossoli, His Excellency no longer enjoyed the little favors he was used to. He was placed in a common shed and put to work. His companions took turns in sparing him the more humiliating tasks like latrine duty, but never, of his own initiative, did he shirk a job, even though manual labor weighed heavily on him, for he was no longer young. Digging, or carrying bricks, often with a grimace of pain, he would keep a sharp eye open to see that no one gave a poor show, and at day's end he would reprimand those who needed it. To him, they were all officers and gentlemen, and such did they continue to feel under the flash of his monocle and the lash of his words. Desperately, heroically, he struggled to keep his nails spotless and his cheeks shaven. He never complained.

Neither then, nor later, was the motive for the June 22 massacre ever made clear. The order came from Milan, some said as a reprisal for something which had happened in Genoa. Lieutenant Dickermann read out the sixty-five names drawn by lot from those of the four hundred inmates lined up in a square. Among the first was the name Bertoni. No one stepped forward. "Bertoni!" roared Dickermann. "Ber-to-ni!" and he stared at the point where Della Rovere stood. Did Dickermann understand, or did he merely

---

[4] *S.S. men* The German storm troopers.

[5] "*Du bist ein Schwein, Bertoni!*" German: "You are a pig, Bertoni!"

choose to humor a dying man? "*Gut, gut,*" he chuckled. "Della Rovere, *wie Sie wollen.* . . ." [6] All held their breath as they watched His Excellency slip his monocle into place and take three slow steps forward. "*General* Della Rovere, please!" he corrected, taking his place by the other doomed men. With the nail of his right forefinger he began to clean the nail of his left—both marvelously steady.

The sixty-five were manacled, blindfolded, and pushed against the wall. Only His Excellency refused to have his eyes covered and was humored. Then the machine guns were set. His Excellency took a step forward. "Hold it! Stop!" cried Dickermann reaching for his revolver. His Excellency took another step. "Gentlemen!" he cried with a voice like a bugle. "In this supreme moment let our thoughts rise . . ." But Dickermann's "Fire!" and the opening crash of the guns cut him short. They all went down. But the General was the only one who did not squirm on the ground, and his monocle remained miraculously in its place. It was still on when they dropped him into the common trench, and he is still wearing it, I assume, there in his coffin.

That coffin which today, June 22, anniversary of the massacre, stands before me in the Milan cathedral, does not contain the body of the imaginary General Della Rovere—true enough! Merely the remains of the former jailbird Bertoni, a Genoese, by profession cardsharp and thief, who, when arrested by the Germans for some petty crime, offered to spy for them in prison by impersonating a non-existent general, and succeeded only too well. . . .

Does it really matter? Surely the Cardinal Archbishop did no wrong in blessing this body together with the others?

For, after all, Bertoni, the cardsharp, the thief, the spy, was indeed a general at the hour of death, and undoubtedly he died convinced that he was the friend of Badoglio's and "technical adviser" to Alexander. But for him, I would never have felt a hero for one night in my cell. . . . And P. and F. would not have walked to the firing squad as colonels should. . . . Because of him, those who lacked courage found it, and Number 215 stopped whimpering for his wife and children. . . .

Peace to his twisted soul.

[*translated by* UGUCCIONE RANIERI]

For Discussion

1. The noble General Della Rovere turns out to be a cardsharp, Bertoni, whom the Germans have planted as a spy on his fellow Italians. What effect does Bertoni's impersonation have upon his own character? What effect does it have upon the men he is supposed to betray? What is the attitude that the Germans take toward him? Why?

2. How do you account for General Della Rovere's actions at the execution? Why does he not plead for his life? Have the Germans made a mistake in

executing him? Why do the Germans execute him along with the other sixty-three prisoners?

3. Notice that in "His Excellency" the author makes himself a character in his own story. Does Montanelli condemn Bertoni? Does he praise him? Does he make Bertoni the hero or the villain of the story? Would it be fair to say that General Della Rovere is the hero and Bertoni the villain?

4. We usually condemn a person who pretends to be something other than what he really is. What makes Bertoni's impersonation a special case? Did he have a right to be buried as General Della Rovere together with the sixty-three martyrs?

---

[6] "*Gut, gut. Della Rovere, wie Sie wollen* . . ." German: "Good, good. Della Rovere, if you prefer . . ."

The Knives

VALENTINE KATAEV

Set in modern Russia, "The Knives" is a comedy based on the same classic plot that Shakespeare used in Romeo and Juliet. *A young man in love finds the path to his sweetheart blocked by her hostile father. But Pashka, the boisterous hero, does not give up easily. Using imagination and wit, he contrives a plan to overcome the barrier to his happiness.*

A SUNDAY'S STROLL in the public gardens is the very thing to show what a man's good for.

Pashka Kokushkin began his Sunday's stroll in the Fresh Ponds at six in the evening. He bought two packets of roasted sunflower seeds from a woman and walked at a leisurely pace along the main avenue. On the way he spoke to a gipsy.

"Let me read your hand, my fine young gentleman. I'll tell you all the truth. I'll tell you what your heart is set on and I'll tell you what's on your mind. I'll tell you it all and hide nothing, and you've only to give the old gipsy ten kopeks for the pleasure it'll be to you. If I tell your fortune, all will be well with you. If I don't you'll be sorry."

Pashka thought it over.

"Fortune telling is rubbish and—a silly superstition. All the same, here's a copper for you. You can carry on, though you'll only tell a pack of lies."

The gipsy put the coin in the pocket of her garish skirt and showed her black teeth.

"There's a pleasant meeting in store for you, young man, and because of this meeting your heart will have sorrow. An old man stands in your way, but don't fear anything. Fear only the knife. The knife will cause you a lot of trouble. Don't fear your friends—fear your enemies, and the green parrot will bring you luck. Go on your way with a brave heart!"

The gipsy bent her lean body forward and walked away with dignity, shuffling the soles of her dusky feet over the ground.

"Lies well, the rascal," Pashka said, winked, laughed out loud and went on his way.

As he went he sampled all the pleasures life had to offer. First he weighed himself on a rickety weighing machine; it registered a hundred and seventy-five pounds. Then he tried his strength and, nearly sinking to his knees with the exertion, he made the quivering pointer reach "strong man." After this he strolled on for a while and tested his nerves with electricity. He grasped the brass rod with both hands; there was a tingling in his wrists and a tickling as of ants, his wrists filled with soda water, his palms stuck to the brass rod—but his nerves were proved to be strong.

Finally he sat on a chair in front of a backcloth suspended from a tree and displaying the Kremlin as seen from the Stone Bridge, crossed his legs, made a very fierce face and had his photograph taken. In ten minutes Pashka received the still wet print and gazed upon it for a long time with great satisfaction: his check cap, his own familiar nose, his shirt with open collar, his coat—all faultless—pleased him well. It was not easy to believe that this strikingly handsome fellow and himself were one and the same.

"Not bad," he said as he carefully rolled up the sticky photograph and marched off to the landing stage.

To exhaust the stock of Sunday delights Pashka had now only to ogle some girls as they passed and take them for a row. Meanwhile he walked on and arrived at an unusually popular booth. A crowd blocked its wide-open doors. The ring of metal and loud laughter could be heard from within.

"What's going on here?" Pashka asked an undersized Guardsman who was pushing his way in.

"Throwing rings. It's a game. If you throw straight you get a samovar." [1]

Pashka peered inquisitively into the brilliantly lighted interior over the heads of the crowd. The whole of the back wall was hung with red cotton. In front of it were three tiers of knives stuck on end. Among the knives enticing prizes were displayed. On the lowest tier—boxes, candies, cakes; on the middle one—alarm clocks, casseroles, caps; and on the top one, just below the roof in semi-darkness, particularly seductive articles—two balalaikas,[2] a samovar, yellow elastic-sided boots, an Italian concertina, a cuckoo-clock and a phonograph. You threw the rings and if you got one over a knife you won the article lying beside it. But it was almost impossible to throw a ring over a knife, for the knives were very flexible and the rings rebounded from them. Most amusing!

Pashka elbowed his way into the booth. A little old man with silver spectacles on his nose stood behind the counter, giving out the rings, forty throws for twenty-five kopeks. A heated young man with a moist shock of hair was laughing uproariously as he threw his last five rings. His coat flapped, the metal rings flew from his clumsy fingers, struck against the knives and fell with a clatter into the sack hanging beneath. The gaping throng laughed. The young fellow's face flushed. The knives rang and vibrated in ever-widening circles as the rings struck them.

The fellow cried out at last, "There's a ruble and a half chucked away. I might at least have got a Balaev cake!" And he vanished crestfallen among the crowd.

"Last Sunday someone won a pair of boots," said a youth in patched trousers, "and spent ten rubles to get them."

"Let me have a go," Pashka said, pushing his way up to the counter. "Just for the fun of the thing."

The old man handed him the rings.

---

[1] *samovar* A large Russian urn used for making tea.

[2] *balalaika* A Russian stringed instrument, somewhat like a guitar.

"Now then," Pashka asked prosily, "if you hit a knife at the bottom, you win a Balaev cake. Is that it?"

"That's so," the old man said with indifference.

"And next row, an alarm clock?"

The old man nodded.

"Fine. And for a samovar, I suppose, you have to aim right under the roof?"

"Get your cake first. Then you can start talking," someone in the crowd remarked impatiently. "Get on! Make a start!"

Pashka put his photograph down on the counter, pushed the crowd aside with his elbows, took his stance, aimed—but suddenly the ring flew from his grasp, fell on its side and rolled away. Pashka had turned to stone. On a chair beside the shelves, with her hands demurely folded in her lap, sat a young, smartly-dressed girl, whose beauty was such that his eyes were blinded. The girl got up quickly from her chair, picked up the ring and handed it back to Pashka without raising her eyes; but at the last moment she smiled faintly and stealthily, only with the corners of her mouth—and Pashka was a lost man.

"Now then, what's up with you? Get on and win your samovar," the eager onlookers shouted behind him.

Pashka awoke and began to sling the rings one after the other, seeing nothing but the girl's lowered eyelids and her little mouth arched in the middle like a cherry. When he had thrown all forty rings she collected them and put them silently on the counter. But this time she did not smile. She only raised her grey eyes to Pashka and stroked back an ash-blonde lock that had fallen forward from behind her ear. Pashka paid another twenty-five kopeks. The rings flew at random. The gaping crowd laughed and surged at his back. The knives hummed like bees. The old man scratched his nose in complete indifference with a hooked forefinger.

When he had squandered a ruble and not made a single hit Pashka forlornly left the crowd and walked under the lime trees along by the water which was dyed a rosy pink with the sunset. A light mist lay over the pond. The air was cool about his ears. The lights of a movie theater were reflected as pillars of flame in the tinted water. Girls in twos with short-cropped heads and green and blue combs in their hair and their arms round each other's waists passed Pashka and nudged each other and turned round to giggle at him, "Isn't he too lovely, that boy." But Pashka went on without paying any attention and hummed to himself in a dream:

"The gipsy told your fortune, the gipsy told your fortune, the gipsy told your fortune, gazing on your hand."

Before the night was over he had lost his heart finally and irrevocably.

For a whole month Pashka went to the booth every Sunday to throw the rings. He threw half his earnings away. He did not take his holiday—he had quite forgotten it was his turn. He became quite crazy. The girl handed him the rings with lowered eyes as before. Only sometimes she smiled as if to herself. And sometimes when she suddenly caught sight of Pashka in the crowds she blushed so deeply that even her shoulders through the thin muslin seemed to glow like dark-cheeked peaches. In spite of all he could do, Pashka never succeeded in having a private word with her; either people got in the way or else the old man was watching them over his spectacles with angry eyes, scratching his nose at the same time with his hooked finger, as though threatening and warning Pashka: "Keep your hands off the girl. She is not for you. Get out of it." But once Pashka did succeed in speaking to her for one second. There were not many people there and the old man had just run round to the back of the booth with a stick to chase away the ragged children.

"Pardon me," Pashka said and his heart stood still, "what is your name?"

"Ludmilla," the girl whispered quickly with glowing cheeks. "I know you well. You once left your photograph behind on the counter and I've kept it. I've lost my heart completely —it's so beautiful."

She put one finger to her neck and pointed to the corner of the crumpled print against her collar bone. When she looked up she was blushing like a rose. "And what's your name?"

"Pashka. Won't you come to the Coliseum with me? It's quite a good show: *The Billionairess.*"

"I couldn't. Father never lets me out of his sight."

"Come all the same."

"God forbid! If I went out he would never let me in again. And Mother is even worse. She has a stall at Sucharev Market in her own name. It's horrible how strict parents are. Simply frightful. We live in Prosvirin Street, not far from here, number two, in the yard to the left as you go in."

"What are we to do, then, Ludmillotchka?" [3]

"We can't do anything. Quick, throw your rings. Father's coming."

Pashka had hardly begun throwing when her father came in with the stick in his hand. He gave his daughter an angry look. So Pashka went away without having come to any arrangement. And when he went the Sunday after—the booth was shut and barred. On the signboard was: "Champion American Quoits, 40 throws 25 kopeks." A green parrot with a red tail was painted on a blue background. In his beak he held a ring, and the wind blew the yellow leaves of the lime trees past the parrot and whirled them all round the booth; the flowerbeds were over and done, not a soul was to be seen. Autumn had come.

Then Pashka remembered the gipsy's words: "An old man stands in your way . . . the knife

[3] *Ludmillotchka* The suffix -*otchka* is a Russian diminutive which shows affection.

will cause you a lot of trouble . . . the green parrot will bring you luck"—and the fury of rage he got into with the old crone passes description. He shook his fist at the parrot and went on through the dreary, yellowing gardens in a gusty wind that blew from all sides at once. He found Prosvirin Street. It was a sombre day, grey and autumnal. Number two —there it was, green and white, with a small, poverty-stricken church opposite. Pashka entered the courtyard and turned to the left. But he had no idea where to go next. Then a street organ began to play in the middle of the yard; on it was perched a green parrot with a red tail, and it looked at Pashka out of round, unabashed and heavily lidded eyes. Then a little window opened on the second floor. A delicate little hand emerged and threw a coin wrapped in paper into the yard below. Through the double window over the padding of felt, decorated with gaily colored snippets of wool, between the curtains and the pot-plants, Pashka caught sight of Ludmilla. She looked joyfully down at him, caressed the window with her pretty cheeks, made signs with her dainty little fingers, extended her arms, shook her head, nodded—there was no making head or tail of what she meant. Pashka too began to talk with his hands: "Come down, never mind your parents; I cannot live without you," but then a fat, moustachio'd woman in a Turkish shawl blotted Ludmilla out, shut the window with a bang and menaced Pashka with her finger.

Pashka dragged himself home, spent two weeks of torment, prowled round Prosvirin Street by night and terrified passers-by, who took him for a thief, got into desperate straits; and on the third Sunday cleaned his coat and trousers with cold tea, put on a pink tie, polished his shoes and went straight to beard the lion in his den—to offer his heart and hand. Ludmillotchka herself opened the door, gasped with astonishment and clutched at her heart; but Pashka marched straight past her into the room where her parents were drinking tea with milk after their devotions [4] and said:

"Your pardon, little Father, and yours, little Mother,[5] but I cannot live without Ludmillotchka. I was lost the moment I set eyes on her. Do as you please—here I am, master smith of the 6th class, plus bonuses, member of the union since 1917, drink no spirits, pay alimony to nobody, so there's no trouble in that way either."

"I am no little Father to you," the old man screamed in an inhuman voice, "and my wife is not your little Mother. Do you understand that?"

"And what do you mean by listening to the street organ in the yard under the windows and bursting in on strangers in their own house?" the wife added in a bass voice. "So take that. The idea! We have very different suitors in mind. Think of it, 6th class! Last year even a house-owner spoke for Ludmilla and we turned him down. Kindly leave the house, comrade! And the girl—under lock and key is well enough. We want no smiths here, not to mention Reds."

"I make up to a thousand rubles in hard cash by the Champion Quoits alone in the season," the father put in pugnaciously, "and the prizes alone are worth four hundred rubles. Ludmillotchka wants a husband with capital to extend the business. So—good day. Do you hear?"

"Then you won't let me have her?" Pashka asked in a voice of despair.

"No," the old man squealed.

"Very well," Pashka said threateningly. "If it's a matter of capital to extend the business, that puts the stopper on it. But you haven't heard the last of me. I'll lead you a dance yet. Good-bye, Ludmillotchka, hold on and—wait!"

Ludmillotchka, however, was sitting in the passage on a chest, wringing her hands.

Pashka set his teeth and went to Sucharev

Market and bought himself a sharp kitchen knife. When he got home he shut himself up. Winter came and went. Pashka went deliberately to work. Not an hour was given up to frivolity; at nights he lay low at home and his neighbours heard a subdued ringing noise proceeding from his room. Perhaps he was learning to play the guitar. No one could say. The river rose. The sun got warmer, the trees budded and put on their greenery, the rowing boats were transported on trucks to the Fresh Ponds. The photographers hung their Kremlins and moonlit nights in the walks. Of an evening the gardens were frequented by the strolling couples.

Pashka went regularly Sunday by Sunday to see whether the booth was open yet. It was shut. The green parrot with a red tail sat against its blue weathered background, holding a ring in its beak, and the fresh green of the lime trees waved above it. Pashka was lean and sombre. One fine Sunday the booth was open. The gaping crowd surged round the entrance. The lights shone brightly within, the ring of metal and bursts of laughter could be heard.

Pashka shouldered his way through the crowd and stepped politely up to the counter. His eyes shone like steel above his strong cheek bones. Ludmilla was collecting the rings. No sooner had he entered than all the color left her face and she went a transparent white. Her eyes were dark and her little mouth no longer resembled a cherry. Her father adjusted his spectacles and took a step back.

"By your leave, friends," Pashka said gruffly, shouldering a fellow aside who was throwing his rings, and without a glance at the old man he made a sign to the girl. She handed him the rings as though she were nearly fainting. He touched her cold fingers and tossed a three ruble piece down on the counter.

"You ought to have hired a cart, friend, for the samovar." There was a titter at his back.

Without turning round, Pashka took hold of the ring and flung it negligently. A brief tinkle

[4] *devotions* Family prayers.
[5] *little Father, little Mother* In Russia, a familiar and respectful term of address to any older person.

was heard. The ring had fallen over the knife without so much as touching it. The old man scratched his nose hurriedly and uneasily put a box of Balaev candy down in front of Pashka. Pashka pushed it aside and threw his second ring as casually as he had the first. It fell just as easily and surely over the second blade. The old man scarcely had time to trot to the shelves before three more rings lightly skimmed the air and with scarcely a sound encircled three more knives. The crowd was dumb.

The old man turned his little face to Pashka and blinked. A dark drop of sweat stood out like a wart on his forehead. His trousers slipped down a little and bagged out. Pashka stood leaning elegantly on the counter with feet crossed and jingled his handful of rings.

"Well, Papa, what about Ludmillotchka now?" he asked quietly, looking aside with an air of indifference.

"I won't let you have her," her father answered in his high-pitched voice.

"You won't," Pashka said sleepily. "Right. Hey, you," he called out to a boy, "run to the Pokrovski gate for a cart and you shall have the samovar. Out of the way, Papa."

Pashka's face went steely. The veins stood out and branched on his brow. He braced himself and lightly raised his arm. Sparks shot from his finger tips. The knives quivered and sang under the assault of the rings. The crowd roared and raged and grew to a mob. People ran to the booth from all sides. Pashka scarcely troubled to take aim. He was frightful to look upon. Not a ring fell into the sack. In five minutes all was over. Pashka wiped his forehead with his sleeve. The crowd made way. The cart was drawn up outside the booth.

"Load up," Pashka said.

"What do you mean to do?" the old man asked in agony, hopping from one foot to another round the shelves.

"Do? Nothing. Chuck 'em all into the pond and have done with it."

"Yes, but why, comrade?" the old fellow whimpered like a woman. "The goods alone are worth four hundred rubles, let alone the business."

"I would not care—even if they were worth a thousand. The plunder belongs to me. I haven't stolen it. I won it honestly. The people here are my witnesses. I practised all winter and not a wink of sleep have I had. I do what I like. If I like, I keep the loot. If I don't like, I chuck it into the water."

"That's quite right," the crowd roared enthusiastically. "Take your oath on it! But not the phonograph. Don't chuck that in too."

Volunteers soon had the cart loaded to the very top.

"Off you go," Pashka commanded.

"Where are you going?" the old man blubbered. "I shan't dare show my nose at my home again after this. . . . Are you really going to sink all of it?"

"Yes," Pashka said. "Drive onto the landing stage."

"Have you no shame in the sight of God?"

The cart moved off surrounded by a living ring of cheering people and did not stop until it reached the landing stage. Pashka took the leather boots from the top of the pile and threw them into the water. The crowd gasped.

"Stop," the old man cried in a voice not his own. "Don't throw them in the water."

Pashka laid his hand on top of the loot and said quietly, lowering his eyes:

"For the last time, Papa. I speak to you frankly, as man to man. Let all here bear me witness. Give me the girl and you can have your junk and I'll never again come within a hundred yards of your booth as long as I live. But otherwise I'll blow your whole show sky-high, Papa. I cannot live a day longer without Ludmillotchka."

"Take her!" the old man squealed. "Curse you—take her!"

"Ludmillotchka," Pashka said as he left the cart. His face was pale.

She stood beside him, hiding her face in her sleeve in her embarrassment. Even her little hands were red with shame.

"The show is over, comrades. You can go," Pashka said, taking the girl by the arm as carefully as if she were made of porcelain.

The scent of lilac filled the whole gardens. Lilac was everywhere, lilac petals in the hair, lilac petals in the water. The moon, high in the dark violet-blue of the sky above the lime trees, was as sharp as a knife. And its new-born light broke in reflections on the water, melting into rings large and small, just like gold wedding rings, come to life.

[*translated by* BASIL CREIGHTON]

For Discussion

1. An author's attitude toward his subject determines a story's mood. What is the mood of "The Knives"? Does Kataev show sympathy toward certain characters? Does he show disapproval of others? Illustrate.

2. What sort of person is Pashka? Do you feel that if he had failed to win Ludmilla his life would suffer a violent change? Does Pashka have any personal qualities that might not be considered virtues?

3. Has the author prepared the reader for Pashka's first sight of Ludmilla? How does he let us know what is on Pashka's mind even before Pashka himself knows?

4. What is the basis of Ludmilla's father's disapproval of Pashka? How does Pashka overcome this? What other ways might he have used?

5. Would an unhappy ending spoil this story? Try to invent an unhappy ending that would still be consistent with the character of Pashka.

The Snob

MORLEY CALLAGHAN

"This above all," Polonius advises his son Laertes in Shakespeare's Hamlet, *"To thine own self be true." Polonius's advice seems logical and emotionally sound, and yet the job of remaining true to oneself is not always a simple process. The image we want to present to others does not always match the self we try to hide. "The Snob" is the story of a young man who, in his anxiety to make the perfect impression on his young lady, denies a part of himself. And, like many human beings who fall prey to self-deceit, he accuses another of the weaknesses he despises in himself.*

IT WAS at the book counter in the department store that John Harcourt, the student, caught a glimpse of his father. At first he could not be sure in the crowd that pushed along the aisle, but there was something about the color of the back of the elderly man's neck, something about the faded felt hat, that he knew very well. Harcourt was standing with the girl he loved, buying a book for her. All afternoon he had been talking to her, eagerly, but with an anxious diffidence, as if there still remained in him an innocent wonder that she should be delighted to be with him. From underneath her wide-brimmed straw hat, her face, so fair and beautifully strong with its expression of cool independence, kept turning up to him and sometimes smiled at what he said. That was the way they always talked, never daring to show much full, strong feeling. Harcourt had just bought the book, and had reached into his pocket for the money with a free, ready gesture to make it appear that he was accustomed to buying books for young ladies, when the white-haired man in the faded felt hat, at the other end of the counter, turned half toward him, and Harcourt knew he was standing only a few feet away from his father.

The young man's easy words trailed away and his voice became little more than a whisper, as if he were afraid that everyone in the store might recognize it. There was rising in him a dreadful uneasiness; something very precious that he wanted to hold seemed close to destruction. His father, standing at the end of the bargain counter, was planted squarely on his two feet, turning a book over thoughtfully in his hands. Then he took out his glasses from an old, worn leather case and adjusted them on the

MORLEY CALLAGHAN (*1903–   *) *was
trained as a lawyer, but early in life
gave up law for literature. He is one
of Canada's leading writers, and his stories
and novels have been reprinted
throughout the world.*

---

end of his nose, looking down over them at the
book. His coat was thrown open, two buttons
on his vest were undone, his gray hair was too
long, and in his rather shabby clothes he looked
very much like a workingman, a carpenter
perhaps. Such a resentment rose in young Harcourt that he wanted to cry out bitterly, "Why
does he dress as if he never owned a decent
suit in his life? He doesn't care what the whole
world thinks of him. He never did. I've told
him a hundred times he ought to wear his good
clothes when he goes out. Mother's told him
the same thing. He just laughs. And now Grace
may see him. Grace will meet him."

So young Harcourt stood still, with his head
down, feeling that something very painful was
impending. Once he looked anxiously at Grace,
who had turned to the bargain counter. Among
those people drifting aimlessly by with hot red
faces, getting in each other's way, using their
elbows but keeping their faces detached and
wooden, she looked tall and splendidly alone.
She was so sure of herself, her relation to the
people in the aisles, the clerks behind the counters, the books on the shelves, and everything
around her. Still keeping his head down and
moving close, he whispered uneasily, "Let's go
and have tea somewhere, Grace."

"In a minute, dear," she said.

"Let's go now."

"In just a minute, dear," she repeated absently.

"There's not a breath of air in here. Let's go
now."

"What makes you so impatient?"

"There's nothing but old books on that
counter."

"There may be something here I've wanted

all my life," she said, smiling at him brightly
and not noticing the uneasiness in his face.

So Harcourt had to move slowly behind her,
getting closer to his father all the time. He
could feel the space that separated them nar-
rowing. Once he looked up with a vague, sidelong glance. But his father, red-faced and happy,
was still reading the book, only now there was
a meditative expression on his face, as if something in the book had stirred him and he intended to stay there reading for some time.

Old Harcourt had lots of time to amuse himself, because he was on a pension after working
hard all his life. He had sent John to the university and he was eager to have him distinguish
himself. Every night when John came home,
whether it was early or late, he used to go into
his father and mother's bedroom and turn on
the light and talk to them about the interesting
things that had happened to him during the day.
They listened and shared this new world with
him. They both sat up in their night clothes and,
while his mother asked all the questions, his
father listened attentively with his head cocked
on one side and a smile or a frown on his face.
The memory of all this was in John now, and
there was also a desperate longing and a pain
within him growing harder to bear as he glanced
fearfully at his father, but he thought stubbornly, "I can't introduce him. It'll be easier
for everybody if he doesn't see us. I'm not
ashamed. But it will be easier. It'll be more sensible. It'll only embarrass him to see Grace." By
this time he knew he was ashamed, but he felt
that his shame was justified, for Grace's father
had the smooth, confident manner of a man who
had lived all his life among people who were
rich and sure of themselves. Often when he
had been in Grace's home talking politely to her
mother, John had kept on thinking of the plain-
ness of his own home and of his parents' laughing, good-natured untidiness, and he resolved
desperately that he must make Grace's people
admire him.

He looked up cautiously, for they were about

eight feet away from his father, but at that moment his father, too, looked up and John's glance shifted swiftly far over the aisle, over the counters, seeing nothing. As his father's blue, calm eyes stared steadily over the glasses, there was an instant when their glances might have met. Neither one could have been certain, yet John, as he turned away and began to talk hurriedly to Grace, knew surely that his father had seen him. He knew it by the steady calmness in his father's blue eyes. John's shame grew, and then humiliation sickened him as he waited and did nothing.

His father turned away, going down the aisle, walking erectly in his shabby clothes, his shoulders very straight, never once looking back. His father would walk slowly down the street, he knew, with that meditative expression deepening and becoming grave.

Young Harcourt stood beside Grace, brushing against her soft shoulder, and made faintly aware again of the delicate scent she used. There, so close beside him, she was holding within her everything he wanted to reach out for, only now he felt a sharp hostility that made him sullen and silent. "You were right, John," she was drawling in her soft voice. "It does get unbearable in here on a hot day. Do let's go now. Have you ever noticed that department stores after a time can make you really hate people?" But she smiled when she spoke, so he might see that she really hated no one.

"You don't like people, do you?" he said sharply.

"People? What people? What do you mean?"

"I mean," he went on irritably, "you don't like the kind of people you bump into here, for example."

"Not especially. Who does? What are you talking about?"

"Anybody could see you don't," he said recklessly, full of a savage eagerness to hurt her. "I say you don't like simple, honest people, the kind of people you meet all over the city." He blurted the words out as if he wanted to shake her, but he was longing to say, "You wouldn't like my family. Why couldn't I take you home to have dinner with them? You'd turn up your nose at them, because they've no pretensions. As soon as my father saw you, he knew you wouldn't want to meet him. I could tell by the way he turned."

His father was on his way home now, he knew, and that evening at dinner they would meet. His mother and sister would talk rapidly, but his father would say nothing to him, or to anyone. There would only be Harcourt's memory of the level look in the blue eyes, and the knowledge of his father's pain as he walked away.

Grace watched John's gloomy face as they walked through the store, and she knew he was nursing some private rage, and so her own resentment and exasperation kept growing, and she said crisply, "You're entitled to your moods on a hot afternoon, I suppose, but if I feel I don't like it here, then I don't like it. You wanted to go yourself. Who likes to spend very much time in a department store on a hot afternoon? I begin to hate every stupid person that bangs into me, everybody near me. What does that make me?"

"It makes you a snob."

"So I'm a snob now?" she asked angrily.

"Certainly you're a snob," he said. They were at the door and going out to the street. As they walked in the sunlight, in the crowd moving slowly down the street, he was groping for words to describe the secret thoughts he had always had about her. "I've always known how you'd feel about people I like who didn't fit into your private world," he said.

"You're a very stupid person," she said. Her face was flushed now, and it was hard for her to express her indignation, so she stared straight ahead as she walked along.

They had never talked in this way, and now they were both quickly eager to hurt each other. With a flow of words, she started to argue with him, then she checked herself and said calmly, "Listen, John, I imagine you're tired of my company. There's no sense in having tea together. I think I'd better leave you right here."

"That's fine," he said. "Good afternoon."

"Good-by."

"Good-by."

She started to go, she had gone two paces, but he reached out desperately and held her arm, and he was frightened, and pleading, "Please don't go, Grace."

All the anger and irritation had left him; there was just a desperate anxiety in his voice as he pleaded, "Please forgive me. I've no right to talk to you like that. I don't know why I'm so rude or what's the matter. I'm ridiculous. I'm very, very ridiculous. Please, you must forgive me. Don't leave me."

He had never talked to her so brokenly, and his sincerity, the depth of his feeling, began to stir her. While she listened, feeling all the yearning in him, they seemed to have been brought closer together, by opposing each other, than ever before, and she began to feel almost shy. "I don't know what's the matter. I suppose we're both irritable. It must be the weather," she said. "But I'm not angry, John."

He nodded his head miserably. He longed to tell her that he was sure she would have been charming to his father, but he had never felt so wretched in his life. He held her arm tight, as if he must hold it or what he wanted most in the world would slip away from him, yet he kept thinking, as he would ever think, of his father walking away quietly with his head never turning.

For Discussion

1. From what the author describes of John Harcourt's father, what sort of man does he seem to be? Can you justify John Harcourt's embarrassment? Do many young people go through a "stage" where their parents become something to hide rather than a source of pride?

2. Mark Twain once said that when he was sixteen, his father was extremely dull and unaware; when he was in his twenties, his father was still dull and unaware, but he had learned a little; by the time he was forty, his father had grown into the wisest man in the world. How does this apply to "The Snob"?

3. When Callaghan writes that John Harcourt "had reached into his pocket for the money with a free,

ready gesture to make it appear that he was accustomed to buying books for young ladies," what does he show us about the young man's personality that prepares us for the heartless treatment of his father that comes later?

4. How does the author make the reader censure John Harcourt's cruelty in the beginning of the story and then feel sorry for him later? Does John Harcourt administer justice to himself? Explain your answer.

5. Explain how John's argument with Grace is really a process of self-accusation. What might be a psychological reason for John's anger with Grace? Which of the two is the snob?

The Sorrel Colt

BENITO LYNCH

The world through a child's eyes is a large and threatening place. In this story of life on the Argentine pampas, a boy finds himself trapped in a world of adult values. He confronts his responsibilities by surrendering what he loves best.

I

TIRED OF playing "Tiger," a game of his own invention which consisted of chasing through the tree-tops after his brother Leo, who defended himself bravely, using the green figs as ammunition, Mario went out to the back gate of the villa; and there, in the noonday sun, he leaned against one of the old pillars and gazed at the street, waiting patiently for Leo, still perched on the topmost branch of a fig-tree and eager to continue the fight, to grow weary of shouting "Nitwit!" and "Jackass!" at him—when an unexpected sight filled him with pleasant surprise.

Turning the corner of the villa, a man riding a pot-bellied mare, followed by a tiny little colt, had just appeared on the street, and was slowly approaching.

"Say!"

And Mario, with his eyes wide open and his face beaming, went to the edge of the path to get a better view of the procession.

"A colt!" . . . One would have to know how much it meant, then, to Mario, to get a colt of his own, that is, a horse in proportion to his size! . . .

This was his "fad," his passion, his everlasting dream. But, unfortunately—and this he knew from experience—his parents wanted no animals at the villa because they would eat up the plants and strip the bark off the tree-trunks.

Over at "The Ranch," anything their hearts desired: namely, a docile little pony, old and big-headed. But here, at the villa, no "beasts" at all!

For this reason, Mario was about to resign himself, as on other occasions, to watch indifferently the little marvel's passing, when an extraordinary thing happened.

Just as he came face to face with him, without slackening his trot and almost without turning his face, the man riding the mare, a big, robust young fellow with a sullen face and a red beret, let loose to Mario with this wonderful proposal.

"Hey, kid! . . . If you want this colt, I'll give him to you. I'm taking him out in the fields to kill him!"

When Mario heard this, he felt the ground quake under his feet, his eyes cloud over, and the blood rush to his head; but oh! he knew the rules of the house so thoroughly that he didn't

BENITO LYNCH (*1880–1951*) *was born in Argentina of a French mother and Irish father. He grew up on a ranch in the pampas in the province of Buenos Aires. The gauchos (the Argentine cowboys) and their way of life provided him with the material for his best and most typical tales.*

---

hesitate a second and, red as a tomato, he refused, ashamed:

"No . . . Thank you . . . no! . . ."

The brawny young man shrugged his shoulders slightly and, without another word, went his way through the sunlight that flooded the street, while following the weary gait of his mare, came that marvelous sorrel[1] colt, who trotted proudly over the clods of dried mud and who, with his fluffy, yellowish tail, tried to brush off the flies just like a grown-up horse.

"Mamma! . . ."

And dashing headlong like a colt and without time to say anything to his brother, who, ignorant of everything and still at the top of his fig-tree, took advantage of his swift flight to pelt him with a few figs, Mario appeared under the arbor, stumbling over everything in his path:

"Oh Mamma! Oh Mamma!"

His mother, who was sewing in her arm-chair in the shade of the young vines, rose from her chair with a start:

"Good Heavens, son, what's the matter?"

"Nothing, mamma, nothing . . . just a man!"

"What, son, what?"

"Just a man was driving a beautiful little colt, and he wanted to give it to me! . . ."

"Mercy, what a fright you gave me!" Then his mother smiled; but he, in his excitement, went on without hearing her.

"A beautiful little colt, mamma, a tiny little sorrel colt, this big . . . and the man was going to kill him, mamma! . . ."

And now something else stupendous happened, for contrary to all expectations and logic, Mario heard his mother say, with genuine concern:

"Really? . . . Well! . . . Why didn't you accept it, silly? Specially now that we're going to 'The Ranch!'"

In the face of so unusual, so unjustified, and so surprising a remark, his jaw dropped a foot, but he was so "colt crazy" that he didn't stop to ask questions and with an "I'll call him, then," as vibrant and shrill as a neigh, he started running towards the gate.

"Careful, son!" cried his mother.

Careful nothing! . . . Mario ran so fast that his brother didn't manage to throw a single fig at him as he passed.

When he went out on the street, the sun's glare dazzled him. Not a single colt or mare or man anywhere. . . . But soon his anxious eyes caught a glimpse of the red beret, off there in the distance, bobbing along in the rhythm of a trot in a cloud of dust.

And in vain the ridges of dry mud made him stumble and fall several times, in vain he felt choked up with emotion, in vain the laundress's hateful little curs came out to greet him—nothing nor anyone could stop Mario from running.

Inside of two blocks he was within earshot of the supreme arbiter of his happiness, who was moseying along dejectedly at a trot on a humble, pot-bellied mare.

"Hey! Hey! Mister, mister! . . ."

When the brawny young man heard him, he reined in his mount and waited for Mario, frowning hard.

"What do you want, huh?"

"The colt! . . . I want the colt!" Mario panted breathlessly and he stretched out his arms towards the animal, as if they were to receive it, like a package in a store.

The man made a doubtful, wry face.

"All right," he said. "Take hold of him."

---

[1] *sorrel*   A reddish-brown color.

"To Mario he was the finest colt there was, and the most beautiful future race-horse . . ."

And at once he added, looking down at his hands:

"Did you bring something to do it with?"

Mario blushed again.

"No . . . I didn't . . ."

He looked around, embarrassed, as though he expected to find a halter hidden somewhere in the grass. . . .

The man dismounted and went to unhook a piece of wire that happened to be hanging from the thorny *cina-cina* [2] fence, while the boy watched him, filled with emotion.

II

Only Mario knew what it meant to him—that little sorrel colt who destroyed plants, who bit and kicked, who refused to budge when he didn't want to; who once tore out a lock of Mario's hair with one bite, probably thinking it was grass, but who ate sugar from his hand and neighed as soon as he saw him in the distance! . . .

He was his love, his worry, his guiding star, his spiritual light. So much so, that his parents became accustomed to using the colt as a means of taming the little boy, and keeping him in line.

"If you don't study, you can't go out on the colt this afternoon . . . If you misbehave, we'll take away the colt . . . If you do this or don't do that . . ."

Always the colt loomed up against Mario's rebellions like the elaborate standard of some invincible legion in the thick of battle. . . .

The threat had such power over him that in no time he would sheathe his arrogance just as any fighter sheathes his knife at the arrival of the sheriff. For that sorrel colt was such a wonder, so gentle, so affectionate, and so clever!

[2] *cina-cina* A kind of hedge.

The horse-tamer at "The Ranch"—a skilled braider—made him a little halter that was a marvel, a truly exquisite lacework of strips of tan leather and, little by little, the other farm-hands, either out of affection for Mario or out of rivalry with the trainer, made all the rest of the accessories, until he had a complete little riding outfit that was admired by "everyone."

To Mario he was the finest colt there was, and the most beautiful future race-horse the world had ever seen—and so firm was his conviction in this respect that the taunts of his brother Leo, who persisted in calling the sorrel colt "jackass" and other such fine names, struck him as veritable blasphemies.

On the other hand, when the foreman of "The Ranch" said, after sizing up the colt through half-closed eyes:

"In my opinion, he'll be a real beauty, that one"—to Mario the foreman seemed the most likable and most intelligent of men. . . .

III

Mario's father wanted to start a garden on the grounds adjoining "The Ranch," and it happened that the "hateful colt"—which is what some now called him, including the boy's mother, probably because he had trampled on some of her newborn chicks—seemed bent on opposing the project, judging by the vehemence with which he attacked the tender seedlings whenever he got loose. Mario had been warned from the very beginning not to forget to tie up the colt at night; but it also so happened that Mario forgot that he had forgotten so many times already, until at last, one morning, his father, exasperated, said to him, shaking his forefinger emphatically and in rhythm with his words:

"The first day that colt destroys another plant, that very day I'll turn him out into the fields. . . ."

"Ooooh! . . . Into the fields! . . . Turn him out into the *fields!* . . ."

Did Mario's father happen to have any idea of what turning him into the fields meant to the boy?

He would have to be eight years old like him, to think the way he thought, and love his sorrel colt the way he loved him, to appreciate the real enormity of the threat. . . .

"The fields! . . . Turn him out into the *fields!* . . ." To Mario the fields were something tempestuous, boundless, and abysmal; putting the colt out there would be as atrocious and inhuman as casting a newborn babe into the sea.

No wonder, then, that he was not careless again; or that a whole, long week went by without the sorrel colt inflicting the slightest damage on the most insignificant little flower . . .

IV

At daybreak of a radiant February morning, Mario was lying across his bed with his feet up against the wall, "confiding" some of his plans for the sorrel colt's bright future to his brother Leo, when his mother unexpectedly entered the bedroom.

"So there you are!" she said, all upset. "So there you are! Have you seen your colt?"

Mario turned crimson and then pale.

"What? My what, mamma?"

"Your colt got loose in the garden again and destroyed a whole lot of things."

To Mario it seemed as if the universe were crashing down on top of him.

"But . . . how?" he managed to say. "But, how? . . ."

"Well, I don't know how," his mother answered, "but you can't say I haven't warned you time and again! . . . Now your father . . ."

"But I did tie him up . . . I *did* tie him up . . ."

And as Mario hurriedly got dressed, his hands shook, and he saw everything blurred, as if that room were filling up with smoke.

V

It was a real disaster. Never had the colt dared do so much. This time he had not only trampled the sod of the flower-beds and knocked down with his rump a certain cane trellis over which a vine had started to climb with great elegance, but had carried his mischief to the point of uprooting and pawing with his hoof several rare carnation plants, arranged in an elegant design . . .

"What have you done? What have you done, Baby?"

And as if in a dream, and almost without knowing what he was doing, Mario knelt on the damp ground and began feverishly replanting the flowers while "Baby," "the wretch," stood still with his head down, the muzzle of his head-stall loose, and a certain air of cynical indifference about his whole "person."

VI

Like a sleepwalker, as if treading on a soft wool mattress, Mario led the colt by the halter down the middle of the wide, sloping road lined with towering populars, which ended there, at the white picket cow-gate which opened on the desolate immensity of the wild fields.

How the blood pounded in the child's brain, how he saw things half-obliterated through a fog, and how he still heard his father's awful threat ringing in his ears! . . .

"Take that colt and put him out into the fields!"

Mario did not cry because he could not, for his throat was in the grip of a steel claw. He walked like an automaton, so strangely, in fact, that only his mother noticed from the patio. . . .

It was that for Mario, the other side of that cow-gate was the end of everything; it was the whirlpool where in a few seconds he and all existence would sink down fatally after the sorrel colt. . . .

When Mario had gone halfway there, his mother could stand it no longer and moaned, nervously clutching his father's arm.

"Enough, Juan, enough," she said.

"All right! . . . Call him! . . ."

But just as Leo started out swiftly, the mother uttered a sharp cry and the father broke into a frantic run.

There, beside the cow-gate, Mario, with his canvas apron, had just fallen on the grass, like a gentle bird hit by a bullet. . . .

VII

. . . A few days later, when Mario could at last sit up in bed, his parents, laughing, but with their eyelids red and their faces pale from the long vigils, ushered the sorrel colt into the bedroom, pulling him by the halter and pushing on his rump . . .

[*translated by* ANGEL FLORES]

For Discussion

1. What is Mario's conception of the adult world? Does it seem to him different from his own world? What is the significance of this difference? Why is he surprised at his mother's suggestion to accept the colt? Do Mario's mother and father appear to be unreasonable and unsympathetic?

2. To Mario the "fields were something tempestous, boundless and abysmal." Is there a wider significance to this concept of the fields? If so, what is it?

3. When Mario takes it upon himself to send the colt to the fields, has he taken a step toward maturity? Is his illness at this point a device by the author to bring about the parents' repentance? Or does it

seem more like a short sleep from which Mario awakens a new person, his childhood forever behind him?

4. Try to state in a brief paragraph the principal lesson of life that Mario learns.

5. A story must be written from a "point of view." That is to say, the events are seen through the eyes of the author, of a narrator, or of one or several of the characters in the story. In some stories the point of view shifts from time to time. Examine "The Sorrel Colt." Try to determine the point of view of each part of the story. If the point of view shifts, show where the changes take place.

The Use of Force

WILLIAM CARLOS WILLIAMS

Much of modern literature—fiction, drama, and poetry—has sought material in the events of everyday life. When a writer merely catalogues the sights and sounds of ordinary lives, with no selectivity, "realism" can be very dull. When presented with great artistry, as in "The Use of Force," a simple "slice of life"—a doctor's visit to a patient—can take on a firm structure and great power. On the surface this small kitchen drama seems no more than an anecdote. A grown man tries to force open the mouth of a stubborn little girl. But as the struggle intensifies, the doctor recognizes the signs of deeper conflict. Note that Dr. Williams has eliminated the use of quotation marks for his dialogue. The reader must determine from the context or change of tone where the characters' speeches begin and end.

THEY WERE new patients to me, all I had was the name, Olson. Please come down as soon as you can, my daughter is very sick.

When I arrived I was met by the mother, a big startled looking woman, very clean and apologetic who merely said, Is this the doctor? and let me in. In the back, she added. You must excuse us, doctor, we have her in the kitchen where it is warm. It is very damp here sometimes.

The child was fully dressed and sitting on her father's lap near the kitchen table. He tried to get up, but I motioned for him not to bother, took off my overcoat and started to look things over. I could see that they were all very nervous, eyeing me up and down distrustfully. As often, in such cases, they weren't telling me more than they had to, it was up to me to tell them; that's why they were spending three dollars on me.

The child was fairly eating me up with her cold, steady eyes, and no expression to her face whatever. She did not move and seemed, inwardly, quiet; an unusually attractive little thing, and as strong as a heifer in appearance. But her face was flushed, she was breathing rapidly, and I realized that she had a high fever. She had magnificent blonde hair, in profusion. One of those picture children often reproduced in advertising leaflets and the photogravure sections of the Sunday papers.

She's had a fever for three days, began the father and we don't know what it comes from. My wife has given her things, you know, like people do, but it don't do no good. And there's been a lot of sickness around. So we tho't you'd better look her over and tell us what is the matter.

As doctors often do I took a trial shot at it as a point of departure. Has she had a sore throat?

Both parents answered me together, No . . . No, she says her throat don't hurt her.

Does your throat hurt you? added the mother to the child. But the little girl's expression didn't change nor did she move her eyes from my face.

Have you looked?

I tried to, said the mother, but I couldn't see.

As it happens we had been having a number of cases of diphtheria in the school to which this child went during that month and we were all, quite apparently, thinking of that, though no one had as yet spoken of the thing.

Well, I said, suppose we take a look at the throat first. I smiled in my best professional manner and asking for the child's first name I said, come on, Mathilda, open your mouth and let's take a look at your throat.

Nothing doing.

Aw, come on, I coaxed, just open your mouth wide and let me take a look. Look, I said opening both hands wide, I haven't anything in my hands. Just open up and let me see.

Such a nice man, put in the mother. Look how kind he is to you. Come on, do what he tells you to. He won't hurt you.

At that I ground my teeth in disgust. If only they wouldn't use the word "hurt" I might be able to get somewhere. But I did not allow myself to be hurried or disturbed but speaking quietly and slowly I approached the child again.

As I moved my chair a little nearer suddenly with one catlike movement both her hands clawed instinctively for my eyes and she almost reached them too. In fact she knocked my glasses flying and they fell, though unbroken, several feet away from me on the kitchen floor.

Both the mother and father almost turned themselves inside out in embarrassment and apology. You bad girl, said the mother, taking her and shaking her by one arm. Look what you've done. The nice man . . .

For heaven's sake, I broke in. Don't call me a nice man to her. I'm here to look at her throat on the chance that she might have diphtheria and possibly die of it. But that's nothing to her. Look here, I said to the child, we're going to look at your throat. You're old enough to understand what I'm saying. Will you open it now by yourself or shall we have to open it for you?

Not a move. Even her expression hadn't changed. Her breaths however were coming faster and faster. Then the battle began. I had to do it. I had to have a throat culture for her own protection. But first I told the parents that it was entirely up to them. I explained the danger but said that I would not insist on a throat examination so long as they would take the responsibility.

If you don't do what the doctor says you'll have to go to the hospital, the mother admonished her severely.

Oh yeah? I had to smile to myself. After all, I had already fallen in love with the savage brat, the parents were contemptible to me. In the ensuing struggle they grew more and more abject, crushed, exhausted while she surely rose to magnificent heights of insane fury of effort bred of her terror of me.

WILLIAM CARLOS WILLIAMS (*1883–1963*) *lived all of his life in Rutherford, New Jersey. He is best known as a poet, yet he also wrote excellent novels* (The Build Up) *as well as stories, plays, and an autobiography. He was a physician by profession and spent most of his life attending his factory-worker patients. His work takes root in the American sights, sounds, and emotions that he found about him; it is characterized by the title of one of his books,* Life Along the Passaic River. *Yet Dr. Williams was never content merely to record commonplace surfaces and conversations. By the rigorous discipline of his language, he transformed the ordinary into the poetic.*

The father tried his best, and he was a big man but the fact that she was his daughter, his shame at her behavior and his dread of hurting her made him release her just at the critical moment several times when I had almost achieved success, till I wanted to kill him. But his dread also that she might have diphtheria made him tell me to go on, go on though he himself was almost fainting, while the mother moved back and forth behind us raising and lowering her hands in an agony of apprehension.

Put her in front of you on your lap, I ordered, and hold both her wrists.

But as soon as he did the child let out a scream. Don't, you're hurting me. Let go of my hands. Let them go I tell you. Then she shrieked terrifyingly, hysterically. Stop it! Stop it! You're killing me!

Do you think she can stand it, doctor! said the mother.

You get out, said the husband to his wife. Do you want her to die of diphtheria?

Come on now, hold her, I said.

Then I grasped the child's head with my left hand and tried to get the wooden tongue depressor between her teeth. She fought, with clenched teeth, desperately! But now I also had grown furious—at a child. I tried to hold myself down but I couldn't. I know how to expose a throat for inspection. And I did my best. When finally I got the wooden spatula behind the last teeth and just the point of it into the mouth cavity, she opened up for an instant but before I could see anything she came down again and gripping the wooden blade between her molars she reduced it to splinters before I could get it out again.

Aren't you ashamed, the mother yelled at her. Aren't you ashamed to act like that in front of the doctor?

Get me a smooth-handled spoon of some sort, I told the mother. We're going through with this. The child's mouth was already bleeding. Her tongue was cut and she was screaming in wild hysterical shrieks. Perhaps I should have desisted and come back in an hour or more. No doubt it would have been better. But I have seen at least two children lying dead in bed of neglect in such cases, and feeling that I must get a diagnosis now or never I went at it again. But the worst of it was that I too had got beyond reason. I could have torn the child apart in my own fury and enjoyed it. It was a pleasure to attack her. My face was burning with it.

The little brat must be protected against her own idiocy, one says to one's self at such times. Others must be protected against her. It is social necessity. And all these things are true. But a blind fury, a feeling of adult shame, bred of a longing for muscular release are the operatives. One goes on to the end.

In a final unreasoning assault I overpowered the child's neck and jaws. I forced the heavy silver spoon back of her teeth and down her throat till she gagged. And there it was—both tonsils covered with membrane. She had fought valiantly to keep me from knowing her secret. She had been hiding that sore throat for three days at least and lying to her parents in order to escape just such an outcome as this.

Now truly she *was* furious. She had been on the defensive before but now she attacked. Tried to get off her father's lap and fly at me while tears of defeat blinded her eyes.

For Discussion

1. The art of "The Use of Force" is in the amount of material that is effortlessly presented within a very short space. Note how little Williams tells us about his characters and about the house and kitchen where the drama takes place. And yet the setting is completely real, and the presence of each character is truly felt. What is the doctor's attitude toward the parents? Their attitude toward him? The parents' attitude toward the child? The doctor's attitude toward her? How does the child feel toward her parents? Toward the doctor? All these attitudes are clearly established in the story, sometimes merely by the tone of voice in which the characters speak. How do these attitudes change during the course of the story?

2. Is the little girl simply fighting to conceal her sore throat, or do her infected tonsils represent something more important? How does the possibility of diphtheria complicate the doctor's duty to make a correct diagnosis? Explain why the doctor's discovery of the little girl's secret changes her tactics from defensive to aggressive.

3. Does the struggle between the little girl and the doctor suggest a larger conflict of the individual with society? In this battle, what arguments favor society in the person of the doctor? What arguments favor the position of the little girl?

4. When the doctor says, "I had already fallen in love with the savage brat," what does he mean? Does the author make it believable that the doctor can feel disgust, annoyance, rage, and love for the child all at once?

5. Why will the parents not tell the doctor any more than they have to?

6. There are two voices arguing with each other within the doctor. Try to identify them.

The End of a Good Man

SEAN O'FAOLAIN

This story, set in modern Dublin, presents another conflict of wills—this time between a young man and his racing pigeon. The fact that the hero's adversary is only a bird gives the story a comic tone. But the effects of the struggle upon both Larry and his pigeon, Brian Boru, are far from comic.

MEN WHO go into competition with the world are broken into fragments by the world, and it is such men we love to analyze. But men who do not go into competition with the world remain intact, and these men we cannot analyze. They are always contented men, with modest ambitions. Larry Dunne was that kind of man. All that there is to say about him, therefore, is that he bred pigeons and was happy.

And yet, this unconditional lump of reality, this unrefracted thought in the mind of God, suddenly did fall into fragments. He fell for the same reason as Adam. For when God was saying, "Orchards for Adam," and "Finance for J. P. Morgan," and "Politics for Teddy Roosevelt," and "Pigeons for Larry Dunne," He must have added (*sotto voce*), "*But one pigeon he must never control.*" And it was to that one pigeon, that one ambition, that Larry Dunne gave his heart. The pigeon's name was Brian Boru.[1] Larry got him on his thirty-fifth birthday from his father.

Any evening that summer you could have met Larry at the pigeon club—it sat every night under the canal bridge on the towpath—and you might have guessed in what direction his heart was already moving by the way he talked endlessly without ever mentioning the fatal bird. You might have heard him, towering over the rest of the club, talking of his runts, tumblers, pouters, homers, racers,[2] without ever mentioning Brian Boru; you might have heard how he had a jacobin, and nearly had a scandaroon; how "pigeons, mind you, must never be washed, only sprayed with rain water. And what's more, pigeons should be sprayed from the shoulders down—never the head, unless you want them to die of meningitis." What a scoundrel the man in Saint Rita's Terrace was, a low fellow who kept budgerigars[3] and had once actually said that pigeons were mere riffraff. How his father had stolen a sacred pigeon out of an Indian temple, when he was in Rangoon with the Royal

---

[1] *Brian Boru* The pigeon derived his name from one of the legendary heroes of Ireland.

[2] *Runts, tumblers, pouters, homers, racers, jacobins, scandaroons* Types of pigeons.

[3] *budgerigars* Type of parakeet.

Irish, and how the rajah chased him into the jungle for two miles trying to catch him. "And what's more, you should never dry a pigeon, unless, to be sure, you wrapped him up in warm flannel—which isn't the same thing." And anyway, what were budgerigars, only pups off parrots? "They are not even called budgerigars! They call them budgies—as if anyone would ever dare to call a pigeon a pidgy! Doesn't it show yeh?"

But whatever he spoke of, or whomever he spoke to, you might notice that he never spoke to one little runt of a man who always listened to him with a sly, sneering smile on his face. That was the club member whose Michael Collins the Second [4] had beaten Larry's Brian Boru in every race since the season began—beaten the bird that had laid its beak on Larry's heart.

Nobody knew the history of this Brian Boru. Larry's father swore he was the great-grandson of the Indian rajah's sacred pigeon, but that, of course, was a tall yarn. Whatever its pedigree, the bird was a marvel. Such speed! Such direction! Such a homer! A bird that had only one flaw! Time and again, when there was a race, Larry had seen that faint speck of joy come into the sky over the flat counties and the checkered market gardens where he lived, each time half an hour, at the very least, ahead of every other bird in the team; and on one occasion as much as fifty-eight minutes ahead of them, and that in the teeth of a thirty-mile gale.

For while other birds had to follow the guiding shore line, or the railway line that dodged the hills, Brian came sailing over mountaintop and moor like an arrow from the bow. Time and again, after greeting him with an adoring shout, Larry had gone tearing back down the lane to his tumble-down cottage, roaring to his da [5] to get out the decoys, and

to light the primus stove for some new concoction whose smell was to tempt Brian Boru down to his loft. Back then to the bridge, waving to the sky, calling the bird by name as it came nearer and nearer to the parapet on which stood the club's timepiece—a clock with a glass front on which there was a blue-and-green painting of a waterfall. (A bird was not officially home until its owner had tipped the waterfall with its beak.)

But . . . time and again the one flaw told. Brian Boru would circle, and Brian Boru would sink, and inevitably Brian Boru would rise again. After about thirty minutes of this he would come down to the telegraph pole over Larry's back yard, and stay there until some slow coach [6] like Michael Collins the Second had walked off with the race. The bird so loved the air that it could not settle down.

"Oh!" Larry had been heard to moan, as he looked up at the telegraph pole. "Isn't it a sign? Isn't it a symbol? Isn't that poor Ireland all over again? First in the race. Fast as the lightning. But she won't settle down! That bird has too much spirit—he's a highflier—and aren't we the same? Always up in the air. Can't come down to earth." And then he would beseech the bird, as it looked down at him over its prima-donna chest with a bleary eye, rather like an old damp-nosed judge falling asleep on his bench: "O Brian Boru! Yeh sweet limb o' the divil, will you come down? Look! I've custards for yeh. I have yer loft lined with the sweetest straw." And he would start clucking and chortling at it. "Coordle-coordle-coordle, Brian Boru-u-u-yu." Or: "Tchook, tchuc, thc, thc, thc, thc. Ychook, thc, thc . . . oh, but I'll tchook you if I lay me hands on you, you criminal type from British India! Brian, my *darling*, aren't you *going* to come *down* to me?"

Brian would snuggle his beak on his chest, or make a contemptuous noise like a snore.

Then, that night at the bridge—for on race

---

[4] *Michael Collins the Second* A pigeon named after the famous Irish patriot.

[5] *da* Short for dad.

[6] *slow coach* Slang for a slow person or thing.

SEAN O'FAOLAIN (1900–) is an Irish novelist, biographer, and literary critic who lives in County Dublin. He has distinguished himself as one of the great modern storytellers who, through a love that embraces the faults and virtues of his subjects, has given artistic expression to his country and its people. The comic and the tragic come together in his romantic, unpredictable characters. A precise craftsman, Sean O'Faolain says of his work, "Half of the art of writing is rewriting" and his stories reflect the care that has gone into their composition.

---

nights Larry simply had to talk about Brian Boru:

"It's not fair," Larry would protest. "The rules should be altered. That bird is not being given his due. That bird is suffering an injustice. Sure, it's only plain, honest reason. The bird is first home in every race—will any member of the club deny it?"

"No, Larry!" they would reply, appeasingly. "No! He's a grand bird, we all admit it, but a bird who won't settle is no good. And, for another thing, as we're sick and tired of telling you, supposing two birds come into sight at one and the same time, who the blazes is going to tell which one of them is first past the winning post—if there's going to be no winning post?"

"Ah!" Larry would roar. "But sure this bird is home hours before any of your so-called pigeons—cripples, I call them." And then, true to his happy, lighthearted nature, he could not help laughing and making a joke of it. Six feet two, and as innocent as a child. "Did I call them cripples? Cripples is too good for them. The one half of ye must be breeding yeer birds from a cross between penguins and pelicans!"

At which he would recover something of his natural good humor again, and go off chortling—

a chortle that would die as he remembered what began it.

As the season approached its end the bird got fat, and Larry got thin; but the bird retained its speed, and Larry became slow-moving and sullen. Those who had always known him for a gay fellow shook their heads sadly over it. He still entered Brian for the races; but each Saturday, now, he would barely stroll to the bridge when the regular two hours were passed since the birds had been released down the country. And when he saw the familiar speck in the sky he would actually turn his back on it.

It was the Easter Monday race that brought things to a head. That day a passing stranger said to him, as Brian Boru came into sight, "Whose bird is that?"

Larry, leaning with his back and two elbows on the parapet, gave an idle glance over his shoulder at the sky.

"Him? He's my bird. But—eh—he's not in the race, you know. He's what you might call a gentleman pigeon. He's doing it for fun. That bird, sir, could win any race he wanted to. But the way it is with him, he couldn't be bothered. Pride is what's wrong with that bird, sir. Pride! Pride, they say, made the angels fall. Maybe it did. I wish something would make that fellow fall."

Whereupon, Larry, as if a new understanding of the nature of pigeons had suddenly been vouchsafed to him, turned and gave the circling speck a terrible look. It was the look of a man struck by rejected love. Just at that moment it was that the man who owned Michael Collins the Second said the fatal word, as they all remembered and often recounted long after. He was a shrimp of a creature, a Tom Thumb of a man, who worked as a boots [7] in a hotel and bred his pigeons out of his tips. Seeing that look of misery in Larry's face he laughed and said, "Why don't you breed budgerigars, Larry? At least you could take them out of their cage and kiss 'em." The row of pigeon fanciers, staring

---

[7] *boots* A shoeshine boy.

up at the sky, chuckled. They did not see the look of hate in Larry's face, or notice the way he slouched away home to his cabin.

There, as he was at his tea, he suddenly heard the clatter of wings like tearing silk and, looking up through his cabin window, he saw his bird in its loft among the custards and dainties, and now and again it glanced indifferently towards the cabin door. Pushing aside his cup, Larry said to his father—the old man recorded it when there was no use in recording it—"I wish to God, Da, you never gave me that pigeon. That bird isn't human. He despises me." And he put his head between his hands.

Later in the night, while the drizzle of rain fell on him, and the red reflections of the city illuminated the sky, he stood outside until his hair was pricked with the dew of the drizzle, talking now to himself, now to Brian; and though his father kept coming to the door, telling him not to be behaving like a child of two, Larry would not stir. He was like a boy hanging about under the window of his beloved.

"Is it the way you're faulting me?" he whispered. "Is there something you think I ought to do? But what is there I can do? I can't alter the rules, and you won't come down! I know it's a dishonor. It's a dishonor for both of us. I know that, Brian my darling, just as well as you know it. But I don't think it's my fault. I brought you up well. I did my best for you. I swear to God above this night I'd lay down my life for you. But, bar flying up in the air myself and bringing you down, what *can* I do?"

From the loft no reply, except the deep breathing of sleep.

Once more he entered the bird. Once more the pigeon scorned the earth. Once more the boots mentioned budgerigars, and this time he added that canaries can at least sing. Once more, Michael Collins won the race. That finished it. Larry went home, and on the following Monday he sold every bird, box, loft, packet of food, and medicine bottle that he possessed. With the money he bought an old Smith and Wesson, thirty-two bore, and five rounds of ammunition from a former pal of the I.R.A.[8] Then, for the last time, he entered the bird, saw it come, as always, first of the team up against the clouds that floated like bridesmaids over the hedgerows; saw through the veils of the sun how Brian swerved, and circled, and sank . . . and rose again; and did so his usual number of times before making for the inaccessible perch on the telegraph pole. While the dozen heads along the bridge shook their commiseration, Larry gripped his revolver in his pocket, and waited for the boots to laugh. The boots laughed. At that Larry's body took on the old fighting slouch; he pulled his hat savagely down over one eye; he buttoned his coat across his chest; he became the old down-looking gunman he had been fifteen years ago when he was in the I.R.A. Then with a roll of his shoulders like a militiaman, a trick learned from his soldier da, he looked at the boots between the shoulder blades, put on the final bit of the gunman's manner—the ominously casual strolling gait—and walked quietly down the lane. There he found Brian on the pole.

"Brian," he whispered, but without hope, "will you come down to me now?"

8 *I.R.A.* Irish Republican Army: an outlawed secret military organization which agitated against England.

The bird rose and flew away, circled and came back again.

"So yeh won't come down?" whispered Larry out of the corner of his mouth. The bird looked haughtily over the lane roofs, as if contemplating another circle of flight. Before it could stir the shot cracked. With one head-sinking tumble it fell with a plop to the ground. Larry stooped, lifted the hot, twitching body in his palms, gave it one agonized look, and pelted back to the bridge, roaring like a maniac.

"By the Lord Almighty!" they said, when they saw him coming, screeching, with the bird in his palms. "Brian Boru is after winning at last!"

Shouldering their cluster right and left, Larry snapped the beak to the glass of the clock, displayed the celluoid ring on the stiff ankle, and shouted, pale as the clouds, "Has he won?"

It was only then that they saw the blood oozing down between his trembling fingers; but before they could tell him what they thought of him they saw the mad look in his eyes, and the way his hand stole to his pocket.

"Well?" yelled Larry at the boots. "Has he won? Or has he not won? Or maybe you'll say there's a rule that a dead bird can't win a race?"

"He's w-w-won, all right," trembled the boots.

"Gimme his prize!" said Larry.

In fear they gave it to him. It was a new dovecot, painted a lovely green. (*Eau de canal,*[9] the boots called it afterwards, being the sarcastic brute he was.) Larry took the dovecot, and with the reddening beak hanging from his fist he slouched away. On Monday he sold the dovecot, had the bird stuffed and put in the window of his lane cabin for the world to see.

You never see Larry Dunne at the canal bridge now. He walks moodily by himself along the towpaths, idly flickering a little twig against the hedges: or he sits with his father at the other side of the fire, learning off bits from his favorite book, *Who's Who*, or he sits gazing into the dancing devils of flame. The sky outside is lurid with the lights of Dublin. And in the little curtained window, the pigeon looks with two glassy eyes out over the damp market gardens and the heavy, odorous night fields at the bloody sky.

For Discussion

1. What kind of man is Larry Dunne? What is the difference between his behavior when he is alone and when he is among his friends? Is he a simple man? Does he change during the story? How?

2. Medieval moralists taught that in order to escape the destructive forces of Fortune, one must never allow himself to be placed in a position from which he might fall, or in which he might fail. Does this apply to Larry Dunne? Is Brian Boru the only reason for his despair?

3. When Larry says of Brian Boru, "Isn't it a sign? Isn't it a symbol? Isn't that poor Ireland all over again?" what does he mean? What are the qualities of Ireland that Larry sees in the bird?

Does the bird reflect any of the qualities of its master?

4. What is the irony of Larry Dunne's solution to the problem? Why does he have Brian Boru stuffed and mounted? Does Larry Dunne enjoy his misery? Is it possible that Larry Dunne created his own grief in the form of Brian Boru?

5. What does the storyteller mean when he says that Larry Dunne fell for the same reason as Adam? In what ways does this story repeat the story of the Garden of Eden?

---

[9] *eau de canal* French: canal water. The boots implies that the dovecot was the same color as the water in the canal.

The Guest

ALBERT CAMUS

Algeria, a North African country torn by the inner friction of two cultures, was long a stronghold of colonialism. Inhabited by early Arab conquerors and by Moors expelled from Spain by Ferdinand and Isabella, Algeria remained a Moslem nation until the French occupation in 1830. Prosperity attracted French citizens, who settled in this land of soft climate on the shores of the Mediterranean Sea. French political domination gave the Europeans an economic and social advantage over the Moslems. The Moslems suffered racial discrimination, even though they far outnumbered the colons—*the French Algerians. After the Second World War the Moslems showed open disapproval of French rule and began to agitate for self-government. Incidents of terrorism occurred. The Europeans, who had no intentions of abandoning all that they had worked to achieve, retaliated with equal measures of cruelty. Hatred roamed the streets. For years, both French and Moslem citizens died in bombings and raids. The struggle for Algerian independence spread and brought violence even to the streets of Paris. It is against this background of civil war and terrorism that "The Guest" takes place. Albert Camus, himself an Algerian* colon, *looks beyond political and racial differences in this story. Here two men momentarily transcend the hostility that separates them from each other as enemies.*

THE SCHOOLMASTER was watching the two men climb toward him. One was on horseback, the other on foot. They had not yet tackled the abrupt rise leading to the schoolhouse built on the hillside. They were toiling onward, making slow progress in the snow, among the stones, on the vast expanse of the high, deserted plateau. From time to time the horse stumbled. Without hearing anything yet, he could see the breath issuing from the horse's nostrils. One of the men, at least, knew the region. They were following the trail although it had disappeared days ago under a layer of dirty white snow. The schoolmaster calculated that it would take

ALBERT CAMUS (1913–1959) was born in Mondori, a town in northeastern Algeria. His Alsatian father died during the First World War, and his Spanish mother struggled to raise her family. Albert Camus attended public schools and worked his way through the University of Algiers. He graduated in 1936 and became vitally interested in the theater. With the drama group L'Equipe ("The Team"), *he participated as an actor and as a director. In 1937 he published his first book, a collection of personal essays entitled* L'envers et l'endroit. *The money from this enabled him to travel to Central Europe, Italy, and France. His experiences on this journey excited him with new ideas and stimulated new writing projects, but he returned to Algiers as a journalist. In 1940 he joined the staff of* Paris-Soir, *a Parisian newspaper. The war with Germany interrupted his career, and he became active in the French Resistance by editing an underground paper,* Combat. *After the war, Albert Camus produced the plays, novels, and essays on man's behavior that won him the Nobel Prize in literature in 1957. During his life he worked ceaselessly for humanitarian causes. He spoke out against all forms of aggression and exploitation.* The Myth of Sisyphus *(1942),* The Stranger *(1946),* Caligula *(1938),* The Plague *(1948), and* The Rebel *(1951), all portray man's moral dilemma in the modern world. Albert Camus' life ended in an auto accident in 1959.*

---

them half an hour to get onto the hill. It was cold; he went back into the school to get a sweater.

He crossed the empty, frigid classroom. On the blackboard the four rivers of France, drawn with four different colored chalks, had been flowing toward their estuaries for the past three days. Snow had suddenly fallen in mid-October after eight months of drought without the transition of rain, and the twenty pupils, more or less, who lived in the villages scattered over the plateau had stopped coming. With fair weather they would return. Daru now heated only the single room that was his lodging, adjoining the classroom and giving also onto the plateau to the east. Like the class windows, his window looked to the south too. On that side the school was a few kilometers from the point where the plateau began to slope toward the south. In clear weather could be seen the purple mass of the mountain range where the gap opened onto the desert.

Somewhat warmed, Daru returned to the window from which he had first seen the two men. They were no longer visible. Hence they must have tackled the rise. The sky was not so dark, for the snow had stopped falling during the night. The morning had opened with a dirty light which had scarcely become brighter as the ceiling of clouds lifted. At two in the afternoon it seemed as if the day were merely beginning. But still this was better than those three days when the thick snow was falling amidst unbroken darkness with little gusts of wind that rattled the double door of the classroom. Then Daru had spent long hours in his room, leaving it only to go to the shed and feed the chickens or get some coal. Fortunately the delivery truck from Tadjid, the nearest village to the north, had brought his supplies two days before the blizzard. It would return in forty-eight hours.

Besides, he had enough to resist a siege, for the little room was cluttered with bags of wheat that the administration left as a stock to distribute to those of his pupils whose families had suffered from the drought. Actually they had all been victims because they were all poor. Every day Daru would distribute a ration to the children. They had missed it, he knew, during these bad days. Possibly one of the fathers or big brothers would come this afternoon and he could supply them with grain. It was just a matter of carrying them over to the next harvest. Now shiploads of wheat were arriving from France and the worst was over. But it would be hard to forget that poverty, that army of ragged ghosts wandering in the sunlight, the plateaus burned to a cinder month after month, the earth shriveled up little by little, literally scorched, every stone bursting into dust under one's foot. The sheep had died then by thousands and even a few men, here and there, sometimes without anyone's knowing.

In contrast with such poverty, he who lived almost like a monk in his remote schoolhouse, nonetheless satisfied with the little he had and with the rough life, had felt like a lord with his whitewashed walls, his narrow couch, his unpainted shelves, his well, and his weekly provision of water and food. And suddenly this snow, without warning, without the foretaste of rain. This is the way the region was, cruel to live in, even without men—who didn't help matters either. But Daru had been born here. Everywhere else, he felt exiled.

He stepped out onto the terrace in front of the schoolhouse. The two men were now halfway up the slope. He recognized the horseman as Balducci, the old gendarme[1] he had known for a long time. Balducci was holding on the end of a rope an Arab who was walking behind him with hands bound and head lowered. The gendarme waved a greeting to which Daru did not reply, lost as he was in contemplation of the Arab dressed in a faded blue jellaba,[2] his feet in sandals but covered with socks of heavy raw wool, his head surmounted by a narrow, short *chèche*.[3] They were approaching. Balducci was holding back his horse in order not to hurt the Arab, and the group was advancing slowly.

Within earshot, Balducci shouted: "One hour to do the three kilometers from El Ameur!" Daru did not answer. Short and square in his

thick sweater, he watched them climb. Not once had the Arab raised his head. "Hello," said Daru when they got up onto the terrace. "Come in and warm up." Balducci painfully got down from his horse without letting go the rope. From under his bristling mustache he smiled at the schoolmaster. His little dark eyes, deep-set under a tanned forehead, and his mouth surrounded with wrinkles made him look attentive and studious. Daru took the bridle, led the horse to the shed, and came back to the two men, who were now waiting for him in the school. He led them into his room. "I am going to heat up the classroom," he said. "We'll be more comfortable there." When he entered the room again, Balducci was on the couch. He had undone the rope tying him to the Arab, who had squatted near the stove. His hands still bound, the *chèche* pushed back on his head, he was looking toward the window. At first Daru noticed only his huge lips, fat, smooth, almost Negroid; yet his nose was straight, his eyes were dark and full of fever. The *chèche* revealed an obstinate forehead and, under the weathered skin now rather discolored by the cold, the whole face had a restless and rebellious look that struck Daru when the Arab, turning his face toward him, looked him straight in the eyes. "Go into the other room," said the schoolmaster, "and I'll make you some mint tea." "Thanks," Balducci said. "What a chore! How I long for retirement." And addressing his prisoner in Arabic: "Come on, you." The Arab got up and, slowly, holding his bound wrists in front of him, went into the classroom.

With the tea, Daru brought a chair. But Balducci was already enthroned on the nearest pupil's desk and the Arab had squatted against the teacher's platform facing the stove, which stood between the desk and the window. When he held out the glass of tea to the prisoner, Daru hesitated at the sight of his bound hands. "He might perhaps be untied." "Sure," said Balducci. "That was for the trip." He started to get to his feet. But Daru, setting the glass on the floor, had knelt beside the Arab. Without saying any-

[1] *gendarme* Policeman.
[2] *jellaba* A hooded cloak, worn by the Arabs.
[3] *chèche* An Arab's cylindrical skullcap.

thing, the Arab watched him with his feverish eyes. Once his hands were free, he rubbed his swollen wrists against each other, took the glass of tea, and sucked up the burning liquid in swift little sips.

"Good," said Daru. "And where are you headed?"

Balducci withdrew his mustache from the tea. "Here, son."

"Odd pupils! And you're spending the night?"

"No. I'm going back to El Ameur. And you will deliver this fellow to Tinguit. He is expected at police headquarters."

Balducci was looking at Daru with a friendly little smile.

"What's this story?" asked the schoolmaster. "Are you pulling my leg?"

"No, son. Those are the orders."

"The orders? I'm not . . ." Daru hesitated, not wanting to hurt the old Corsican.[4] "I mean, that's not my job."

"What! What's the meaning of that? In wartime people do all kinds of jobs."

"Then I'll wait for the declaration of war!"

Balducci nodded.

"O.K. But the orders exist and they concern you too. Things are brewing, it appears. There is talk of a forthcoming revolt. We are mobilized, in a way."

Daru still had his obstinate look.

"Listen, son," Balducci said. "I like you and you must understand. There's only a dozen of us at El Ameur to patrol throughout the whole territory of a small department and I must get back in a hurry. I was told to hand this guy over to you and return without delay. He couldn't be kept there. His village was beginning to stir; they wanted to take him back. You must take him to Tinguit tomorrow before the day is over. Twenty kilometers shouldn't faze a husky fellow like you. After that, all will be over. You'll come back to your pupils and your comfortable life."

[4] *Corsican* Many of the "French" settlers in Algiers are actually immigrants from Corsica.

Behind the wall the horse could be heard snorting and pawing the earth. Daru was looking out the window. Decidedly, the weather was clearing and the light was increasing over the snowy plateau. When all the snow was melted, the sun would take over again and once more would burn the fields of stone. For days, still, the unchanging sky would shed its dry light on the solitary expanse where nothing had any connection with man.

"After all," he said, turning around toward Balducci, "what did he do?" And, before the gendarme had opened his mouth, he asked: "Does he speak French?"

"No, not a word. We had been looking for him for a month, but they were hiding him. He killed his cousin."

"Is he against us?"

"I don't think so. But you can never be sure."

"Why did he kill?"

"A family squabble, I think. One owed the other grain, it seems. It's not at all clear. In short, he killed his cousin with a billhook. You know, like a sheep, *kreezk!*"

Balducci made the gesture of drawing a blade across his throat and the Arab, his attention attracted, watched him with a sort of anxiety. Daru felt a sudden wrath against the man, against all men with their rotten spite, their tireless hates, their blood lust.

But the kettle was singing on the stove. He served Balducci more tea, hesitated, then served the Arab again, who, a second time, drank avidly. His raised arms made the jellaba fall open and the schoolmaster saw his thin, muscular chest.

"Thanks, kid," Balducci said. "And now, I'm off."

He got up and went toward the Arab, taking a small rope from his pocket.

"What are you doing?" Daru asked dryly.

Balducci, disconcerted, showed him the rope.

"Don't bother."

The old gendarme hesitated. "It's up to you. Of course, you are armed?"

"I have my shotgun."

"Where?"

"In the trunk."

"You ought to have it near your bed."

"Why? I have nothing to fear."

"You're crazy, son. If there's an uprising, no one is safe, we're all in the same boat."

"I'll defend myself. I'll have time to see them coming."

Balducci began to laugh, then suddenly the mustache covered the white teeth.

"You'll have time? O.K. That's just what I was saying. You have always been a little cracked. That's why I like you, my son was like that."

At the same time he took out his revolver and put it on the desk.

"Keep it; I don't need two weapons from here to El Ameur."

The revolver shone against the black paint of the table. When the gendarme turned toward him, the schoolmaster caught the smell of leather and horseflesh.

"Listen, Balducci," Daru said suddenly, "every bit of this disgusts me, and first of all your fellow here. But I won't hand him over. Fight, yes, if I have to. But not that."

The old gendarme stood in front of him and looked at him severely.

"You're being a fool," he said slowly. "I don't like it either. You don't get used to putting a rope on a man even after years of it, and you're even ashamed—yes, ashamed. But you can't let them have their way."

"I won't hand him over," Daru said again.

"It's an order, son, and I repeat it."

"That's right. Repeat to them what I've said to you: I won't hand him over."

Balducci made a visible effort to reflect. He looked at the Arab and at Daru. At last he decided.

"No, I won't tell them anything. If you want to drop us, go ahead; I'll not denounce you. I have an order to deliver the prisoner and I'm doing so. And now you'll just sign this paper for me."

"There's no need. I'll not deny that you left him with me."

"Don't be mean with me. I know you'll tell the truth. You're from hereabouts and you are a man. But you must sign, that's the rule."

Daru opened his drawer, took out a little square bottle of purple ink, the red wooden penholder with the "sergeant-major" pen he used for making models of penmanship, and signed. The gendarme carefully folded the paper and put it into his wallet. Then he moved toward the door.

"I'll see you off," Daru said.

"No," said Balducci. "There's no use being polite. You insulted me."

He looked at the Arab, motionless in the same spot, sniffed peevishly, and turned away toward the door. "Good-by, son," he said. The door shut behind him. Balducci appeared suddenly outside the window and then disappeared. His footsteps were muffled by the snow. The horse stirred on the other side of the wall and several chickens fluttered in fright. A moment later Balducci reappeared outside the window leading the horse by the bridle. He walked toward the little rise without turning around and disappeared from sight with the horse following him. A big stone could be heard bouncing down. Daru walked back toward the prisoner, who, without stirring, never took his eyes off him. "Wait," the schoolmaster said in Arabic and went toward the bedroom. As he was going through the door, he had a second thought, went to the desk, took the revolver, and stuck it in his pocket. Then, without looking back, he went into his room.

For some time he lay on his couch watching the sky gradually close over, listening to the silence. It was this silence that had seemed painful to him during the first days here, after the war. He had requested a post in the little town at the base of the foothills separating the upper plateaus from the desert. There, rocky walls, green and black to the north, pink and lavender to the south, marked the frontier of eternal summer. He had been named to a post farther north, on the plateau itself. In the beginning, the solitude and the silence had been hard for him on these wastelands peopled only by stones. Occasionally, furrows suggested cultivation, but they had been dug to uncover a certain kind of stone good for building. The only plowing here was to harvest rocks. Elsewhere a thin layer of soil accumulated in the hollows would be scraped out to enrich paltry village gardens. This is the way it was: bare rock covered three quarters of the region. Towns sprang up, flourished, then disappeared; men came by, loved one another or fought bitterly, then died. No one in this desert, neither he nor his guest, mattered. And yet, outside this desert neither of them, Daru knew, could have really lived.

When he got up, no noise came from the classroom. He was amazed at the unmixed joy he derived from the mere thought that the Arab might have fled and that he would be alone with no decision to make. But the prisoner was there. He had merely stretched out between the stove and the desk. With eyes open, he was staring at the ceiling. In that position, his thick lips were particularly noticeable, giving him a pouting look. "Come," said Daru. The Arab got up and followed him. In the bedroom, the schoolmaster pointed to a chair near the table under the window. The Arab sat down without taking his eyes off Daru.

"Are you hungry?"

"Yes," the prisoner said.

Daru set the table for two. He took flour and oil, shaped a cake in a frying-pan, and lighted the little stove that functioned on bottled gas. While the cake was cooking, he went out to the shed to get cheese, eggs, dates, and condensed milk. When the cake was done he set it on the window sill to cool, heated some condensed milk diluted with water, and beat up the eggs into an omelette. In one of his motions he knocked against the revolver stuck in his right pocket. He set the bowl down, went into the classroom, and put the revolver in his desk drawer. When he came back to the room, night was falling. He put on the light and served the

Arab. "Eat," he said. The Arab took a piece of the cake, lifted it eagerly to his mouth, and stopped short.

"And you?" he asked.

"After you. I'll eat too."

The thick lips opened slightly. The Arab hesitated, then bit into the cake determinedly.

The meal over, the Arab looked at the schoolmaster. "Are you the judge?"

"No, I'm simply keeping you until tomorrow."

"Why do you eat with me?"

"I'm hungry."

The Arab fell silent. Daru got up and went out. He brought back a folding bed from the shed, set it up between the table and the stove, perpendicular to his own bed. From a large suitcase which, upright in a corner, served as a shelf for papers, he took two blankets and arranged them on the camp bed. Then he stopped, felt useless, and sat down on his bed. There was nothing more to do or to get ready. He had to look at this man. He looked at him, therefore, trying to imagine his face bursting with rage. He couldn't do so. He could see nothing but the dark yet shining eyes and the animal mouth.

"Why did you kill him?" he asked in a voice whose hostile tone surprised him.

The Arab looked away.

"He ran away. I ran after him."

He raised his eyes to Daru again and they were full of a sort of woeful interrogation. "Now what will they do to me?"

"Are you afraid?"

He stiffened, turning his eyes away.

"Are you sorry?"

The Arab stared at him openmouthed. Obviously he did not understand. Daru's annoyance was growing. At the same time he felt awkward and self-conscious with his big body wedged between the two beds.

"Lie down there," he said impatiently. "That's your bed."

The Arab didn't move. He called to Daru:

"Tell me!"

The schoolmaster looked at him.

"Is the gendarme coming back tomorrow?"

"I don't know."

"Are you coming with us?"

"I don't know. Why?"

The prisoner got up and stretched out on top of the blankets, his feet toward the window. The light from the electric bulb shone straight into his eyes and he closed them at once.

"Why?" Daru repeated, standing beside the bed.

The Arab opened his eyes under the blinding light and looked at him, trying not to blink.

"Come with us," he said.

In the middle of the night, Daru was still not asleep. He had gone to bed after undressing completely; he generally slept naked. But when he suddenly realized that he had nothing on, he hesitated. He felt vulnerable and the temptation came to him to put his clothes back on. Then he shrugged his shoulders; after all, he wasn't a child and, if need be, he could break his adversary in two. From his bed he could observe him, lying on his back, still motionless with his eyes closed under the harsh light. When Daru turned out the light, the darkness seemed to coagulate all of a sudden. Little by little, the night came back to life in the window where the starless sky was stirring gently. The schoolmaster soon made out the body lying at his feet. The Arab still did not move, but his eyes seemed open. A faint wind was prowling around the schoolhouse. Perhaps it would drive away the clouds and the sun would reappear.

During the night the wind increased. The hens fluttered a little and then were silent. The Arab turned over on his side with his back to Daru, who thought he heard him moan. Then he listened for his guest's breathing, become heavier and more regular. He listened to that breath so close to him and mused without being able to go to sleep. In this room where he had been sleeping alone for a year, this presence bothered him. But it bothered him also by imposing on him a sort of brotherhood he knew well but refused to accept in the present circumstances.

Men who shared the same rooms, soldiers or prisoners, develop a strange alliance as if, having cast off their armor with their clothing, they fraternized every evening, over and above their differences, in the ancient community of dream and fatigue. But Daru shook himself; he didn't like such musings, and it was essential to sleep.

A little later, however, when the Arab stirred slightly, the schoolmaster was still not asleep. When the prisoner made a second move, he stiffened, on the alert. The Arab was lifting himself slowly on his arms with almost the motion of a sleepwalker. Seated upright in bed, he waited motionless without turning his head toward Daru, as if he were listening attentively. Daru did not stir; it had just occurred to him that the revolver was still in the drawer of his desk. It was better to act at once. Yet he continued to observe the prisoner, who, with the same slithery motion, put his feet on the ground, waited again, then began to stand up slowly. Daru was about to call out to him when the Arab began to walk, in a quite natural but extraordinarily silent way. He was heading toward the door at the end of the room that opened into the shed. He lifted the latch with precaution and went out, pushing the door behind him but without shutting it. Daru had not stirred. "He is running away," he merely thought. "Good riddance!" Yet he listened attentively. The hens were not fluttering; the guest must be on the plateau. A faint sound of water reached him, and he didn't know what it was until the Arab again stood framed in the doorway, closed the door carefully, and came back to bed without a sound. Then Daru turned his back on him and fell asleep. Still later he seemed, from the depths of his sleep, to hear furtive steps around the schoolhouse. "I'm dreaming! I'm dreaming!" he repeated to himself. And he went on sleeping.

When he awoke, the sky was clear; the loose window let in a cold, pure air. The Arab was asleep, hunched up under the blankets now, his mouth open, utterly relaxed. But when Daru shook him, he started dreadfully, staring at

Daru with wild eyes as if he had never seen him and such a frightened expression that the schoolmaster stepped back. "Don't be afraid. It's me. You must eat." The Arab nodded his head and said yes. Calm had returned to his face, but his expression was vacant and listless.

The coffee was ready. They drank it seated together on the folding bed as they munched their pieces of the cake. Then Daru led the Arab under the shed and showed him the faucet where he washed. He went back into the room, folded the blankets and the bed, made his own bed and put the room in order. Then he went through the classroom and out onto the terrace. The sun was already rising in the blue sky; a soft, bright light was bathing the deserted plateau. On the ridge the snow was melting in spots. The stones were about to reappear. Crouched on the edge of the plateau, the schoolmaster looked at the deserted expanse. He thought of Balducci. He had hurt him, for he had sent him off in a way as if he didn't want to be associated with him. He could still hear the gendarme's farewell and, without knowing why, he felt strangely empty and vulnerable. At that moment, from the other side of the schoolhouse, the prisoner coughed. Daru listened to him almost despite himself and then, furious, threw a pebble that whistled through the air before sinking into the snow. That man's stupid crime revolted him, but to hand him over was contrary to honor. Merely thinking of it made him smart with humiliation. And he cursed at one and the same time his own people who had sent him this Arab and the Arab too who had dared to kill and not managed to get away. Daru got up, walked in a circle on the terrace, waited motionless, and then went back into the schoolhouse.

The Arab, leaning over the cement floor of the shed, was washing his teeth with two fingers. Daru looked at him and said: "Come." He went back into the room ahead of the prisoner. He slipped a hunting-jacket on over his sweater and put on walking-shoes. Standing, he waited until the Arab had put on his *chèche* and sandals.

They went into the classroom and the schoolmaster pointed to the exit, saying: "Go ahead." The fellow didn't budge. "I'm coming," said Daru. The Arab went out. Daru went back into the room and made a package of pieces of rusk, dates, and sugar. In the classroom, before going out, he hesitated a second in front of his desk, then crossed the threshold and locked the door. "That's the way," he said. He started toward the east, followed by the prisoner. But, a short distance from the schoolhouse, he thought he heard a slight sound behind them. He retraced his steps and examined the surroundings of the house; there was no one there. The Arab watched him without seeming to understand. "Come on," said Daru.

They walked for an hour and rested beside a sharp peak of limestone. The snow was melting faster and faster and the sun was drinking up the puddles at once, rapidly cleaning the plateau, which gradually dried and vibrated like the air itself. When they resumed walking, the ground rang under their feet. From time to time a bird rent the space in front of them with a joyful cry. Daru breathed in deeply the fresh morning light. He felt a sort of rapture before the vast familiar expanse, now almost entirely yellow under its dome of blue sky. They walked an hour more, descending toward the south. They reached a level height made up of crumbly rocks. From there on, the plateau sloped down, eastward, toward a low plain where there were a few spindly trees and, to the south, toward outcroppings of rock that gave the landscape a chaotic look.

Daru surveyed the two directions. There was nothing but the sky on the horizon. Not a man could be seen. He turned toward the Arab, who was looking at him blankly. Daru held out the package to him. "Take it," he said. "There are dates, bread, and sugar. You can hold out for two days. Here are a thousand francs too." The Arab took the package and the money but kept his full hands at chest level as if he didn't know what to do with what was being given him. "Now look," the schoolmaster said as he pointed in the direction of the east, "there's the way to Tinguit. You have a two-hour walk. At Tinguit you'll find the administration and the police. They are expecting you." The Arab looked toward the east, still holding the package and the money against his chest. Daru took his elbow and turned him rather roughly toward the south. At the foot of the height on which they stood could be seen a faint path. "That's the trail across the plateau. In a day's walk from here you'll find pasturelands and the first nomads. They'll take you in and shelter you according to their law." The Arab had now turned toward Daru and a sort of panic was visible in his expression. "Listen," he said. Daru shook his head: "No, be quiet. Now I'm leaving you." He turned his back on him, took two long steps in the direction of the school, looked hesitantly at the motionless Arab, and started off again. For a few minutes he heard nothing but his own step resounding on the cold ground and did not turn his head. A moment later, however, he turned around. The Arab was still there on the edge of the hill, his arms hanging now, and he was looking at the schoolmaster. Daru felt something rise in this throat. But he swore with impatience, waved vaguely, and started

off again. He had already gone some distance when he again stopped and looked. There was no longer anyone on the hill.

Daru hesitated. The sun was now rather high in the sky and was beginning to beat down on his head. The schoolmaster retraced his steps, at first somewhat uncertainly, then with decision. When he reached the little hill, he was bathed in sweat. He climbed it as fast as he could and stopped, out of breath, at the top. The rock-fields to the south stood out sharply against the blue sky, but on the plain to the east a steamy heat was already rising. And in that slight haze, Daru, with heavy heart, made out the Arab walking slowly on the road to prison.

A little later, standing before the window of the classroom, the schoolmaster was watching the clear light bathing the whole surface of the plateau, but he hardly saw it. Behind him on the blackboard, among the winding French rivers, sprawled the clumsily chalked-up words he had just read: "You handed over our brother. You will pay for this." Daru looked at the sky, the plateau, and, beyond, the invisible lands stretching all the way to the sea. In this vast landscape he had loved so much, he was alone.

[*translated by* JUSTIN O'BRIEN]

For Discussion

1. Often it is simpler to think in terms of abstractions rather than make a sincere effort to understand all the complications that exist within another man or another group. Which of the two men, Daru or Balducci, thinks of the Arab in terms of an abstraction? Which of the two tries to understand him as a man? Explain.

2. The Arab is a murderer. Does Camus make the Arab a murderer purposely to create a more difficult test for Daru? Explain.

3. When Daru gives the Arab his choice of freedom or prison, is he avoiding his own responsibility? In one or two sentences, define Daru's real responsibility. Is it to Balducci? To the French

government that pays his wages? To the Arab? To himself? Does he take an easy way out? How will Balducci react to what he does? What does the message on the blackboard indicate?

4. What does the last scene prove of the Arab? Is he a brave man? Why does he choose the road to prison? To please Daru, who has been kind to him? Can you suggest other reasons?

5. Is Daru a hero? What kind of heroism does he enact? What does the last sentence of the story mean? Does Daru do a good deed for his fellow man for which he will receive punishment? Explain how, in times of war or hostility, kindness can be a crime.

M·D·XXVII·

HANS HOLBEIN THE YOUNGER

Sir Thomas More

(The Frick Collection)

UNIT 3: BIOGRAPHY AND AUTOBIOGRAPHY

Biography is both a science

and an art. The scientific part of a biographer's work lies in the discovery and arrangement of facts. He must assemble and evaluate the manuscripts, gossip, reports, and letters that surround the life of his subject. Without this basis in fact, a biography is worthless. Yet the mere facts do not tell the whole story of a man's life. The biographer must add art to science. He must exercise his imagination and his knowledge of human nature in order to bring all the separate facts together into a whole. He must be able to relate the life he is writing about to the culture and history that surrounded it. Most of all, through his skill as a writer, the biographer must bring his subject to life. In a good biography or autobiography, the reader can come to know outstanding men and women and share the experiences of their lives.

Many people (and some biographers) have the mistaken idea that biography is written in praise of great men. The fact is that the best biographies attempt to produce an honest and complete representation of a man or woman. The subject may be a benefactor of humanity, such as Helen Keller, or he may be a monster, such as Adolf Hitler. No man, no matter how famous or infamous, is either all good or all evil. Oliver Cromwell, Lord Protector of England, once told an artist about to do his portrait that he wanted to be painted "warts and all." As readers, we want from biography and autobiography neither praise nor blame but reality. We want to see both the positive and negative qualities that make a man unique. We want to see how those qualities combine to produce greatness.

The selections included in this unit show how biography as a literary type can vary widely in its style and approach. Eve Curie's subject was her own mother, the discoverer of radium, Madame Curie. But the daughter has not allowed her fondness for her mother to distort the picture she draws. "Four Years in a Shed" is an exercise in objectivity: if we did not already know that the writer was Madame Curie's own daughter,

we would not be able to discover it from the writing. Samuel Eliot Morison's portrait of Columbus is the work of a great scholar and historian. It is based on years of research, yet Morison does not allow his scholarship to give him an excuse for dryness. He brings Columbus's adventure, and especially his voyage, to life. The small facts, such as the song the Spanish sailors sang, become a vivid recreation of history. If the work of Eve Curie and of Morison may be called portraits, Deems Taylor's brief life of Richard Wagner is only a sketch. It was more quickly written and is more quickly read. "The Monster" is not meant to be a well-rounded study. It is a vivid impression of only one aspect of the great composer's character.

The method of Van Wyck Brooks's "Helen Keller" is an unusual one: he brings Miss Keller before the reader's eyes by reprinting entries in his own diary. The result is a vivid and human study. Michel del Castillo's "Christmas in a Concentration Camp" is from a book which was published as a novel. Yet in fact his novel was a very lightly fictionalized account of his own childhood. The experiences recounted in the book, *A Child of Our Time*, are so painful that del Castillo probably felt it wise to add a touch of objectivity by using the name "Tanguy" for himself.

The literary method behind these biographical selections varies widely, yet the selections have two things in common. All are based upon events that really happened. Each allows the reader a chance to involve himself with another life.

Four Years in a Shed

EVE CURIE

Eve Curie's biography of her mother, Madame Curie, is a modern classic. "Four Years in a Shed" tells of the events leading up to the central adventure of Marie Curie's life—the discovery of radium. For four years, Marie and Pierre Curie were alone, with nothing but their own will and enthusiasm to sustain them. As much as possible, they sacrificed their private lives to science. Their daughter's book is more than the story of a scientific quest; it is also the account of a great test of the human spirit.

A MAN chosen at random from a crowd to read an account of the discovery of radium would not have doubted for one moment that radium existed: beings whose critical sense has not been sharpened and simultaneously deformed by specialized culture keep their imaginations fresh. They are ready to accept an unexpected fact, however extraordinary it may appear, and to wonder at it.

The physicist colleagues of the Curies received the news in slightly different fashion. The special properties of polonium and radium upset fundamental theories in which scientists had believed for centuries. How was one to explain the spontaneous radiation of the radioactive bodies? The discovery upset a world of acquired knowledge and contradicted the most firmly established ideas on the composition of matter. Thus the physicist kept on the reserve. He was violently interested in Pierre and Marie's work, he could perceive its infinite developments, but before being convinced he awaited the acquisition of decisive results.

The attitude of the chemist was even more downright. By definition, a chemist only believes in the existence of a new substance when he has seen the substance, touched it, weighed and examined it, confronted it with acids, bottled it, and when he has determined its "atomic weight."

Now, up to the present, nobody had "seen" radium. Nobody knew the atomic weight of radium. And the chemists, faithful to their principles, concluded: "No atomic weight, no radium. Show us some radium and we will believe you."

To show polonium and radium to the incredulous, to prove to the world the existence of their "children," and to complete their own conviction, M. and Mme. Curie were now to labor for four years.

The aim was to obtain pure radium and polonium. In the most strongly radioactive products the scientists had prepared, these substances figured only in imperceptible traces. Pierre and Marie already knew the method by

EVE CURIE (*1904–   *), *the daughter of Marie and Pierre Curie, has won recognition as a pianist and war correspondent as well as a biographer. Her book* Madame Curie *has been translated into twenty-five languages.*

which they could hope to isolate the new metals, but the separation could not be made except by treating very large quantities of crude material.

Here arose three agonizing questions:

How were they to get a sufficient quantity of ore? What premises could they use to effect their treatment? What money was there to pay the inevitable cost of the work?

Pitchblende, in which polonium and radium were hidden, was a costly ore, treated at the St. Joachimsthal mines in Bohemia for the extraction of uranium salts used in the manufacture of glass. Tons of pitchblende would cost a great deal: a great deal too much for the Curie household.

Ingenuity was to make up for wealth. According to the expectation of the two scientists, the extraction of uranium should leave, intact in the ore, such traces of polonium and radium as the ore contains. There was no reason why these traces should not be found in the residue. And, whereas crude pitchblende was costly, its residue after treatment had very slight value. By asking an Austrian colleague for a recommendation to the directors of the mine of St. Joachimsthal would it not be possible to obtain a considerable quantity of such residue for a reasonable price?

It was simple enough: but somebody had to think of it.

It was necessary, of course, to buy this crude material and pay for its transportation to Paris. Pierre and Marie appropriated the required sum from their very slight savings. They were not so foolish as to ask for official credits. . . . If two physicists on the scent of an immense discovery had asked the University of Paris or the French government for a grant to buy pitchblende residue they would have been laughed at. In any case their letter would have been lost in the files of some office, and they would have had to wait months for a reply, probably unfavorable in the end. Out of the traditions and principles of the French Revolution, which had created the metric system, founded the Normal School, and encouraged science in many circumstances, the State seemed to have retained, after more than a century, only the deplorable words pronounced by Fouquier-Tinville at the trial in which Lavoisier was condemned to the guillotine: "The Republic has no need for scientists."

But at least could there not be found, in the numerous buildings attached to the Sorbonne,[1] some kind of suitable workroom to lend to the Curie couple? Apparently not. After vain attempts, Pierre and Marie staggered back to their point of departure, which is to say to the School of Physics where Pierre taught, to the little room where Marie had done her first experiments. The room gave on a courtyard, and on the other side of the yard there was a wooden shack, an abandoned shed, with a skylight roof in such bad condition that it admitted the rain. The Faculty of Medicine had formerly used the place as a dissecting room, but for a long time now it had not even been considered fit to house the cadavers. No floor: an uncertain layer of bitumen covered the earth. It was furnished with some worn kitchen tables, a blackboard which had landed there for no known reason, and an old cast-iron stove with a rusty pipe.

A workman would not willingly have worked in such a place: Marie and Pierre, nevertheless, resigned themselves to it. The shed had one advantage: it was so untempting, so miserable, that nobody thought of refusing them the use of it. Schutzenberger, the director of the school, had always been very kind to

---

[1] *Sorbonne* France's leading university.

Pierre Curie and no doubt regretted that he had nothing better to offer. However that may be, he offered nothing else; and the couple, very pleased at not being put out into the street with their material, thanked him, saying that "this would do" and they would "make the best of it."

As they were taking possession of the shed, a reply arrived from Austria. Good news! By extraordinary luck, the residue of recent extractions of uranium had not been scattered. The useless material had been piled up in a no-man's land planted with pine trees, near the mine of St. Joachimsthal. Thanks to the intercession of Professor Suess and the Academy of Science of Vienna, the Austrian government, which was the proprietor of the State factory there, decided to present a ton of residue to the two French lunatics who thought they needed it. If, later on, they wish to be sent a greater quantity of the material, they could obtain it at the mine on the best terms. For the moment the Curies had to pay only the transportation charges on a ton of ore.

One morning a heavy wagon, like those which deliver coal, drew up in the Rue Lhomond before the School of Physics. Pierre and Marie were notified. They hurried bareheaded into the street in their laboratory gowns. Pierre, who was never agitated, kept his calm; but the more exuberant Marie could not contain her joy at the sight of the sacks that were being unloaded. It was pitchblende, *her* pitchblende, for which she had received a notice some days before from the freight station. Full of curiosity and impatience, she wanted to open one of the sacks and contemplate her treasure without further waiting. She cut the strings, undid the coarse sackcloth and plunged her two hands into the dull brown ore, still mixed with pine needles from Bohemia.

There was where radium was hidden. It was from there that Marie must extract it, even if she had to treat a mountain of this inert stuff like dust on the road.

Marya Sklodovska had lived through the most intoxicating moments of her student life in a garret; Marie Curie was to know wonderful joys again in a dilapidated shed. It was a strange sort of beginning over again, in which a sharp subtle happiness (which probably no woman before Marie had ever experienced) twice elected the most miserable setting.

The shed in the Rue Lhomond surpassed the most pessimistic expectations of discomfort. In summer, because of its skylights, it was as stifling as a hothouse. In winter one did not know whether to wish for rain or frost; if it rained, the water fell drop by drop, with a soft, nerve-racking noise, on the ground or on the worktables, in places which the physicists had to mark in order to avoid putting apparatus there. If it froze, one froze. There was no recourse. The stove, even when it was stoked white, was a complete disappointment. If one went near enough to touch it one received a little heat, but two steps away and one was back in the zone of ice.

It was almost better for Marie and Pierre to get used to the cruelty of the outside temperature, since their technical installation—hardly existent—possessed no chimneys to carry off noxious gases, and the greater part of their treatment had to be made in the open air, in the courtyard. When a shower came the physicists hastily moved their apparatus inside: to keep on working without being suffocated they set up draughts between the opened door and windows.

Marie probably did not boast to Dr. Vanthier of this very peculiar cure for attacks of tuberculosis.

We had no money, no laboratory and no help in the conduct of this important and difficult task [she was to write later]. It was like creating something out of nothing, and if Casimir Dluski once called my student years "the heroic years of my sister-in-law's life," I may say without exaggeration that this period was, for my husband and myself, the heroic period of our common existence.

. . . And yet it was in this miserable old shed that the best and happiest years of our life were spent, entirely consecrated to work. I sometimes passed the whole day stirring a mass in ebullition,[2] with an iron rod nearly as big as myself. In the evening I was broken with fatigue.

In such conditions M. and Mme. Curie worked for four years from 1898 to 1902.

During the first year they busied themselves with the chemical separation of radium and polonium and they studied the radiation of the products (more and more active) thus obtained. Before long they considered it more practical to separate their efforts. Pierre Curie tried to determine the properties of radium, and to know the new metal better. Marie continued those chemical treatments which would permit her to obtain salts of pure radium.

In this division of labor Marie had chosen the "man's job." She accomplished the toil of a day laborer. Inside the shed her husband was absorbed by delicate experiments. In the courtyard, dressed in her old dust-covered and acid-stained smock, her hair blown by the wind, surrounded by smoke which stung her eyes and throat, Marie was a sort of factory all by herself.

I came to treat as many as twenty kilograms of matter at a time [she writes], which had the effect of filling the shed with great jars full of precipitates and liquids. It was killing work to carry the receivers, to pour off the liquids and to stir, for hours at a stretch, the boiling matter in a smelting basin.

Radium showed no intention of allowing itself to be known by human creatures. Where were the days when Marie naïvely expected the radium content of pitchblende to be *one per cent?* The radiation of the new substance was so powerful that a tiny quantity of radium, disseminated through the ore, was the source of striking phenomena which could be easily observed and measured. The difficult, the impossible thing, was to isolate this minute quantity, to separate it from the gangue [3] in which it was so intimately mixed.

The days of work became months and years: Pierre and Marie were not discouraged. This material which resisted them, which defended its secrets, fascinated them. United by their tenderness, united by their intellectual passions, they had, in a wooden shack, the "anti-natural" existence for which they had both been made, she as well as he.

At this period we were entirely absorbed by the new realm that was, thanks to an unhoped-for-discovery, opening before us [Marie was to write]. In spite of the difficulties of our working conditions, we felt very happy. Our days were spent at the laboratory. In our poor shed there reigned a great tranquillity: sometimes, as we watched over some operation, we would walk up and down, talking about work in the present and in the future; when we were cold a cup of hot tea taken near the stove comforted us. We lived in our single preoccupation as if in a dream.

. . . We saw only very few persons at the laboratory; among the physicists and chemists there were a few who came from time to time, either to see our experiments or to ask for advice from Pierre Curie, whose competence in several branches of physics was well-known. Then took place some conversations before the blackboard—the sort of conversation one remembers well because it acts as a stimulant for scientific interest and the ardor for work without interrupting the course of reflection and without troubling that atmosphere of peace and meditation which is the true atmosphere of a laboratory.

Whenever Pierre and Marie, alone in this poor place, left their apparatus for a moment and quietly let their tongues run on, their talk about their beloved radium passed from the transcendent to the childish.

"I wonder what *It* will be like, what *It* will look like," Marie said one day with the feverish curiosity of a child who has been promised a

---

[2] *in ebullition*   In a state of boiling.

[3] *gangue*   Stony or earthy substance.

toy. "Pierre, what form do you imagine *It* will take?"

"I don't know," the physicist answered gently. "I should like it to have a very beautiful color. . . ."

It is odd to observe that in Marie Curie's correspondence we find, upon this prodigious effort, none of the sensitive comments, decked out with imagery, which used to flash suddenly amid the familiarity of her letters. Was it because the years of exile had somewhat relaxed the young woman's intimacy with her people? Was she too pressed by work to find time?

The essential reason for this reserve is perhaps to be sought elsewhere. It was not by chance that Mme. Curie's letters ceased to be original at the exact moment when the story of her life became exceptional. As student, teacher or young wife, Marie could tell her story. . . . But now she was isolated by all that was secret and inexpressible in her scientific vocation. Among those she loved there was no longer anybody able to understand, to realize her worries and her difficult design. She could share her obsessions with only one person, Pierre Curie, companion. To him alone could she confide rare thoughts and dreams. Marie, from now on, was to present to all others, however near they might be to her heart, an almost commonplace picture of herself. She was to paint for them only the bourgeois side of her life. She was to find sometimes accents full of contained emotion to express her happiness as a woman. But of her work she was to speak only in laconic, inexpressive little phrases: news in three lines, without even attempting to suggest the wonders that work meant to her.

Here we feel an absolute determination not to illustrate the singular profession she had chosen by literature. Through subtle modesty, and also through horror of vain talk and everything superfluous, Marie concealed herself, dug herself in; or rather, she offered only one of her profiles. Shyness, boredom, or reason, whatever

"Our work on radioactivity began in solitude."

Marie Curie in her laboratory

it may have been, the scientist of genius effaced and dissimulated herself behind "a woman like all others."

Marie to Bronya, 1899:

Our life is always the same. We work a lot but we sleep well, so our health does not suffer. The evenings are taken up by caring for the child. In the morning I dress her and give her her food, then I can generally go out at about nine. During the whole of this year we have not been either to the theater or a concert, and we have not paid one visit. For that matter, we feel very well. . . . I miss my family enormously, above all you, my dears, and Father. I often think of my isolation with grief. I cannot complain of anything else, for our health is not bad, the child is growing well, and I have the best husband one could dream of; I could never have imagined finding one like him. He is a true gift of heaven, and the more we live together the more we love each other.

Our work is progressing. I shall soon have a lecture to deliver on the subject. It should have been last Saturday but I was prevented from giving it, so it will no doubt be this Saturday, or else in a fortnight.

This work, which is so dryly mentioned in passing, was in fact progressing magnificently. In the course of the years 1899 and 1900 Pierre and Marie Curie published a report on the discovery of "induced radioactivity" due to radium, another on the effects of radioactivity, and another on the electric charge carried by the rays. And at last they drew up, for the Congress of Physics of 1900, a general report on the radioactive substances, which aroused immense interest among the scientists of Europe.

The development of the new science of radioactivity was rapid, overwhelming—the Curies needed fellow workers. Up to now they had had only the intermittent help of a laboratory assistant named Petit, an honest man who came to work for them outside his hours of service—working out of personal enthusiasm, almost in secret. But they now required technicians of the first order. Their discovery had important extensions in the domain of chemistry, which demanded attentive study. They wished to associate competent research workers with them.

Our work on radioactivity began in solitude [Marie was to write]. But before the breadth of the task it became more and more evident that collaboration would be useful. Already in 1898 one of the laboratory chiefs of the school, G. Bémont, had given us some passing help. Toward 1900 Pierre Curie entered into relations with a young chemist, André Debierne, assistant in the laboratory of Professor Friedel, who esteemed him highly. André Debierne willingly accepted work on radioactivity. He undertook especially the research of a new radio element, the existence of which was suspected in the group of iron and rare clays. He discovered this element, named "actinium." Even though he worked in the physico-chemical laboratory at the Sorbonne directed by Jean Perrin, he frequently came to see us in our shed and soon became a very close friend to us, to Dr. Curie and later on to our children.

Thus, even before radium and polonium were isolated, a French scientist, André Debierne, had discovered a "brother," *actinium.*

At about the same period [Marie tells us], a young physicist, Georges Sagnac, engaged in studying X-rays, came frequently to talk to Pierre Curie about the analogies that might exist between these rays, their secondary rays, and the radiation of radioactive bodies. Together they performed a work on the electric charge carried by these secondary rays.

Marie continued to treat, kilogram by kilogram, the tons of pitchblende residue which were sent her on several occasions from St. Joachimsthal. With her terrible patience, she was able to be, every day for four years, a physicist, a chemist, a specialized worker, an engineer and a laboring man all at once. Thanks to her brain and muscle, the old tables in the shed held more and more concentrated products—products more and more rich in radium. Mme. Curie was approaching the end: she no longer stood in the courtyard, enveloped in bitter smoke, to watch the heavy basins of material in fusion. She was now at the stage of purification and of the "fractional crystallization" of strongly radioactive solutions. But the poverty of her haphazard equipment hindered her work more than ever. It was now that she needed a spotlessly clean workroom and apparatus perfectly protected against cold, heat and dirt. In this shed, open to every wind, iron and coal dust was afloat which, to Marie's despair, mixed itself into the products purified with so much care. Her heart sometimes constricted before these little daily accidents, which took so much of her time and her strength.

Pierre was so tired of the interminable struggle that he would have been quite ready to abandon it. Of course, he did not dream of dropping the study of radium and of radioactivity. But he would willingly have renounced, for the time being, the special operation of preparing pure radium. The obstacles seemed insurmountable. Could they not resume this work later on, under better conditions? More attached to the meaning of natural phenomena than to their material reality, Pierre Curie was exasperated to see the paltry results to which Marie's exhausting effort had led. He advised an armistice.

He counted without his wife's character. Marie wanted to isolate radium and she would isolate it. She scorned fatigue and difficulties, and even the gaps in her own knowledge which complicated her task. After all, she was only a very young scientist: she still had not the certainty and great culture Pierre had acquired by twenty years' work, and sometimes she stumbled across phenomena or methods of calculation which she knew very little, and for which she had to make hasty studies.

So much the worse! With stubborn eyes under her great brow, she clung to her apparatus and her test tubes.

In 1902, forty-five months after the day on which the Curies announced the probable existence of radium, Marie finally carried off the victory in this war of attrition: she succeeded in preparing a decigram of pure radium, and made a first determination of the atomic weight of the new substance, which was 225.

The incredulous chemist—of whom there were still a few—could only bow before the facts, before the superhuman obstinacy of a woman.

Radium officially existed.

It was nine o'clock at night. Pierre and Marie Curie were in their little house at 108 Boulevard Kellermann, where they had been living since 1900. The house suited them well. From the boulevard, where three rows of trees half hid the fortifications, could be seen only a dull wall and a tiny door. But behind the one-story house, hidden from all eyes, there was a narrow provincial garden, rather pretty and very quiet, and from the "barrier" of Gentilly they could escape on their bicycles toward the suburbs and the woods. . . .

Old Dr. Curie, who lived with the couple, had retired to his room. Marie had bathed her child and put it to bed, and had stayed for a long time beside the cot. This was a rite. When Irène did not feel her mother near her at night she would call out for her incessantly, with that "Mé!" which was to be our substitute for "Mamma" always. And Marie, yielding to the implacability of the four-year-old baby, climbed the stairs, seated herself beside the child and stayed there in the darkness until the young voice gave way to light, regular breathing. Only then would she go down again to Pierre, who was growing impatient. In spite of his kindness, he was the most possessive and jealous of husbands. He was so used to the constant presence of his wife that her least eclipse kept him from thinking freely. If Marie delayed too long near her daughter, he received her on her return with a reproach so unjust as to be comic:

"You never think of anything but that child!"

Pierre walked slowly about the room. Marie sat down and made some stitches on the hem of Irène's new apron. One of her principles was never to buy ready-made clothes for the child: she thought them too fancy and impractical. In the days when Bronya was in Paris the two sisters cut out their children's dresses together, according to patterns of their own invention. These patterns still served for Marie.

But this evening she could not fix her attention. Nervous, she got up; then, suddenly:

"Suppose we go down there for a moment?"

There was a note of supplication in her voice

—altogether superfluous, for Pierre, like herself, longed to go back to the shed they had left two hours before. Radium, fanciful as a living creature, endearing as a love, called them back to its dwelling, to the wretched laboratory.

The day's work had been hard, and it would have been more reasonable for the couple to rest. But Pierre and Marie were not always reasonable. As soon as they had put on their coats and told Dr. Curie of their flight, they were in the street. They went on foot, arm in arm, exchanging few words. After the crowded streets of this queer district, with its factory buildings, wastelands and poor tenements, they arrived in the Rue Lhomond and crossed the little courtyard. Pierre put the key in the lock. The door squeaked, as it had squeaked thousands of times, and admitted them to their realm, to their dream.

"Don't light the lamps!" Marie said in the darkness. Then she added with a little laugh:

"Do you remember the day when you said to me 'I should like the radium to have a beautiful color'?"

The reality was more entrancing than the simple wish of long ago. Radium had something better than "a beautiful color": it was spontaneously luminous. And in the somber shed where, in the absence of cupboards, the precious particles in their tiny glass receivers were placed on tables or on shelves nailed to the wall, their phosphorescent bluish outlines gleamed, suspended in the night.

"Look . . . Look!" the young woman murmured.

She went forward cautiously, looked for and found a straw-bottomed chair. She sat down in the darkness and silence. Their two faces turned toward the pale glimmering, the mysterious sources of radiation, toward radium—their radium. Her body leaning forward, her head eager, Marie took up again the attitude which had been hers an hour earlier at the bedside of her sleeping child.

Her companion's hand lightly touched her hair.

She was to remember forever this evening of glowworms, this magic.

For Discussion

1. Carefully read the first two sentences of this biography. What do they mean? How does this idea apply to the next section which describes the skepticism of the scientific world to the Curies' theory? Could this sort of thing happen today? Suggest examples.

2. As the years pass in the work to isolate radium, in what ways do Marie and Pierre Curie change? Are they drawn closer together as husband and wife? Does their obsession with their work cause them to neglect their child?

3. How does Marie Curie's attitude toward radium change as she approaches the end of the experiment? What is the significance of Marie's sitting in the dark beside her child at home and sitting in the dark watching the glowing tubes of radium?

What is the author trying to express through these two images?

4. Do Marie and Pierre Curie seem to be working for fame? For money? Can you suggest anything else that drives them on to complete their task?

5. In the poem, "Two Tramps in Mud Time," the American poet Robert Frost writes:

> My object in life is to unite
> My avocation and my vocation
> As my two eyes make one in sight.
> Only where love and need are one,
> And the work is play for mortal stakes,
> Is the deed ever really done
> For Heaven and the future's sakes.

Does this apply to Marie and Pierre Curie? Explain.

Leeuwenhoek: First of the Microbe Hunters

PAUL DE KRUIF

The telescope opened man's eyes to the vast external universe beyond his planet. The microscope magnified his vision to see the busy infinity that existed in a drop of water, in a speck of dirt. The discovery of the microscope led to scientific and medical triumphs that revealed the structure of matter and the sources of disease. Antony Leeuwenhoek, a dry-goods store owner and janitor, was the first man to realize the importance of microscopic investigation. Like Marie Curie, he left the comforts of an ordinary human life far behind him in order to devote himself completely to his great discoveries. Paul De Kruif presents the life of this stubborn Dutchman in a way that enables us to see the human drama behind his contribution to humanity.

I

TWO HUNDRED AND FIFTY years ago an obscure man named Leeuwenhoek looked for the first time into a mysterious new world peopled with a thousand different kinds of tiny beings, some ferocious and deadly, others friendly and useful, many of them more important to mankind than any continent or archipelago.

Leeuwenhoek, unsung and scarce remembered, is now almost as unknown as his strange little animals and plants were at the time he discovered them. This is the story of Leeuwenhoek, the first of the microbe hunters. . . .

Take yourself back to Leeuwenhoek's day, two hundred and fifty years ago, and imagine yourself just through high school, getting ready to choose a career, wanting to know—

You have lately recovered from an attack of mumps, you ask your father what is the cause of mumps, and he tells you a mumpish evil spirit has got into you. His theory may not impress you much, but you decide to make believe you believe him and not to wonder any more about what is mumps—because if you publicly don't believe him you are in for a beating and may even be turned out of the house. Your father is Authority.

PAUL DE KRUIF (*1890–*　　) *was born in Michigan. Trained as a scientist, he worked as a bacteriologist until 1917. He collaborated with Sinclair Lewis on* Arrowsmith, *Lewis's novel about the medical profession. His own books are dramatized popular presentations of the lives and works of scientists. The two best known are* Microbe Hunters (*1920*) *and* Hunger Fighters (*1939*).

That was the world about three hundred years ago, when Leeuwenhoek was born. It had hardly begun to shake itself free from superstitions, it was barely beginning to blush for its ignorance. It was a world where science (which only means trying to find truth by careful observation and clear thinking) was just learning to toddle on vague and wobbly legs. It was a world where Servetus was burned to death for daring to cut up and examine the body of a dead man, where Galileo was shut up for life for daring to prove that the earth moved around the sun.

Antony Leeuwenhoek was born in 1632 amid the blue windmills and low streets and high canals of Delft, in Holland. His family were burghers of an intensely respectable kind and I say intensely respectable because they were basket-makers and brewers, and brewers are respectable and highly honored in Holland. Leeuwenhoek's father died early and his mother sent him to school to learn to be a government official, but he left school at sixteen to be an apprentice in a dry-goods store in Amsterdam. That was his university. . . .

At the age of twenty-one he left the dry-goods store, went back to Delft, married, set up a dry-goods store of his own there. For twenty years after that very little is known about him, except that he had two wives (in succession) and several children most of whom died, but there is no doubt that during this time he was appointed janitor of the city hall of Delft, and

that he developed a most idiotic love for grinding lenses. He had heard that if you very carefully ground very little lenses out of clear glass, you would see things look much bigger than they appeared to the naked eye. . . .

It would be great fun to look through a lens and see things bigger than your naked eye showed them to you! But *buy* lenses? Not Leeuwenhoek! There never was a more suspicious man. Buy lenses? He would make them himself! During these twenty years of his obscurity he went to spectacle-makers and got the rudiments of lens-grinding. He visited alchemists and apothecaries [1] and put his nose into their secret ways of getting metals from ores, he began fumblingly to learn the craft of the gold- and silversmiths. He was a most pernickety man and was not satisfied with grinding lenses as good as those of the best lens-grinder in Holland, they had to be better than the best, and then he still fussed over them for long hours. Next he mounted these lenses in little oblongs of copper or silver or gold, which he had extracted himself, over hot fires, among strange smells and fumes. . . .

Of course his neighbors thought he was a bit cracked but Leeuwenhoek went on burning and blistering his hands. Working forgetful of his family and regardless of his friends, he bent solitary to subtle tasks in still nights. The good neighbors sniggered, while that man found a way to make a tiny lens, less than one-eight of an inch across, so symmetrical, so perfect, that it showed little things to him with a fantastic clear enormousness. . . .

Now this self-satisfied dry-goods dealer began to turn his lenses onto everything he could get hold of. He looked through them at the muscle fibers of a whale and the scales of his own skin. He went to the butcher shop and begged or bought ox-eyes and was amazed at how prettily the crystalline lens of the eye of

---

[1] *alchemists and apothecaries* The alchemists were trying to turn base metals into gold and to find magical substances. *Apothecaries:* druggists.

the ox is put together. He peered for hours at the build of the hairs of a sheep, of a beaver, of an elk, that were transformed from their fineness into great rough logs under his bit of glass. He delicately dissected the head of a fly; he stuck its brain on the fine needle of his microscope—how he admired the clear details of the marvelous big brain of that fly! He examined the cross-sections of the wood of a dozen different trees and squinted at the seeds of plants. He grunted "Impossible!" when he first spied the outlandish large perfection of the sting of a flea and the legs of a louse. That man Leeuwenhoek was like a puppy who sniffs—with a totally impolite disregard of discrimination—at every object of the world around him!

II

But at this time, in the middle of the seventeenth century, great things were astir in the world. Here and there in France and England and Italy rare men were thumbing their noses at almost everything that passed for knowledge. "We will no longer take Aristotle's say-so, nor the Pope's say-so," said these rebels. "We will trust only the perpetually repeated observations of our own eyes and the careful weighings of our scales; we will listen to the answers experiments give us and no other answers!" So in England a few of these revolutionists started a society called The Invisible College; it had to be invisible because that man Cromwell might have hung them for plotters and heretics if he had heard of the strange questions they were trying to settle.

. . . Remember that one of the members of this college was Robert Boyle, founder of the science of chemistry, and another was Isaac Newton. Such was the Invisible College, and presently, when Charles II came to the throne, it rose from its depths as a sort of blind-pig scientific society to the dignity of the name of the Royal Society of England. And they were

Antony Leeuwenhoek's first audience! There was one man in Delft who did not laugh at Antony Leeuwenhoek, and that was Regnier de Graaf, whom the Lords and Gentlemen of the Royal Society had made a corresponding member because he had written them of interesting things he had found in the human ovary. Already Leeuwenhoek was rather surly and suspected everybody, but he let de Graaf peep through those magic eyes of his, those little lenses whose equal did not exist in Europe or England or the whole world for that matter. What de Graaf saw through those microscopes made him ashamed of his own fame and he hurried to write to the Royal Society:

"Get Antony Leeuwenhoek to write you telling of his discoveries."

And Leeuwenhoek answered the request of the Royal Society with all the confidence of an ignorant man who fails to realize the profound wisdom of the philosophers he addresses. It was a long letter, it rambled over every subject under the sun, it was written with a comical artlessness in the conversational Dutch that was the only language he knew. The title of that letter was: "A Specimen of Some Observations made by a Microscope contrived by Mr. Leeuwenhoek, concerning Mould upon the Skin, Flesh, etc.; the Sting of a Bee, etc." The Royal Society was amazed, the sophisticated and learned gentlemen were amused—but principally the Royal Society was astounded by the marvelous things Leeuwenhoek told them he could see through his new lenses. The Secretary of the Royal Society thanked Leeuwenhoek and told him he hoped his first communication would be followed by others. It was, by hundreds of others over a period of fifty years. They were talkative letters full of salty remarks about his ignorant neighbors, of exposures of charlatans and of skilled explodings of superstitions, of chatter about his personal health—but sandwiched between paragraphs and pages of this homely stuff, in almost every letter, those Lords and Gentlemen of the Royal Society had the honor of reading immortal and gloriously accurate descriptions of the discoveries made by the magic eye of that janitor and shopkeeper. What discoveries!

. . . When Leeuwenhoek was born there were no microscopes but only crude hand-lenses that would hardly make a ten-cent piece look as large as a quarter. Through these—without his incessant grinding of his own marvelous lenses—that Dutchman might have looked till he grew old without discovering any creature smaller than a cheese-mite. You have read that he made better and better lenses with the fanatical persistence of a lunatic; that he examined everything, the most intimate things and the most shocking things, with the silly curiosity of a puppy. Yes, and all this squinting at bee-stings and mustache hairs and what-not were needful to prepare him for that sudden day when he looked through his toy of a gold-mounted lens at a fraction of a small drop of clear rain water to discover—

What he saw that day starts this history. Leeuwenhoek was a maniac observer, and who but such a strange man would have thought to turn his lens on clear, pure water, just come down from the sky? What could there be in water but just—water? You can imagine his daughter Maria—she was nineteen and she took such care of her slightly insane father!—watching him take a little tube of glass, heat it red-hot in a flame, draw it out to the thinnest of a hair. . . .

He squints through his lens. He mutters guttural words under his breath.

Then suddenly the excited voice of Leeuwenhoek: "Come here! Hurry! There are little animals in this rain water. . . . They swim! They play around! They are a thousand times smaller than any creatures we can see with our eyes alone. . . . Look! See what I have discovered!"

Leeuwenhoek's day of days had come. . . . This janitor of Delft had stolen upon and peeped into a fantastic sub-visible world of little things, creatures that had lived, had bred, had battled, had died, completely hidden from and unknown to all men from the beginning of time. Beasts these were of a kind that ravaged and annihilated whole races of men ten millions times larger than they were themselves. Beings these were, more terrible than fire-spitting dragons or hydra-headed monsters.[2] They were silent assassins that murdered babes in warm cradles and kings in sheltered places. It was this invisible, insignificant, but implacable—and sometimes friendly—world that Leeuwenhoek had looked into for the first time of all men of all countries.

This was Leeuwenhoek's day of days. . . .

III

. . . How marvelous it would be to step into that simple Dutchman's shoes, to be inside his brain and body, to feel his excitement—it is almost nausea!—at his first peep at those cavorting "wretched beasties."

That was what he called them, and this Leeuwenhoek was an unsure man. Those animals were too tremendously small to be true, they were too strange to be true. So he looked again, till his hands were cramped with holding his microscope and his eyes full of that smarting water that comes from too-long looking. But he was right! Here they were again, not one kind of little creature, but here was another, larger than the first, "moving about very nimbly because they were furnished with divers incredibly thin feet." Wait! Here is a third kind—and a fourth, so tiny I can't make out his shape. But he is alive! He goes about, dashing over great distances in this world of his water-drop in the little tube. . . . What nimble creatures!

"They stop, they stand still as 'twere upon a point, and then turn themselves round with that swiftness, as we see a top turn round, the circumference they make being no bigger than that

---

[2] *hydra-headed monsters* The Hydra was a nine-headed monster slain by Hercules. When one of its heads was cut off, two more would grow in its place.

of a fine grain of sand." So wrote Leeuwen-hoek. . . .

But where did these outlandish little inhabitants of the rainwater come from? Had they come down from the sky? Had they crawled invisibly over the side of the pot from the ground? Or had they been created out of nothing by a God full of whims? Well, there was only one way to find out where they came from. "I will experiment!" he muttered.

. . . Then he took a big porcelain dish, "glazed blue within," he washed it clean, out into the rain he went with it and put it on top of a big box so that the falling raindrops would splash no mud into the dish. The first water he threw out to clean it still more thoroughly. Then intently he collected the next bit in one of his slender pipes, into his study he went with it. . . .

"I have proved it! This water has not a single little creature in it! They do not come down from the sky!"

But he kept that water; hour after hour, day after day he squinted at it—and on the fourth day he saw those wee beasts beginning to appear in the water along with bits of dust and little flecks of thread and lint. That was a man from Missouri! [3] Imagine a world of men who would submit all of their cocksure judgments to the ordeal of the common-sense experiments of a Leeuwenhoek!

Did he write to the Royal Society to tell them of this entirely unsuspected world of life he had discovered? Not yet! He was a slow man. He turned his lens onto all kinds of water, water kept in the close air of his study, water in a pot kept on the high roof of his house, water from the not-too-clean canals of Delft and water from the deep cold well in his garden. Everywhere he found those beasts. He gaped at their enormous littleness, he found many thousands of them did not equal a grain of sand in bigness, he compared them to a cheese-mite and they

were to this filthy little creature as a bee is to a horse. He was never tired with watching them "swim about among one another gently with a swarm of mosquitoes in the air. . . ."

Of course this man was a groper. He was a groper and a stumbler as all men are gropers, devoid of prescience, and stumblers, finding what they never set out to find. His new beasties were marvelous but they were not enough for him, he was always poking into everything, trying to see more closely, trying to find reasons. Why is the sharp taste of pepper? That was what he asked himself one day, and he guessed: "There must be little points on the particles of pepper and these points jab the tongue when you eat pepper. . . ."

But are there such little points?

He fussed with dry pepper. He sneezed. He sweat, but he couldn't get the grains of pepper small enough to put under his lens. So, to soften it, he put it to soak for several weeks in water. Then with fine needles he pried the almost invisible specks of the pepper apart, and sucked them up in a little drop of water into one of his hair-fine glass tubes. He looked—

Here was something to make even this determined man scatter-brained. He forgot about possible small sharp points on the pepper. With the interest of an intent little boy he watched the antics of "an incredible number of little animals, of various sorts, which move very prettily, which tumble about and sidewise, this way and that!"

So it was Leeuwenhoek stumbled on a magnificent way to grow his new little animals.

And now to write all this to the great men off there in London! Artlessly he described his own astonishment to them. Long page after page in a superbly neat handwriting with little common words he told them that you could put a million of these little animals into a coarse grain of sand and that one drop of his pepper-water, where they grew and multiplied so well, held more than two-million seven-hundred-thousand of them. . . .

---

[3] *man from Missouri* One who must see something with his own eyes before he will believe it.

This letter was translated into English. It was read before the learned skeptics . . . and it bowled the learned body over! What! The Dutchman said he had discovered beasts so small that you could put as many of them into one little drop of water as there were people in his native country? Nonsense! The cheese mite was absolutely and without doubt the smallest creature God had created.

But a few of the members did not scoff. This Leeuwenhoek was a confoundedly accurate man: everything he had ever written to them they had found to be true. . . . So a letter went back to the scientific janitor, begging him to write them in detail the way he had made his microscope, and his method of observing.

. . . He replied to them in a long letter assuring them he never told anything too big. He explained his calculations (and modern microbe hunters with all of their apparatus make only slightly more accurate ones!); he wrote these calculations out, divisions, multiplications, additions, until his letter looked like a child's exercise in arithmetic. He finished by saying that many people of Delft had seen—with applause! —these strange new animals under his lens. He would send them affidavits from prominent citizens of Delft—two men of God, one notary public, and eight other persons worthy to be believed. But he wouldn't tell them how he made his microscopes.

That was a suspicious man! He held his little machines up for people to look through, but let them so much as touch the microscope to help themselves to see better and he might order them out of his house. . . . He was like a child anxious and proud to show a large red apple to his playmates but loath to let them touch it for fear they might take a bite out of it.

So the Royal Society commissioned Robert Hooke and Nehemiah Grew to build the very best microscopes, and brew pepper water from the finest quality of black pepper. And, on the 15th of November, 1677, Hooke came carrying his microscope to the meeting—agog—for Antony Leeuwenhoek had not lied. Here they were, those enchanted beasts! The members rose from their seats and crowded round the microscope. They peered, they exclaimed: this man must be a wizard observer! That was a proud day for Leeuwenhoek. And a little later the Royal Society made him a Fellow, sending him a gorgeous diploma of membership in a silver case with the coat of arms of the society on the cover. "I will serve you faithfully during the rest of my life," he wrote them. And he was as good as his word, for he mailed them those conversational mixtures of gossip and science till he died at the age of ninety. But send them a microscope? Very sorry, but that was impossible to do, while he lived.

IV

Those little animals were everywhere! He told the Royal Society of finding swarms of those sub-visible beings in his mouth—of all places: "Although I am now fifty years old," he wrote, "I have uncommonly well-preserved teeth, because it is my custom every morning to rub my teeth very hard with salt, and after cleaning my large teeth with a quill, to rub them vigorously with a cloth. . . ." But there still were little bits of white stuff between his teeth, when he looked at them with a magnifying mirror. . . .

What was this white stuff made of?

From his teeth he scraped a bit of this stuff, mixed it with pure rain water, stuck it in a little tube on to the needle of his microscope, closed the door of his study—

What was this that rose from the gray dimness of his lens into clear distinctness as he brought the tube into the focus? Here was an unbelievably tiny creature, leaping about in the water of the tube "like the fish called a pike." There was a second kind that swam forward a little way, then whirled about suddenly, then tumbled over itself in pretty somersaults. There were some beings that moved sluggishly and looked like wee bent sticks, nothing more, but that Dutchman squinted at them till his eyes were red-rimmed—and they moved, they were alive, no doubt of it! There was a menagerie in his mouth! There were creatures shaped like flexible rods that went to and fro with the stately carriage of bishops in procession, there were spirals that whirled through the water like violently animated corkscrews. . . .

You may wonder that Leeuwenhoek nowhere in any of those hundreds of letters makes any mention of the harm these mysterious new little animals might do to men. He had come upon them in drinking water, spied upon them in the mouth; as the years went by he discovered them in the intestines of frogs and horses, and even in his own discharges; in swarms he found them on those rare occasions when, as he says, "he was troubled with a looseness." But not for a moment did he guess that his trouble was caused by those little beasts, and from his unimaginativeness and his carefulness not to jump to conclusions modern microbe hunters—if they only had time to study his writings—could learn a great deal. . . .

The years went by. He tended his little dry-goods store, he saw to it the city hall of Delft was properly swept out, he grew more and more crusty and suspicious, he looked longer and longer hours through his hundreds of microscopes, he made a hundred amazing discoveries. In the tail of a little fish stuck head first into a glass tube he saw for the first time of all men the capillary blood vessels through which blood goes from the arteries to the veins—so he completed the Englishman Harvey's discovery of the circulation of the blood. The most sacred and improper and romantic things in life were only material for the probing, tireless eyes of his lenses. . . . The years went by and all Europe knew about him. Peter the Great of Russia came to pay his respects to him, and the Queen of England journeyed to Delft only to look at the wonders to be seen through the lenses of his microscopes. He exploded countless superstitions for the Royal Society, and aside from Isaac Newton and Robert Boyle he was the most famous of their members. But did these honors turn his head? They couldn't turn his

head because he had from the first a sufficiently high opinion of himself! His arrogance was limitless—but it was equaled by his humility when he thought of that misty unknown that he knew surrounded himself and all men. . . .

He was an amazingly healthy man, and at the age of eighty his hand hardly trembled as he held up his microscope for visitors to peep at his little animals or to exclaim at the unborn oysters. . . . Years after his discovery of the microbes in his mouth one morning in the midst of his coffee drinkings he looked once more at the stuff between his teeth—

What was this? There was not a single little animal to be found. Or there were no living animals rather, for he thought he could make out the bodies of myriads of dead ones—and maybe one or two that moved feebly, as if they were sick. "Blessed Saints!" he growled: "I hope some great Lord of the Royal Society doesn't try to find those creatures in his mouth, and fail, and then deny my observations. . . ."

But look here! He had been drinking coffee, so hot it had blistered his lips, almost. He had looked for the little animals in the white stuff from between his front teeth. It was just after the coffee he had looked there—Well?

With the help of a magnifying mirror he went at his back teeth. Presto! "With great surprise I saw an incredibly large number of little animals, and in such an unbelievable quantity of the aforementioned stuff, that it is not to be conceived of by those who have not seen it with their own eyes." Then he made delicate experiments in tubes, heating the water with its tiny population to a temperature a little warmer than that of a hot bath. In a moment the creatures stopped their agile runnings to and fro. He cooled the water. They did not come back to life—so! It was that hot coffee that had killed the beasties in his front teeth! . . .

If Antony Leeuwenhoek failed to see the germs that cause human disease, if he had too little imagination to predict the rôle of assassin for his wretched creatures, he did show that sub-visible beasts could devour and kill living beings much larger than they were themselves. He was fussing with mussels, shellfish that he dredged up out of the canals of Delft. He found thousands of them unborn inside their mothers. He tried to make these young ones develop outside their mothers in a glass of canal water. "I wonder," he muttered, "why our canals are not choked with mussels, when the mothers have each one so many young ones inside them!" Day after day he poked about in his glass of water with its slimy mass of embryos, he turned his lens on to them to see if they were growing— but what was this? Astounded he watched the fishy stuff disappear from between their shells —it was being gobbled up by thousands of tiny microbes that were attacking the mussels greedily. . . .

"Life lives on life—it is cruel, but it is God's will," he pondered. "And it is for our good, of course, because if there weren't little animals to eat up the young mussels, our canals would be choked by those shellfish, for each mother has more than a thousand young ones at a time!" So Antony Leeuwenhoek accepted everything and praised everything, and in this he was a child of his time, for in his century searchers had not yet, like Pasteur who came after them, begun to challenge God, to shake their fists at the meaningless cruelties of nature toward mankind, her children. . . .

He passed eighty, and his teeth came loose as they had to even in his strong body; he didn't complain at the inexorable arrival of the winter of his life, but he jerked out that old tooth and turned his lens onto the little creatures he found within that hollow root—why shouldn't he study them once more? There might be some little detail he had missed those hundred other times! Friends came to him at eighty-five and told him to take it easy and leave his studies. He wrinkled his brow and opened wide his still bright eyes: "The fruits that ripen in autumn last the longest!" he told them—he called eighty-five the autumn of his life! . . .

That was the first of the microbe hunters. In 1723, when he was ninety-one years old and on his deathbed, he sent for his friend Hoogvliet. He could not lift his hand. His once glowing eyes were rheumy and their lids were beginning to stick fast with the cement of death. He mumbled:

"Hoogvliet, my friend, be so good as to have those two letters on the table translated into Latin. . . . Send them to London to the Royal Society. . . ."

So he kept his promise made fifty years before, and Hoogvliet wrote, along with those last letters: "I send you, learned sirs, this last gift of my dying friend, hoping that his final word will be agreeable to you."

For Discussion

1. In what ways was Leeuwenhoek an ideal scientist? In what ways was he not? Describe his method of investigation.

2. Would you say that Antony Leeuwenhoek led a happy life? Give reasons for your answer.

3. What is the difference between the public's attitude toward science today and the attitude in Leeuwenhoek's time? Does this add or detract from the greatness of Leeuwenhoek's achievement? Explain.

4. What does the fact that Leeuwenhoek wanted to make lenses "better than the best" reveal about his character? Did his neighbors' critical attitude toward Leeuwenhoek make him want to change? What do his letters to the Royal Academy suggest about Leeuwenhoek as a man?

5. What qualities has Leeuwenhoek in common with other great scientists? What are the qualities that seem to work to his disadvantage in such a comparison?

Christopher Columbus, Mariner

SAMUEL ELIOT MORISON

Of all the adventurers who have sailed into the unknown, Christopher Columbus remains the symbol of dedication to an ideal. All who came after him have been measured against his persistence and courage. Samuel Eliot Morison depicts him as a freckle-faced redhead who, as a boy, held a great dream in his blue eyes. The laughter of his critics, the difficulty of raising funds for his expedition, and the temptation to turn back, all faded before his indomitable will to succeed. In his biography of Columbus, Morison places emphasis upon Columbus as a sailor. The general outline of the explorer's story is known to every child. Morison's writing brings the reality of the achievement freshly before the reader's eyes. He supplies the small, harsh details of Columbus's life and voyage as well as the romance.

CHRISTOPHER COLUMBUS, discoverer of the New World, was first and foremost a sailor. Born and reared in Genoa, one of the oldest European seafaring communities, as a youth he made several voyages in the Mediterranean, where the greatest mariners of antiquity were bred. At the age of twenty-four, by a lucky chance he was thrown into Lisbon, center of European oceanic enterprise; and there, while employed partly in making charts and partly on long voyages under the Portuguese flag, he conceived the great enterprise that few but a sailor would have planned, and none but a sailor could have executed. That enterprise was simply to reach "The Indies"—Eastern Asia—by sailing west. It took him about ten years to obtain support for this idea, and he never did execute it, because a vast continent stood in the way. America was discovered by Columbus purely by accident and was named for a man who had nothing to do with it; we now honor Columbus for doing something that he never intended to do, and never knew that he had done. Yet we are right in so honoring him, because no other sailor had

SAMUEL ELIOT MORISON (*1887–   ) was born in Boston. He has spent most of his mature life as professor of history at Harvard University, with time out for service in both the Army and the Navy of the United States. He became a high-ranking officer in the Navy and was appointed official historian of naval operations in the Second World War. Morison is an expert yachtsman. In preparing to write his biography of Columbus, he himself sailed Columbus's route across the Atlantic.*

---

the persistence, the knowledge and the sheer guts to sail thousands of miles into the unknown ocean until he found land.

This was the most spectacular and most far-reaching geographical discovery in recorded human history. Moreover, apart from the magnitude of his achievement, Columbus was a highly interesting character. Born at the crossroads between the Middle Ages and the Renaissance, he showed the qualities of both eras. He had the firm religious faith, the *a priori* [1] reasoning and the close communion with the Unseen typical of the early Christian centuries. Yet he also had the scientific curiosity, the zest for life, the feeling for beauty and the striving for novelty that we associate with the advancement of learning. And he was one of the greatest seamen of all time.

The little we know about the Discoverer's childhood and early youth can be quickly told. He had very little formal schooling, spoke the Genoese dialect, which was almost unintelligible to other Italians, and never learned to read and write until he went to Portugal. As everyone who described him in later life said that he had a long face, an aquiline nose, ruddy complexion and red hair, we can picture him as a little,

---

[1] *a priori* A mode of thought which derives consequences from self-evident principles by the use of reason alone.

---

freckle-faced redhead with blue eyes. One imagines that he was a dreamy little boy and very religious for one of his age, and he must have disliked working in his father's loom shed, as he took every opportunity to go to sea.

In later life Columbus said that he first went to sea in 1461 when he was ten years old. Probably his seafaring at that age did not amount to much; maybe his father let him sail with a neighbor to Portofino to load dried fish, or even over to Corsica, which would have seemed like a foreign voyage to a little boy. What sailor can forget his first cruise? Every incident, every turn of wind, every vessel or person you meet stays in your memory for years. What pride and joy to be given the tiller while the skipper goes below and the mate snoozes on the sunny side of the deck! What a thrill to sight five mountains above the horizon, to watch them rise, spread out and merge into one as you approach! Then, to go ashore, to swap your jackknife for a curiosity, to see the island gradually sink below the horizon on the homeward passage, and to swagger ashore feeling you are a real old salt! Such things a sailor never forgets.

In May, 1476, in his twenty-fifth year, came the adventure that changed the course of Christopher's life. Genoa organized an armed convoy to carry a valuable cargo to Northern Europe, and in this convoy Christopher sailed as seaman in a Flemish vessel named *Bechalla*. On August 13, when it had passed the Strait of Gibraltar and was off the southern coast of Portugal, the fleet was attacked by a French task force. The battle raged all day, and by nightfall three Genoese ships and four of the enemy's had gone down. *Bechalla* was one of the casualties. Christopher, though wounded, managed to grasp a floating sweep and, by alternately kicking it ahead and resting on it, reached the shore six miles distant. The people of Lagos, near which he landed, treated him kindly, and on learning that his younger brother Bartholomew was living at Lisbon, sent him thither as soon as he could travel.

That was one of the best things that could have happened to Christopher Columbus.

Portugal was then the liveliest and most progressive country in Europe, and Lisbon the center for exploration and discovery. Almost half a century earlier the Infante Dom Henrique, the Portuguese prince whom we call Henry the Navigator, had set up a combined hydrographic and marine intelligence office at Cape St. Vincent, which attracted ambitious seamen from all over the Mediterranean. He subsidized voyages out into the Atlantic and down along the west coast of Africa. His captains discovered the seven islands of the Azores, one-third of the way to America; the Portuguese colonized not only the Azores but the Madeira group which had been discovered earlier, and the Cape Verde Islands off Africa.

Lisbon, moreover, was a learned city where it was easy for a newcomer like Columbus to learn Latin and modern languages and to acquire books that increased his knowledge of the world. Bartholomew, who had already joined the Genoese community there, was employed in one of the chart-making establishments, where he got a job for Christopher, and before long the Columbus brothers had a thriving chart business of their own. That put them in close touch with master mariners and the like, for all charts at that time were based on information and rough sketches that seamen brought home. The two brothers would manage to be on hand whenever a ship returned from Africa or the Western Islands to invite the master or pilot to dine or drink with them, and would extract from him all the data they could for correcting their charts of known countries or extending those of the African coast. It may well be that in one of these conferences a grizzled captain, looking at a chart of the known world, remarked. "I'm sick of sailing along the fever-stricken Guinea coast, chaffering with local chiefs for a cargo of blackamoors; why can't we sail due west beyond the Azores, till we hit the Golden East, and make a real killing? . . ."

We do not know how Columbus came by the idea of sailing west to reach the East, but once he had it, that was the truth for him; he was the sort of man in whom action is the complement of a dream. Like the pioneers of aviation, he was considered a little touched in the head: one who would fly in the face of God. And the worst of it was that he had to persuade stupid people in high places that his Enterprise of the Indies, as he called it, was plausible, because he wanted money, men and equipment to carry it out. More maritime experience than that of foremost hand and apprentice chartmaker was needed before he could hope to convince anyone. And that he obtained, under the Portuguese flag.

Christopher Columbus, now aged thirty-one or -two, had "arrived," according to the standards of his day. He was a master mariner in the Portuguese merchant service, then the finest and most far-ranging merchant marine in the world. He had sailed from above the Arctic Circle to the Equator, and from the eastern Aegean to the outer Azores. He had learned all of practical navigation that could be acquired by entering ships "through the hawse hole" and working up to the captain's cabin. He could make charts and figure latitude from the North Star. Besides, he was an avid reader of books on geography and cosmography. He was connected by marriage to two important families of Portugal. He had business connections with a leading merchant-banker house of Genoa. Columbus had only to continue in this career, persevere in the African trade with its many opportunities to make something on the side, and retire after a few years, a rich man. Or the King might give him one of the royal caravels [2] to explore the African coast, as Diego Cão was doing in 1482–83; and Cão, for discovering a new farthest south on the African coast, was knighted and ennobled in 1484.

But Christopher had other ideas and a vaster

[2] *caravel* A small sailing vessel.

ambition. His mind was seething with the notion of sailing west to the Orient, acquiring wealth beyond the dreams of avarice, and glory exceeding that of any earlier mariner. . . .

In 1484 he made his first effort to interest a prince—John II, King of Portugal, a nephew of Henry the Navigator who was intensely interested in new discoveries. According to the contemporary Portuguese historians and chroniclers, the Columbian project was exactly the same then as later—to reach Japan by sailing west and to discover other islands en route. "The King," says one of the historians, "as he observed this *Christovão Colom* to be a big talker and boastful . . . and full of fancy and imagination with his Isle *Cypango* . . . gave him small credit." Nevertheless, the King committed the project to a junta [3] consisting of a prominent churchman and two Jewish physicians of reputed skill in celestial navigation. They turned it down, flat. Their reasons for so doing are not recorded, but we may assume that they had a more accurate idea of the distance to be covered than did Columbus.

In 1485, the same year that the Portuguese committee turned him down, his wife Dona Felipa died at Lisbon. That broke his strongest tie with Portugal. Nobody there would stake him if the King would not, so Columbus decided to try his luck in Spain. He knew no one there except a sister of his late wife who was married to a Spaniard in Huelva, so to that part of Spain, the County of Niebla adjoining Portugal, Columbus took ship with his five-year-old son Diego.

It must have been with sinking heart that Columbus entered the Rio Saltés and sighted the sleepy little ports of Huelva and Palos, a sad contrast to bright, bustling Lisbon. As his ship rounded into the Rio Tinto, he observed on a bluff the buildings of the Franciscan friary of La Rábida. That suggested a solution to his problem of what to do with Diego, as the Franciscans were known to take "boarders." So,

after landing at Palos, he walked with his little son four miles to the friary, knocked at the gate and asked the porter for a drink of water and some bread for the boy. Fortunately, Antonio de Marchena, a highly intelligent Franciscan who had studied astronomy, came to the gate and got into conversation with Columbus. He invited both father and son to stay, accepted Diego as a pupil and introduced Columbus to the Count of Medina Celi, a grandee of Spain and also an important shipowner of Cadiz.

Medina Celi, of whom Columbus asked "three or four well-equipped caravels, and no more," had almost decided to underwrite the enterprise when it occurred to him to ask permission of the Queen. He did so, and Isabella refused, believing that so important an enterprise as that of Columbus should be conducted by the crown. But this transfer from Count to Queen postponed Columbus's voyage some six years.

On May Day 1486, almost a year from the time he had first set foot in Spain, Columbus was received by the Queen in the Alcazar that still stands at Cordova. Isabella the Catholic was one of the ablest European sovereigns in an age of strong kings. She had an intuitive faculty for choosing the right man for a job, and for doing the right thing at the right time. She was very close to Columbus's age and similar to him in temperament, and in coloring—blue eyes and auburn hair. Her marriage with Ferdinand of Aragon had united all "the Spains," excepting Portugal, to which she was allied, and the remnant of the Moorish Caliphate of Cordova, which she had resolved to conquer. Some spark of understanding evidently passed between Christopher and Isabella at their first meeting, and although she turned down his enterprise more than once, he found that he could count on her in the end. On this occasion she appointed a special commission under Hernando de Talavera, her confessor, to examine the Great Project and recommend whether she should accept or reject it, or allow Medina Celi to back it.

Then began a period of almost six years, the

[3] *junta* A committee.

most unhappy in Columbus's entire life. He had to sustain a continual battle against prejudice, contumely and sheer indifference. A proud, sensitive man who *knew* that his project was feasible and that it would open new pathways to maritime achievement and opportunity, he had to endure clownish witticisms and crackpot jests by ignorant courtiers, to be treated worse than a beggar, and at times actually to suffer want. Worst of all, perhaps, he learned by experience the meaning of the phrase "*cosas de España*," [4] the irritating procrastination of Spaniards, who never seemed to be able to make up their minds, to carry out a plain order, or to make a firm decision without fees or favors. In later years he often alluded bitterly to these experiences and tactlessly contrasted the enormous wealth and power he had conferred on Spain with his pitiable and protracted efforts to obtain a fair hearing.

At about Christmas time 1491, Columbus again appeared at court, which was then being held in the fortified camp of Santa Fe during the siege of Granada. A new commission was appointed, and the Royal Council reviewed their findings. The exact details are not known, but it seems probable that the commission, reading the Queen's mind, recommended that Columbus be allowed to try this project, and that the Council rejected it because of the price he asked. For this extraordinary man, despite poverty, delays and discouragement, had actually raised his demands. In 1485 he had been willing to sail west for Medina Celi on an expense-account basis, without any particular honors or emoluments. Now he demanded not only ennoblement and the title of admiral, but also that he be made governor and viceroy of any new lands he might discover, that both titles be hereditary in his family, and that he and his heirs be given a ten per cent cut on the trade. He had suffered so many outrages and insults during his long residence in Spain that—by San Fernando!—he would not glorify Spain for

nothing. If the sovereigns would grant him, contingent on his success, such rank, titles and property that he and his issue could hold up their heads with Spanish grandees, well and good; but no more bargaining. Take it, Your Majesties, or leave it.

Leave it they did, in January, 1492, immediately after the fall of Granada. Ferdinand and Isabella told him this at an audience that the King, at least, intended to be final. Columbus saddled his mule, packed the saddlebags with his charts and other exhibits, and started for Seville with his faithful friend Juan Pérez, intending to take ship for France and join Bartholomew in a fresh appeal to Charles VIII.

Just as, in Oriental bargaining, a storekeeper will often run after a departing customer to accept his last offer, so it happened here. Luis de Santangel, keeper of King Ferdinand's privy purse, called on the Queen the very day that Columbus left Santa Fe and urged her to meet Columbus's terms. The expedition, he pointed out, would not cost as much as a week's entertainment of a fellow sovereign, and he would undertake to raise the money himself. As for the honors and emoluments, Columbus asked only for a promise of them in the event of his success, and if he did succeed, they would be a small price to pay for the discovery of new islands and a western route to the Indies. Isabella, who had probably felt that way all along, jumped at this, her really last chance. She even proposed to pledge her crown jewels for the expenses, but Santangel said that would not be necessary. And she sent a messenger who overtook Columbus at a village four miles from Santa Fe, and brought him back. . . .

Although it was now settled in principle, the success of the Enterprise depended on an infinite number of practical details. First, it was decided to fit out the fleet and recruit the men at Palos, the little port in the Niebla where Columbus had first set foot in Spain, and for several reasons. Columbus had made friends there of the Pinzón family, leading shipowners and master mariners;

[4] "*cosas de España*" Spanish ways.

both ships and sailors were available. And Palos had committed some municipal misdemeanor for which the Queen conveniently fined her two well-equipped caravels. Columbus made a public appearance in the Church of St. George, Palos, on May 23, 1492, with his friend Fray Juan Pérez, while a notary read the royal order that "within ten days" the two caravels were to be provided and crews recruited, with four months' advance pay.

Ten days, of course, was preposterous, and it actually took about three months for Columbus to get to sea. He had been promised three caravels, not two, but it so happened that a ship from Galicia, owned and captained by Juan de la Cosa, was then in port, and Columbus chartered her as his flagship.

Santa María, as this ship was called, is the most famous of Columbus's ships. She left her bones on a reef off Hispaniola, and no picture or model of her has survived, but several conjectural models have been made and two full-size "replicas" have been constructed in Spain. The original *Santa María* was probably of about one hundred tons' burthen, which meant that her cargo capacity was one hundred "tuns" or double hogsheads of wine.

A Spanish ship in those days had an official name, usually that of a saint, and a nickname which the sailors used; *Santa María* was *La Gallega*, "The Galician." One of the two caravels provided by the town of Palos was named *Santa Clara*, but she is universally known by her nickname *Niña*, so given because she belonged

"*. . . he conceived the great enterprise that few but a sailor would have planned . . .*"

Columbus and His Son at La Rabida, *a painting by Eugene Delacroix*

to the Niño family of Palos. *Niña* was Columbus's favorite.

Pinta, also a locally built caravel, was probably a little larger than *Niña*, and square-rigged from the first. Her real name we do not know; *Pinta* probably was derived from a former owner named Pinto. She was a smart sailor; the New World was first sighted from her deck and she was first home to Spain.

Almost all the enlisted men—stewards, boatswains, calkers, able seamen and "gromets," or ship's boys—were from the Niebla or near-by towns of Andalusia like Seville, Cordova and Jerez de la Frontera. Each seaman received about the equivalent of $7 in gold per month, the petty officers twice that and the boys about $4.60. Encouraged by an ancient pilot who was sure he had just missed the Indies on a Portuguese voyage westward forty years earlier, these men and boys overcame the natural conservatism of a mariner in the hope of glory, gold and adventure. Those who survived won plenty of the first two, and all shared in one of the greatest adventures of history—Columbus's First Voyage.

By the second day of August, 1492, everything at last was ready. That night every man and boy of the fleet confessed his sins, received absolution and made his communion at the church of Palos, which by happy coincidence was dedicated to Saint George, patron saint of Genoa. Columbus went on board his flagship in the small hours of Friday the third and gave the signal to get under way. Before the sun rose, all three vessels had anchors aweigh, and with sails hanging limp from their yards were floating down the Rio Tinto on the morning ebb, using their long sweeps to maintain steerageway. As they swung into the Saltés and passed La Rábida close aboard, they could hear the friars chanting the ancient hymn "*Iam lucis orto sidere*" with its haunting refrain "*Et nunc et in perpetuum*," which we render, "Evermore and evermore."

Columbus's plan for the voyage was simple, and its simplicity insured his success. Not for him the boisterous head winds, the monstrous seas and the dark, unbridled waters of the North Atlantic, which had already baffled so many Portuguese. He would run south before the prevailing northerlies to the Canary Islands, and there make, as it were, a right-angle turn; for he had observed on his African voyages that the winter winds in the latitude of the Canaries blew from the east, and that the ocean around them, more often than not, was calm as a millpond.

On September 2 all three ships were anchored off San Sebastián, the port of that island. Columbus then met for the first time Doña Beatriz de Bobadilla, widow of the former captain of the island. Beatriz was a beautiful lady still under thirty, and Columbus is said to have fallen in love with her; but if that is true, he did not love her warmly enough to tarry to the next full moon. Additional ship's stores were quickly hoisted on board and struck below, and on September 6, 1492, the fleet weighed anchor for the last time in the Old World. They had still another island to pass, the lofty Ferro or Hierro. Owing to calms and variables Ferro and the twelve-thousand-foot peak of Tenerife were in sight until the ninth, but by nightfall that day, every trace of land had sunk below the eastern horizon, and the three vessels were alone on an uncharted ocean. Columbus himself gave out the course: "West; nothing to the north, nothing to the south." . . .

One reason Columbus always wanted two or more vessels was to have someone to rescue survivors in case of sinking. But he made an unusual record for that era by never losing a ship at sea, unless we count the *Santa María*, grounded without loss of life. Comforts and conveniences were almost totally lacking. Cooking was done on deck over a bed of sand in a wooden firebox protected from the wind by a hood. The diet was a monotonous one of salt meat, hardtack and dried peas. For drink they had wine, while it lasted, and water in casks, which often went bad. Only the Captain General and the ships' captains had cabins with bunks; the others slept where they could, in their clothes.

In those days, sailors were the most religious of laymen. On each vessel a boy was charged with singing a ditty at daybreak, which began:

> Blessed be the light of day
> And the Holy Cross, we say;

after which he recited the Lord's Prayer and the Ave Maria, and invoked a blessing on the ship's company. Every half-hour a boy sang out when turning the glass. For instance, at what we would call five bells, he sang:

> Five is past and six floweth,
> More shall flow if God willeth,
> Count and pass make voyage fast.

After sunset, and before the first night watch was set, all hands were called to evening prayers. The service began with the boy whose duty it was to light the binnacle lamp singing:

> God give us a good night and good sailing;
> May our ship make a good passage,
> Sir Captain and Master and good company.

All hands then said the Lord's Prayer, the Creed and the Ave Maria, and concluded by singing the *Salve Regina*.[5] As Columbus himself said, "Seamen sing or say it after their own fashion," bawling it out in several keys at once and murdering the stately Latin words. But was it the less acceptable to the Virgin, under whose protection all sailors felt secure?

Now the boy who turns up the glass for the eighth time sings:

> The watch is called,
> The glass floweth.
> We shall make a good voyage
> If God willeth.

---

[5] *Salve Regina* "Hail, Holy Queen."

And as the vessels sail westward through the soft tropic night, rolling and pitching, sails bellying and slatting, cordage straining, bows throwing foam, every half-hour is marked by this chantey:

> To our God let's pray
> To give us a good voyage,
> And through the Blessed Mother,
> Our advocate on high,
> Protect us from the waterspout
> And send no tempest nigh.

So much for the sea ritual that went on every day, whatever the weather. Now for the events of the voyage.

On September 9, the day he dropped the last land below the horizon, Columbus decided to keep a true reckoning of his course for his own use and a false one to give out to the people, so that they would not be frightened at sailing so far from land.

During the first ten days (September 9 to 18), the easterly trade wind blew steadily, and the fleet made 1,163 nautical miles westward. This was the honeymoon of the voyage. "*Que era plazer grande el gusto de las mañanas*"—"What a delight was the savor of the mornings!" wrote Columbus in his Journal. That entry speaks to the heart of anyone who has sailed in the trades; it recalls the beauty of the dawn, kindling clouds and sails rose color, the smell of dew drying on a wooden deck, and, something Columbus didn't have, the first cup of coffee.

On September 19, only ten days out from Ferro, the fleet temporarily ran into an area of variable winds and rain. But the seamen who, on the tenth day of the northeast trades, were beginning to wonder whether they could ever beat back home were cheered by the change of wind.

During the next five days only 234 miles were made good. During this spell of moderate weather it was easy to converse from ship to ship and to talk about this or that island, St.

Brendan's or Antilia, which they might pick up. In the middle of one of these colloquies, a seaman of *Pinta* gave the "Land Ho!" and everyone thought he saw an island against the setting sun. Columbus fell on his knees to thank God, ordered "*Gloria in excelsis Deo*" [6] to be sung by all hands, and set a course for the island. But at dawn no island was visible; there was none. It was simply a cloud bank above the western horizon resembling land, a common phenomenon at sea. Martin Alonso Pinzón apparently wished to beat about and search for this island, but Columbus refused, because, he said, "his object was to reach the Indies, and if he delayed, it would not have made sense."

The trade wind now returned, but moderately, and during the six days September 26 to October 1, the fleet made only 382 miles. Under these circumstances the people began to mutter and grumble. Three weeks was probably more than they had ever been outside sight of land before. They were all getting on each other's nerves, as happens even nowadays on a long voyage to a known destination. There was nothing for the men to do in the light wind except to follow the ship's routine, and troll for fish. Grievances, real or imaginary, were blown up; cliques were formed; Spain was farther away every minute, and what lay ahead? Probably nothing, except in the eye of that cursed Genoese. Let's make him turn back, or throw him overboard!

On October 7, when there was another false landfall, great flocks of birds passed over the ships, flying west-southwest; this was the autumn migration from eastern North America to the West Indies. Columbus decided that he had better follow the birds rather than his chart, and changed course accordingly that evening. That was "good joss"; [7] it was his shortest course to the nearest land. Now, every night,

the men were heartened by seeing against the moon (full on October 5) flocks of birds flying their way. But by the tenth, mutiny flared up again. No land for thirty-one days. Even by the phony reckoning which Columbus gave out they had sailed much farther west than anyone had expected. Enough of this nonsense, sailing west to nowhere; let the Captain General turn back or else—! Columbus, says the record, "cheered them as best he could, holding out good hope of the advantages they might gain; and, he added, it was useless to complain, *since he had come to go to the Indies, and so had to continue until he found them, with Our Lord's help.*"

Signs of land, such as branches of trees with green leaves and flowers, became so frequent that the people were content with their Captain General's decision, and the mutinous mutterings died out in the keen anticipation of making a landfall in the Indies.

As the sun set under a clear horizon October 11, the northeast trade breezed up to gale force, and the three ships tore along at nine knots. But Columbus refused to shorten sail. He signaled everyone to keep a particularly sharp watch, and offered extra rewards for first landfall in addition to the year's pay promised by the sovereigns. That night of destiny was clear and beautiful with a late rising moon, but the sea was the roughest of the entire passage. The men were tense and expectant, the officers testy and anxious, the Captain General serene in the confidence that presently God would reveal to him the promised Indies.

At 10 P.M., an hour before moonrise, Columbus and a seaman, almost simultaneously, thought they saw a light "like a little wax candle rising and falling." Others said they saw it too, but most did not; and after a few minutes it disappeared. Volumes have been written to explain what this light was or might have been. To a seaman it requires no explanation. It was an illusion, created by overtense watchfulness. When uncertain of your exact position, and straining to make a night landfall, you are

---

[6] "*Gloria in excelsis Deo*" "Glory to God upon high."

[7] "*good joss*" Good fortune.

apt to see imaginary lights and flashes and to hear nonexistent bells and breakers.

On rush the ships, pitching, rolling, throwing spray—white waves at their bows and white wakes reflecting the moon. *Pinta* is perhaps half a mile in the lead. *Santa María* on her port quarter, *Niña* on the other side. Now one, now another forges ahead, but they are all making the greatest speed of which they are capable. With the sixth glass of the night watch, the last sands are running out of an era that began with the dawn of history. A few minutes now and destiny will turn up a glass the flow of whose sands we are still watching. Not since the birth of Christ has there been a night so full of meaning for the human race.

At 2 A.M., October 12, Rodrigo de Triana, lookout on *Pinta*, sees something like a white cliff shining in the moonlight, and sings out, "Tierra! tierra!" "Land! land!" Captain Pinzón verifies the landfall, fires a gun as agreed, and shortens sail to allow the flagship to catch up. As *Santa María* approaches, the Captain General shouts across the rushing waters, "Señor Martín Alonso, you *did* find land! Five thousand *maravedis* [8] for you as a bonus!"

Yes, land it was this time, a little island of the Bahamas group. The fleet was headed for the sand cliffs on its windward side and would have been wrecked had it held course. But these seamen were too expert to allow that to happen. The Captain General ordered sail to be shortened and the fleet to jog off and on until daylight, which was equivalent to a southwesterly drift clear of the island. At dawn they made full sail, passed the southern point of the island and sought an opening on the west coast, through the barrier reef. Before noon they found it, sailed into the shallow bay now called Long or Fernandez, and anchored in the lee of the land, in five fathoms.

Here on a gleaming beach of white coral occurred the famous first landing of Columbus. The Captain General (now by general consent called Admiral) went ashore in the flagship's boat with the royal standard of Castile displayed, the two Captains Pinzón in their boats, flying the banner of the Expedition—the green crowned cross on a white field. "And, all having rendered thanks to Our Lord, kneeling on the ground, embracing it with tears of joy for the immeasurable mercy of having reached it, the Admiral rose and gave this island the name *San Salvador*"—Holy Savior.

For Discussion

1. How did circumstances seem to dictate Columbus as the man to attempt to find the western route to the Orient?

2. From the facts presented in "Christopher Columbus, Mariner," could you reconstruct a day aboard the *Santa María?* Describe the crew.

3. Does the fact that Christopher Columbus's discovery of America was an accident lessen the heroism of the venture? Is the spirit of Columbus still evident in the modern world? Give a few examples.

4. Was Columbus's journey across an unchartered ocean a headstrong dare or a "calculated risk" based on experience, study, and knowledge of the sea?

5. What does Morison mean when he writes: "Not since the birth of Christ has there been a night so full of meaning for the human race"? Suggest how the discovery of the New World changed old ways of thinking. How did the presence of a vast new continent create a new relationship between European nations? How might this be seen as a parallel to the present competition for the control of outer space?

---

[8] *maravedi* A Spanish coin.

The Monster

DEEMS TAYLOR

The Romantic artist often sees himself as a being set apart from the rest of humanity. He feels that he must be some kind of "monster" in order to create great art. The Irish poet, William Butler Yeats, wrote:

> *The intellect of man is forced to choose*
> *Perfection of the life, or of the work,*
> *And if it take the second must refuse*
> *A heavenly mansion, raging in the dark.*

The subject of this profile chose perfection in his work, and much of his life was indeed a "raging in the dark."

HE WAS an undersized little man, with a head too big for his body—a sickly little man. His nerves were bad. He had skin trouble. It was agony for him to wear anything next to his skin coarser than silk. And he had delusions of grandeur.

He was a monster of conceit. Never for one minute did he look at the world or at people, except in relation to himself. He was not only the most important person in the world, to himself; in his own eyes he was the only person who existed. He believed himself to be one of the greatest dramatists in the world, one of the greatest thinkers, and one of the greatest composers. To hear him talk, he was Shakespeare, and Beethoven, and Plato, rolled into one. And you would have had no difficulty in hearing him talk. He was one of the most exhaustive conversationalists that ever lived. An evening with him was an evening spent in listening to a monologue. Sometimes he was brilliant; sometimes he was maddeningly tiresome. But whether he was being brilliant or dull, he had one sole topic of conversation: himself. What *he* thought and what *he* did.

He had a mania for being in the right. The slightest hint of disagreement, from anyone, on the most trivial point, was enough to set him off on a harangue that might last for hours, in which he proved himself right in so many ways, that in the end his hearer, stunned and deafened, would agree with him, for the sake of peace.

It never occurred to him that he and his doing were not of the most intense and fascinating interest to anyone with whom he came in contact. He had theories about almost any subject under the sun, including vegetarianism, the drama, politics, and music; and in support of these theories he wrote pamphlets, letters, books . . . thousands upon thousands of words, hundreds and hundreds of pages. He not only wrote these things, and published them—usually at somebody else's expense—but he would sit and read them aloud, for hours, to his friends and his family.

DEEMS TAYLOR (*1885–*) *is an American composer and music critic. Two of his operas have been presented at the Metropolitan Opera House in New York,* The King's Henchman *and* Peter Ibbetson.

He wrote operas; and no sooner did he have the synopsis of a story, but he would invite—or rather summon—a crowd of his friends to his house and read it aloud to them. Not for criticism. For applause. When the complete poem was written, the friends had to come again, and hear *that* read aloud. Then he would publish the poem, sometimes years before the music that went with it was written. He played the piano like a composer, in the worst sense of what that implies, and he would sit down at the piano before parties that included some of the finest pianists of his time, and play for them, by the hour—his own music, needless to say. He had a composer's voice. And he would invite eminent vocalists to his house, and sing them his operas, taking all the parts.

He had the emotional stability of a six-year-old child. When he felt out of sorts, he would rave and stamp, or sink into suicidal gloom and talk darkly of going to the East to end his days as a Buddhist monk. Ten minutes later, when something pleased him, he would rush out of doors and run around the garden, or jump up and down on the sofa, or stand on his head. He could be grief-stricken over the death of a pet dog, and he could be callous and heartless to a degree that would have made a Roman emperor shudder.

He was almost innocent of any sense of responsibility. Not only did he seem incapable of supporting himself, but it never occurred to him that he was under any obligation to do so. He was convinced that the world owed him a living. In support of this belief, he borrowed money from everybody who was good for a loan—men, women, friends, or strangers. He wrote begging letters by the score, sometimes groveling without shame, at others loftily offering his intended benefactor the privilege of contributing to his support, and being mortally offended if the recipient declined the honor. I have found no record of his ever paying or repaying money to anyone who did not have a legal claim upon it.

What money he could lay his hands on he spent like an Indian rajah. The mere prospect of a performance of one of his operas was enough to set him to running up bills amounting to ten times the amount of his prospective royalties. On an income that would reduce a more scrupulous man to doing his own laundry, he would keep two servants. Without enough money in his pocket to pay his rent, he would have the walls and ceiling of his study lined with pink silk. No one will ever know—certainly he never knew—how much money he owed. We do know that his greatest benefactor gave him $6,000 to pay the most pressing of his debts in one city, and a year later had to give him $16,000 to enable him to live in another city without being thrown into jail for debt. . . .

He was completely selfish in his personal relationships. His liking for his friends was measured solely by the completeness of their devotion to him, or by their usefulness to him, whether financial or artistic. The minute they failed him—even by so much as refusing a dinner invitation—or began to lessen in usefulness, he cast them off without a second thought. At the end of his life he had exactly one friend left whom he had known even in middle age.

He had a genius for making enemies. He would insult a man who disagreed with him about the weather. He would pull endless wires in order to meet some man who admired his work and was able and anxious to be of use to him—and would proceed to make a mortal enemy of him with some idiotic and wholly uncalled-for exhibition of arrogance and bad manners. A character in one of his operas was a caricature of one of the most powerful music critics of his day. Not content with burlesquing him, he invited the critic to his house and read him the libretto aloud in front of his friends.

The name of this monster was Richard Wagner. Everything that I have said about him you can find on record—in newspapers, in police reports, in the testimony of people who knew him, in his own letters, between the lines of his autobiography. And the curious thing about this record is that it doesn't matter in the least.

Because this undersized, sickly, disagreeable, fascinating little man was right all the time. The joke was on us. He *was* one of the world's great dramatists; he *was* a great thinker; he *was* one of the most stupendous musical geniuses that, up to now, the world has even seen. The world did owe him a living. People couldn't know those things at the time, I suppose; and yet to us, who know his music, it does seem as though they should have known. What if he did talk about himself all the time? If he talked about himself for twenty-four hours every day for the span of his life, he would not have uttered half the number of words that other men have spoken and written about him since his death.

When you consider what he wrote—thirteen operas and music dramas, eleven of them still holding the stage, eight of them unquestionably worth ranking among the world's great musico-dramatic masterpieces—when you listen to what he wrote, the debts and heartaches that people had to endure from him don't seem much of a price. Eduard Hanslick, the critic whom he caricatured in *Die Meistersinger*[1] and who hated him ever after, now lives only because he was caricatured in *Die Meistersinger*. The women whose hearts he broke are long since dead; and the man who could never love anyone but himself has made them deathless atonement, I think, with *Tristan und Isolde*. Think of the luxury with which for a time, at least, fate rewarded Napoleon, the man who ruined France and looted Europe; and then perhaps you will agree that a few thousand dollars' worth of debts were not too heavy a price to pay for the *Ring* trilogy.

What if he was faithless to his friends and to his wives? He had one mistress to whom he was faithful to the day of his death: Music. Not for a single moment did he ever compromise with what he believed, with what he dreamed. There is not a line of his music that could have been conceived by a little mind. Even when he is dull, or downright bad, he is dull in the grand manner. There is greatness about his worst mistakes. Listening to his music, one does not forgive him for what he may or may not have been. It is not a matter of forgiveness. It is a matter of being dumb with wonder that his poor brain and body didn't burst under the torment of the demon of creative energy that lived inside him, struggling, clawing, scratching to be released; tearing, shrieking at him to write the music that was in him. The miracle is that what he did in the little space of seventy years could have been done at all, even by a great genius. Is it any wonder that he had no time to be a man?

For Discussion

1. Did Richard Wagner have any doubts about himself as a great composer? Was his constant posturing a sign of confidence?

2. This profile is divided into two parts. What is the point of division? Why did the author choose this type of structure?

3. The introduction to this unit mentions Oliver Cromwell's order to his portrait painter that he wanted to be represented "warts and all." Does Deems Taylor use a "warts and all" method in presenting Richard Wagner? Might there be other details that the author seems to have neglected? Does he mention one social virtue that Wagner might have possessed? Can you explain why?

---

[1] *Die Meistersinger* Wagner's only comic opera.

Lafayette, the Runaway General

RUSSELL FREEDMAN

The American Revolution excited the interest of many European believers in the cause of liberty. Thomas Paine, a British writer, came to America and wrote eloquent tracts for the colonists. The Polish officers Pulaski and Kosciusko offered their military knowledge to the Continental Army. The most romantic figure among these volunteers was the Marquis de Lafayette. All Americans are aware of his contribution to the cause of the Revolution. Few know that he was no more than a teen-ager when he received his commission as a major general in Washington's army.

IN MARCH, 1777, a mysterious young stranger appeared in Chaillot, a village outside Paris. He moved quietly into a gardener's house and soon became the main topic of conversation in town. No one knew who he was, where he had come from or what he was doing in Chaillot.

The gardener was little help in clearing up the mystery. He refused to talk about his guest. He said only that the stranger was a gentleman who wished to remain anonymous. Aside from that, he merely shrugged his shoulders at neighbors' questions and called the stranger "the gentleman on the first floor."

For three days, no one in Chaillot saw the stranger leave his room. But several townspeople noticed that he received visitors from time to time. Late one evening, two riders on horseback galloped into town, dismounted furtively before the gardener's house and slipped quickly inside.

Wrapped in their dark cloaks, they had the distinct air of men who feared they were being followed. The neighbors peered through their windows, wondering what on earth was going on.

While the neighbors wondered and speculated, a hushed, hurried conference was taking place in the house. One of the participants was an American, a representative of the colonial rebels who were at that moment fighting their War of Independence against England. Another was a French army officer, a close associate of an influential behind-the-scenes figure in French politics. The third was a wealthy, 19-year-old nobleman named Gilbert de Lafayette. He was "the gentleman on the first floor."

Lafayette hardly looked like the central character in a cloak and dagger mystery. He was a rather awkward young man with a long, pointed nose, an unusually high forehead and a deadly serious expression. His build was slight, his face freckled and his reddish hair powdered, in the style of the French court. He did not present a very dashing appearance.

But he had other assets. He belonged to a powerful aristocratic family, possessed an enormous personal fortune and was a member of the royal court at Versailles. Now, he was about to stake everything on the first great adventure of his life. He was going to sail off and join the American insurgents in their battle for liberty. Lafayette had solemnly pledged his honor, his life and his fortune to the American cause.

There was just one problem: before he could sail off to America, he would have to run away from France. France was not directly involved in the Revolutionary War, and the French government did not want to jeopardize its neutrality. For this reason, the government had forbidden its citizens to go to the aid of the colonists. To complicate matters further, Lafayette's legal guardian disapproved of the rebels and had ordered the young nobleman to mind his own business and stay home.

Yet Lafayette had no intention of staying home. All his life he had waited for an opportunity to distinguish himself in battle and uphold his family's gallant military tradition. That opportunity was now at hand. Despite all opposition, he planned to escape from France and embark for America with a small group of fellow volunteers. The secret meeting in Chaillot, where he was hiding out, climaxed months of careful preparation.

The meeting lasted only a few minutes. When Lafayette's visitors were ready to leave, the American extended his hand. "Good luck," he said. "I needn't remind you that your journey requires the utmost caution. You must proceed to Bordeaux as rapidly and as discreetly as possible. I shall be waiting to hear of your safe arrival in America."

Then the French officer placed his hand on Lafayette's shoulder. "As for me, my young friend, I shall see you in the morning. The carriage will be here promptly at daybreak." With a smile, he added: "Sleep well."

Promptly at daybreak the next morning, the mysterious "gentleman on the first floor" left Chaillot as suddenly as he had arrived. One of the curious neighbors saw him climb into a waiting carriage and speed away in the direction of Paris.

Young Gilbert de Lafayette, who had never in his life set foot on a battlefield, was off to play a crucial role in the creation of the United States of America.

Traditionally, the men of the Lafayette family showed heroism in battle. For hundreds of years they had ridden away to war, resplendent in their uniforms, the family banner flapping in the breeze. Gilbert de Lafayette was the last of his line, and as a child, he heard the stories of his gallant ancestors time and time again. He listened gravely, for it was a proud heritage.

He spent a lonely childhood growing up in Chavaniac, age-old home of the Lafayettes. His only real playmate was a girl, his older cousin. It was impossible to make friends with the village children. Gilbert, after all, was the feudal lord of Chavaniac, the ranking nobleman for miles around, and the peasant children kept a respectful distance. Whenever he walked through town, the boys lifted their hats and the girls curtsied. So did their elders.

Chavaniac was a quiet place, hidden in the hills in the remote province of Auvergne, about 300 miles from Paris. The Lafayette chateau, a formidable stone building flanked on both sides by towers, stood high on a hill overlooking the red tile roofs of the village. The chateau had so many rooms that Lafayette wasn't sure which was the one he had been born in. In nearly every one of those rooms, Gilbert's heroic forefathers stared down at him from dark oil paintings.

Three years later, when the boy was eleven,

his childhood came to an end. His mother returned from Paris and told him he was now old enough to join her in the capital and begin his education as a gentleman. "Look at you," she said. "My little lord, tramping through the forest, running about the hills. Before you realize it, Gilbert, you will be presented at court. It is not too early to begin learning your responsibilities."

Gilbert didn't have to be convinced. He had always wanted to visit Paris, yet had never been more than a few miles away from home. He pestered Madame Lafayette with so many questions, she wished she had kept her plans secret until the last minute. "Gilbert!" she exclaimed at last, "You *must* learn that a gentleman does not ask so many questions."

When it was finally time to depart, Gilbert clambered into the coach after his mother and stared out the window as they drove slowly down the hill and through the village. The people of Chavaniac had lined both sides of the road to bid adieu to their little lord.

Instead of being the reigning lord for miles around, Gilbert was just a frightened country boy in Paris. The polished manners and slick sophistication of the capital were unfamiliar and often confusing. Though he would someday inherit a great fortune, his prospects of wealth came from his mother's side of the family, not his father's, and some aristocrats politely regarded him as the son of a minor backwoods nobleman. For the first time in his life, he felt self-conscious and ill at ease.

Soon after arriving in Paris, he was enrolled in the Collège du Plessis, a fashionable boarding school for young aristocrats. Gilbert had never seen anything like the elegant manners and dress of his classmates, but he did his best to imitate them. He wore embroidered coats, silk stockings and buckled shoes. His hair was powdered and pomaded. A small sword dangled at his side as a mark of rank. But despite the fancy clothes, he was still a country boy. All the time he had been growing up in the provinces, his classmates had been living in Paris,

taking lessons from their dance masters and being instructed in the fine art of repartee.

Young Lafayette was often the target of jokes, but he had one quality which eventually won the respect of his classmates. Perhaps he was awkward, but he was also strong-willed and high-spirited. Maybe he wasn't a clever conversationalist, yet he wasn't afraid to speak his thoughts. Once, he tried to raise a rebellion among the students because he felt a classmate had been unjustly punished. In spite of his efforts, the revolt failed. Gilbert's fellow students told him they agreed with him, but they were afraid to join him.

Gilbert's mother died suddenly when the boy was 13. A few weeks later, his grandfather also died and the heartbroken youngster came into his vast inheritance. Gilbert was left under the stern guardianship of his great grandfather, the Comte de La Rivière.

The comte was a proud aristocrat of the old school, a lieutenant general in the king's armies and a holder of the Grand Cross of the Royal and Military Order of St. Louis. He saw to it that Gilbert began his own military career without delay and obtained the boy a cadet's commission in the celebrated Black Musketeers, so-called because of their sleek, black horses. This was the elite corps later immortalized by Alexandre Dumas in *The Three Musketeers*.

Gilbert continued to live at school, but was excused from classes to attend the Musketeers' training exercises and regimental ceremonies. Here was what he had always looked forward to. Sword rattling and spurs jangling, he rode in regimental parades in full dress uniform—a scarlet jacket embellished with gold braid, white breeches, glistening black boots, and a long blue cape bearing a silver cross encircled by flames.

Now that Gilbert's military career was launched, his great grandfather began looking about for a suitable wedding match. By custom, marriages were usually arranged as economic and social alliances among noble families. Gilbert's guardian, the Comte de La Rivière, set his sights on one of the proudest and most powerful families in France. He approached the Duc d'Ayen about a possible match between young Lafayette and the duc's second daughter, Adrienne.

The Duc d'Ayen was not enthusiastic at first, since his family outranked the Lafayettes. But as the Comte de La Rivière pointed out, Gilbert was one of France's wealthiest young men. The duc considered this. He also considered that he had five daughters, and a marriage to an acceptable nobleman would have to be arranged for every one of them. After giving the matter much thought, the duc finally agreed; Gilbert would marry Adrienne.

The next step was to draw up a marriage contract. Each family was required to give a full accounting of its assets and a dowry had to be agreed on. The negotiations dragged out for the next five months, with dozens of attorneys and family representatives taking part. Then Adrienne's mother complained bitterly that her daughter was too young to marry immediately. She also insisted—holding views on marriage far in advance of her time—that the young people must have the final say in the matter. The ceremony was put off for a year so Gilbert and his bride-to-be could get better acquainted.

There was no problem. Adrienne was already infatuated with the Black Musketeer, and Gilbert was attracted to the quiet girl who seemed to understand his own lonely moods. According to their own testimony, they fell in love long before the wedding ceremony on April 11, 1774. Since the Duc d'Ayen had not quite accepted the fact that his new son-in-law was slightly inferior in rank, he spared no expense, and the wedding was one of the most impressive events of the Paris season. Gilbert was not yet 17. Adrienne was two years younger.

The newlyweds were expected to take their place at the royal court, but they weren't very successful at Versailles. At heart, Adrienne was a serious, deeply religious girl. When she was expecting her first child, she gladly retired from court life for the time being. For his part, Gilbert still felt somewhat out of place in Paris.

His awkward manners led to one of the most humiliating incidents of his life. At a grand ball one evening, Lafayette was honored by a dance with Marie Antoinette. When the music ended, the queen turned to him and announced scornfully, "I shall dance with you no more. You are too clumsy."

Clumsy or not, Gilbert had social obligations as a young nobleman, and for a time, he tried to play an active role at court. Yet the trivial preoccupations of Paris and Versailles bored and frustrated him. As a result, he became increasingly withdrawn and reserved.

Beneath his quiet reserve, however, was a mounting restlessness and discontent. Inwardly, Gilbert was every bit as strong-willed and rebellious as he had been during his student days. Usually, he kept himself in check, but occasionally, when he permitted his resentments to flare up, his outspoken views antagonized fellow aristocrats.

Gilbert's father-in-law was disturbed by the young man's lack of social aggressiveness. He obtained an appointment for Lafayette to the household of the Comte d'Artois, a brother of the king. Most courtiers would have considered this appointment an enviable honor, but Lafayette decided it was high time he asserted his personal independence. He didn't particularly like the Comte d'Artois, and within a few days he had deliberately insulted the king's brother, knowing quite well that his royal appointment would be withdrawn.

Gilbert was proud of this moment of defiance; he considered it an act of courage and integrity. To most people at court, however, the episode simply illustrated that he was a social blunderer. And his haughty father-in-law was shocked.

The insult ruined Lafayette's chances of ever becoming a successful courtier. He didn't care. Now he could concentrate on what he considered his true calling—his military career. He was no longer a fledgling cadet in the Black

Musketeers. Since his marriage, he had been a lieutenant in the Noailles Dragoons, a cavalry regiment under the hereditary patronage of his wife's family. Though his father-in-law had arranged for his commission, this was no reflection on Lafayette. Traditionally, officers' posts in many French units were confined to the members of certain powerful families.

Willingly committed to the life of a professional soldier, Lafayette showed little interest in salvaging his social reputation. He had been promised a captain's commission on his 18th birthday. Eventually, he could look forward to assuming command of the Noailles Dragoons. Someday, he would have a chance to prove his worth as a soldier, as had his ancestors before him.

For a brief time, Lafayette was content. On his 18th birthday in 1775, he received his captain's commission. Three months later, Adrienne presented him with their first child, a girl named Henriette. His marriage was happy and his prospering military career provided the foundations of his self-respect.

Then his career was cut short abruptly. France had been at peace for more than a decade, and early in 1776, a new minister of war embarked on a vigorous reform program. Entire units were demobilized; long lists of officers were removed from active duty. One of the first officers to be swept aside was the newly commissioned Captain Lafayette. He had no battle experience to his credit and his commission was solely the result of family influence. His services could easily be dispensed with.

Lafayette had deliberately antagonized the court so he could concentrate on being a soldier. Now his commission meant nothing. Though he still retained the privileges of his rank, it might be years before he could return to active duty. Meanwhile, he would have to put up with the life of a hanger-on at the court which had written him off as a social misfit.

How could he prove to himself and to his contemporaries that he was not destined to be a failure in all he undertook? Events taking place 3,000 miles away were to be his answer.

By 1775, the long-standing quarrel between England and her American colonies had erupted into open rebellion. British troops exchanged shots with the colonists at Concord and Lexington. Toward the middle of the year, the Continental Congress appointed George Washington commander-in-chief of the insurgent army. "Give me liberty or give me death!" shouted Patrick Henry, and his words became the battlecry of the revolution.

Before long, the colonies began to establish diplomatic contact with friendly powers, and in 1776, an American named Silas Deane arrived in Paris. His job was to gain French aid and support. He found the French government willing to help the rebels—but only in secret.

At that time, France and England were old and bitter enemies. France had neither forgotten nor forgiven her humiliating loss of Canada in the recent Seven Years' War and was interested in doing anything possible to undermine the far-flung British Empire. Now, the rebellious Americans offered a rare chance to strike back at Great Britain. France, however, could not side openly with the Americans; she was not yet willing to risk war on behalf of the untried little nation across the sea. Consequently, all negotiations with Silas Deane had to be carried on with utmost caution.

Deane was seeking financial help, arms, equipment and a possible future alliance. Since he also felt that the new American army needed trained, experienced officers, he began to recruit French volunteers. The French government was aware of this activity, but took no official part. Instead, Deane met potential recruits with the help of several influential men in Paris. He offered better pay and higher ranks than many volunteers could obtain in the French army, so he was soon able to report to Congress that he was "well-nigh harassed to death with applications of officers to go to America."

Lafayette had been watching the progress of the American Revolution with mounting interest. He found much to admire in the rebels. Here were men who weren't afraid to fight for their principles. Their aggressive spirit of independence appealed to him; their political ideals had captured his imagination and crystallized some of the vague democratic notions taking shape in his own mind.

When Lafayette learned that French officers were volunteering to fight in America, he wanted to go, too. Why not? He had ruined his chances at court; his military career was stymied; he had to depend on his wife's family for advancement in anything he attempted. Here at last was a chance to break away from his futile existence in Paris. Here was an opportunity to bolster his sagging self-respect, to win distinction as a soldier, to show everyone he could live up to his titles and justify his family name.

Deane wasn't impressed with the new volunteer. He needed trained, efficient officers to augment the American forces and here was a 19-year-old boy who had never fired a shot in battle. When Lafayette admitted that his father-in-law wouldn't consent to his venture, Deane advised him to abandon the idea and return home. Lafayette was crestfallen, but he wouldn't go home.

As Deane talked to the hopeful recruit, it occurred to him that Lafayette's high birth and titles might compensate for his youth and inexperience. Gilbert was the first prominent aristocrat to volunteer. No one paid much attention when an obscure soldier-adventurer went off to fight in a foreign war, but if a nobleman actually attached to the court sailed for America, all France would sit up and take notice.

In fact, Deane reasoned, Lafayette's departure would be all the more dramatic if he held a high rank. Kalb had been granted a major general's commission, but he was unknown outside of military circles. Why not give young Lafayette the same commission? If he left for America as a major general, it would probably cause a sensation in Paris.

Lafayette enthusiastically encouraged this line of reasoning. He helpfully pointed out that if he were given such a high rank, he would certainly be able to obtain his father-in-law's consent.

Deane promised the commission, but he still wasn't quite sure he was doing the right thing. When the contract was drawn up, on December 7, 1776, Deane went to great pains to explain exactly why he had granted the 19-year-old marquis such an extraordinary honor:

The desire which the Marquis de Lafayette shows of serving among the troops of the United States of North America, and the interest which he takes in the justice of their cause, make him wish to distinguish himself in this war, and to render himself as useful as he possibly can; but not thinking that he can obtain leave of his family to pass the seas and serve in a foreign country . . . I have thought I could not better serve my country, and those who have entrusted me, than by granting to him, in the name of the very honorable Congress, the rank of major-general . . . His birth, his alliances, the great dignities which his family hold at this Court, his considerable estates in this realm, his personal merit, his reputation . . . and, above all, his zeal for the liberty of our provinces, are such as have only been able to engage me to promise him the rank of major-general.

Before Lafayette could confront his father-in-law with this unexpected triumph, complicating factors came into the picture. The British ambassador in Paris issued a strong complaint about the French volunteers openly sailing for America. Forced to make a greater show of neutrality, the French government prohibited further sailings. It was widely understood, however, that this order was just a formality. At that very time, France was secretly sending arms, clothing and equipment to the Americans. Her volunteers would just have to leave more surreptitiously in the future so they would escape the notice of the British ambassador.

Nonetheless, the government had expressed an official policy. Now, Lafayette feared his father-in-law would use this policy as an excuse to put an end to his plans—despite his major general's commission. For the time being, he decided to say nothing. Besides, he had thought of an excellent way to spend some of his fortune, and his father-in-law would probably raise the roof if he learned of this latest project. He went back to see Silas Deane. "Up to now, sir," he said, "you have seen nothing but my zeal. But now I am going to turn it to some account. I intend to buy a ship to transport your officers."

Deane could hardly believe it, but he quickly accepted the offer. At the moment, it seemed the only way of gettting the volunteers on the high seas. They agreed that Lafayette would remain in Paris while an agent traveled to the seaport city of Bordeaux to search for a suitable vessel.

To offset any suspicions while the ship was being overhauled, Lafayette decided to visit London, where an uncle of his served as French ambassador. Who would suspect he was planning to fight England while he was enjoying a vacation there? He left for London in mid-February, 1777. Kalb was to notify him there when work on the *Victoire* was completed. . . .

As preparations for sailing got underway, Lafayette wrote a hasty letter to Silas Deane:

The only favor that I wish is that I be afforded every possible opportunity to use my fortune, my labors, all the resources of my imagination and to shed my blood for my brothers and my friends . . . You may feel entirely at ease as far as my family is concerned, and even about that order that I received. Once I am gone, everybody will be of my opinion. Once I have conquered, everyone will applaud my enterprise.

They were applauding before he ever reached America. As Silas Deane had predicted, Lafayette's dramatic escape created a sensation in Paris. People spoke of nothing else. The awkward young aristocrat who had been a failure at court and useless in the army had suddenly asserted himself. He had left a beautiful wife and a life of luxury to fight for liberty in a land he had never seen. Officially, the king's ministers assumed an attitude of injured innocence. They pretended to be angry over the affair. But privately, they praised the conduct of the runaway marquis. Even Marie Antoinette, who had once insulted Lafayette, was now reported to admire his courage.

Meanwhile, Lafayette, Kalb and their little band of volunteers were sailing toward the insurgent colonies under the constant threat of British privateers. The *Victoire* was too heavy and slow to escape prying warships and inadequately equipped to fight them off. To avoid capture by the British, Lafayette and Kalb had agreed to blow up their ship if they were overtaken on the high seas, but the 54-day voyage was uneventful. On Friday, June 13, 1777, the *Victoire*'s crew sighted land and the lumbering vessel finally dropped anchor off a quiet South Carolina beach, far from the British warships that were blockading the American coast.

As Lafayette stepped ashore, he kneeled on the sand, raised his sword and solemnly vowed to devote his life to the American cause. His troubles, however, were not yet over. True enough, he had already overcome the opposition of his own government. Now he would have to face up to the opposition of the United States Congress.

The French officers spent a full month traveling 600 miles over primitive, rutted roads to the American capital at Philadelphia. They expected a warm welcome, but when they attempted to present their credentials to Congress, Chairman James Lovell of the Foreign Affairs Committee told them: "It seems that French officers have a great fancy to enter our service without being invited. It is true we were in need of officers last year, but now we have experienced men and plenty of them."

In the past year, Congress had been dismayed at the number of self-seeking adventurers coming over from Europe, mercenaries who regarded the revolution as a happy hunting ground to advance their personal fortunes. There were, of course, many excellent European officers in the American army; some of them gave their lives for the American cause. But most European volunteers were irresponsible soldiers of fortune who were neither a credit nor a help to the Americans. As a result—shortly before Lafayette and his party arrived in Philadelphia—Congress had imposed a ban on any further volunteers.

Lafayette and his companions knew nothing of the troubles the Americans had been having. They knew only that they had spent more than three exhausting months traveling from Europe to Philadelphia and had arrived brimming with goodwill. They had come to offer their lives for liberty, not to be turned away curtly at the doors of Congress.

That evening, Lafayette wrote a letter to Congress. He carefully explained the circumstances under which the French officers had come to America. Then he added: "After the sacrifices I have made for independence, I consider that I have the right to ask two favors: that of serving without pay, at my own expense, and that of serving as a volunteer (that is to say, in the ranks)."

The letter caused quite a stir when it was read on the floor of Congress the next day. No French officer had ever offered to serve without pay. None had even hinted he would serve in the ranks. Impressed, the congressmen asked to see Lafayette's credentials. Silas Deane's glowing recommendation settled the matter. The young marquis and his companions were admitted into the service of the United States. The congressmen accepted Lafayette's offer to serve without pay, but they had no intention of placing him in the ranks. On July 31, 1777, Congress passed a resolution confirming the commission of the 19-year-old major general:

Whereas the Marquis de Lafayette, out of his great zeal to the cause of liberty, in which the United States are engaged, has left his family and connections, and at his own expense come over to offer his services to the United States without pension or particular allowance, and is anxious to

A portrait of Lafayette at the age of thirty-four by the French painter Court

risk his life in our cause—Resolved, that his service be accepted, and that in consideration of his zeal, illustrious family and connections he have rank and commission of Major General in the Army of the United States.

In formally accepting the commission, Lafayette told Congress: "I wish to serve under General Washington 'til such time as he may think it proper to entrust me with a division of the army."

Lafayette's wish was granted and he was directed to report to Washington's headquarters. When he arrived, he was shocked at the army's ragged condition. The troops were poorly armed. They wore every imaginable kind of clothing, from grey canvas hunting shirts and overalls, to makeshift combinations of patched and tattered uniforms. Many men were barefoot.

"We are bound to be embarrassed," said Washington, "at showing ourselves to an officer coming directly from the French troops."

"I am here, sir," replied Lafayette humbly, "to learn and not to teach."

Washington was pleased by this answer, but there was another reason for his embarrassment besides the shabby condition of his army. He did not quite know what to do with the zealous Frenchman. All the enthusiasm in the world could not compensate for Lafayette's complete lack of military experience. And he was scarcely old enough to be a lieutenant.

Washington wrote an inquiring letter to Congress. Had he clearly understood the situation? Was he supposed to take the marquis' rank seriously? Congress replied that for the time being, Lafayette's commission might be considered honorary. The marquis could remain at Washington's headquarters as an aide, and be given a responsible command whenever Washington thought best.

The American general was not too happy with this arrangement. He felt the presence of the boy general had a demoralizing effect on his veteran officers. Despite his misgivings, he could not help liking the young man who appeared so anxious to prove his courage and ability. Before long, a friendship began to develop between the 45-year-old American who had never fathered a son, and the 19-year-old nobleman who had never seen his father. It was a friendship that was to last the rest of their lives.

Lafayette's baptism of fire came the week of his 20th birthday, at the Battle of Brandywine Creek on September 11, 1777. Washington's army, camped outside Philadelphia, was caught by surprise when British forces suddenly crossed the Brandywine and attacked from the rear. The Americans were forced to retreat and Lafayette finally faced the test he had been waiting for all his life. He did himself proud. While rallying his disorganized troops, he was shot in the leg. Ignoring the wound, he managed to bring some order out of the wild rout, saving lives and valuable equipment.

"The English have honored me with a musket ball in the leg," he wrote to his wife. "But it is a trifle, my dearest love; the ball touched neither bone nor nerve, and I have escaped with the obligation of lying on my back for some time, which puts me much out of humor."

Though he was much out of humor, he was immensely proud of his wound. It was a badge of courage and honor, the first entry on the credentials which would admit him to the ranks of his gallant ancestors. The wound was still raw when he insisted on rejoining the army. He was back in action before he could fit a boot over his badly swollen leg.

Encouraged by the young man's conduct under fire, Washington decided to give him more responsibility. It was a fortunate decision. This fledgling general was destined to play a surprisingly important role in the Revolutionary War.

Beginning with the Battle of Brandywine Creek, Lafayette displayed an unmistakable military flair. Washington soon recognized this and put him in command of a small division. Before he could see much action, however, the army retired to winter headquarters at Valley Forge and Lafayette shared that grim ordeal with his troops.

Early that spring Lafayette was back on the battlefield. In the following months, his tactical genius became increasingly apparent. He distinguished himself in several major engagements, notably the Battle of Barren Hill (now Lafayette Hill) near Philadelphia in May, 1778, and the Battle of Monmouth, New Jersey, two months later. The young Frenchman's courage in action won him a special commendation from Congress.

Meanwhile, momentous news had arrived from Europe. France had entered the war. She had recognized the independence of the 13 colonies and signed an alliance with the United States. Lafayette felt obligated to return home and place himself at the disposal of his own government; he obtained a temporary leave-of-absence from the American army. When he left for Europe in January, 1779, he carried a letter from Congress addressed to King Louis XVI.

The letter praised "This noble young man whom we have found wise in council, brave in battle, patient in the midst of the fatigues of war."

The runaway general was greeted as a homecoming hero when he arrived in France—but not until he had submitted to a necessary formality. As soon as he stepped ashore, he was arrested. Since he had defied a royal command in going to America, the king thought it prudent to make a public gesture of disapproval. Lafayette was condemned to spend eight days under house arrest, in his own house. King Louis XVI was slightly embarrassed by the whole affair, and when the "sentence" expired, the King was the first to receive Lafayette.

Actually, the mock penalty was more a favor than a reprimand. It meant Lafayette had a full week to rest up after his voyage and enjoy a reunion with his family. Even his father-in-law was glad to see him. The duc had decided to let bygones be bygones. Lafayette, after all, had brought the family more fame and prestige than it had enjoyed in centuries.

Lafayette spent a year in France. Much of this time he served as an unofficial ambassador, negotiating with his own government on behalf of the United States. Until then, France had sent only a few ships across the Atlantic, and the war was dragging on with no end in sight. Lafayette managed to win additional financial aid for America and helped to persuade his government to dispatch a powerful fleet and 6,000 infantrymen, under command of Lieutenant General Rochambeau. These reinforcements were to tip the balance in favor of the American cause.

Lafayette returned to the United States in May, 1780, in time to play a vital role in the decisive campaign of the war. Early in 1781, Washington placed the young general in command of some 1,200 troops and ordered him to march on Virginia and meet the marauding British forces under command of Lord Cornwallis. Lafayette's little army was soon reinforced, but even so, he was outnumbered about five to one. Cornwallis boasted, "The boy cannot escape me."

Cornwallis was mistaken. He did not escape "the boy."

Lafayette knew his own forces weren't strong enough to risk a pitched battle. Instead, he turned the lopsided odds to his own advantage by constantly harassing the British in a dazzling series of hit-and-run maneuvers. By the middle of the summer, he had chased Cornwallis across Virginia and bottled him up on the Yorktown peninsula, where the telling battle of the war took place.

With Cornwallis cornered, Lafayette sent out a hasty call for more reinforcements. First to appear was a French fleet. As the warships sat menacingly offshore, Washington's army and the French army under command of Rochambeau rushed down from the north to join Lafayette's waiting troops. The combined French and American forces were placed under Washington's command and the siege of Yorktown began. Cornwallis was surrounded and could do nothing but watch in dismay as the town was blown to bits around him. Finally, out of food and ammunition, he surrendered on October 18, 1781. For all practical purposes, the War of Independence was won.

When word of the victory reached Paris, the foreign minister, who had once forbidden Lafayette to leave France, wrote: "Your name is held in veneration. Although you were not in supreme command of this operation, your . . . preliminary movements laid the foundations of success."

Two months after the Battle of Yorktown, Lafayette was granted an indefinite leave-of-absence and he again returned to France. This time there was no formal reprimand awaiting him. There was only acclaim. He was decorated by the king, consulted by the Foreign Office and given a general's commission in the French army. He was hailed in the streets, cheered at the opera and politely applauded in the smart

Paris salons. He was probably the most celebrated hero of the time—"a hero of two worlds," as someone called him.

His earlier lack of success at court forgotten, Lafayette enjoyed playing the part of a hero. He no longer had to prove himself, and now he had something far more important on his mind. In working for his own glory, he had come to worship the one principle that would guide him the rest of his life—the principle of political liberty.

"Working for my own glory," he once wrote, "will become working for their welfare. The welfare of America is intimately linked with the welfare of all humanity. She is going to become the respected and secure refuge of virtue, good character, tolerance, equality and a peaceful liberty."

Lafayette devoted the rest of his long life to winning the same liberty for his own countrymen as he had helped win for Americans. He was a leading figure in the French Revolution, a bloody, chaotic affair which kept France in turmoil for years. He lost his fortune and his freedom, spending time in prison and exile. In his lifetime, his hopes for a truly democratic France were never realized. Yet he never lost his confidence in the ultimate triumph of his cause. "His confidence in the triumph of liberty," said a friend, "is the same as that of a pious man in the hereafter."

In 1824, when Lafayette was 66 years old, he returned to America at the invitation of Congress. As the nation's guest, he toured each of the 24 states, and wherever he went, from Boston to New Orleans to Fayetteville, the North Carolina city named after him, he was greeted by emotional demonstrations. Probably no other foreign visitor, before or since, has received a warmer welcome to the United States. When one eager well-wisher congratulated him on his ability to speak to Americans in their own language, he replied, "Why shouldn't I? I am an American who has just returned from a long trip to Europe."

The tour lasted 15 months. Then Lafayette sailed back to France aboard an American ship named the *Brandywine* in his honor. The *Brandywine* was loaded down with thousands of gifts and souvenirs, but the most unusual item aboard was something Lafayette had given himself. It was a large chest filled with American soil. In accordance with his wishes, he was buried in that soil when he died ten years later.

For Discussion

1. The author of this biography emphasizes opposites in the character of Lafayette: his awkward appearance opposed to his strong will and high spirit; his aristocratic background opposed to his desire to fight for other men's political freedom. Are there other pairs of opposites? What do they signify?

2. Do you feel that Lafayette's desire to impress his countrymen with noble deeds was stronger than his urge to help the cause of freedom? If a nearer, more convenient war had been going on, do you think that Lafayette would have forsaken the remote struggle in America? Does his escape from Paris seem like a publicity scheme? How does his role in the French Revolution help us to understand Lafayette's true sympathy for the rising spirit of democracy?

3. What were the qualities in the rebellious colonists that Lafayette admired most? Does he see a reflection of any of his own qualities in their awkward attempt to overcome the oppression of British authority?

4. Is the life of Lafayette simply a success story? Are there factors which complicate his fight to throw over his past? Why did he go to war for men he had never known, in a country he had never seen?

5. There have been many men and women who have needed to prove themselves. How does Lafayette fit into this pattern? Was his heroism only a by-product of the urge to prove himself to his own countrymen? What evidence is there that his motives underwent a change when he was actually in America?

Christmas in a Concentration Camp

MICHEL DEL CASTILLO

Tanguy, the hero of this selection, is actually a self-portrait of the author, Michel del Castillo. His story, A Child of Our Time, *is the account of his own growing up. Imprisoned by the Nazis during the second World War, Tanguy manages to find a good friend in his fellow prisoner Gunther. "Christmas in a Concentration Camp" tells how these two were able to keep their spirits alive in the midst of horrors.*

The nightmare of the concentration camp will cast a ghostly shadow across the pages of twentieth-century history. Human beings herded like animals behind barbed wire present a contradiction to any civilized ideals invoked by their captors. Yet this inferno of human misery gave birth to stories of man's endurance and of his ability to love in the midst of hate.

CHRISTMAS 1942.

It was a Christmas that Tanguy was never to forget, a brief truce created out of concerted hope in that world of silence and death. A few days beforehand the prisoners began to scrub out their barrack huts and decorate them with pine branches and colored paper garlands. They even tacked up Christmas messages on the doors.

Then it was Christmas Day.

The evening inspection was shorter than usual, and the commandant wished the prisoners a happy Christmas. Then the loudspeakers began to broadcast carols. The soup had potato-peelings floating in it and was less reddish in color than usual. Everyone agreed that the bread ration had been increased a little.

The atmosphere in the camp was completely transformed. Even those who most habitually quarreled and insulted each other now spoke in friendly tones. They gave each other cigarette butts and inquired after their companions' health. They even behaved kindly to Gunther; [1] and one of them who had always shown himself

[1] *Gunther* A young German pianist and fellow prisoner, the author's closest friend in the concentration camp.

145

MICHEL DEL CASTILLO (*1933–*   ) *was born in Spain. He was brought to France as a small boy, and there he was imprisoned by the Nazis during the Second World War. He has written the frightening story of his own youth in* A Child of Our Time.

───────────────

particularly hostile to the young German went so far as to shake hands with him.

In the endless sea of hatred which formed their lives this day stood out, a peaceful island. The prisoners lay on their bunks and dreamed of their own countries and homes, of other, pre-war Christmases. For this one evening they felt themselves in touch once more with the rest of the world; and they knew instinctively that the linking thread was hope. Hope for a more just and better world; hope for true peace to men of good will; above all, the hope of spending future Christmases in their own homes again, and becoming men once more.

"*Stille Nacht, heilige Nacht*" [2]—all over the world, they knew, in countless different tongues, this carol was being sung and heard; and everywhere men dreamed of this same peace promised to men of good will.

Tanguy, too, lay and dreamed. He felt surging up in him an infinite nostalgia for every Christmas he had never known: the Christmas Days he should have spent in the peaceful company of his family, with a beautiful glittering Christmas tree. He felt in himself the collective nostalgia of all children who, without parents and without love, still dream of the Christmas season. The unspoken yearning of children everywhere stirred in him: those that Dickens portrayed in his *Christmas Carol*, all orphans and charity boys and every one, boy or girl, that had never known true affection. He felt in his innermost heart what all these poor deprived creatures felt: the lack of any happy memories.

[2] "*Stille Nacht, heilige Nacht*" "Silent Night, Holy Night."

Gunther came over to Tanguy's bunk. His face, in the dim evening light, seemed more fine-drawn and beautiful than ever, Tanguy thought. Gunther smiled at him and wished him a happy Christmas.

"Happy Christmas, Gunther."

"Look," Gunther said, "I've brought you a present. Not much, but all I could find. Let it be a token of my affection for you."

Tanguy tried to smile his thanks, but instead he found himself blushing and stammering and very close to tears. Clumsily he opened the parcel. It contained a book: Tolstoy's *Resurrection*.

He thanked Gunther in a choking voice.

Gunther was standing over him, and Tanguy still stared at his face by the faint light of the winter moon. The child's emotions were violently aroused, and yet he could find nothing to say to express his gratitude, though there was much he wanted to tell Gunther. He sat there on his bunk in an agony of indecision, clasping his present in both hands. He was so happy that it hurt.

"Tanguy—there's something I wanted to say to you—"

"Yes?" Tanguy asked eagerly.

Gunther seemed to hesitate. Then, in a nervous voice, he said: "If something . . . happens to me one day, get up on my bunk and pry up the nearest board. Under it you will find a tiny gold medallion. I was wearing it on the day of my arrest. It belonged to my mother. I bequeath it to you."

"But what do you think is going to happen to you?"

"I don't know. It doesn't matter, anyway. Happy Christmas!"

"Happy Christmas, Gunther. And—you know—"

"I know. And now," Gunther said, in a different voice, "now I'm going to give the staff my Christmas recital. You're going to hear it too. The commandant has decided that prisoners are entitled to some music tonight. The curfew is being put back two hours. I'm going to play a Mozart sonata which'll be wasted on the S.S. —but at least I'll have the satisfaction of knowing that you'll be in the audience."

"Thank you, Gunther—that makes it a real Christmas for me."

"Perhaps Christmas has more true reality here than anywhere else," the German said. "Here that dream of hope and love, the Christmas spirit, has more solemn undertones than the free world knows, or cares to know."

Tanguy was silent for a moment, and examined his book, deeply moved. The words for which he fumbled would not come; they suddenly seemed to have lost any meaning. Doggedly he returned to the attack.

"Gunther—"

"M'm?"

"It's the first Christmas I've had—in my whole life—with decorations, and someone giving me a present. You know?"

"I know."

"He felt them dreaming, as he dreamed, of a world without wars, concentration camps, hatred, or betrayal."

Children leaving the Buchenwald concentration camp after its capture by the U.S. Army

"All the same, I'm glad to have spent it with you. I shall never forget tonight."

"Others will forget for you. Christmas will go back to being a mere orgy—getting drunk on beer or champagne, expensive dinners, theaters, promiscuousness. There will be very few for whom Christmas will still symbolize a living hope: the hope of that peace which is sworn to those who earn it. But perhaps mankind will never earn it."

Tanguy lay in his bunk and listened to Gunther's playing over the loudspeaker. . . . Gunther's interpretation and re-creation of his chosen pieces seemed to come from another world. Tanguy pictured his long fingers fluttering up and down the keyboard while his eyes stared into space, absorbed. He felt that through the medium of this music, with its melancholy serenity, Gunther was trying to impart some essential truth to his young mind —something so beautiful that words were inadequate to express it, and only music would suffice. He listened with rapt attention. All was forgotten: his hunger, the fear he had felt during the past few weeks, his frost-bitten hands, the whole wretchedness of his ruined childhood.

In the silent, sleeping barracks Tanguy sensed the secret thoughts, collective and individual, of his companions. He knew which prisoners were reliving their moments of former happiness, and which, like himself, must be regretting the happiness they might have had if life had not denied it to them. He felt them dreaming, as he dreamed, of a world without wars, concentration camps, hatred, or betrayal. And perhaps, he thought, on some remote station platform other children now traveling to other camps must be dreaming of the happier Christmases they had once known.

When Gunther's recital was over, the commandant had records of Wagner relayed over the loudspeakers. Tanguy knew the *Tannhaüser* overture, but it was the first time he had heard it played in the camp. He listened with intense pleasure. Gunther had once explained the libretto to him, and now in his mind's eye he seemed to see the Pilgrim's Chorus moving across a huge, brightly lit stage.

Presently Gunther came back, carrying his usual booty. Tanguy sat on his bed in happy anticipation while Gunther meticulously divided the bread, chocolate, and orange he had been given. Then the two friends ate their Christmas dinner in silence, while the music played on, penetrating to every corner of the camp, feeding the nostalgic dreams which all prisoners cherish.

For Discussion

1. What is the significance of the gifts offered to Tanguy by Gunther? What might the book represent? What might the gold medallion represent?

2. Why does Gunther say that the Mozart sonata would be wasted on the S.S.? What does this suggest about his attitude toward the Germans who run the concentration camp?

3. When Gunther suggests that something might happen to him one day, what does he mean? How does this dark note make his enjoyment of Christmas more intense?

4. When a person has no future to anticipate, his past becomes a refuge to which he can retreat for comfort. How does this apply to Tanguy? Why does the author tell us that Tanguy had never known Christmas before? What effect does that have on the Christmas he experiences in the concentration camp?

5. How do Tanguy and Gunther triumph over their surroundings? When Gunther says, "Christmas will go back to being a mere orgy," what does he mean? Why does he say that perhaps mankind will never earn peace?

Helen Keller

VAN WYCK BROOKS

We tend to pity a person who loses the use of one of the senses. Most men would consider a lifetime of darkness and silence a living death. But Helen Keller, afflicted with the loss of sight and hearing when she was nineteen months old, has won world-wide admiration for the keenness of her intellect and for her poetic sensibility. For more than half a century she has numbered famous men and women among her closest friends. She has written books, traveled and lectured in every part of the world, and even appeared in vaudeville and in the movies. Blind and deaf throughout her life, she has become one of the most notable persons of her era.

This account of Helen Keller is written by her friend and neighbor Van Wyck Brooks, himself a great American literary critic and scholar. His method of presenting his subject is unusual but effective: diary entries describing his meetings with Helen Keller. These intimate glimpses tell us more about her than would a formal biography. Notice as you read that you come to "know" Helen Keller as a charming woman and as a most interested and interesting conversationalist. You become so absorbed by her as a person that soon you forget she is both blind and deaf.

I

WHEN I was in St. Augustine, Florida, in the winter of 1932, Helen Keller appeared at the Cathedral Lyceum, and I went to see and hear her there, drawn by curiosity, such as one feels for any world-famous person. For Helen Keller was not only famous but she had been so from the age of ten, when she had sat on Edward Everett Hale's [1] knee and Queen Victoria asked Phillips Brooks [2] about her. A ship was named after her in 1890, and, while Oliver Wendell Holmes had published a letter of hers in one

---

[1] *Edward Everett Hale (1822–1909)* American clergyman and writer.
[2] *Phillips Brooks (1835–1893)* Episcopal bishop and writer.

VAN WYCK BROOKS (*1886–1963*) *was born
in New Jersey. Soon after his graduation
from Harvard, he began his life-long
study of thought and writing in America.
He published important criticisms
of Mark Twain, Henry James, Emerson,
Thoreau, Whitman, and Melville. His
best-known books concern New England
writers of the nineteenth century:* The
Flowering of New England *and* New
England, Indian Summer.

---

of his books, she had visited Whittier in his house on the Merrimac River. President Grover Cleveland had received her in the White House, as other presidents were to do in after years, and Mark Twain had said that the two most interesting characters of the nineteenth century were, quite simply, Napoleon and Helen Keller. Yet there she was in St. Augustine, still young, in 1932, and here she continues to be twenty-two years later.

I remember one phrase she uttered then, interpreted by her companion (for, never having her own voice, her speech was turbid): a phrase referring to the subway in New York that "opened its jaws like a great beast," which struck me at the moment as reminiscent of the prophets in the Bible. I was not aware then how steeped she was in the language of the Bible, which I later heard her expound with Biblical scholars; nor did I know how familiar she was, literally, with the jaws of beasts, for she had once stroked a lion's mouth. The lion, it is true, was young and well fed in advance, but nevertheless she entered its cage boldly; for her "teacher," as she always called Anne Sullivan, the extraordinary woman who developed her mind, wished her to meet experiences of every sort.

The daughter of a Confederate officer, Miss Keller was born on an Alabama farm and knew cows, mules, and horses from her earliest childhood; they had eaten apples from her hand and never harmed her; and her teacher, feeling that she should know wild animals as well, introduced her early to the zoo of a circus. She shook hands with a bear, she patted a leopard, she was lifted up to feel the ears of a giraffe. She encouraged elephants to wind their trunks about her neck and big snakes wrapped their coils about her, so that Helen Keller, for this reason partly, grew up without fear, and she has remained both physically and morally fearless. The only animals she has not touched are the panther and the tiger, for the tiger is "wanton," as I once heard her say, an appropriate word but characteristic of a mind that has been fed from books instead of the give-and-take of everyday talk.

At that time I knew little of Helen Keller's life and mind, and I could not have guessed that a few years later I was to be her neighbor, seeing her often. My old friend the sculptor Jo Davidson brought us together, just as her own feeling for sculpture had drawn her to Jo Davidson, because Helen Keller "saw" with her hands. She has "ten eyes for sculpture," as Professor Gaetano Salvemini said when, in 1950, she visited Florence, and he arranged for her to see Michelangelo's Medici tombs and the sculpture of Donatello in the Bargello. Salvemini had movable scaffolds set up so that she could pass her hands over the Medici heads and St. John the Baptist, the figures of Night and Day and Madonna and Child; and our friend Jo, who was present, said he had never seen these sculptures before as when he watched her hands wandering over the forms. She peered as it were into every crevice and the subtlest modulations, exclaiming with pleasure as she divined the open mouth of the singing youth and murmuring over the suckling infant, "Innocent greed!" She had quoted in *The World I Live In* a saying of Ghiberti [3] about some sculptured figure he had seen in Rome, that "its most exquisite

[3] *Ghiberti* Fifteenth-century Florentine painter and sculptor.

beauties could not be discovered by the sight but only by the touch of the hand passed over it." To how much else and to how many others her "seeing hand" has led her first or last! It has been her passport to the world outside her.

For the world in which she lives herself is built of touch-sensations, devoid of physical color and devoid of sound, and she has written much about the hand by which she lives and which takes the place of the hearing and sight of others. Exploring the faces of her friends and people whom she has just met, she reads them as if she were clairvoyant, and she can distinguish the Yankee twang and the Southern drawl she has never heard by touching two or three spots on the throats of the speakers.

She says that hands are quite as easy to recognize as faces and reveal the secrets of the character more openly, in fact, and she can tell from hands at once whether people have large natures or whether they have only "dormouse valor." In the soft smooth roundness of certain hands, especially of the rich who have never known toil, she feels a certain chaos of the undeveloped; and, in her land of darkness and silence, she can feel with her own hands the beautiful, the strong, the weak, the comic.

She had early learned geography from maps that her teacher made out of clay or sand on the banks of the Tennessee river, feeling mountains and valleys and following the course of other rivers, and she relates in *The Story of My Life* how, in 1893, she virtually saw with her fingers the World's Fair in Chicago. It is true that the inventor of the telephone, Alexander Graham Bell, one of her early admirers, was there with her and described to her some of the sights in the deaf-and-dumb "system," but he had arranged for her to touch all the objects in the bazaars, the relics of ancient Mexico, the Viking ship. She had taken in with her finger tips the Arabian Nights of the fair as she had learned to read from the raised letters of Braille.

It is natural that Helen Keller has dwelt at length in her books on the hand by which alone the blind are able to see. She very early dedicated her own life to the cause of the education of the blind—doubly handicapped as she was and the only one so handicapped who has ever become a thoroughly well-educated person. (The only possible exception is Robert Smithdas, who graduated from St. John's University in 1952.) Because she was handicapped, because two of her senses were cut off, nature augmented her three remaining senses, not the sense of touch alone but the sense of taste and the sense of smell, which others regard, she says, as a "fallen angel."

In her these are all exceptionally acute and alert. She tells in her *Journal* how in London, passing through a gate, she knew at once by the smell of burning leaves, with the smell of the grass, that she was in Green Park, and she says she can always distinguish Fifth Avenue from humbler New York streets by the odors issuing from the doors as she walks past. She knows the cosmetics that women are using and the kind of coffee they are roasting within and whether they use candles and burn soft coal or wood, just as she recognized St. Louis from the smell of the breweries miles away and Peoria from the smell of the whisky stills. "Listening" with her feet, she says, in a hotel dining-room, she knows the moods and characters of people who walk past her, whether they are firm or indecisive, active or lazy, careless, timid, weary, angry, or sad; and she will exclaim, "What lovely white lilacs!", knowing they are white by touch or smell, for in texture and perfume white lilacs differ from purple. Sometimes, hearing her say these things, I have thought of Edward Sheldon, my blind friend who remarked to Cornelia Otis Skinner,[4] "Your hair is dark, isn't it? I can tell from your voice." Helen Keller, who cannot hear voices, feels vibrations. When an orchestra plays, she follows the music waves along the floor; and, detecting

[4] *Cornelia Otis Skinner* An American actress.

on her desk upstairs the vibration of the bell from the pantry below, she answers with a shuffle of the feet, "Coming down!"

All this gave rise in early years to legends of a "wonder girl" that always annoyed Helen Keller—for she is the embodiment of humor and simple good sense—as well as to rumors in Europe that she was the last word in "American bluff," which led to various efforts to discredit and expose her. The girl who had "found the Blue Bird," as Maeterlinck [5] put it, was said never to be tired or discouraged or sad, and all sorts of supernatural faculties were attributed to her, especially the gift of making uncanny predictions.

But, while Anne Sullivan took pains to keep her from being a prodigy, and no one found anything to expose, it was impossible to conceal the fact that she had a remarkable mind and even perhaps a still more remarkable will. Speaking of this, Emma Goldman [6] said she proved that the human will had "an almost illimitable power"; and what could one say of an intellect as handicapped as hers that, at eighteen, carried her so far in so many directions? If she did not master, she learned much of geometry, algebra, physics, with botany, zoology, and the philosophy that she knew well, while she wrote good letters in French, as later she spoke German, reading Latin too when she went to college. Unable to hear lectures or take notes, she graduated with honors at Radcliffe, where she wrote her autobiography in the class of Mr. Copeland, the famous "Copey" who said she showed that she could write better, in some of her work, than any other man or woman he had had as a pupil.

It was Anne Sullivan who had invented the methods of connecting mind with mind that made all this possible, of course—and that

[5] *Maurice Maeterlinck (1862–1949)* Belgian poet and dramatist, author of *The Blue Bird* and 1911 winner of the Nobel Prize in literature.
[6] *Emma Goldman* Russian-born anarchist who spent many years in America.

seemed to be "superhuman," as Einstein remarked; although Helen all but outstripped her perceptive teacher and retained all that she took in. Few of the required books were printed for the blind, and she had to have whole books spelled into her hand, while, always examining, observing, reflecting, surrounded by darkness and silence, she wrote that she found music and brightness within. Through all her thoughts flashed what she supposed was color. With her native traits of pluck and courage, energy, tenacity, she was tough-minded and independent also, and her only fear was of writing something that she had been told or that she had read, something that was not out of her own life and mind.

II

This was the girl who had evolved from the headstrong child whom Anne Sullivan had found in Alabama and whom she had taken at the age of eight to the Perkins Institution in Boston where Helen afterward visited off and on. There she encountered Laura Bridgman, the first deaf-and-dumb person who had ever been taught to communicate with her fellow-creatures, Dr. Howe's celebrated pupil whom Dickens had written about and who was a contrast indeed to the "young colt" Helen. Laura Bridgman was shocked, in fact, by her impulsive movements and rebuked her for being too forward, robust as she was, while the statue-like motionless Laura, with her cool hands, struck Helen as like a flower that has grown in the shade.

A much more interesting personality, and ruddily healthy from the start, Helen herself was to grow up fond of sports, riding a horse and a bicycle tandem, playing cards and chess and all but completely self-reliant. Moreover, she was never guarded from the knowledge of evil, and, fully informed as she always was about the seamy sides of life, the mind that she developed was realistic. Nothing could have been more tonic than Helen Keller's bringing up, under the guidance of Anne Sullivan, on the farm in Alabama. They read and studied out of doors on the river-bank, in the woods, in the fields, in the shade, as Helen remembered, of a wild tulip tree, and the fragrance of the mimosa blossoms, the pine needles, and the grapes were blended with all her early lessons. She learned about the sun and rain, and how birds build their nests, about squirrels, frogs, wild flowers, rabbits, and insects; and, as it came back to her, everything that sang or bloomed, buzzed or hummed was part of her education.

It might have been supposed, meanwhile, that the Perkins Institution also influenced Helen in various ways, for she carried through life what seemed to be the stamp of the reformist mind that the great Dr. Howe represented. An old Yankee abolitionist, Samuel Gridley Howe was concerned for all the desolate and all the oppressed, and Helen has written with the same indignation and grief about lynching and anti-Semitism and the case of Sacco and Vanzetti.[7] Usually on the unpopular side, and for years a follower of Debs,[8] she was almost a social outcast in certain circles when Mark Twain, who hated injustice—and was a special friend of hers—said there were worse things than being blind. It was worse to have eyes and not to see. Helen liked Mark Twain all the better because, as she wrote in *Midstream*, he did not temper his words to suit feminine ears, because "his talk was fragrant with tobacco and flamboyant with profanity," while, with his tender heart, he matched her tough mind. It pleased her when, bidding her good night, he said she would find in the bathroom not only Bourbon and Scotch but plenty of cigars.

She has become a world citizen who stands for the real America that public men so often misrepresent. She has understood Japan and Greece and especially perhaps the Bible lands, Egypt, Lebanon, Syria, Israel, where she has lectured at universities from Cairo to Jerusalem and where new schools for the blind have risen as she passed. Reaching out to meet the minds of all sorts and conditions of men, she comprehends their needs and aspirations, so that she is a true spokesman of our multiracial country that is already a vestibule of the coming "one world."

III

Now it happens that, living myself in Connecticut, not far from Helen Keller, I have taken a few notes about her in recent years, jotting down chance remarks of hers and other memoranda, comments that from time to time she has suggested. I offer some of these, unconnected as they are, as follows.

July 1945

Helen has been out picking blueberries today. She has only to touch them to know when they are ripe.

The paths and garden at her house are all so perfectly kept that I exclaimed over them. Helen does it. In summer she is up at five every morning, edging the driveway and the paths. She asks Herbert [Herbert Haas, who drives the car and runs the house] what she should do next. Then she weeds the flower beds. She distinguishes by touch between the flowers and the weeds.

Dinner with Helen and Salvemini at Professor Robert Pfeiffer's. Our Florentine hostess Mrs. Pfeiffer played an Italian song. Helen stood by with her left hand on the piano top, waving her right hand, keeping time. In this way she knows by heart Beethoven's "Ninth Symphony" and recognizes many other compositions.

---

[7] *Sacco and Vanzetti* Italian-born Americans who were executed for murder in 1927. The Sacco–Vanzetti affair was one of the most controversial cases of its time, for many Americans believed that the men were convicted because of their politics.

[8] *Eugene Debs* American Socialist leader.

Helen Keller at the age of eighteen, with her teacher Anne Sullivan

Someone asked her how she tells the difference between day and night. "Oh," she said, "in the day the air is lighter, odors are lighter, and there is more motion and more vibration in the atmosphere. At night there is less vibration; the air is dense and one feels less motion in things."

With Helen and Polly Thomson [Anne Sullivan's successor] in New York, at a small political meeting in the Hotel Astor. Maury Maverick was with us, just back from England, marveling over the work of the English surgeons in the war. Vice-President Truman had come up from Washington to make a short speech, and we were all introduced to him. Later Helen said, "He has an open hand. There are no crooks in his fingers." She grasps character instantly. Truman was deeply touched by Helen. He was in tears when she spoke to him.

September 1945

Today, more than usually, an air of Scotland pervades Helen's house. In the first place, it is called Arcan Ridge after an old farmhouse in the Scottish Highlands, and Polly Thomson, who has been with Helen since

1914, speaks with a livelier than ever Scottish accent. But this evening William Allan Neilson comes to dinner, the president of Smith College who was one of Helen's professors at Radcliffe and learned the manual alphabet to talk with her there. (He was one of my old professors at Harvard too, and now he is the only person living who, meeting me, aged sixty, invariably addresses me as "Boy.") Neilson still speaks broad Scots, almost every word with "hair on it," as Rudolph Ruzicka said of another Scotsman.

After dinner the talk fell on Scottish songs. Helen went upstairs to her study—for she knows her way perfectly about the house—and brought down a two-volume collection of Scottish songs in Braille which the publishers in Edinburgh had sent her. She read the table of contents with her fingers rapidly, found a song she wanted, turned the pages and read it out to us—a Highland "wail from Skye," as Polly put it.

With Helen and Polly to the harvest festival at the Jewish Theological Seminary far uptown in New York. Midday meal in the Sukkah, the festival tent set up in the quadrangle. The walls were hung with all the fruits of the season, or all the fruits of the Holy Land that are mentioned in the Bible. We sat with the president of the Seminary, Dr. Louis Finkelstein, and the famous Hebrew scholar, Dr. Saul Lieberman. For a moment I thought of the New Testament scene in in the Temple at Jerusalem, for Helen surprised these great Jewish doctors with her knowledge of the Bible. I remembered what she wrote in *Midstream*: she had read her Braille Bible so often that in many places the dots had been rubbed off.

Listening to the Hebrew grace with her fingers on Dr. Finkelstein's lips, she said, "It is like the voice of the Lord upon many waters, the Lord of Glory, thundering."

Then she said, "The Bible is the only book that reaches up to the times in which we live.

It speaks knowingly of the sun, the skies, the sea, and the beauty of distant stars. . . . There are no differences in men. Differences are only as the variation in shadows cast by the sun."

After lunch we rode down town in a Broadway bus to the Grand Central Station. Helen likes to feel the crowd around her. Suddenly she said, "There is a painter in the bus." I looked around and, sure enough, there was a house painter sitting in a corner at the other end of the bus, twenty feet away.

July 1946

Dinner at Helen's. She is ready for any adventure. We talked about the gypsies and Conrad Bercovici,[9] and I told her how Bercovici had taken me through the East Side one night where the gypsies were camping out in the cellars of old warehouses. Obliged to come into the city so that their children could go to school, they lived in these abandoned cellars just as they lived on the road in summer. They even set up tents and built campfires on the concrete floors, while their young women told fortunes on the streets.

In Polly's hand Helen's fingers rippled with excitement. She asked me to remind Bercovici of his promise to take her through the East Side and show her the gypsies.

October 1949

Helen comes to dinner. . . . One of our friends asked Helen how she had come to understand abstractions. She said she had found that good apples were sweet and that there were also bad apples that were bitter. Then she learned to think of the sweetness and bitterness apart from the apples. She grasped the idea of sweetness and bitterness in themselves.

The fact is that Helen has a philosophic mind. She relates in her little book *My Religion* how, when she was twelve or so,

[9] *Conrad Bercovici* An American writer.

she suddenly said to her teacher, "I have been in Athens." She meant, of course, in imagination, for she had been reading about Greece, but observe what followed in her thinking. She instantly perceived that the "realness" of her mind was independent of conditions of place and body, that she had vividly seen and felt a place thousands of miles away precisely because she had a mind. How else could one explain this being "in Athens"? From that moment, she continued, "Deafness and blindness were of no real account. They were to be relegated to the outer circle of my life."

Is not that real philosophy, the life of reason?

Christmas 1951

Helen has a way of bursting out with the most surprising remarks at table. Today she was full of Thucydides and the Peloponnesian war, about which she had been reading this Christmas morning. "What a stupid war!—the stupidest war in history," she said, shaking her head in mournful disapproval. She had been brooding and grieving over this war, which destroyed the democracy of Athens. For the rest, she was sure there was nothing about war that Thucydides did not know.

The other day she burst out about a certain Evelyn Cheesman, an English entomologist who had written wonderful things, she said, about insects. Helen had read her in one of the Braille magazines, no doubt—whether English, American, French, or German, for Helen reads them all.

Polly took her up. "What's this, Helen? Who is this Evelyn Cheesman?" Polly likes to tease her, and she is sometimes severe with her. For instance, if Helen makes a mistake in typewriting one of her letters Polly makes her copy the page again. (Usually Helen's typing is like an expert stenographer's, but the other day there were a few dim lines in one of her letters and she added this postscript: "Polly says the writing of this machine

doesn't please her critical eye. My apologies. H. K.")

To return to the lady entomologist, Helen is charmingly eager about these shining new bits of knowledge. She has the earnest innocence of a ten-year-old child. Often, on the other hand, she speaks like an oracle, or, as one might say, an Asiatic sage. In spite of her incessant work, much of her life is still spent in solitary meditation, alone in the dark with her own thoughts, or with the Bible or the classics; and, as she lives in her way as the old prophets lived in the desert, many of her words inspire a kind of reverential wonder. She naturally uses archaic and poetic expressions of the sort that children pick up in their reading, words that are seldom heard in the ordinary talk that she only hears when the ever-alert Polly passes it on to her.

(I must add, what all their friends know, that Polly is in her way as extraordinary a person as Helen. Without her vitality and her diplomatic sense what could Helen do in her journeys about the world? And what inexhaustible buoyancy both of them have! I have seen them together on a midnight train, when everyone else was asleep, smiling and chatting like birds on a branch in the morning.)

June 1953

Helen is seventy-three years old today. She lives much in eternity and much in history, but she only lives in time when she is able to keep up with the news. This week she returned from a two-months' absence in South America, and she has not had a moment yet to catch up with the newspapers and magazines.

What variety there is in her mind! She is interested in everything. One day she recalled to me the dancing of La Argentina, though how she conceived of this so well I cannot imagine. Another day she quoted at length from a poem by Robinson Jeffers, who once told me he had seen Helen's name in the register of a hotel in the Orkney Islands. And what happy phrases come to her mind. Some children spelled words into her hand and she said their small fingers were like "the wild flowers of conversation."

About Hellen Keller, it seems to me, William James [10] uttered the last word when he wrote, "The sum of it is that you are a *blessing*"; a verdict that has been ratified in hundreds of hospitals throughout the world where she has all but raised the dead. Some day the story will be told of the miracles she has performed, or what would have passed for miracles in less case-hardened ages, when the blind have opened inward eyes and really seen life for the first time after Helen Keller has walked and talked with them.

How many, meanwhile, may have thought of her while reading the colonel's soliloquy at the end of Arthur Koestler's *The Age of Longing*, observing that American women are all too busy "playing bridge" to be "cut out for the part of martyrs and saints. . . . American womanhood," the colonel went on, "has produced no Maid of Orleans, no Rosa Luxemburgs or Madame Curies, no Brontës or Florence Nightingales or Krupskayas," [11] and one might add that it seldom produces anyone as rash as various people who generalize about it. For how many types there are in our teeming population! One might easily suggest a list to set beside the list this fictional colonel has drawn from three or four countries. The names of Jane Addams and Emily Dickinson [12] would appear somewhere on such a list, and I dare say that for not a few the name of Helen Keller would figure as leading all the rest.

For Discussion

1. How does the story of Helen Keller remind the reader that he does not see all there is to see around him or hear all there is to hear?

2. Explain how it might be said that people with healthy eyes fail to see? For an experiment, blindfold a friend. Give him an unfamiliar object to explore with his hands. Record his description and compare it with a description made by a person who has seen the object.

3. Is there a greatness in Helen Keller apart from her success in the struggle to overcome her physical handicaps? Can you define it?

4. Does the story of Helen Keller evoke pity for a woman who has suffered a great deal? Does Helen Keller's life seem more rich and more exciting than that of most people? Why?

5. In the essay, "Three Days to See," Helen Keller writes, "We should live each day with a gentleness, a vigor, and a keenness of appreciation which are often lost when time stretches before us in the constant panorama of more days and months and years to come." Does this sound as if it had been spoken by a person who has been cut off from the sights and sounds of the world? Discuss this statement as a philosophy of life.

[11] *Maid of Orleans and so forth*   All women of action or achievement: *Maid of Orleans*—Joan of Arc; *Rosa Luxemburg*—Russian-born German revolutionist; *Madame Curie*—discoverer of radium; *Charlotte, Emily, and Anne Brontë*—English novelists; *Florence Nightingale* —British reformer of the nursing profession; *Krupskaya* —Russian revolutionist, wife of Lenin.

[10] *William James* Famous American psychologist, teacher, and writer.

[12] *Jane Addams and Emily Dickinson* American social reformer and American poet.

UNIT 4: DRAMA

Conflict and imitation are

the fundamentals of drama. Not action itself, but the *imitation* of an action makes a play. For the audience, drama provides a means of interpreting human experience and a means of sharing it as well. In all ages and in all cultures, men have devised ways of representing action: ritual dances, verse tragedies, slapstick comedies, radio plays, operas, puppet shows.

The roots of drama extend deep into primitive rituals. The ancient Greeks

159

gathered in the woods around a statue of the god Dionysus. From these ceremonies grew the forms of classical Greek tragedy and comedy. Centuries later, at Eastertime, Christians presented dramatizations of the stations of the Cross. These in time became the miracle and morality plays that entertained and instructed audiences gathered in the market places throughout the Middle Ages and the early Renaissance.

The forms of drama are many: they may or may not employ language, dancing, music, costumes, masks, scenery, or pantomime. A play may be as short as a two-minute humorous skit, or it may, like the classical Greek trilogies or the Passion Play at Oberammergau, take most of a day to perform. The theater itself may be anywhere: a completely equipped modern auditorium, an off-Broadway basement, a tent, or a platform in the open air. One thing remains common to all plays and to all theaters—they aim to satisfy man's need to cry, laugh, shudder at the spectacle of himself.

Ideally a play is not meant to be read, but to be performed. Here is the most obvious difference between the drama and other forms of literature. A play is meant to be "acted out," even if the theater happens to be only the mind of the reader. Some plays are said to "read" better than others. This means only that they are easier to visualize from the printed page. Of the two plays in this unit, Shaw's *Arms and the Man* probably loses less in print than does the Japanese Nōh play *The Dwarf Trees*. Shaw's characters move and speak in a realistic setting which most playgoers may imagine without difficulty. Unless one has had the rare opportunity of seeing a Japanese theater company in action, it is hard to imagine the kind of costumes, music, dancing, acting, singing, and pantomime that would go into an authentic performance of *The Dwarf Trees*.

It is difficult to judge the merits of a play merely from reading it. Most theatergoers have had the experience of finding that a play they thought dull in print suddenly comes to life in the hands of skillful actors. But plays can still be read. Over the centuries, for every person who has been fortunate enough to see a fine production of a play by Shakespeare, hundreds have delighted in reading his comedies, tragedies, and histories. In fact, critics sometimes believe (as with Shakespeare's *King Lear*) that a certain play is so great that no actual production could ever do it justice. The "ideal" production the reader stages in his own mind may be more exciting than any he is likely to see in a theater. Reading a play requires an active, creative participation on the part of the reader. For an hour or two, his study becomes a stage, and he himself is in turn actor, actress, choreographer, designer, and director.

The theater is a place of entertainment. But it is important to understand that even while a good play is entertaining, it may also be a serious comment on life. Moreover, a comedy by a writer such as Shakespeare, Molière, or Thornton Wilder may be every bit as "serious" as a tragedy or a play with an obvious social message. Oscar Wilde's *The Importance of Being Earnest* is a good example of this. An audience laughs its way through that comedy from beginning to end. It appears to be pure fun. Critics who have looked carefully at *The Importance of Being Earnest*, however, have found that its foolery is based on a sharp criticism of the artificial aspects of society. Even the bubbling operettas of Gilbert and Sullivan, *Pinafore, The Mikado*, and *Trial by Jury*, have a serious foundation.

The theater is a place in which the human race explores its own mind and soul. It is a place of spectacle, tears, horror, ideas, and laughter. Much that is presented in the name of theater is trash. But the list of the very greatest writers who have chosen the stage for their medium of expression includes such names as Sophocles, Shakespeare, Goethe, Lope de Vega, Molière, Chekhov, Pirandello, O'Casey, Eliot, Ibsen, Shaw, and O'Neill.

Arms and the Man

GEORGE BERNARD SHAW

Romantic and sentimental ideas about war and love are the subject of this comedy by George Bernard Shaw. With wit, laughter, and paradox he punctures these romantic notions as he forces his characters to throw away the attitudes they have found in books and to face the reality of their lives and actions. The conflict in Arms and the Man *is between the unique personalities of the characters and their own conventional social ideas.*

More than any previous playwright, Shaw brought ideas into the theater. His characters, however, do not merely sit around discussing those ideas. Rather, they embody conflicting concepts by their contrasting personalities. In this play two attitudes toward war are represented by the romantic, aristocrat Sergius, and the realistic commoner Bluntschli. Two attitudes toward love are found in the down-to-earth servant Louka and her romantic mistress Raina. Arms and the Man *abounds with comments on society, economics, and psychology. But to say this is to make the play sound like a solemn essay. It is not. Shaw's art lies in the fact that all his serious questions and comments are put forth as a light and amusing comedy about young people in love.*

Characters

CATHERINE, *an aristocratic Bulgarian lady, Raina's mother and Petkoff's wife*

RAINA, *a romantic young lady, engaged to Sergius*

LOUKA, *an ambitious servant girl*

BLUNTSCHLI, *a Swiss, serving as an officer in the Serbian army*

A RUSSIAN OFFICER, *on the Bulgarian side*

NICOLA, *a servant of the Petkoff's, in love with Louka*

PETKOFF, *a Major in the Bulgarian army, Raina's father and Catherine's husband*

SERGIUS SARANOFF, *a dashing, aristocratic Major in the Bulgarian army, engaged to Raina*

GEORGE BERNARD SHAW (*1856–1950*) *was born in Dublin, Ireland. Rebellious from the beginning, he left school at fourteen. At the age of twenty, he went to London where he became a journalist. He was the best music critic and dramatic critic of his time, championing the new music of Wagner and the new theater of Ibsen. It was not until he was in his late thirties that Shaw began to write for the stage. For years he struggled to have his "dramas of ideas" produced, for the theater of his day was almost entirely given over to trivial entertainment. Shaw was a reformer and propagandist. By shocking the public and by making it laugh, he aimed to make it think. All the social conventions of his time became targets for his wit. By 1915 he was an international celebrity, and in 1925 he won the Nobel Prize in literature. In all, he wrote close to fifty plays between 1892 and 1939. Among the best are* Saint Joan, Androcles and the Lion, Major Barbara, Pygmalion, Man and Superman, Candida, Heartbreak House, *and* Caesar and Cleopatra.

Act 1

Night: A lady's bedchamber in Bulgaria, in a small town near the Dragoman Pass, late in November in the year 1885. Through an open window with a little balcony a peak of the Balkans, wonderfully white and beautiful in the starlit snow, seems quite close at hand, though it is really miles away. The interior of the room is not like anything to be seen in the west of Europe. It is half rich Bulgarian, half cheap Viennese. Above the head of the bed, which stands against a little wall cutting off the left hand corner of the room, is a painted wooden shrine, blue and gold, with an ivory image of Christ, and a light hanging before it in a pierced metal ball suspended by three chains. The principal seat, placed towards the other side of the room and opposite the window, is a Turkish ottoman. The counterpaine and hangings of the bed, the window curtains, the little carpet, and all the ornamental textile fabrics in the room are oriental and gorgeous; the paper on the walls is occidental and paltry. The washstand, against the wall on the side nearest the ottoman and window, consists of an enamelled iron basin with a pail beneath it in a painted metal frame, and a single towel on the rail at the side. The dressing table, between the bed and the window, is a common pine table, covered with a cloth of many colours, with an expensive toilet mirror on it. The door is on the side nearest the bed; and there is a chest of drawers between. This chest of drawers is also covered by a variegated native cloth; and on it there is a pile of paper backed novels, a box of chocolate creams, and a miniature easel with a large photograph of an extremely handsome officer, whose lofty bearing and magnetic glance can be felt even from the portrait. The room is lighted by a candle on the chest of drawers, and another on the dressing table with a box of matches beside it.

The window is hinged doorwise and stands wide open. Outside, a pair of wooden shutters, opening outwards, also stand open. On the balcony a young lady, intensely conscious of the romantic beauty of the night, and of the fact that her own youth and beauty are part of it, is gazing at the snowy Balkans. She is in her nightgown, well covered by a long mantle of furs, worth, on a moderate estimate, about three times the furniture of the room.

Her reverie is interrupted by her mother, Catherine Petkoff, a woman over forty, imperiously energetic, with magnificent black hair and eyes, who might be a very splendid specimen of the wife of a mountain farmer, but is determined to be a Viennese lady, and to that end wears a fashionable tea gown on all occasions.

CATHERINE [*entering hastily, full of good news*]: Raina! [*She pronounces it Rah-eena, with the stress on the ee.*] Raina! [*She goes to the bed, expecting to find Raina there.*] Why, where—? [*Raina looks into the room.*] Heavens, child! are you out in the night air instead of in your bed? Youll [1] catch your death. Louka told me you were asleep.

RAINA [*dreamily*]:   I sent her away. I wanted to be alone. The stars are so beautiful! What is the matter?

CATHERINE: Such news! There has been a battle.

RAINA [*her eyes dilating*]: Ah! [*She comes eagerly to Catherine.*]

CATHERINE: A great battle at Slivnitza! A victory! And it was won by Sergius.

RAINA [*with a cry of delight*]: Ah! [*They embrace rapturously.*] Oh, mother! [*Then, with sudden anxiety*] is father safe?

CATHERINE: Of course! he sends me the news. Sergius is the hero of the hour, the idol of the regiment.

RAINA: Tell me, tell me. How was it? [*Ecstatically*] Oh, mother! mother! mother! [*She pulls her mother down on the ottoman; and they kiss one another frantically.*]

CATHERINE [*with surging enthusiasm*]:   You cant guess how splendid it is. A cavalry charge! think of that! He defied our Russian commanders [2]—acted without orders—led a charge on his own responsibility—headed it himself—was the first man to sweep through their guns. Cant you see it, Raina: our gallant splendid Bulgarians with their swords and eyes flashing, thundering down like an avalanche and scattering the wretched Serbs and their dandified Austrian officers like chaff. And you! you kept Sergius waiting a year before you would be betrothed to him. Oh, if you have a drop of Bulgarian blood in your veins, you will worship him when he comes back.

RAINA: What will he care for my poor little worship after the acclamations of a whole army of heroes? But no matter: I am so happy! so proud! [*She rises and walks about excitedly.*] It proves that all our ideas were real after all.

CATHERINE [*indignantly*]:   Our ideas real! What do you mean?

RAINA: Our ideas of what Sergius would do. Our patriotism. Our heroic ideals. I sometimes used to doubt whether they were anything but dreams. Oh, what faithless little creatures girls are! When I buckled on Sergius's sword he looked so noble: it was treason to think of disillusion or humiliation or failure. And yet—and yet—[*She sits down again suddenly.*] Promise me youll never tell him.

1 *youll*   Shaw had very personal ideas about spelling: he wrote *youll* for *you'll*, *dont* for *don't*, and so forth. In this book, the editors have followed Shaw's own text.

2 *our Russian commanders*   During the latter part of the nineteenth century, Bulgaria was struggling for its independence from the Serbs and Turks. In the wars that form a background for this play, the Austrians were aiding the Serbs and the Russians were aiding the Bulgarians.

CATHERINE: Dont ask me for promises until I know what I'm promising.

RAINA: Well, it came into my head just as he was holding me in his arms and looking into my eyes, that perhaps we only had our heroic ideas because we are so fond of reading Byron and Pushkin,[3] and because we were so delighted with the opera that season at Bucharest. Real life is so seldom like that! indeed never, as far as I knew it then. [*Remorsefully*] Only think, mother: I doubted him: I wondered whether all his heroic qualities and his soldiership might not prove mere imagination when he went into a real battle. I had an uneasy fear that he might cut a poor figure there beside all those clever officers from the Tsar's court.

CATHERINE: A poor figure! Shame on you! The Serbs have Austrian officers who are just as clever as the Russians; but we have beaten them in every battle for all that.

RAINA [*laughing and snuggling against her mother*]: Yes: I was only a prosaic little coward. Oh, to think that it was all true! that Sergius is just as splendid and noble as he looks! that the world is really a glorious world for women who can see its glory and men who can act its romance! What happiness! what unspeakable fulfilment!

They are interrupted by the entry of Louka, a handsome proud girl in a pretty Bulgarian peasant's dress with double apron, so defiant that her servility to Raina is almost insolent. She is afraid of Catherine, but even with her goes as far as she dares.

LOUKA: If you please, madam, all the windows are to be closed and the shutters made fast. They say there may be shooting in the streets. [*Raina and Catherine rise together, alarmed.*] The Serbs are being chased right back through the pass; and they say they may

---

[3] *Byron and Pushkin* Pushkin, the great Russian poet, and Lord Byron, the English poet, both wrote highly romantic works from which Raina has devised her ideas about life.

---

run into the town. Our cavalry will be after them; and our people will be ready for them, you may be sure, now theyre running away. [*She goes out on the balcony, and pulls the outside shutters to; then steps back into the room.*]

CATHERINE [*businesslike, housekeeping instincts aroused*]: I must see that everything is made safe downstairs.

RAINA: I wish our people were not so cruel. What glory is there in killing wretched fugitives?

CATHERINE: Cruel! Do you suppose they would hesitate to kill you—or worse?

RAINA [*to Louka*]: Leave the shutters so that I can just close them if I hear any noise.

CATHERINE [*authoritatively, turning on her way to the door*]: Oh no, dear: you must keep them fastened. You would be sure to drop off to sleep and leave them open. Make them fast, Louka.

LOUKA: Yes, madam. [*She fastens them.*]

RAINA: Dont be anxious about me. The moment I hear a shot, I shall blow out the candles and roll myself up in bed with my ears well covered.

CATHERINE: Quite the wisest thing you can do, my love. Goodnight.

RAINA: Goodnight. [*Her emotion comes back for a moment.*] Wish me joy. [*They kiss.*] This is the happiest night of my life—if only there are no fugitives.

CATHERINE: Go to bed, dear; and dont think of them. [*She goes out.*]

LOUKA [*secretly to Raina*]: If you would like the shutters open, just give them a push like this. [*She pushes them: they open: she pulls them to again.*] One of them ought to be bolted at the bottom; but the bolt's gone.

RAINA [*with dignity, reproving her*]: Thanks, Louka; but we must do what we are told. [*Louka makes a grimace.*] Goodnight.

LOUKA [*carelessly*]: Goodnight. [*She goes out, swaggering.*]

Raina, left alone, takes off her fur cloak and

throws it on the ottoman. Then she goes to the chest of drawers, and adores the portrait there with feelings that are beyond all expression. She does not kiss it or press it to her breast, or shew[4] it any mark of bodily affection; but she takes it in her hands and elevates it, like a priestess.

RAINA [*looking up at the picture*]: Oh, I shall never be unworthy of you any more, my soul's hero: never, never, never. [*She replaces it reverently. Then she selects a novel from the little pile of books. She turns over the leaves dreamily; finds her page; turns the book inside out at it; and, with a happy sigh, gets into bed and prepares to read herself to sleep. But before abandoning herself to fiction, she raises her eyes once more, thinking of the blessed reality, and murmurs.*] My hero! my hero!

A distant shot breaks the quiet of the night. She starts, listening; and two more shots, much nearer, follow, startling her so that she scrambles out of bed, and hastily blows out the candle on the chest of drawers. Then, putting her fingers in her ears, she runs to the dressing table, blows out the light there, and hurries back to bed in the dark, nothing being visible but the glimmer of the light in the pierced ball before the image, and the starlight seen through the slits at the top of the shutters. The firing breaks out again: there is a startling fusillade quite close at hand. Whilst it is still echoing, the shutters disappear, pulled open from without; and for an instant the rectangle of snowy starlight flashes out with the figure of a man silhouetted in black upon it. The shutters close immediately; and the room is dark again. But the silence is now broken by the sound of panting. Then there is a scratch; and the flame of a match is seen in the middle of the room.

RAINA [*crouching on the bed*]: Who's there? [*The match is out instantly.*] Who's there? Who is that?

[4] *shew* Shaw preferred this spelling for "show."

A MAN'S VOICE [*in the darkness, subduedly, but threateningly*]: Sh—sh! Dont call out; or youll be shot. Be good; and no harm will happen to you. [*She is heard leaving her bed, and making for the door.*] Take care: it's no use trying to run away.

RAINA: But who—

THE VOICE [*warning*]: Remember: if you raise your voice my revolver will go off. [*Commandingly*] Strike a light and let me see you. Do you hear. [*Another moment of silence and darkness as she retreats to the chest of drawers. Then she lights a candle; and the mystery is at an end. He is a man of about 35, in a deplorable plight, bespattered with mud and blood and snow, his belt and the strap of his revolver case keeping together the torn ruins of the blue tunic of a Serbian artillery officer. All that the candlelight and his unwashed unkempt condition make it possible to discern is that he is of middling stature and undistinguished appearance, with strong neck and shoulders, roundish obstinate looking head covered with short crisp bronze curls, clear quick eyes and good brows and mouth, hopelessly prosaic nose like that of a strong minded baby, trim soldierlike carriage and energetic manner, and with all his wits about him in spite of his desperate predicament: even with a sense of the humor of it, without, however, the least intention of trifling with it or throwing away a chance. Reckoning up what he can guess about Raina: her age, her social position, her character, and the extent to which she is frightened, he continues, more politely but still most determinedly.*] Excuse my disturbing you; but you recognize my uniform? Serb! If I'm caught I shall be killed. [*Menacingly*] Do you understand that?

RAINA: Yes.

THE MAN: Well, I don't intend to get killed if I can help it. [*Still more formidably*] Do you understand that? [*He locks the door quickly but quietly.*]

RAINA [*disdainfully*]: I suppose not. [*She draws herself up superbly, and looks him straight in the face, adding, with cutting emphasis*] Some soldiers, I know, are afraid to die.

THE MAN [*with grim goodhumor*]: All of them, dear lady, all of them, believe me. It is our duty to live as long as we can. Now, if you raise an alarm—

RAINA [*cutting him short*]: You will shoot me. How do you know that *I* am afraid to die?

THE MAN [*cunningly*]: Ah; but suppose I dont shoot you, what will happen then? A lot of your cavalry will burst into this pretty room of yours and slaughter me here like a pig; for I'll fight like a demon: they shant get me into the street to amuse themselves with: I know what they are. Are you prepared to receive that sort of company in your present undress? [*Raina, suddenly conscious of her nightgown, instinctively shrinks and gathers it more closely about her neck. He watches her and adds pitilessly*] Hardly presentable, eh? [*She turns to the ottoman. He raises his pistol instantly, and cries*] Stop! [*She stops.*] Where are you going?

RAINA [*with dignified patience*]: Only to get my cloak.

THE MAN [*passing swiftly to the ottoman and snatching the cloak*]: A good idea! I'll keep the cloak; and you'll take care that nobody comes in and sees you without it. This is a better weapon than the revolver: eh? [*He throws the pistol down on the ottoman.*]

RAINA [*revolted*]: It is not the weapon of a gentleman!

THE MAN: It's good enough for a man with only you to stand between him and death. [*As they look at one another for a moment, Raina hardly able to believe that even a Serbian officer can be so cynically and self-ishly unchivalrous, they are startled by a sharp fusillade in the street. The chill of imminent death hushes the man's voice as he adds*] Do you hear? If you are going to bring those blackguards in on me you shall receive them as you are.

Clamor and disturbance. The pursuers in the street batter at the house door, shouting Open the door! Open the door! Wake up, will you! *A man servant's voice calls to them angrily from within* This is Major Petkoff's house: you cant come in here; *but a renewal of the clamor, and a torrent of blows on the door, end with his letting a chain down with a clank, followed by a rush of heavy footsteps and a din of triumphant yells, dominated at last by the voice of Catherine, indignantly addressing an officer with* What does this mean, sir? Do you know where you are? *The noise subsides suddenly.*

LOUKA [*outside, knocking at the bedroom door*]: My lady! my lady! get up quick and open the door. If you dont they will break it down.

The fugitive throws up his head with the gesture of a man who sees that it is all over with him, and drops the manner he has been assuming to intimidate Raina.

THE MAN [*sincerely and kindly*]: No use, dear: I'm done for. [*Flinging the cloak to her*] Quick! wrap yourself up: they're coming.

RAINA. Oh, thank you: [*She wraps herself up with intense relief.*]

THE MAN [*between his teeth*]: Dont mention it.

RAINA [*anxiously*]: What will you do?

THE MAN [*grimly*]: The first man in will find out. Keep out of the way; and dont look. It won't last long; but it will not be nice. [*He draws his sabre and faces the door, waiting.*]

RAINA [*impulsively*]: I'll help you. I'll save you.

THE MAN: You cant.

RAINA: I can. I'll hide you. [*She drags him towards the window.*] Here! behind the curtains.

THE MAN [*yielding to her*]: Theres just half a chance, if you keep your head.

RAINA [*drawing the curtain before him*]: S-sh! [*She makes for the ottoman.*]

THE MAN [*putting out his head*]: Remember—

RAINA [*running back to him*]: Yes?

THE MAN: —nine soldiers out of ten are born fools.

RAINA: Oh! [*She draws the curtain angrily before him.*]

THE MAN [*looking out at the other side*]: If they find me, I promise you a fight: a devil of a fight.

She stamps at him. He disappears hastily. She takes off her cloak, and throws it across the foot of the bed. Then, with a sleepy, disturbed air, she opens the door. Louka enters excitedly.

LOUKA: One of those beasts of Serbs has been seen climbing up the waterpipe to your balcony. Our men want to search for him; and they are so wild and drunk and furious. [*She makes for the other side of the room to get as far from the door as possible.*] My lady says you are to dress at once and to—[*She sees the revolver lying on the ottoman, and stops petrified.*]

RAINA [*as if annoyed at being disturbed*]: They shall not search here. Why have they been let in?

CATHERINE [*coming in hastily*]: Raina, darling, are you safe? Have you seen anyone or heard anything?

RAINA: I heard the shooting. Surely the soldiers will not dare come in here?

CATHERINE: I have found a Russian officer, thank Heaven: he knows Sergius. [*Speaking through the door to someone outside*] Sir: will you come in now. My daughter will receive you.

A young Russian officer, in Bulgarian uniform. enters, sword in hand.

OFFICER [*with soft feline politeness and stiff military carriage*]: Good evening, gracious lady. I am sorry to intrude; but there is a Serb hiding on the balcony. Will you and the gracious lady your mother please to withdraw whilst we search?

RAINA [*petulantly*]: Nonsense, sir: you can see that there is no one on the balcony. [*She throws the shutters wide open and stands with her back to the curtain where the man is hidden, pointing to the moonlit balcony. A couple of shots are fired right under the window; and a bullet shatters the glass opposite Raina, who winks and gasps, but stands her ground; whilst Catherine screams, and the officer, with a cry of* Take care! *rushes to the balcony.*]

THE OFFICER [*on the balcony, shouting savagely down to the street*] Cease firing there, you fools: do you hear? Cease firing! [*He glares down for a moment; then turns to Raina, trying to resume his polite manner.*] Could anyone have got in without your knowledge? Were you asleep?

RAINA. No: I have not been to bed.

THE OFFICER [*impatiently, coming back into the room*]: Your neighbors have their heads so full of runaway Serbs that they see them everywhere. [*Politely*] Gracious lady: a thousand pardons. Goodnight. [*Military bow, which Raina returns coldly. Another to Catherine, who follows him out.*]

Raina closes the shutters. She turns and sees Louka, who has been watching the scene curiously.

RAINA: Dont leave my mother, Louka, until the soldiers go away.

Louka glances at Raina, at the ottoman, at the curtain; then purses her lips secretively, laughs insolently, and goes out. Raina, highly offended by this demonstration, follows her to the door, and shuts it behind her with a slam, locking it violently. The man immediately steps out from behind the curtain, sheathing his sabre. Then, dismissing the danger from his mind in a businesslike way, he comes affably to Raina.

THE MAN: A narrow shave; but a miss is as good as a mile. Dear young lady: your servant to the death. I wish for your sake I had joined the Bulgarian army instead of the other one. I am not a native Serb.

RAINA [*haughtily*]: No: you are one of the Austrians who set the Serbs on to rob us of our national liberty, and who officer their army for them. We hate them!

THE MAN: Austrian! not I. Dont hate me, dear young lady. I am a Swiss, fighting merely as a professional soldier. I joined the Serbs because they came first on the road from Switzerland. Be generous: youve beaten us hollow.

RAINA: Have I not been generous?

THE MAN: Noble! Heroic! But I'm not saved yet. This particular rush will soon pass through; but the pursuit will go on all night by fits and starts. I must take my chance to get off in a quiet interval. [*Pleasantly*] You don't mind my waiting just a minute or two, do you?

RAINA [*putting on her most genteel society manner*]: Oh, not at all. Wont you sit down?

THE MAN: Thanks. [*He sits on the foot of the bed.*]

  Raina walks with studied elegance to the ottoman and sits down. Unfortunately she sits on the pistol, and jumps up with a shriek. The man, all nerves, shies like a frightened horse to the other side of the room.

THE MAN [*irritably*]: Dont frighten me like that. What is it?

RAINA: Your revolver! It was staring that officer in the face all the time. What an escape!

THE MAN [*vexed at being unnecessarily terrified*]: Oh, is that all?

RAINA [*staring at him rather superciliously as she conceives a poorer and poorer opinion of him, and feels proportionately more and more at her ease*]: I am sorry I frightened you. [*She takes up the pistol and hands it to him.*] Pray take it to protect yourself against me.

THE MAN [*grinning wearily at the sarcasm as he takes the pistol*]: No use, dear young lady: there's nothing in it. It's not loaded. [*He*

makes a grimace at it, and drops it despairingly into his revolver case.]

RAINA: Load it by all means.

THE MAN: Ive no ammunition. What use are cartridges in battle? I always carry chocolate instead; and I finished the last cake of that hours ago.

RAINA [*outraged in her most cherished ideals of manhood*]: Chocolate! Do you stuff your pockets with sweets—like a schoolboy—even in the field?

THE MAN [*grinning*]: Yes: isnt it contemptible? [*Hungrily*] I wish I had some now.

RAINA: Allow me. [*She sails away scornfully to the chest of drawers, and returns with the box of confectionery in her hand.*] I am sorry I have eaten them all except these. [*She offers him the box.*]

THE MAN [*ravenously*]: Youre an angel! [*He gobbles the contents.*] Creams! Delicious! [*He looks anxiously to see whether there are any more. There are none: he can only scrape the box with his fingers and suck them. When that nourishment is exhausted he accepts the inevitable with pathetic goodhumor, and says, with grateful emotion*] Bless you, dear lady! You can always tell an old soldier by the inside of his holsters and cartridge boxes. The young ones carry pistols and cartridges: the old ones, grub. Thank you. [*He hands back the box. She snatches it contemptuously from him and throws it away. He shies again, as if she had meant to strike him.*] Ugh! Dont do things so suddenly, gracious lady. It's mean to revenge yourself because I frightened you just now.

RAINA [*loftily*]: Frighten me! Do you know, sir, that though I am only a woman, I think I am at heart as brave as you.

THE MAN: I should think so. You havnt been under fire for three days as I have. I can stand two days without shewing it much; but no man can stand three days: I'm as nervous as a mouse. [*He sits down on the ottoman, and takes his head in his hands.*] Would you like to see me cry?

RAINA [*alarmed*]: No.

THE MAN: If you would, all you have to do is to scold me just as if I were a little boy and you my nurse. If I were in camp now, theyd play all sorts of tricks on me.

RAINA [*a little moved*]: I'm sorry. I wont scold you. [*Touched by the sympathy in her tone, he raises his head and looks gratefully at her: she immediately draws back and says stiffly.*] You must excuse me: our soldiers are not like that. [*She moves away from the ottoman.*]

THE MAN: Oh yes they are. There are only two sorts of soldiers: old ones and young ones. I've served fourteen years: half of your fellows never smelt powder before. Why, how is it that youve just beaten us? Sheer ignorance of the art of war, nothing else. [*Indignantly*] I never saw anything so unprofessional.

RAINA [*ironically*]: Oh! was it unprofessional to beat you?

THE MAN: Well, come! is it professional to throw a regiment of cavalry on a battery of machine guns, with the dead certainty that if the guns go off not a horse or man will ever get within fifty yards of the fire? I couldn't believe my eyes when I saw it.

RAINA [*eagerly turning to him, as all her enthusiasm and her dreams of glory rush back on her*]: Did you see the great cavalry charge? Oh, tell me about it. Describe it to me.

THE MAN: You never saw a cavalry charge, did you?

RAINA: How could I?

THE MAN: Ah, perhaps not. No: of course not! Well, it's a funny sight. It's like slinging a handful of peas against a window pane: first one comes; then two or three close behind him; and then all the rest in a lump.

RAINA [*her eyes dilating as she raises her clasped hands ecstatically*]: Yes, first One! the bravest of the brave!

THE MAN [*prosaically*]: Hm! you should see the poor devil pulling at his horse.

RAINA: Why should he pull at his horse?

THE MAN [*impatient of so stupid a question*]: It's running away with him, of course: do you suppose the fellow wants to get there before the others and be killed? Then they all come. You can tell the young ones by their wildness and their slashing. The old ones come bunched up under the number one guard: they know that theyre mere projectiles, and that it's no use trying to fight. The wounds are mostly broken knees, from the horses cannoning together.

RAINA: Ugh! But I dont believe the first man is a coward. I know he is a hero!

THE MAN [*goodhumoredly*]: Thats what youd have said if youd seen the first man in the charge today.

RAINA [*breathless, forgiving him everything*]: Ah, I knew it! Tell me. Tell me about him.

THE MAN: He did it like an operatic tenor. A regular handsome fellow, with flashing eyes and lovely moustache, shouting his warcry and charging like Don Quixote at the windmills. We did laugh.

RAINA: You dared to laugh!

THE MAN: Yes; but when the sergeant ran up as white as a sheet, and told us theyd sent us the wrong ammunition, and that we couldnt fire a round for the next ten minutes, we laughed at the other side of our mouths. I never felt so sick in my life; though Ive been in one or two very tight places. And I hadnt even a revolver cartridge: only chocolate. We'd no bayonets: nothing. Of course, they just cut us to bits. And there was Don Quixote flourishing like a drum major, thinking he'd done the cleverest thing ever known, whereas he ought to be courtmartialled for it. Of all the fools ever let loose on a field of battle, that man must be the very maddest. He and his regiment simply committed suicide; only the pistol missed fire: thats all.

RAINA [*deeply wounded, but steadfastly loyal to her ideals*]: Indeed! Would you know him again if you saw him?

THE MAN: Shall I ever forget him!

She again goes to the chest of drawers. He watches her with a vague hope that she may have something more for him to eat. She takes the portrait from its stand and brings it to him.

RAINA: That is a photograph of the gentleman—the patriot and hero—to whom I am betrothed.

THE MAN [*recognizing it with a shock*]:   I'm really very sorry. [*Looking at her*] Was it fair to lead me on? [*He looks at the portrait again.*] Yes: thats Don Quixote: not a doubt of it. [*He stifles a laugh.*]

RAINA [*quickly*]:   Why do you laugh?

THE MAN [*apologetic, but still greatly tickled*]:   I didnt laugh, I assure you. At least I didnt mean to. But when I think of him charging the windmills and imagining he was doing the finest thing—[*He chokes with suppressed laughter.*]

RAINA [*sternly*]:   Give me back the portrait, sir.

THE MAN [*with sincere remorse*]:   Of course. Certainly. I'm really very sorry. [*He hands her the picture. She deliberately kisses it and looks him straight in the face before returning to the chest of drawers to replace it. He follows her, apologizing.*] Perhaps I'm quite wrong, you know: no doubt I am. Most likely he had got wind of the cartridge business somehow, and knew it was a safe job.

RAINA: That is to say, he was a pretender and a coward! You did not dare say that before.

THE MAN [*with a comic gesture of despair*]:   It's no use, dear lady: I cant make you see it from the professional point of view. [*As he turns away to get back to the ottoman, a couple of distant shots threaten renewed trouble.*]

RAINA [*sternly, as she sees him listening to the shots*]:   So much the better for you!

THE MAN [*turning*]:   How?

RAINA: You are my enemy; and you are at my mercy. What would I do if I were a professional soldier?

THE MAN: Ah, true, dear young lady: youre always right. I know how good youve been to me: to my last hour I shall remember those three chocolate creams. It was unsoldierly; but it was angelic.

RAINA [*coldly*]:   Thank you. And now I will do a soldierly thing. You cannot stay here after what you have just said about my future husband; but I will go out on the balcony and see whether it is safe for you to climb down into the street. [*She turns to the window.*]

THE MAN [*changing countenance*]:   Down that waterpipe! Stop! Wait! I cant! I darent! The very thought of it makes me giddy. I came up it fast enough with death behind me. But to face it now in cold blood—! [*He sinks on the ottoman.*] It's no use: I give up: I'm beaten. Give the alarm. [*He drops his head on his hands in the deepest dejection.*]

RAINA [*disarmed by pity*]:   Come: don't be disheartened. [*She stoops over him almost maternally: he shakes his head.*] Oh, you are a very poor soldier: a chocolate cream soldier! Come, cheer up! it takes less courage to climb down than to face capture: remember that.

THE MAN [*dreamily, lulled by her voice*]:   No: capture only means death; and death is sleep: oh, sleep, sleep, sleep, undisturbed sleep! Climbing down the pipe means doing something—exerting myself—thinking! Death ten times over first.

RAINA [*softly and wonderingly, catching the rhythm of his weariness*]:   Are you as sleepy as that?

THE MAN: Ive not had two hours undisturbed sleep since I joined. I havnt closed my eyes for forty-eight hours.

RAINA [*at her wit's end*]:   But what am I to do with you?

THE MAN [*staggering up, roused by her desperation*]:   Of course. I must do something. [*He shakes himself; pulls himself together; and speaks with rallied vigor and courage.*] You see, sleep or no sleep, hunger or no hunger, tired or not tired, you can always do a thing when you know it must be done. Well, that pipe must be got down: [*He hits himself on the chest.*] do you hear that, you chocolate cream soldier? [*He turns to the window.*]

RAINA [*anxiously*]: But if you fall?

THE MAN. I shall sleep as if the stones were a feather bed. Goodbye. [*He makes boldly for the window; and his hand is on the shutter when there is a terrible burst of firing in the street beneath.*]

RAINA [*rushing to him*]: Stop! [*She seizes him recklessly, and pulls him quite round.*] Theyll kill you.

THE MAN [*coolly, but attentively*]: Never mind: this sort of thing is all in my day's work. I'm bound to take my chance. [*Decisively*] Now do what I tell you. Put out the candle; so that they shant see the light when I open the shutters. And keep away from the window, whatever you do. If they see me theyre sure to have a shot at me.

RAINA [*clinging to him*]: Theyre sure to see you: it's bright moonlight. I'll save you. Oh, how can you be so indifferent! You want me to save you, dont you?

THE MAN: I really dont want to be troublesome. [*She shakes him in her impatience.*] I am not indifferent, dear young lady, I assure you. But how is it to be done?

RAINA: Come away from the window. [*She takes him firmly back to the middle of the room. The moment she releases him he turns mechanically towards the window again. She seizes him and turns him back, exclaiming*] Please! [*He becomes motionless, like a hypnotized rabbit, his fatigue gaining fast on him. She releases him, and addresses him patronizingly.*] Now listen. You must trust to our hospitality. You do not yet know in whose house you are. I am a Petkoff.

THE MAN: A pet what?

RAINA [*rather indignantly*]: I mean that I belong to the family of the Petkoffs, the richest and best known in our country.

THE MAN: Oh yes, of course. I beg your pardon. The Petkoffs, to be sure. How stupid of me!

RAINA: You know you never heard of them until this moment. How can you stoop to pretend!

THE MAN: Forgive me: I'm too tired to think; and the change of subject was too much for me. Dont scold me.

RAINA: I forgot. It might make you cry. [*He nods quite seriously. She pouts and then resumes her patronizing tone.*] I must tell you that my father holds the highest command of any Bulgarian in our army. He is [*proudly*] a Major.

THE MAN [*pretending to be deeply impressed*]: A Major! Bless me! Think of that!

RAINA: You shewed great ignorance in thinking that it was necessary to climb up to the balcony because ours is the only private house that has two rows of windows. There is a flight of stairs inside to get up and down by.

THE MAN: Stairs! How grand! You live in great luxury indeed, dear young lady.

RAINA: Do you know what a library is?

THE MAN: A library? A roomful of books?

RAINA: Yes. We have one, the only one in Bulgaria.

THE MAN: Actually a real library! I should like to see that.

RAINA [*affectedly*]: I tell you these things to shew you that you are not in the house of ignorant country folk who would kill you the moment they saw your Serbian uniform, but among civilized people. We go to Bucharest every year for the opera season; and I have spent a whole month in Vienna.

THE MAN: I saw that, dear young lady. I saw at once that you knew the world.

RAINA: Have you ever seen the opera of Ernani? [5]

THE MAN: Is that the one with the devil in it in red velvet, and a soldiers' chorus?

RAINA [*contemptuously*]: No!

[5] *Ernani* Verdi's opera was based on a highly romantic play by Victor Hugo.

THE MAN [*stifling a heavy sigh of weariness*]: Then I dont know it.

RAINA: I thought you might have remembered the great scene where Ernani, flying from his foes just as you are tonight, takes refuge in the castle of his bitterest enemy, an old Castilian noble. The noble refuses to give him up. His guest is sacred to him.

THE MAN [*quickly, waking up a little*]: Have your people got that notion?

RAINA [*with dignity*]: My mother and I can understand that notion, as you call it. And if instead of threatening me with your pistol as you did you had simply thrown yourself as a fugitive on our hospitality, you would have been as safe as in your father's house.

THE MAN: Quite sure?

RAINA [*turning her back on him in disgust*]: Oh, it is useless to try to make you understand.

THE MAN: Dont be angry: you see how awkward it would be for me if there was any mistake. My father is a very hospitable man: he keeps six hotels; but I couldnt trust him as far as that. What about your father?

RAINA: He is away at Slivnitza fighting for his country. I answer for your safety. There is my hand in pledge of it. Will that reassure you? [*She offers him her hand.*]

THE MAN [*looking dubiously at his own hand*]: Better not touch my hand, dear young lady. I must have a wash first.

RAINA [*touched*]: That is very nice of you. I see that you are a gentleman.

THE MAN [*puzzled*]: Eh?

RAINA: You must not think I am surprised. Bulgarians of really good standing—people in our position—wash their hands nearly every day. So you see I can appreciate your delicacy. You may take my hand. [*She offers it again.*]

THE MAN [*kissing it with his hands behind his back*]: Thanks, gracious young lady: I feel safe at last. And now would you mind breaking the news to your mother? I had better not stay here secretly longer than is necessary.

RAINA: If you will be so good as to keep perfectly still whilst I am away.

THE MAN: Certainly. [*He sits down on the ottoman.*]

Raina goes to the bed and wraps herself in the fur cloak. His eyes close. She goes to the door. Turning for a last look at him, she sees that he is dropping off to sleep.

RAINA [*at the door*]: You are not going asleep, are you? [*He murmurs inarticulately: she runs to him and shakes him.*] Do you hear? Wake up: you are falling asleep.

THE MAN: Eh? Falling aslee—? Oh no: not the least in the world: I was only thinking. It's all right: I'm wide awake.

RAINA [*severely*]: Will you please stand up while I am away. [*He rises reluctantly.*] All the time, mind.

THE MAN [*standing unsteadily*]: Certainly. Certainly: you may depend on me.

Raina looks doubtfully at him. He smiles weakly. She goes reluctantly, turning again at the door, and almost catching him in the act of yawning. She goes out.

THE MAN [*drowsily*]: Sleep, sleep, sleep, sleep, slee—[*The words trail off into a murmur. He wakes again with a shock on the point of falling.*] Where am I? Thats what I want to know: where am I? Must keep awake. Nothing keeps me awake except danger: remember that: [*intently*] danger, danger, danger, dan—[*trailing off again: another shock*] Wheres danger? Mus' find it. [*He starts off vaguely round the room in search of it.*] What am I looking for? Sleep—danger—dont know. [*He stumbles against the bed.*] Ah yes: now I know. All right now. I'm to go to bed, but not to sleep. Be sure not to sleep, because of danger. Not to lie down either, only sit down. [*He sits on the bed. A blissful expression comes into his face.*] Ah! [*With a happy sigh he sinks back at full length; lifts his boots into the bed with a final effort; and falls fast asleep instantly.*]

Catherine comes in, followed by Raina.

RAINA [*looking at the ottoman*]: He's gone! I left him here.

CATHERINE: Here! Then he must have climbed down from the—

RAINA [*seeing him*]: Oh! [*She points.*]

CATHERINE [*scandalized*]: Well! [*She strides to the bed, Raina following until she is opposite her on the other side.*] He's fast asleep. The brute!

RAINA [*anxiously*]: Sh!

CATHERINE [*shaking him*]: Sir! [*Shaking him again, harder*] Sir! [*Vehemently, shaking very hard*] Sir!!!

RAINA [*catching her arm*]: Dont, mamma; the poor darling is worn out. Let him sleep.

CATHERINE [*letting him go. and turning amazed to Raina*]: The poor darling! Raina!!! [*She looks sternly at her daughter.*]

The man sleeps profoundly.

Act II

The sixth of March, 1886. In the garden of Major Petkoff's house. It is a fine spring morning: the garden looks fresh and pretty. Beyond the paling the tops of a couple of minarets can be seen, shewing that there is a valley there, with the little town in it. A few miles further the Balkan mountains rise and shut in the landscape. Looking towards them from within the garden, the side of the house is seen on the left, with a garden door reached by a little flight of steps. On the right the stable yard, with its gateway, encroaches on the garden. There are fruit bushes along the paling and house, covered with washing spread out to dry. A path runs by the house, and rises by two steps at the corner, where it turns out of sight. In the middle, a small table, with two bent wood chairs at it, is laid for breakfast with Turkish coffee pot, cups, rolls, etc.; but the cups have been used and the bread broken. There is a wooden garden seat against the wall on the right.

Louka is standing between the table and the house, turning her back with angry disdain on a man servant who is lecturing her. He is a middle-aged man of cool temperament and low but clear and keen intelligence, with the complacency of the servant who values himself on his rank in servitude, and the imperturbability of the accurate calculator who has no illusions. He wears a white Bulgarian costume: jacket with embroidered border, sash, wide knickerbockers, and decorated gaiters. His head is shaved up to the crown, giving him a high Japanese forehead. His name is Nicola.

NICOLA: Be warned in time, Louka: mend your manners. I know the mistress. She is so grand that she never dreams that any servant could dare be disrespectful to her; but if she once suspects that you are defying her, out you go.

LOUKA: I do defy her. I will defy her. What do I care for her?

NICOLA: If you quarrel with the family, I never can marry you. It's the same as if you quarrelled with me!

LOUKA: You take her part against me, do you?

NICOLA [*sedately*]: I shall always be dependent on the good will of the family. When I leave their service and start a shop in Sofia, their custom will be half my capital: their bad word would ruin me.

LOUKA: You have no spirit. I should like to catch them saying a word against me!

NICOLA [*pityingly*]: I should have expected more sense from you, Louka. But youre young: youre young!

LOUKA: Yes; and you like me the better for it, dont you? But I know some family secrets they wouldn't care to have told, young as I am. Let them quarrel with me if they dare!

NICOLA [*with compassionate superiority*]: Do you know what they would do if they heard you talk like that?

LOUKA: What could they do?

NICOLA: Discharge you for untruthfulness. Who would believe any stories you told after that? Who would give you another situation? Who in this house would dare be seen speaking to you ever again? How long would your father be left on his little farm? Child: you don't know the power such high people have over the like of you and me when we try to rise out of our poverty against them. [*He goes close to her and lowers his voice.*] Look at me, ten years in their service. Do you think I know no secrets? I know things about the mistress that she wouldnt have the master know for a thousand levas. I know things about him that she wouldnt let him hear the last of for six months if I blabbed them to her. I know things about Raina that would break off her match with Sergius if—

LOUKA [*turning on him quickly*]: How do you know? I never told you!

NICOLA [*opening his eyes cunningly*]: So thats your little secret, is it? I thought it might be something like that. Well, you take my advice and be respectful and make the mistress feel that no matter what you know or dont know, she can depend on you to hold your tongue and serve the family faithfully. Thats what they like; and thats how youll make most out of them.

LOUKA [*with searching scorn*]: You have the soul of a servant, Nicola.

NICOLA [*complacently*]: Yes: thats the secret of success in service.

A loud knocking with a whip handle on a wooden door is heard from the stable yard.

MALE VOICE OUTSIDE: Hollo! Hollo there! Nicola!

LOUKA: Master! back from the war!

NICOLA [*quickly*]: My word for it, Louka, the war's over. Off with you and get some fresh coffee. [*He runs out into the stable yard.*]

LOUKA [*as she collects the coffee pot and cups on the tray, and carries it into the house*]: Youll never put the soul of a servant into me.

Major Petkoff comes from the stable yard, followed by Nicola. He is a cheerful, excitable, insignificant, unpolished man of about 50, naturally unambitious except as to his income and his importance in local society, but just now greatly pleased with the military rank which the war has thrust on him as a man of consequence in his town. The fever of plucky patriotism which the Serbian attack roused in all the Bulgarians has pulled him through the war; but he is obviously glad to be home again.

PETKOFF [*pointing to the table with his whip*]: Breakfast out here, eh?

NICOLA: Yes, sir. The mistress and Miss Raina have just gone in.

PETKOFF [*sitting down and taking a roll*]: Go in and say Ive come; and get me some fresh coffee.

NICOLA: It's coming, sir. [*He goes to the house door. Louka with fresh coffee, a clean cup, and a brandy bottle on her tray, meets him.*] Have you told the mistress?

LOUKA: Yes: she's coming.

Nicola goes into the house. Louka brings the coffee to the table.

PETKOFF. Well: the Serbs havnt run away with you, have they?

LOUKA: No, sir.

PETKOFF: Thats right. Have you brought me some cognac?

LOUKA [*putting the bottle on the table*]: Here, sir.

PETKOFF: Thats right. [*He pours some into his coffee.*]

Catherine, who, at this early hour made only a very perfunctory toilet, wears a Bulgarian apron over a once brilliant but now half worn-out dressing gown, and a colored handkerchief tied over her thick black hair, comes from the house with Turkish slippers on her bare feet, looking astonishingly handsome and stately under all the circumstances. Louka goes into the house.

CATHERINE: My dear Paul: what a surprise for us! [*She stoops over the back of his chair to kiss him.*] Have they brought you fresh coffee?

PETKOFF: Yes: Louka's been looking after me. The war's over. The treaty was signed three days ago at Bucharest; and the decree for our army to demobilize was issued yesterday.

CATHERINE [*springing erect, with flashing eyes*]: Paul: have you let the Austrians force you to make peace?

PETKOFF [*submissively*]: My dear: they didn't consult me. What could *I* do? [*She sits down and turns away from him.*] But of course we saw to it that the treaty was an honorable one. It declares peace—

CATHERINE [*outraged*]: Peace!

PETKOFF [*appeasing her*]: —but not friendly relations: remember that. They wanted to put that in; but I insisted on its being struck out. What more could I do?

CATHERINE: You could have annexed Serbia and made Prince Alexander [6] Emperor of the Balkans. Thats what I would have done.

PETKOFF: I dont doubt it in the least, my dear. But I should have had to subdue the whole Austrian Empire first; and that would have kept me too long away from you. I missed you greatly.

CATHERINE [*relenting*]: Ah! [*She stretches her hand affectionately across the table to squeeze his.*]

[6] *Prince Alexander* The Bulgarian leader.

PETKOFF: And how have you been, my dear?

CATHERINE: Oh, my usual sore throats: thats all.

PETKOFF [*with conviction*]: That comes from washing your neck every day. Ive often told you so.

CATHERINE: Nonsense, Paul!

PETKOFF [*over his coffee and cigaret*]: I dont believe in going too far with these modern customs. All this washing cant be good for the health; it's not natural. There was an Englishman at Philippopolis who used to wet himself all over with cold water every morning when he got up. Disgusting! It all comes from the English: their climate makes them so dirty that they have to be perpetually washing themselves. Look at my father! he never had a bath in his life; and he lived to be ninety-eight, the healthiest man in Bulgaria. I dont mind a good wash once a week to keep up my position; but once a day is carrying the thing to a ridiculous extreme.

CATHERINE: You are a barbarian at heart still, Paul. I hope you behaved yourself before all those Russian officers.

PETKOFF: I did my best. I took care to let them know that we have a library.

CATHERINE: Ah; but you didnt tell them that we have an electric bell in it? I have had one put up.

PETKOFF: Whats an electric bell?

CATHERINE: You touch a button; something tinkles in the kitchen; and then Nicola comes up.

PETKOFF: Why not shout for him?

CATHERINE: Civilized people never shout for their servants. Ive learnt that while you were away.

PETKOFF: Well, I'll tell you something Ive learnt too. Civilized people dont hang out their washing to dry where visitors can see it; so youd better have all that [*Indicating the clothes on the bushes*] put somewhere else.

CATHERINE: Oh, thats absurd, Paul: I dont believe really refined people notice such things.

SERGIUS [*knocking at the stable gates*]: Gate, Nicola!

PETKOFF: Theres Sergius. [*Shouting*] Hollo, Nicola!

CATHERINE: Oh, dont shout, Paul: it really isnt nice.

PETKOFF: Bosh! [*He shouts louder than before.*] Nicola!

NICOLA [*appearing at the house door*]: Yes, sir.

PETKOFF: Are you deaf? Dont you hear Major Saranoff knocking? Bring him round this way. [*He pronounces the name with the stress on the second syllable: Sarahnoff.*]

NICOLA: Yes, Major. [*He goes into the stable yard.*]

PETKOFF: You must talk to him, my dear, until Raina takes him off our hands. He bores my life out about our not promoting him. Over my head, if you please.

CATHERINE: He certainly ought to be promoted when he marries Raina. Besides, the country should insist on having at least one native general.

PETKOFF: Yes; so that he could throw away whole brigades instead of regiments. It's no use, my dear: he hasnt the slightest chance of promotion until we're quite sure that the peace will be a lasting one.

NICOLA [*at the gate, announcing*]: Major Sergius Saranoff! [*He goes into the house and returns presently with a third chair, which he places at the table. He then withdraws.*]

    Major Sergius Saranoff, the original of the portrait in Raina's room, is a tall romantically handsome man, with the physical hardihood, the high spirit, and the susceptible imagination of an untamed mountaineer chieftain. But his remarkable personal distinction is of a characteristically civilized type. The ridges of his eyebrows, curving with an interrogative twist round the projections at the outer corners; his jealously observant eye; his nose, thin, keen, and apprehensive in spite of the pugnacious high bridge and large nostril; his assertive chin would not be out of place in a Parisian salon, shewing that the clever imaginative barbarian has an acute critical faculty which has been thrown into intense activity by the arrival of western civilization in the Balkans. The result is precisely what the advent of nineteenth century thought first produced in England: to wit, Byronism. By his brooding on the perpetual failure, not only of others, but of himself, to live up to his ideals; by his consequent cynical scorn for humanity; by his jejune credulity as to the absolute validity of his concepts and the unworthiness of the world in disregarding them; by his wincings and mockeries under the sting of the petty disillusions which every hour spent among men brings to his sensitive observation, he has acquired the half tragic, half ironic air, the mysterious moodiness, the suggestion of a strange and terrible history that has left nothing but undying remorse, by which Childe Harold [7] fascinated the grandmothers of his English contemporaries. It is clear that here or nowhere is Raina's ideal hero. Catherine is hardly less enthusiastic about him than her daughter, and much less reserved in shewing her enthusiasm. As he enters from the stable gate, she rises effusively to greet him. Petkoff is distinctly less disposed to make a fuss about him.*

PETKOFF: Here already, Sergius! Glad to see you.

CATHERINE: My dear Sergius! [*She holds out both her hands.*]

SERGIUS [*kissing them with scrupulous gallantry*]: My dear mother, if I may call you so.

PETKOFF [*drily*]: Mother-in-law, Sergius: mother-in-law! Sit down; and have some coffee.

SERGIUS: Thank you: none for me. [*He gets away from the table with a certain distaste for Petkoff's enjoyment of it, and posts himself with conscious dignity against the rail of the steps leading to the house.*]

---

[7] *Childe Harold*   Hero of a poem by Byron.

CATHERINE: You look superb. The campaign has improved you, Sergius. Everybody here is mad about you. We were all wild with enthusiasm about that magnificent cavalry charge.

SERGIUS [*with grave irony*]: Madam: it was the cradle and the grave of my military reputation.

CATHERINE: How so?

SERGIUS: I won the battle the wrong way when our worthy Russian generals were losing it the right way. In short, I upset their plans, and wounded their self-esteem. Two Cossack colonels had their regiments routed on the most correct principles of scientific warfare. Two major-generals got killed strictly according to military etiquette. The two colonels are now major-generals; and I am still a simple major.

CATHERINE: You shall not remain so, Sergius. The women are on your side; and they will see that justice is done you.

SERGIUS: It is too late. I have only waited for the peace to send in my resignation.

PETKOFF [*dropping his cup in his amazement*]: Your resignation!

CATHERINE: Oh, you must withdraw it!

SERGIUS [*with resolute measured emphasis, folding his arms*]: I never withdraw.

PETKOFF [*vexed*]: Now who could have supposed you were going to do such a thing?

SERGIUS [*with fire*]: Everyone that knew me. But enough of myself and my affairs. How is Raina; and where is Raina?

RAINA [*suddenly coming round the corner of the house and standing at the top of the steps in the path*]: Raina is here.

She makes a charming picture as they turn to look at her. She wears an underdress of pale green silk, draped with an overdress of thin ecru canvas embroidered with gold. She is crowned with a dainty eastern cap of gold tinsel. Sergius goes impulsively to meet her. Posing regally, she presents her hand: he drops chivalrously on one knee and kisses it.

PETKOFF [*aside to Catherine, beaming with parental pride*]: Pretty, isnt it? She always appears at the right moment.

CATHERINE [*impatiently*]: Yes; she listens for it. It is an abominable habit.

Sergius leads Raina forward with splendid gallantry. When they arrive at the table, she turns to him with a bend of the head: he bows; and thus they separate, he coming to his place and she going behind her father's chair.

RAINA [*stooping and kissing her father*]: Dear father! Welcome home!

PETKOFF [*patting her cheek*]: My little pet girl. [*He kisses her. She goes to the chair left by Nicola for Sergius, and sits down.*]

CATHERINE: And so youre no longer a soldier, Sergius.

SERGIUS: I am no longer a soldier. Soldiering, my dear madam, is the coward's art of attacking mercilessly when you are strong, and keeping out of harm's way when you are weak. That is the whole secret of successful fighting. Get your enemy at a disadvantage; and never, on any account, fight him on equal terms.

PETKOFF: They wouldnt let us make a fair stand-up fight of it. However, I suppose soldiering has to be a trade like any other trade.

SERGIUS: Precisely. But I have no ambition to shine as a tradesman; so I have taken the advice of that bagman of a captain that settled the exchange of prisoners with us at Pirot, and given it up.

PETKOFF: What! that Swiss fellow? Sergius: I've often thought of that exchange since. He over-reached us about those horses.

SERGIUS: Of course he over-reached us. His father was a hotel and livery stable keeper; and he owed his first step to his knowledge of horse-dealing. [*With mock enthusiasm*] Ah, he was a soldier: every inch a soldier! If only I had bought the horses for my regiment instead of foolishly leading it into danger, I should have been a field-marshal now!

CATHERINE: A Swiss? What was he doing in the Serbian army?

PETKOFF: A volunteer, of course: keen on picking up his profession. [*Chuckling*] We shouldn't have been able to begin fighting if these foreigners hadnt shewed us how to do it: we knew nothing about it; and neither did the Serbs. Egad there'd have been no war without them!

RAINA: Are there many Swiss officers in the Serbian Army?

PETOFF: No. All Austrians, just as our officers were all Russians. This was the only Swiss I came across. I'll never trust a Swiss again. He humbugged us into giving him fifty ablebodied men for two hundred worn out chargers. They werent even eatable!

SERGIUS: We were two children in the hands of that consummate soldier, Major: simply two innocent little children.

RAINA: What was he like?

CATHERINE: Oh, Raina, what a silly question!

SERGIUS: He was like a commercial traveller in uniform. Bourgeois to his boots!

PETKOFF [*grinning*]: Sergius: tell Catherine that queer story his friend told us about how he escaped after Slivnitza. You remember. About his being hid by two women.

SERGIUS [*with bitter irony*]: Oh yes: quite a romance! He was serving in the very battery I so unprofessionally charged. Being a thorough soldier, he ran away like the rest of them, with our cavalry at his heels. To escape their sabres he climbed a waterpipe and made his way into the bedroom of a young Bulgarian lady. The young lady was enchanted by his persuasive commercial traveller's manners. She very modestly entertained him for an hour or so, and then called in her mother lest her conduct should appear unmaidenly. The old lady was equally fascinated; and the fugitive was sent on his way in the morning, disguised in an old coat belonging to the master of the house, who was away at the war.

RAINA [*rising with marked stateliness*]: Your life in the camp has made you coarse, Sergius. I did not think you would have repeated such a story before me. [*She turns away coldly.*]

CATHERINE [*also rising*]: She is right, Sergius. If such women exist, we should be spared the knowledge of them.

PETKOFF: Pooh! nonsense! what does it matter?

SERGIUS [*ashamed*]: No, Petkoff: I was wrong. [*To Raina, with earnest humility*] I beg your pardon. I have behaved abominably. Forgive me, Raina. [*She bows reservedly.*] And you too, madam [*Catherine bows graciously and sits down. He proceeds solemnly, again addressing Raina.*] The glimpses I have had of the seamy side of life during the last few months have made me cynical; but I should not have brought my cynicism here: least of all into your presence, Raina. I—[*Here, turning to the others, he is evidently going to begin a long speech when the Major interrupts him.*]

PETKOFF: Stuff and nonsense, Sergius! That's quite enough fuss about nothing: a soldier's daughter should be able to stand up without flinching to a little strong conversation. [*He rises.*] Come: it's time for us to get to business. We have to make up our minds how those three regiments are to get back to Philippopolis: theres no forage for them on the Sofia route. [*He goes towards the house.*] Come along. [*Sergius is about to follow him when Catherine rises and intervenes.*]

CATHERINE: Oh, Paul, cant you spare Sergius for a few moments? Raina has hardly seen him yet. Perhaps I can help you to settle about the regiments.

SERGIUS [*protesting*]: My dear madam, impossible: you—

CATHERINE [*stopping him playfully*]: You stay here, my dear Sergius: theres no hurry. I have a word or two to say to Paul. [*Sergius instantly bows and steps back.*] Now, dear [*taking Petkoff's arm*]: come and see the electric bell.

PETKOFF: Oh, very well, very well.

They go into the house together affectionately. Sergius, left alone with Raina, looks anxiously at her, fearing that she is still offended. She smiles, and stretches out her arms to him.

SERGIUS [*hastening to her*]: Am I forgiven?

RAINA [*placing her hands on his shoulders as she looks up at him with admiration and worship*]: My hero! My king!

SERGIUS: My Queen! [*He kisses her on the forehead.*]

RAINA: How I have envied you, Sergius! You have been out in the world, on the field of battle, able to prove yourself there worthy of any woman in the world; whilst I have had to sit at home inactive—dreaming—useless—doing nothing that could give me the right to call myself worthy of any man.

SERGIUS: Dearest: all my deeds have been yours. You inspired me. I have gone through the war like a knight in a tournament with his lady looking down at him!

RAINA: And you have never been absent from my thoughts for a moment. [*Very solemnly*] Sergius: I think we two have found the higher love. When I think of you, I feel that I could never do a base deed, or think an ignoble thought.

SERGIUS: My lady and my saint! [*He clasps her reverently.*]

RAINA [*returning his embrace*]: My lord and my—

SERGIUS: Sh—sh! Let me be the worshipper, dear. You little know how unworthy even the best man is of a girl's pure passion!

RAINA: I trust you. I love you. You will never disappoint me, Sergius. [*Louka is heard singing within the house. They quickly release each other.*] I cant pretend to talk indifferently before her: my heart is too full. [*Louka comes from the house with her tray. She goes to the table, and begins to clear it, with her back turned to them.*] I will get my hat; and then we can get out until lunch time. Wouldn't you like that?

SERGIUS: Be quick. If you are away five minutes, it will seem five hours. [*Raina runs to the top of the steps, and turns there to exchange looks with him and wave him a kiss with both hands. He looks after her with emotion for a moment; then turns slowly away, his face radiant with the loftiest exaltation. The movement shifts his field of vision, into the corner of which there now comes the tail of Louka's double apron. His attention is arrested at once. He takes a stealthy look at her, and begins to twirl his moustache mischievously, with his left hand akimbo on his hip. Finally, striking the ground with his heels in something of a cavalry swagger, he strolls over to the other side of the table, opposite her, and says*] Louka: do you know what the higher love is?

LOUKA [*astonished*]: No, sir.

SERGIUS: Very fatiguing thing to keep up for any length of time, Louka. One feels the need of some relief after it.

LOUKA [*innocently*]: Perhaps you would like some coffee, sir? [*She stretches her hand across the table for the coffee pot.*]

SERGIUS [*taking her hand*]: Thank you, Louka.

LOUKA [*pretending to pull*]: Oh, sir, you know I didnt mean that. I'm surprised at you!

SERGIUS [*coming clear of the table and drawing her with him*]: I am surprised at myself, Louka. What would Sergius, the hero of Slivnitza, say if he saw me now? What would Sergius, the apostle of the higher love, say if he saw me now? What would the half dozen Sergiuses who keep popping in and out of this handsome figure of mine say if they caught us here? [*Letting go her hand and slipping his arm dexterously round her waist*] Do you consider my figure handsome, Louka?

LOUKA: Let me go, sir. I shall be disgraced. [*She struggles: he holds her inexorably.*] Oh, will you let go?

SERGIUS [*looking straight into her eyes*]: No.

LOUKA: Then stand back where we cant be seen. Have you no common sense?

SERGIUS: Ah! thats reasonable. [*He takes her into the stable yard gateway, where they are hidden from the house.*]

LOUKA [*plaintively*]:   I may have been seen from the windows: Miss Raina is sure to be spying about after you.

SERGIUS [*stung: letting her go*]:   Take care, Louka. I may be worthless enough to betray the higher love; but do not you insult it.

LOUKA [*demurely*]:   Not for the world, sir, I'm sure. May I go on with my work, please, now?

SERGIUS [*again putting his arm round her*]:   You are a provoking little witch, Louka. If you were in love with me, would you spy out of windows on me?

LOUKA: Well, you see, sir, since you say you are half a dozen different gentlemen all at once, I should have a great deal to look after.

SERGIUS [*charmed*]:   Witty as well as pretty. [*He tries to kiss her.*]

LOUKA [*avoiding him*]:   No: I dont want your kisses. Gentlefolk are all alike: you making love to me behind Miss Raina's back; and she doing the same behind yours.

SERGIUS [*recoiling a step*]:   Louka!

LOUKA: It shews how little you really care.

SERGIUS [*dropping his familiarity, and speaking with freezing politeness*]:   If our conversation is to continue, Louka, you will please remember that a gentleman does not discuss the conduct of the lady he is engaged to with her maid.

LOUKA: It's so hard to know what a gentleman considers right. I thought from your trying to kiss me that you had given up being so particular.

SERGIUS [*turning from her and striking his forehead as he comes back into the garden from the gateway*]:   Devil! devil!

LOUKA: Ha! ha! I expect one of the six of you is very like me, sir; though I am only Miss Raina's maid. [*She goes back to her work at the table, taking no further notice of him.*]

SERGIUS [*speaking to himself*]:   Which of the six is the real man? thats the question that torments me. One of them is a hero, another a buffoon, another a humbug, another perhaps a bit of a blackguard. [*He pauses, and looks furtively at Louka as he adds, with deep bitterness*] And one, at least, is a coward: jealous, like all cowards. [*He goes to the table.*] Louka.

LOUKA: Yes?

SERGIUS: Who is my rival?

LOUKA: You shall never get that out of me, for love or money.

SERGIUS: Why?

LOUKA: Never mind why. Besides, you would tell that I told you; and I should lose my place.

SERGIUS [*holding out his right hand in affirmation*]:   No! on the honor of a—[*He checks himself; and his hand drops, nerveless, as he concludes sardonically*]—of a man capable of behaving as I have been behaving for the last five minutes. Who is he?

LOUKA: I dont know. I never saw him. I only heard his voice through the door of her room.

SERGIUS: How dare you?

LOUKA [*retreating*]:   Oh, I mean no harm; youve no right to take up my words like that. The mistress knows all about it. And I tell you that if that gentleman ever comes here again, Miss Raina will marry him, whether he likes it or not. I know the difference between the sort of manner you and she put on before one another and the real manner.

Sergius shivers as if she had stabbed him. Then, setting his face like iron, he strides grimly to her, and grips her above the elbows with both hands.

SERGIUS: Now listen you to me.

LOUKA [*wincing*]:   Not so tight: youre hurting me.

SERGIUS: That doesnt matter. You have stained my honor by making me a party to your eavesdropping. And you have betrayed your mistress.

LOUKA [*writhing*]:   Please—

SERGIUS: That shews that you are an abominable little clod of common clay, with the soul of a servant. [*He lets her go as if she were an unclean thing, and turns away, dusting his hands of her, to the bench by the wall, where he sits down with averted head, meditating gloomily.*]

LOUKA [*whimpering angrily with her hands up her sleeves, feeling her bruised arms*]: You know how to hurt with your tongue as well as with your hands. But I dont care, now Ive found out that whatever clay I'm made of, youre made of the same. As for her, she's a liar; and her fine airs are a cheat; and I'm worth six of her. [*She shakes the pain off hardily; tosses her head; and sets to work to put the things on the tray.*]

He looks doubtfully at her. She finishes packing the tray, and laps the cloth over the edges, so as to carry all out together. As she stoops to lift it, he rises.

SERGIUS: Louka! [*She stops and looks defiantly at him.*] A gentleman has no right to hurt a woman under any circumstances. [*With profound humility, uncovering his head*] I beg your pardon.

LOUKA: That sort of apology may satisfy a lady. Of what use is it to a servant?

SERGIUS [*rudely crossed in his chivalry, throws it off with a bitter laugh, and says slightingly*]: Oh! you wish to be paid for the hurt! [*He puts on his shako, and takes some money from his pocket.*]

LOUKA [*her eyes filling with tears in spite of herself*]: No: I want my hurt made well.

SERGIUS [*sobered by her tone*]: How?

She rolls up her left sleeve; clasps her arm with the thumb and fingers of her right hand; and looks down at the bruise. Then she raises her head and looks straight at him. Finally, with a superb gesture, she presents her arm to be kissed. Amazed, he looks at her; at the arm; at her again; hesitates; and then, with shuddering intensity, exclaims Never! *and gets away as far as possible from her.*

Her arm drops. Without a word, and with unaffected dignity, she takes her tray, and is approaching the house when Raina returns, wearing a hat and jacket in the height of the Vienna fashion of the previous year, 1885. Louka makes way proudly for her, and then goes into the house.

RAINA: I'm ready. Whats the matter? [*Gaily*] Have you been flirting with Louka?

SERGIUS [*hastily*]: No, no. How can you think such a thing?

RAINA [*ashamed of herself*]: Forgive me, dear: it was only a jest. I am so happy today.

He goes quickly to her, and kisses her hand remorsefully. Catherine comes out and calls to them from the top of the steps.

CATHERINE [*coming down to them*]: I am sorry to disturb you, children; but Paul is distracted over those three regiments. He doesnt know how to send them to Philippopolis; and he objects to every suggestion of mine. You must go and help him, Sergius. He is in the library.

RAINA [*disappointed*]: But we are just going out for a walk.

SERGIUS: I shall not be long. Wait for me just five minutes. [*He runs up the steps to the door.*]

RAINA [*following him to the foot of the steps and looking up at him with timid coquetry*]: I shall go round and wait in full view of the library windows. Be sure you draw father's attention to me. If you are a moment longer than five minutes, I shall go in and fetch you, regiments or no regiments.

SERGIUS [*laughing*]: Very well. [*He goes in.*] *Raina watches him until he is out of her sight. Then, with a perceptible relaxation of manner, she begins to pace up and down the garden in a brown study.*

CATHERINE: Imagine their meeting that Swiss and hearing the whole story! The very first thing your father asked for was the old coat we sent him off in. A nice mess you have got us into!

RAINA [*gazing thoughtfully at the gravel as she walks*]:   The little beast!

CATHERINE: Little beast! What little beast?

RAINA: To go and tell! Oh, if I had him here, I'd cram him with chocolate creams til he couldnt ever speak again!

CATHERINE: Dont talk such stuff. Tell me the truth, Raina. How long was he in your room before you came to me?

RAINA [*whisking round and recommencing her march in the opposite direction*]:   Oh, I forget.

CATHERINE: You cannot forget! Did he really climb up after the soldiers were gone; or was he there when that officer searched the room?

RAINA: No. Yes: I think he must have been there then.

CATHERINE: You think! Oh, Raina! Raina! Will anything ever make you straightforward? If Sergius finds out, it will be all over between you.

RAINA [*with cool impertinence*]:   Oh, I know Sergius is your pet. I sometimes wish you could marry him instead of me. You would just suit him. You would pet him, and spoil him, and mother him to perfection.

CATHERINE [*opening her eyes very widely indeed*]:   Well, upon my word!

RAINA [*capriciously: half to herself*]:   I always feel a longing to do or say something dreadful to him—to shock his propriety—to scandalize the five senses out of him. [*To Catherine, perversely*] I dont care whether he finds out about the chocolate cream soldier or not. I half hope he may. [*She again turns and strolls flippantly away up the path to the corner of the house.*]

CATHERINE: And what should I be able to say to your father, pray?

RAINA [*over her shoulder, from the top of the two steps*]:   Oh, poor father! As if he could help himself! [*She turns the corner and passes out of sight.*]

CATHERINE [*looking after her, her fingers itching*]:   Oh, if you were only ten years younger! [*Louka comes from the house with a salver, which she carries hanging down by her side.*] Well?

LOUKA: Theres a gentleman just called, madam. A Serbian officer.

CATHERINE [*flaming*]:   A Serb! And how dare he—[*checking herself bitterly*] Oh, I forgot. We are at peace now. I suppose we shall have them calling every day to pay their compliments. Well: if he is an officer why dont you tell your master? He is in the library with Major Saranoff. Why do you come to me?

LOUKA: But he asks for you, madam. And I dont think he knows who you are: he said the lady of the house. He gave me this little ticket for you. [*She takes a card out of her bosom; puts it on the salver; and offers it to Catherine.*]

CATHERINE [*reading*]:   "Captain Bluntschli"? That's a German name.

LOUKA: Swiss, madam, I think.

CATHERINE [*with a bound that makes Louka jump back*]:   Swiss! What is he like?

LOUKA [*timidly*]:   He has a big carpet bag, madam.

CATHERINE: Oh Heavens! he's come to return the coat. Send him away: say we're not at home: ask him to leave his address and I'll write to him. Oh stop: that will never do. Wait! [*She throws herself into a chair to think it out. Louka waits.*] The master and Major Saranoff are busy in the library, arnt they?

LOUKA: Yes, madam.

CATHERINE [*decisively*]:   Bring the gentleman out here at once. [*Peremptorily*] And be very polite to him. Dont delay. Here [*impatiently snatching the salver from her*]: leave that here; and go straight back to him.

LOUKA: Yes, madam. [*going*]

CATHERINE: Louka!

LOUKA [*stopping*]:   Yes, madam.

CATHERINE: Is the library door shut?

LOUKA: I think so, madam.

CATHERINE: If not, shut it as you pass through.

LOUKA: Yes, madam. [*going*]

CATHERINE: Stop. [*Louka stops.*] He will have to go that way. [*Indicating the gate of the stable yard*] Tell Nicola to bring his bag here after him. Dont forget.

LOUKA [*surprised*]: His bag?

CATHERINE: Yes: here: as soon as possible. [*Vehemently*] Be quick! [*Louka runs into the house. Catherine snatches her apron off and throws it behind a bush. She then takes up the salver and uses it as a mirror, with the result that the handkerchief tied round her head follows the apron. A touch to her hair and a shake to her dressing gown make her presentable.*] Oh, how? how? how can a man be such a fool! Such a moment to select! [*Louka appears at the door of the house, announcing Captain Bluntschli. She stands aside at the top of the steps to let him pass before she goes in again. He is the man of the midnight adventure in Raina's room, clean, well brushed, smartly uniformed, and out of trouble, but still unmistakably the same man. The moment Louka's back is turned, Catherine swoops on him with impetuous, urgent, coaxing appeal.*] Captain Bluntschli: I am very glad to see you; but you must leave this house at once. [*He raises his eyebrows.*] My husband has just returned with my future son-in-law; and they know nothing. If they did, the consequences would be terrible. You are a foreigner: you do not feel our national animosities as we do. We still hate the Serbs: the effect of the peace on my husband has been to make him feel like a lion baulked of his prey. If he discovers our secret, he will never forgive me; and my daughter's life will hardly be safe. Will you, like the chivalrous gentleman and soldier you are, leave at once before he finds you here?

BLUNTSCHLI [*disappointed, but philosophical*]: At once, gracious lady. I only came to thank you and return the coat you lent me. If you will allow me to take it out of my bag and leave it with your servant as I pass out, I need detain you no further. [*He turns to go into the house.*]

CATHERINE [*catching him by the sleeve*]: Oh, you must not think of going back that way. [*Coaxing him across to the stable gates*] This is the shortest way out. Many thanks. So glad to have been of service to you. Good-bye.

BLUNTSCHLI: But my bag?

CATHERINE: It shall be sent on. You will leave me your address.

BLUNTSCHLI: True. Allow me. [*He takes out his cardcase, and stops to write his address, keeping Catherine in an agony of impatience. As he hands her the card, Petkoff, hatless, rushes from the house in a fluster of hospitality, followed by Sergius.*]

PETKOFF [*as he hurries down the steps*]: My dear Captain Bluntschli—

CATHERINE: Oh Heavens! [*She sinks on the seat against the wall.*]

PETKOFF [*too preoccupied to notice her as he shakes Bluntschli's hand heartily*]: Those stupid people of mine thought I was out here, instead of in the—haw!—library. [*He cannot mention the library without betraying how proud he is of it.*] I saw you through the window. I was wondering why you didnt come in. Saranoff is with me: you remember him, dont you?

SERGIUS [*saluting humorously, and then offering his hand with great charm of manner*]: Welcome, our friend the enemy!

PETKOFF: No longer the enemy, happily. [*Rather anxiously*] I hope youve called as a friend, and not about horses or prisoners.

CATHERINE: Oh, quite as a friend, Paul. I was just asking Captain Bluntschli to stay to lunch; but he declares he must go at once.

SERGIUS [*sardonically*]: Impossible, Bluntschli. We want you here badly. We have to send on three cavalry regiments to Philippopolis; and we dont in the least know how to do it.

BLUNTSCHLI [*suddenly attentive and business-like*]: Philippopolis? The forage is the trouble, I suppose.

PETKOFF [*eagerly*]:   Yes: thats it. [*To Sergius*] He sees the whole thing at once.

BLUNTSCHLI: I think I can shew you how to manage that.

SERGIUS: Invaluable man! Come along! [*Towering over Bluntschli, he puts his hand on his shoulder and takes him to the steps, Petkoff following.*]

    Raina comes from the house as Bluntschli puts his foot on the first step.

RAINA: Oh! The chocolate cream soldier!

    Bluntschli stands rigid. Sergius, amazed, looks at Raina, then at Petkoff, who looks back at him and then at his wife.

CATHERINE [*with commanding presence of mind*]:   My dear Raina, dont you see that we have a guest here? Captain Bluntschli: one of our new Serbian friends.

    Raina bows: Bluntschli bows.

RAINA: How silly of me! [*She comes down into the centre of the group, between Bluntschli and Petkoff.*] I made a beautiful ornament this morning for the ice pudding; and that stupid Nicola has just put down a pile of plates on it and spoilt it. [*To Bluntschli, winningly*] I hope you didnt think that you were the chocolate cream soldier, Captain Bluntschli.

BLUNTSCHLI [*laughing*]:   I assure you I did. [*Stealing a whimsical glance at her*] Your explanation was a relief.

PETKOFF [*Suspiciously, to Raina*]:   And since when, pray, have you taken to cooking?

CATHERINE: Oh, whilst you were away. It is her latest fancy.

PETKOFF [*testily*]:   And has Nicola taken to drinking? He used to be careful enough. First he shews Captain Bluntschli out here when he knew quite well I was in the library; and then he goes downstairs and breaks Raina's chocolate soldier. He must—[*Nicola appears at the top of the steps with the bag. He descends; places it respectfully before Bluntschli; and waits for further orders. General amazement. Nicola, unconscious of the effect he is producing, looks perfectly satisfied with himself. When Petkoff recovers his power of speech, he breaks out at him*] Are you mad, Nicola?

NICOLA [*taken aback*]:   Sir?

PETKOFF: What have you brought that for?

NICOLA: My lady's orders, major. Louka told me that—

CATHERINE [*interrupting him*]:   My orders! Why should I order you to bring Captain Bluntschli's luggage out here? What are you thinking of, Nicola?

NICOLA [*after a moment's bewilderment, picking up the bag as he addresses Bluntschli with the very perfection of servile discretion*]:   I beg your pardon, captain, I am sure. [*To Catherine*] My fault, madame: I hope youll overlook it. [*He bows, and is going to the steps with the bag, when Petkoff addresses him angrily.*]

PETKOFF: Youd better go and slam that bag, too, down on Miss Raina's ice pudding! [*This is too much for Nicola. The bag drops from his hand almost on his master's toes, eliciting a roar of*] Begone, you butter-fingered donkey.

NICOLA [*snatching up the bag, and escaping into the house*]:   Yes, Major.

CATHERINE: Oh, never mind. Paul: dont be angry.

PETKOFF [*blustering*]:   Scoundrel! He's got out of hand while I was away. I'll teach him. Infernal blackguard! The sack next Saturday! I'll clear out the whole establishment—[*He is stifled by the caresses of his wife and daughter, who hang round his neck, petting him.*]

CATHERINE } [*together*] { Now, now, now, it
RAINA   }   { Wow, wow, wow: not

mustnt be angry. He meant no harm. Be good to please me, dear. Sh-sh-sh-sh!
on your first day at home. I'll make another ice pudding. Tch-ch-ch!

PETKOFF [*yielding*]: Oh well, never mind. Come, Bluntschli: lets have no more nonsense about going away. You know very well youre not going back to Switzerland yet. Until you do go back youll stay with us.

RAINA: Oh, do, Captain Bluntschli.

PETKOFF [*to Catherine*]: Now, Catherine: it's of you he's afraid. Press him: and he'll stay.

CATHERINE: Of course I shall be only too delighted if [*appealingly*] Captain Bluntschli really wishes to stay. He knows my wishes.

BLUNTSCHLI [*in his driest military manner*]: I am at madam's orders.

SERGIUS [*cordially*]: That settles it!

PETKOFF [*heartily*]: Of course!

RAINA: You see you must stay.

BLUNTSCHLI [*smiling*]: Well, if I must, I must.
Gesture of despair from Catherine.

Act III

In the library after lunch. It is not much of a library. Its literary equipment consists of a single fixed shelf stocked with old paper covered novels, broken backed, coffee stained, torn and thumbed; and a couple of little hanging shelves with a few gift books on them: the rest of the wall space being occupied by trophies of war and the chase. But it is a most comfortable sitting room. A row of three large windows shews a mountain panorama, just now seen in one of its friendliest aspects in the mellowing afternoon light. In the corner next the right hand window a square earthenware stove, a perfect tower of glistening pottery, rises nearly to the ceiling and guarantees plenty of warmth. The ottoman is like that in Raina's room, and similarly placed; and the window seats are luxurious with decorated cushions. There is one object, however, hopelessly out of keeping with its surroundings. This is a small kitchen table, much the worse for wear, fitted as a writing table with an old canister full of pens, an eggcup filled with ink, and a deplorable scrap of heavily used pink blotting paper.

At the side of this table, which stands to the left of anyone facing the window, Bluntschli is hard at work with a couple of maps before him, writing orders. At the head of it sits Sergius, who is supposed to be also at work, but is actually gnawing the feather of a pen, and contemplating Bluntschli's quick, sure, businesslike progress with a mixture of envious irritation at his own incapacity and awestruck wonder at an ability which seems to him almost miraculous, though its prosaic character forbids him to esteem it. The Major is comfortably established on the ottoman, with a newspaper in his hand and the tube of his hookah within easy reach. Catherine sits at the stove, with her back to them, embroidering. Raina, reclining on the divan, is gazing in a daydream out at the Balkan landscape, with a neglected novel in her lap.

The door is on the same side as the stove, farther from the window. The button of the electric bell is at the opposite side, behind Bluntschli.

PETKOFF [*looking up from his paper to watch how they are getting on at the table*]: Are you sure I cant help in any way, Bluntschli?

BLUNTSCHLI [*without interrupting his writing or looking up*]: Quite sure, thank you. Saranoff and I will manage it.

SERGIUS [*grimly*]: Yes: we'll manage it. He finds out what to do; draws up the orders; and I sign em. Division of labor! [*Bluntschli passes him a paper.*] Another one? Thank you. [*He plants the paper squarely before him; sets his chair carefully parallel to it; and signs with his cheek on his elbow and his protruded tongue following the movements of his pen.*] This hand is more accustomed to the sword than to the pen.

PETKOFF: It's very good of you, Bluntschli: it is indeed, to let yourself be put upon in this way. Now are you quite sure I can do nothing?

CATHERINE [*in a low warning tone*]: You can stop interrupting, Paul.

PETKOFF [*starting and looking round at her*]: Eh? Oh! Quite right. [*He takes his newspaper up again, but presently lets it drop.*] Ah, you havnt been campaigning, Catherine: you dont know how pleasant it is for us to sit here, after a good lunch, with nothing to do but enjoy ourselves. Theres only one thing I want to make me thoroughly comfortable.

CATHERINE: What is that?

PETKOFF: My old coat. I'm not at home in this one: I feel as if I were on parade.

CATHERINE: My dear Paul, how absurd you are about that old coat! It must be hanging in the blue closet where you left it.

PETKOFF: My dear Catherine, I tell you Ive looked there. Am I to believe my own eyes or not? [*Catherine rises and crosses the room to press the button of the electric bell.*] What are you shewing off that bell for? [*She looks at him majestically, and silently resumes her chair and her needlework.*] My dear: if you think the obstinacy of your sex can make a coat out of two old dressing gowns of Raina's, your waterproof, and my mackintosh, youre mistaken. Thats exactly what the blue closet contains at present.

　　Nicola presents himself.

CATHERINE: Nicola: go to the blue closet and bring your master's old coat here: the braided one he wears in the house.

NICOLA: Yes, madame. [*He goes out.*]

PETKOFF: Catherine.

CATHERINE: Yes, Paul.

PETKOFF: I bet you any piece of jewellery you like to order from Sofia against a week's housekeeping money that the coat isnt there.

CATHERINE: Done, Paul!

PETKOFF [*excited by the prospect of a gamble*]: Come: heres an opportunity for some sport. Wholl bet on it? Bluntschli: I'll give you six to one.

BLUNTSCHLI [*imperturbably*]: It would be robbing you, Major. Madame is sure to be right. [*Without looking up, he passes another batch of papers to Sergius.*]

SERGIUS [*also excited*]: Bravo, Switzerland! Major: I bet my best charger against an Arab mare for Raina that Nicola finds the coat in the blue closet.

PETKOFF [*eagerly*]: Your best char—

CATHERINE [*hastily interrupting him*]: Dont be foolish, Paul. An Arabian mare will cost you 50,000 levas.[8]

RAINA [*suddenly coming out of her picturesque revery*]: Really, mother, if you are going to take the jewellery, I don't see why you should grudge me my Arab.

　　Nicola comes back with the coat, and brings it to Petkoff, who can hardly believe his eyes.

CATHERINE: Where was it, Nicola?

NICOLA: Hanging in the blue closet, madame.

PETKOFF: Well, I am d—

CATHERINE [*stopping him*]: Paul!

PETKOFF: I could have sworn it wasnt there. Age is beginning to tell on me. I'm getting hallucinations. [*To Nicola*] Here: help me to change. Excuse me, Bluntschli. [*He begins changing coats, Nicola acting as valet.*] Remember: I didnt take that bet of yours, Sergius. Youd better give Raina that Arab steed yourself, since youve roused her expectations. Eh, Raina? [*He looks round at her; but she is again rapt in the landscape. With a little gush of parental affection and pride, he points her out to them, and says*] She's dreaming, as usual.

---

[8] *leva*　A Bulgarian coin.

SERGIUS: Assuredly she shall not be the loser.

PETKOFF: So much the better for her. *I* shant come off so cheaply, I expect. [*The change is now complete. Nicola goes out with the discarded coat.*] Ah, now I feel at home at last. [*He sits down and takes his newspaper with a grunt of relief.*]

BLUNTSCHLI [*to Sergius, handing a paper*]: Thats the last order.

PETKOFF [*jumping up*]: What! Finished?

BLUNTSCHLI: Finished.

PETKOFF [*with childlike envy*]: Havnt you anything for me to sign?

BLUNTSCHLI: Not necessary. His signature will do.

PETKOFF [*inflating his chest and thumping it*]: Ah well, I think weve done a thundering good day's work. Can I do anything more?

BLUNTSCHLI: You had better both see the fellows that are to take these. [*Sergius rises.*] Pack them off at once; and shew them that Ive marked on the orders the time they should hand them in by. Tell them that if they stop to drink or tell stories—if theyre five minutes late, theyll have the skin taken off their backs.

SERGIUS [*stiffening indignantly*]: I'll say so. [*He strides to the door.*] And if one of them is man enough to spit in my face for insulting him, I'll buy his discharge and give him a pension. [*He goes out.*]

BLUNTSCHLI [*confidentially*]: Just see that he talks to them properly, Major, will you?

PETKOFF [*officiously*]: Quite right, Bluntschli, quite right. I'll see to it. [*He goes to the door importantly, but hesitates on the threshold.*] By the bye, Catherine, you may as well come too. Theyll be far more frightened of you than of me.

CATHERINE [*putting down her embroidery*]: I daresay I had better. You would only splutter at them. [*She goes out, Petkoff holding the door for her and following her.*]

BLUNTSCHLI: What an army! They make cannons out of cherry trees; and the officers send for their wives to keep discipline! [*He begins to fold and docket the papers.*]

Raina, who has risen from the divan, marches slowly down the room with her hands clasped behind her, and looks mischievously at him.

RAINA: You look ever so much nicer than when we last met. [*He looks up, surprised.*] What have you done to yourself?

BLUNTSCHLI: Washed; brushed; good night's sleep and breakfast. Thats all.

RAINA: Did you get back safely that morning?

BLUNTSCHLI: Quite, thanks.

RAINA: Were they angry with you for running away from Sergius's charge?

BLUNTSCHLI [*grinning*]: No: they were glad; because theyd all just run away themselves.

RAINA [*going to the table, and leaning over it towards him*]: It must have made a lovely story for them: all that about me and my room.

BLUNTSCHLI: Capital story. But I only told it to one of them: a particular friend.

RAINA: On whose discretion you could absolutely rely?

BLUNTSCHLI: Absolutely.

RAINA: Hm! He told it all to my father and Sergius the day you exchanged the prisoners. [*She turns away and strolls carelessly across to the other side of the room.*]

BLUNTSCHLI [*deeply concerned, and half incredulous*]: No! You dont mean that, do you?

RAINA [*turning, with sudden earnestness*]: I do indeed. But they dont know that it was in this house you took refuge. If Sergius knew, he would challenge you and kill you in a duel.

BLUNTSCHLI: Bless me! then dont tell him.

RAINA: Please be serious, Captain Bluntschli. Can you not realize what it is to me to deceive him? I want to be quite perfect with Sergius: no meanness, no smallness, no deceit. My relation to him is the one really beautiful and noble part of my life. I hope you can understand that.

BLUNTSCHLI [*sceptically*]: You mean that you wouldnt like him to find out that the story about the ice pudding was a—a—a— You know.

RAINA [*wincing*]: Ah, dont talk of it in that flippant way. I lied: I know it. But I did it to save your life. He would have killed you. That was the second time I ever uttered a falsehood. [*Bluntschli rises quickly and looks doubtfully and somewhat severely at her.*] Do you remember the first time?

BLUNTSCHLI: I! No. Was I present?

RAINA: Yes; and I told the officer who was searching for you that you were not present.

BLUNTSCHLI: True. I should have remembered it.

RAINA [*greatly encouraged*]: Ah, it is natural that you should forget it first. It cost you nothing: it cost me a lie! A lie!

She sits down on the ottoman, looking straight before her with her hands clasped around her knee. Bluntschli, quite touched, goes to the ottoman with a particularly reassuring and considerate air, and sits down beside her.

BLUNTSCHLI: My dear young lady, dont let this worry you. Remember: I'm a soldier. Now what are the two things that happen to a soldier so often that he comes to think nothing of them? One is hearing people tell lies [*Raina recoils*]: the other is getting his life saved in all sorts of ways by all sorts of people.

RAINA [*rising in indignant protest*]: And so he becomes a creature incapable of faith and of gratitude.

BLUNTSCHLI [*making a wry face*]: Do you like gratitude? I dont. If pity is akin to love, gratitude is akin to the other thing.

RAINA: Gratitude! [*Turning on him*] If you are incapable of gratitude you are incapable of any noble sentiment. Even animals are grateful. Oh, I see now exactly what you think of me! You were not surprised to hear me lie. To you it was something I probably did every day! every hour! That is how men think of women. [*She paces the room tragically.*]

BLUNTSCHLI [*dubiously*]: Theres reason in everything. You said youd told only two lies in your whole life. Dear young lady: isnt that rather a short allowance? I'm quite a straightforward man myself; but it wouldnt last me a whole morning.

RAINA [*staring haughtily at him*]: Do you know, sir, that you are insulting me?

BLUNTSCHLI: I cant help it. When you strike that noble attitude and speak in that thrilling voice, I admire you; but I find it impossible to believe a single word you say.

RAINA [*superbly*]: Captain Bluntschli!

BLUNTSCHLI [*unmoved*]: Yes?

RAINA [*standing over him, as if she could not believe her senses*]: Do you mean what you said just now? Do you know what you said just now?

BLUNTSCHLI: I do.

RAINA [*gasping*]: I! I!!! [*She points to herself incredulously, meaning "I, Raina Petkoff tell lies!" He meets her gaze unflinchingly. She suddenly sits down beside him, and adds, with a complete change of manner from the heroic to a babyish familiarity*] How did you find me out?

BLUNTSCHLI [*promptly*]: Instinct, dear young lady. Instinct, and experience of the world.

RAINA [*wonderingly*]: Do you know, you are the first man I ever met who did not take me seriously?

BLUNTSCHLI: You mean, dont you, that I am the first man that has ever taken you quite seriously?

RAINA: Yes: I suppose I do mean that. [*Cosily, quite at her ease with him*] How strange it is to be talked to in such a way! You know, Ive always gone on like that.

BLUNTSCHLI: You mean the—?

RAINA: I mean the noble attitude and the thrilling voice. [*They laugh together.*] I did it when I was a tiny child to my nurse. She believed in it. I do it before my parents. They believe in it. I do it before Sergius. He believes in it.

BLUNTSCHLI: Yes: he's a little in that line himself, isnt he?

RAINA [*startled*]: Oh! Do you think so?

BLUNTSCHLI: You know him better than I do.

RAINA: I wonder—I wonder is he? If I thought that—! [*Discouraged*] Ah, well; what does it matter? I suppose, now youve found me out, you despise me.

BLUNTSCHLI [*warmly, rising*]: No, my dear young lady, no, no, no a thousand times. It's part of your youth: part of your charm. I'm like all the rest of them: the nurse, your parents, Sergius: I'm your infatuated admirer.

RAINA [*pleased*]: Really?

BLUNTSCHLI [*slapping his breast smartly with his hand, German fashion*]: Hand aufs Herz! [9] Really and truly.

RAINA [*very happy*]: But what did you think of me for giving you my portrait?

BLUNTSCHLI [*astonished*]: Your portrait! You never gave me your portrait.

RAINA [*quickly*]: Do you mean to say you never got it?

BLUNTSCHLI: No. [*He sits down beside her, with renewed interest, and says, with some complacency*] When did you send it to me?

RAINA [*indignantly*]: I did not send it to you. [*She turns her head away, and adds, reluctantly*] It was in the pocket of that coat.

BLUNTSCHLI [*pursuing his lips and rounding his eyes*]: Oh-o-oh! I never found it. It must be there still.

RAINA [*springing up*]: There still! for my father to find the first time he puts his hand in his pocket! Oh, how could you be so stupid?

BLUNTSCHLI [*rising also*]: It doesnt matter: I suppose it's only a photograph: how can he tell who it was intended for? Tell him he put it there himself.

RAINA [*bitterly*]: Yes: that is so clever! isnt it? [*Distractedly*] Oh! what shall I do?

BLUNTSCHLI: Ah, I see. You wrote something on it. That was rash.

RAINA [*vexed almost to tears*]: Oh, to have done such a thing for you, who care no more—except to laugh at me—oh! Are you sure nobody has touched it?

BLUNTSCHLI: Well, I can't be quite sure. You see, I couldn't carry it about with me all the time: one cant take much luggage on active service.

RAINA: What did you do with it?

BLUNTSCHLI: When I got through to Pirot I had to put it in safe keeping somehow. I thought of the railway cloak room; but thats the surest place to get looted in modern warfare. So I pawned it.

RAINA: Pawned it!!!

BLUNTSCHLI: I know it doesn't sound nice: but it was much the safest plan. I redeemed it the day before yesterday. Heaven only knows whether the pawnbroker cleared out the pockets or not.

RAINA [*furious: throwing the words right into his face*]: You have a low shopkeeping mind. You think of things that would never come into a gentleman's head.

BLUNTSCHLI [*phlegmatically*]: Thats the Swiss national character, dear lady. [*He returns to the table.*]

RAINA: Oh, I wish I had never met you. [*She flounces away, and sits at the window fuming.*]

Louka comes in with a heap of letters and telegrams on her salver, and crosses, with her bold free gait, to the table. Her left sleeve is looped up to the shoulder with a brooch, shewing her naked arm, with a broad gilt bracelet covering the bruise.

LOUKA [*to Bluntschli*]: For you. [*She empties the salver with a fling on to the table*]: The messenger is waiting. [*She is determined not to be civil to an enemy, even if she must bring him his letters.*]

BLUNTSCHLI [*to Raina*]: Will you excuse me: the last postal delivery that reached me was three weeks ago. These are the subsequent accumulations. Four telegrams: a week old. [*He opens one.*] Oho! Bad news!

[9] *"Hand aufs Herz!"* German: "Hand on the heart!"

RAINA [*rising and advancing a little remorsefully*]:   Bad news?

BLUNTSCHLI: My father's dead. [*He looks at the telegram with his lips pursed, musing on the unexpected change in his arrangements. Louka crosses herself hastily.*]

RAINA: Oh, how very sad!

BLUNTSCHLI: Yes: I shall have to start for home in an hour. He has left a lot of big hotels behind him to be looked after. [*He takes up a fat letter in a long blue envelope.*] Here's a whacking letter from the family solicitor. [*He puts out the enclosures and glances over them.*] Great Heavens! Seventy! Two hundred! [*In a crescendo of dismay*] Four hundred! Four thousand!! Nine thousand six hundred!!! What on earth am I to do with them all?

RAINA [*timidly*]:   Nine thousand hotels?

BLUNTSCHLI: Hotels! nonsense. If you only knew! Oh, it's too ridiculous! Excuse me: I must give my fellow orders about starting. [*He leaves the room hastily, with the documents in his hand.*]

LOUKA [*knowing instinctively that she can annoy Raina by disparaging Bluntschli*]:   He has not much heart, that Swiss. He has not a word of grief for his poor father.

RAINA [*bitterly*]:   Grief! A man who has been doing nothing but killing people for years! What does he care? What does any soldier care? [*She goes to the door, restraining her tears with difficulty.*]

LOUKA: Major Saranoff has been fighting too; and he has plenty of heart left. [*Raina, at the door, draws herself up haughtily and goes out.*] Aha! I thought you wouldnt get much feeling out of your soldier. [*She is following Raina when Nicola enters with an armful of logs for the stove.*]

NICOLA [*grinning amorously at her*]:   Ive been trying all the afternoon to get a minute alone with you, my girl. [*His countenance changes as he notices her arm.*] Why, what fashion is that of wearing your sleeve, child?

LOUKA [*proudly*]:   My own fashion.

NICOLA: Indeed! If the mistress catches you, she'll talk to you. [*He puts the logs down, and seats himself comfortably on the ottoman.*]

LOUKA: Is that any reason why you should take it on yourself to talk to me?

NICOLA: Come! dont be so contrary with me. Ive some good news for you. [*She sits down beside him. He takes out some paper money. Louka, with an eager gleam in her eyes, tries to snatch it; but he shifts it quickly to his left hand, out of her reach.*] See! a twenty leva bill! Sergius gave me that, out of pure swagger. A fool and his money are soon parted. Theres ten levas more. The Swiss gave me that for backing up the mistress' and Raina's lies about him. He's no fool, he isnt. You should have heard old Catherine downstairs as polite as you please to me, telling me not to mind the Major being a little impatient; for they knew what a good servant I was—after making a fool and a liar of me before them all! The twenty will go to our savings; and you shall have the ten to spend if youll only talk to me so as to remind me I'm a human being. I get tired of being a servant occasionally.

LOUKA: Yes: sell your manhood for 30 levas, and buy me for 10! [*Rising scornfully*] Keep your money. You were born to be a servant. I was not. When you set up your shop you will only be everybody's servant instead of somebody's servant. [*She goes moodily to the table and seats herself regally in Sergius's chair.*]

NICOLA [*picking up his logs, and going to the stove*]:   Ah, wait til you see. We shall have our evenings to ourselves; and I shall be master in my own house, I promise you. [*He throws the logs down and kneels at the stove.*]

LOUKA: You shall never be master in mine.

NICOLA [*turning, still on his knees, and squatting down rather forlornly on his calves, daunted by her implacable disdain*]:   You have a great ambition in you, Louka. Remember: if any luck comes to you, it was I that made a woman of you.

LOUKA: You!

NICOLA [*scrambling up and going to her*]: Yes, me. Who was it made you give up wearing a couple of pounds of false black hair on your head and reddening your lips and cheeks like any other Bulgarian girl! I did. Who taught you to trim your nails, and keep your hands clean, and be dainty about yourself, like a fine Russian lady! Me: do you hear that? me! [*She tosses her head defiantly; and he turns away, adding more coolly*] Ive often thought that if Raina were out of the way, and you just a little less of a fool and Sergius just a little more of one, you might come to be one of my grandest customers, instead of only being my wife and costing me money.

LOUKA: I believe you would rather be my servant than my husband. You would make more out of me. Oh, I know that soul of yours.

NICOLA [*going closer to her for greater emphasis*]: Never you mind my soul; but just listen to my advice. If you want to be a lady, your present behaviour to me wont do at all, unless when we're alone. It's too sharp and impudent; and impudence is a sort of familiarity: it shews affection for me. And dont you try being high and mighty with me, either. Youre like all country girls: you think it's genteel to treat a servant the way I treat a stableboy. Thats only your ignorance; and dont you forget it. And dont be so ready to defy everybody. Act as if you expected to have your own way, not as if you expected to be ordered about. The way to get on as a lady is the same as the way to get on as a servant: youve got to know your place: thats the secret of it. And you may depend on me to know my place if you get promoted. Think over it, my girl. I'll stand by you: one servant should always stand by another.

LOUKA [*rising impatiently*]: Oh, I must behave in my own way. You take all the courage out of me with your cold-blooded wisdom. Go

and put those logs in the fire: thats the sort of thing you understand.

Before Nicola can retort, Sergius comes in. He checks himself a moment on seeing Louka; then goes to the stove.

SERGIUS [*to Nicola*]: I am not in the way of your work, I hope.

NICOLA [*in a smooth, elderly manner*]: Oh no, sir: thank you kindly. I was only speaking to this foolish girl about her habit of running up here to the library whenever she gets a chance, to look at the books. Thats the worst of her education, sir: it gives her habits above her station. [*To Louka*] Make that table tidy, Louka, for the Major. [*He goes out sedately.*]

Louka, without looking at Sergius, pretends to arrange the papers on the table. He crosses slowly to her, and studies the arrangement of her sleeve reflectively.

SERGIUS: Let me see: is there a mark there? [*He turns up the bracelet and sees the bruise made by his grasp. She stands motionless, not looking at him: fascinated, but on her guard.*] Ffff! Does it hurt?

LOUKA: Yes.

SERGIUS: Shall I cure it?

LOUKA [*instantly withdrawing herself proudly, but still not looking at him*]: No. You cannot cure it now.

SERGIUS [*masterfully*]: Quite sure? [*He makes a movement as if to take her in his arms.*]

LOUKA: Dont trifle with me, please. An officer should not trifle with a servant.

SERGIUS [*indicating the bruise with a merciless stroke of his forefinger*]: That was no trifle, Louka.

LOUKA [*flinching; then looking at him for the first time*]: Are you sorry?

SERGIUS [*with measured emphasis, folding his arms*]: I am never sorry.

LOUKA [*wistfully*]: I wish I could believe a man could be as unlike a woman as that. I wonder are you really a brave man?

SERGIUS [*unaffectedly, relaxing his attitude*]: Yes: I am a brave man. My heart jumped like a woman's at the first shot; but in the charge

I found that I was brave. Yes: that at least is real about me.

LOUKA: Did you find in the charge that the men whose fathers are poor like mine were any less brave than the men who are rich like you?

SERGIUS [*with bitter levity*]: Not a bit. They all slashed and cursed and yelled like heroes. Psha! the courage to rage and kill is cheap. I have an English bull terrier who has as much of that sort of courage as the whole Bulgarian nation, and the whole Russian nation at its back. But he lets my groom thrash him, all the same. Thats your soldier all over! No, Louka: your poor men can cut throats; but they are afraid of their officers; they put up with insults and blows; they stand by and see one another punished like children: aye, and help to do it when they are ordered. And the officers!!! Well [*with a short harsh laugh*] *I* am an officer. Oh, [*fervently*] give me the man who will defy to the death any power on earth or in heaven that sets itself up against his own will and conscience: he alone is the brave man.

LOUKA: How easy it is to talk! Men never seem to me to grow up: they all have schoolboy's ideas. You dont know what true courage is.

SERGIUS [*ironically*]: Indeed! I am willing to be instructed. [*He sits on the ottoman, sprawling magnificently.*]

LOUKA: Look at me! How much am I allowed to have my own will? I have to get your room ready for you: to sweep and dust, to fetch and carry. How could that degrade me if it did not degrade you to have it done for you? But [*with subdued passion*] if I were Empress of Russia, above everyone in the world, then!! Ah then, though according to you I could shew no courage at all, you should see, you should see.

SERGIUS: What would you do, most noble Empress?

LOUKA: I would marry the man I loved, which no other queen in Europe has the courage to do. If I loved you, though you would be as far beneath me as I am beneath you, I would dare to be the equal of my inferior. Would you dare as much if you loved me? No: if you felt the beginnings of love for me you would not let it grow. You would not dare: you would marry a rich man's daughter because you would be afraid of what other people would say of you.

SERGIUS [*bounding up*]: You lie: it is not so, by all the stars! If I loved you, and I were the Czar himself, I would set you on the throne by my side. You know that I love another woman, a woman as high above you as heaven is above earth. And you are jealous of her.

LOUKA: I have no reason to be. She will never marry you now. The man I told you of has come back. She will marry the Swiss.

SERGIUS [*recoiling*]: The Swiss!

LOUKA: A man worth ten of you. Then you can come to me; and I will refuse you. You are not good enough for me. [*She turns to the door.*]

SERGIUS [*springing after her and catching her fiercely in his arms*]: I will kill the Swiss; and afterwards I will do as I please with you.

LOUKA [*in his arms, passive and steadfast*]: The Swiss will kill you, perhaps. He has beaten you in love. He may beat you in war.

SERGIUS [*tormentedly*]: Do you think I believe that she—she! whose worst thoughts are higher than your best ones, is capable of trifling with another man behind my back?

LOUKA: Do you think she would believe the Swiss if he told her now that I am in your arms?

SERGIUS [*releasing her in despair*]: Damnation! Oh, damnation! Mockery! mockery everywhere! everything I think is mocked by everything I do. [*He strikes himself frantically on the breast.*] Coward! liar! fool! Shall I kill myself like a man, or live and pretend to laugh at myself? [*She again turns to go.*] Louka. [*She stops near the door.*] Remember: you belong to me.

LOUKA [*turning*]: What does that mean? An insult?

SERGIUS [*commandingly*]: It means that you love me, and that I have had you here in my arms, and will perhaps have you there again. Whether that is an insult I neither know nor care: take it as you please. But [*vehemently*] I will not be a coward and a trifler. If I choose to love you, I dare marry you, in spite of all Bulgaria. If these hands ever touch you again, they shall touch my affianced bride.

LOUKA: We shall see whether you dare keep your word. And take care. I will not wait long.

SERGIUS [*again folding his arms and standing motionless in the middle of the room*]: Yes: we shall see. And you shall wait my pleasure.

Bluntschli, much preoccupied, with his papers still in his hand, enters, leaving the door open for Louka to go out. He goes across to the table, glancing at her as he passes. Sergius, without altering his resolute attitude, watches him steadily. Louka goes out, leaving the door open.

BLUNTSCHLI [*absently, sitting at the table as before, and putting down his papers*]: Thats a remarkable looking young woman.

SERGIUS [*gravely, without moving*]: Captain Bluntschli.

BLUNTSCHLI: Eh?

SERGIUS: You have deceived me. You are my rival. I brook no rivals. At six o'clock I shall be in the drilling-ground on the Klissoura road, alone, on horseback, with my sabre. Do you understand?

BLUNTSCHLI [*staring, but sitting quite at his ease*]: Oh, thank you: thats a cavalry man's proposal. I'm in the artillery; and I have the choice of weapons. If I go, I shall take a machine gun. And there shall be no mistake about the cartridges this time.

SERGIUS [*flushing, but with deadly coldness*]: Take care, sir. It is not our custom in Bulgaria to allow invitations of that kind to be trifled with.

BLUNTSCHLI [*warmly*]: Pooh! dont talk to me about Bulgaria. You dont know what fighting is. But have it your own way. Bring your sabre along. I'll meet you.

SERGIUS [*fiercely delighted to find his opponent a man of spirit*]: Well said, Switzer. Shall I lend you my best horse?

BLUNTSCHLI: No: thank you all the same, my dear fellow. [*Raina comes in, and hears the next sentence.*] I shall fight you on foot. Horseback's too dangerous; I dont want to kill you if I can help it.

RAINA [*hurrying forward anxiously*]: I have heard what Captain Bluntschli said, Sergius. You are going to fight. Why? [*Sergius turns away in silence, and goes to the stove, where he stands watching her as she continues, to Bluntschli*] What about?

BLUNTSCHLI: I dont know: he hasnt told me. Better not interfere, dear young lady. No harm will be done: Ive often acted as sword instructor. He wont be able to touch me; and I'll not hurt him. It will save explanations. In the morning I shall be off home; and youll never see me or hear of me again. You and he will then make it up and live happily ever after.

RAINA [*turning away deeply hurt, almost with a sob in her voice*]: I never said I wanted to see you again.

SERGIUS [*striding forward*]: Ha! That is a confession.

RAINA [*haughtily*]: What do you mean?

SERGIUS: You love that man!

RAINA [*scandalized*]: Sergius!

SERGIUS: You allow him to make love to you behind my back, just as you treat me as your affianced husband behind his. Bluntschli: you knew our relations; and you deceived me. It is for that that I call you to account, not for having received favors *I* never enjoyed.

BLUNTSCHLI [*jumping up indignantly*]: Stuff! Rubbish! I have received no favors. Why, the young lady doesnt even know whether I'm married or not.

RAINA [*forgetting herself*]: Oh! [*Collapsing on the ottoman*] Are you?

SERGIUS: You see the young lady's concern, Captain Bluntschli. Denial is useless. You have enjoyed the privilege of being received in her own room, late at night—

BLUNTSCHLI [*interrupting him pepperily*]: Yes, you blockhead! she received me with a pistol at her head. Your cavalry were at my heels. I'd have blown out her brains if she'd uttered a cry.

SERGIUS [*taken aback*]: Bluntschli! Raina: is this true?

RAINA [*rising in wrathful majesty*]: Oh, how dare you, how dare you?

BLUNTSCHLI: Apologize, man: apologize. [*He resumes his seat at the table.*]

SERGIUS [*with the old measured emphasis, folding his arms*]: I never apologize!

RAINA [*passionately*]: This is the doing of that friend of yours, Captain Bluntschli. It is he who is spreading this horrible story about me. [*She walks about excitedly.*]

BLUNTSCHLI: No: he's dead. Burnt alive.

RAINA [*stopping, shocked*]: Burnt alive!

BLUNTSCHLI: Shot in the hip in a woodyard. Couldnt drag himself out. Your fellows' shells set the timber on fire and burnt him, with half a dozen other poor devils in the same predicament.

RAINA: How horrible!

SERGIUS: And how ridiculous! Oh, war! war! the dream of patriots and heroes! A fraud, Bluntschli. A hollow sham, like love.

RAINA [*outraged*]: Like love! You say that before me!

BLUNTSCHLI: Come, Saranoff: that matter is explained.

SERGIUS: A hollow sham, I say. Would you have come back here if nothing had passed between you except at the muzzle of your pistol? Raina is mistaken about your friend who was burnt. He was not my informant.

RAINA: Who then? [*Suddenly guessing the truth*] Ah, Louka! my maid! my servant! You were with her this morning all that time after—after—Oh, what sort of god is this I have been worshipping! [*He meets her gaze with sardonic enjoyment of her disenchantment. Angered all the more, she goes closer to him, and says, in a lower, intenser tone*] Do you know that I looked out of the window as I went upstairs, to have another sight of my hero; and I saw something I did not understand then. I know now that you were making love to her.

SERGIUS [*with grim humor*]: You saw that?

RAINA: Only too well. [*She turns away, and throws herself on the divan under the centre window, quite overcome.*]

SERGIUS [*cynically*]: Raina: our romance is shattered. Life's a farce.

BLUNTSCHLI [*to Raina, whimsically*]: You see: he's found himself out now.

SERGIUS [*going to him*]: Bluntschli: I have allowed you to call me a blockhead. You may now call me a coward as well. I refuse to fight you. Do you know why?

BLUNTSCHLI: No; but it doesnt matter. I didn't ask the reason when you cried on; and I dont ask the reason now that you cry off. I'm a professional soldier! I fight when I have to, and am very glad to get out of it when I havnt to. Youre only an amateur: you think fighting's an amusement.

SERGIUS [*sitting down at the table, nose to nose with him*]: You shall hear the reason all the same, my professional. The reason is that it takes two men—real men—men of heart, blood and honor—to make a genuine combat. I could no more fight with you than I could make love to an ugly woman. Youve no magnetism: youre not a man: youre a machine.

BLUNTSCHLI [*apologetically*]: Quite true, quite true. I always was that sort of chap. I'm very sorry.

SERGIUS: Psha!

BLUNTSCHLI: But now that youve found that life isnt a farce, but something quite sensible and serious, what further obstacle is there to your happiness?

RAINA [*rising*]: You are very solicitous about my happiness and his. Do you forget his new love—Louka? It is not you that he must fight now, but his rival, Nicola.

SERGIUS: Rival!! [*bounding half across the room*]

RAINA: Dont you know that theyre engaged?

SERGIUS: Nicola! Are fresh abysses opening? Nicola!

RAINA [*sarcastically*]: A shocking sacrifice, isnt it? Such beauty! such intellect! such modesty! wasted on a middle-aged servant man. Really, Sergius, you cannot stand by and allow such a thing. It would be unworthy of your chivalry.

SERGIUS [*losing all self-control*]: Viper! Viper! [*He rushes to and fro, raging.*]

BLUNTSCHLI: Look here, Saranoff: youre getting the worst of this.

RAINA [*getting angrier*]: Do you realize what he has done, Captain Bluntschli? He has set this girl as a spy on us; and her reward is that he makes love to her.

SERGIUS: False! Monstrous!

RAINA: Monstrous! [*Confronting him*] Do you deny that she told you about Captain Bluntschli being in my room?

SERGIUS: No; but—

RAINA [*interrupting*]: Do you deny that you were making love to her when she told you?

SERGIUS: No; but I tell you—

RAINA [*cutting him short contemptuously*]: It is unnecessary to tell us anything more. That is quite enough for us. [*She turns away from him and sweeps majestically back to the window.*]

BLUNTSCHLI [*quietly, as Sergius, in an agony of mortification, sinks on the ottoman, clutching his averted head between his fists*]: I told you you were getting the worst of it, Saranoff.

SERGIUS: Tiger cat!

RAINA [*running excitedly to Bluntschli*]: You hear this man calling me names, Captain Bluntschli?

BLUNTSCHLI: What else can he do, dear lady? He must defend himself somehow. Come [*very persuasively*]: dont quarrel. What good does it do?

Raina, with a gasp, sits down on the ottoman, and after a vain effort to look vexedly at Bluntschli, falls a victim to her sense of humor, and actually leans back babyishly against the writhing shoulder of Sergius.

SERGIUS: Engaged to Nicola! Ha! ha! Ah well, Bluntschli, you are right to take this huge imposture of a world coolly.

RAINA [*quaintly to Bluntschli, with an intuitive guess at his state of mind*]: I daresay you think us a couple of grown-up babies, dont you?

SERGIUS [*grinning savagely*]: He does: he does. Swiss civilization nursetending Bulgarian barbarism, eh?

BLUNTSCHLI [*blushing*]: Not at all, I assure you. I'm only very glad to get you two quieted. There! there! let's be pleasant and talk it over in a friendly way. Where is this other young lady?

RAINA: Listening at the door, probably.

SERGIUS [*shivering as if a bullet had struck him, and speaking with quiet but deep indignation*]: I will prove that that, at least, is a calumny. [*He goes with dignity to the door and opens it. A yell of fury bursts from him as he looks out. He darts into the passage, and returns dragging in Louka, whom he flings violently against the table, exclaiming*] Judge her, Bluntschli. You, the cool impartial man: judge the eavesdropper.

Louka stands her ground, proud and silent.

BLUNTSCHLI [*shaking his head*]: I mustnt judge her. I once listened myself outside a tent when there was a mutiny brewing. It's all a question of the degree of provocation. My life was at stake.

LOUKA: My love was at stake. I am not ashamed.

RAINA [*contemptuously*]: Your love! Your curiosity, you mean.

LOUKA [*facing her and returning her contempt with interest*]: My love, stronger than anything you can feel, even for your chocolate cream soldier.

SERGIUS [*with quick suspicion, to Louka*]: What does that mean?

LOUKA [*fiercely*]: I mean—

SERGIUS [*interrupting her slightingly*]: Oh, I remember: the ice pudding. A paltry taunt, girl!

Major Petkoff enters, in his shirtsleeves.

PETKOFF: Excuse my shirtsleeves, gentlemen. Raina: somebody has been wearing that coat of mine: I'll swear it. Somebody with a differently shaped back. It's all burst open at the sleeve. Your mother is mending it. I wish she'd make haste: I shall catch cold. [*He looks more attentively at them.*] Is anything the matter?

RAINA: No. [*She sits down at the stove, with a tranquil air.*]

SERGIUS: Oh no. [*He sits down at the end of the table, as at first.*]

BLUNTSCHLI [*who is already seated*]: Nothing. Nothing.

PETKOFF [*sitting down on the ottoman in his old place*]: Thats all right. [*He notices Louka.*] Anything the matter, Louka?

LOUKA: No, sir.

PETKOFF [*genially*]: Thats all right. [*He sneezes.*] Go and ask your mistress for my coat, like a good girl, will you?

Nicola enters with the coat. Louka makes a pretence of having business in the room by taking the little table with the hookah away to the wall near the windows.

RAINA [*rising quickly as she sees the coat on Nicola's arm*]: Here it is papa. Give it to me Nicola; and do you put some more wood on the fire. [*She takes the coat, and brings it to the Major, who stands up to put it on. Nicola attends to the fire.*]

PETKOFF: [*to Raina, teasing her affectionately*]: Aha! Going to be very good to poor old papa just for one day after his return from the wars, eh?

RAINA [*with solemn reproach*]: Ah, how can you say that to me, father?

PETKOFF: Well, well, only a joke, little one. Come: give me a kiss. [*She kisses him.*] Now give me the coat.

RAINA: No: I am going to put it on for you. Turn your back. [*He turns his back and feels behind him with his arms for the sleeves. She dexterously takes the photograph from the pocket and throws it on the table before Bluntschli, who covers it with a sheet of paper under the very nose of Sergius, who looks on amazed, with his suspicions roused in the highest degree. She then helps Petkoff on with his coat.*] There, dear! Now are you comfortable?

PETKOFF: Quite, little love. Thanks. [*He sits down; and Raina returns to her seat near the stove.*] Oh, by the bye, Ive found something funny. Whats the meaning of this? [*He puts his hand into the picked pocket.*] Eh? Hallo! [*He tries the other pocket.*] Well, I could have sworn—! [*Much puzzled, he tries the breast pocket.*] I wonder—[*trying the original pocket*] Where can it—? [*He rises, exclaiming*] Your mother's taken it!

RAINA [*very red*]: Taken what?

PETKOFF: Your photograph, with the inscription: "Raina, to her Chocolate Cream Soldier: a Souvenir." Now you know theres something more in this than meets the eye; and I'm going to find it out. [*Shouting*] Nicola!

NICOLA [*coming to him*]: Sir!

PETKOFF: Did you spoil any pastry of Miss Raina's this morning?

NICOLA: You heard Miss Raina say that I did, sir.

PETKOFF: I know that, you idiot. Was it true?

NICOLA: I am sure Miss Raina is incapable of saying anything that is not true, sir.

PETKOFF: Are you? Then I'm not. [*Turning to the others*] Come: do you think I dont see it all? [*He goes to Sergius, and slaps him on the shoulder.*] Sergius: youre the chocolate cream soldier, arnt you?

SERGIUS [*starting up*]: I! A chocolate cream soldier! Certainly not.

PETKOFF: Not! [*He looks at them. They are all very serious and very conscious.*] Do you mean to tell me that Raina sends things like that to other men?

SERGIUS [*enigmatically*]: The world is not such an innocent place as we used to think, Petkoff.

BLUNTSCHLI [*rising*]: It's all right, Major. I'm the chocolate cream soldier. [*Petkoff and Sergius are equally astonished.*] The gracious young lady saved my life by giving me chocolate creams when I was starving: shall I ever forget their flavour! My late friend Stolz told you the story of Pirot. I was the fugitive.

PETKOFF: You! [*He gasps.*] Sergius: do you remember how those two women went on this morning when we mentioned it? [*Sergius smiles cynically. Petkoff confronts Raina severely.*] Youre a nice young woman, arnt you?

RAINA [*bitterly*]: Major Saranoff has changed his mind. And when I wrote that on the photograph, I did not know that Captain Bluntschli was married.

BLUNTSCHLI [*startled into vehement protest*]: I'm not married.

RAINA [*with deep reproach*]: You said you were.

BLUNTSCHLI: I did not. I positively did not. I never was married in my life.

PETKOFF [*exasperated*]: Raina: will you kindly inform me, if I am not asking too much, which of these gentlemen you are engaged to?

RAINA: To neither of them. This young lady [*introducing Louka, who faces them all proudly*] is the object of Major Saranoff's affections at present.

PETKOFF: Louka! Are you mad, Sergius? Why, this girl's engaged to Nicola.

NICOLA: I beg your pardon, sir. There is a mistake. Louka is not engaged to me.

PETKOFF: Not engaged to you, you scoundrel! Why, you had twenty-five levas from me on the day of your betrothal; and she had that gilt bracelet from Miss Raina.

NICOLA [*with cool unction*]: We gave it out so, sir. But it was only to give Louka protection. She had a soul above her station; and I have been no more than her confidential servant. I intend, as you know, sir, to set up a shop later on in Sofia; and I look forward to her custom and recommendation should she marry into the nobility. [*He goes out with impressive discretion, leaving them all staring after him.*]

PETKOFF [*breaking the silence*]: Well, I am— hm!

SERGIUS: This is either the finest heroism or the most crawling baseness. Which is it, Bluntschli?

BLUNTSCHLI: Never mind whether it's heroism or baseness. Nicola's the ablest man Ive met in Bulgaria. I'll make him manager of a hotel if he can speak French and German.

LOUKA [*suddenly breaking out at Sergius*]: I have been insulted by everyone here. You set them the example. You owe me an apology.

Sergius, like a repeating clock of which the spring has been touched, immediately begins to fold his arms.

BLUNTSCHLI [*before he can speak*]: It's no use. He never apologizes.

LOUKA: Not to you, his equal and his enemy. To me, his poor servant, he will not refuse to apologize.

SERGIUS [*approvingly*]: You are right. [*He bends his knee in his grandest manner.*] Forgive me.

LOUKA: I forgive you. [*She timidly gives him*

her hand, which he kisses.] That touch makes me your affianced wife.

SERGIUS [*springing up*]:   Ah! I forgot that.

LOUKA [*coldly*]:   You can withdraw if you like.

SERGIUS: Withdraw! Never! You belong to me. [*He puts his arm about her.*]

   Catherine comes in and finds Louka in Sergius' arms, with all the rest gazing at them in bewildered astonishment.

CATHERINE: What does this mean?

   Sergius releases Louka.

PETKOFF: Well, my dear, it appears that Sergius is going to marry Louka instead of Raina. [*She is about to break out indignantly at him: he stops her by exclaiming testily*] Dont blame me: Ive nothing to do with it. [*He retreats to the stove.*]

CATHERINE: Marry Louka! Sergius: you are bound by your word to us!

SERGIUS [*folding his arms*]:   Nothing binds me.

BLUNTSCHLI [*much pleased by this piece of common sense*]:   Saranoff: your hand. My congratulations. These heroics of yours have their practical side after all. [*To Louka*] Gracious young lady: the best wishes of a good Republican! [10] [*He kisses her hand, to Raina's great disgust, and returns to his seat.*]

CATHERINE: Louka: you have been telling stories.

LOUKA: I have done Raina no harm.

CATHERINE [*haughtily*]:   Raina!

   Raina, equally indignant, almost snorts at the liberty.

LOUKA: I have a right to call her Raina: she calls me Louka. I told Major Saranoff she would never marry him if the Swiss gentleman came back.

BLUNTSCHLI [*rising, much surprised*]:   Hallo!

LOUKA [*turning to Raina*]:   I thought you were fonder of him than of Sergius. You know best whether I was right.

[10] *Republican*   Believer in popular government.

BLUNTSCHLI: What nonsense! I assure you, my dear Major, my dear Madame, the gracious young lady simply saved my life, nothing else. She never cared two straws for me. Why, bless my heart and soul, look at the young lady and look at me. She, rich, young, beautiful, with her imagination full of fairy princes and noble natures and cavalry charges and goodness knows what! And I, a commonplace Swiss soldier who hardly knows what a decent life is after fifteen years of barracks and battles: a vagabond, a man who has spoiled all his chances in life through an incurably romantic disposition, a man—

SERGIUS [*starting as if a needle had pricked him and interrupting Bluntschli in incredulous amazement*]:   Excuse me, Bluntschli: what did you say had spoiled your chances in life?

BLUNTSCHLI [*promptly*]:   An incurably romantic disposition. I ran away from home twice when I was a boy. I went into the army instead of into my father's business. I climbed the balcony of this house when a man of sense would have dived into the nearest cellar. I came sneaking back here to have another look at the young lady when any other man of my age would have sent the coat back—

PETKOFF: My coat!

BLUNTSCHLI: —yes: thats the coat I mean—would have sent it back and gone quietly home. Do you suppose I am the sort of fellow a young girl falls in love with? Why, look at our ages! I'm thirty-four: I dont suppose the young lady is much over seventeen. [*This estimate produces a marked sensation, all the rest turning and staring at one another. He proceeds innocently.*] All that adventure which was life or death to me, was only a schoolgirl's game to her—chocolate creams and hide and seek. Heres the proof! [*He takes the photograph from the table.*] Now, I ask you, would a woman who took the affair seriously have sent me this and written on it "Raina, to her Chocolate Cream Soldier: a

Souvenir"? [*He exhibits the photograph triumphantly, as if it settled the matter beyond all possibility of refutation.*]

PETKOFF: Thats what I was looking for. How the deuce did it get there? [*He comes from the stove to look at it, and sits down on the ottoman.*]

BLUNTSCHLI [*to Raina, complacently*]: I have put everything right, I hope, gracious young lady.

RAINA [*going to the table to face him*]: I quite agree with your account of yourself. You are a romantic idiot. [*Bluntschli is unspeakably taken aback.*] Next time, I hope you will know the difference between a schoolgirl of seventeen and a woman of twenty-three.

BLUNTSCHLI [*stupefied*]: Twenty-three.

Raina snaps the photograph contemptuously from his hand; tears it up; throws the pieces in his face; and sweeps back to her former place.

SERGIUS [*with grim enjoyment of his rival's discomfiture*]: Bluntschli: my one last belief is gone. Your sagacity is a fraud, like everything else. You have less sense than even I!

BLUNTSCHLI [*overwhelmed*]: Twenty-three! Twenty-three!! [*He considers.*] Hm! [*Swiftly making up his mind and coming to his host*] In that case, Major Petkoff, I beg to propose formally to become a suitor for your daughter's hand, in place of Major Saranoff retired.

RAINA: You dare!

BLUNTSCHLI: If you were twenty-three when you said those things to me this afternoon, I shall take them seriously.

CATHERINE [*loftily polite*]: I doubt, sir, whether you quite realize either my daughter's position or that of Major Sergius Saranoff, whose place you propose to take. The Petkoffs and the Saranoffs are known as the richest and most important families in the country.

Our position is almost historical: we can go back for twenty years.

PETKOFF: Oh, never mind that, Catherine. [*To Bluntschli*] We should be most happy, Bluntschli, if it were only a question of your position; but hang it, you know, Raina is accustomed to a very comfortable establishment. Sergius keeps twenty horses.

BLUNTSCHLI: But who wants twenty horses? We're not going to keep a circus.

CATHERINE [*severely*]: My daughter, sir, is accustomed to a first-rate stable.

RAINA: Hush, mother: youre making me ridiculous.

BLUNTSCHLI: Oh well, if it comes to a question of an establishment, here goes! [*He darts impetuously to the table; seizes the papers in the blue envelope; and turns to Sergius.*] How many horses did you say?

SERGIUS: Twenty, noble Switzer.

BLUNTSCHLI: I have two hundred horses. [*They are amazed.*] How many carriages?

SERGIUS: Three.

BLUNTSCHLI: I have seventy. Twenty-four of them will hold twelve inside, besides two on the box, without counting the driver and conductor. How many tablecloths have you?

SERGIUS: How the deuce do I know?

BLUNTSCHLI: Have you four thousand?

SERGIUS: No.

BLUNTSCHLI: I have. I have nine thousand six hundred pairs of sheets and blankets, with two thousand four hundred eider-down quilts. I have ten thousand knives and forks, and the same quantity of dessert spoons. I have three hundred servants. I have six palatial establishments, besides two livery stables, a tea garden, and a private house. I have four medals for distinguished services; I have the rank of an officer and the standing of a gentleman; and I have three native languages. Shew me any man in Bulgaria that can offer as much!

PETKOFF [*with childish awe*]: Are you Emperor of Switzerland?

BLUNTSCHLI: My rank is the highest known in Switzerland: I am a free citizen.

CATHERINE: Then, Captain Bluntschli, since you are my daughter's choice—

RAINA [*mutinously*]: He's not.

CATHERINE [*ignoring her*]: —I shall not stand in the way of her happiness. [*Petkoff is about to speak.*] That is Major Petkoff's feeling also.

PETKOFF: Oh, I shall be only too glad. Two hundred horses! Whew!

SERGIUS: What says the lady?

RAINA [*pretending to sulk*]: The lady says that he can keep his tablecloths and his omnibuses. I am not here to be sold to the highest bidder. [*She turns her back on him.*]

BLUNTSCHLI: I wont take that answer. I appealed to you as a fugitive, a beggar, and a starving man. You accepted me. You gave me your hand to kiss, your bed to sleep in, and your roof to shelter me.

RAINA: I did not give them to the Emperor of Switzerland.

BLUNTSCHLI: Thats just what I say. [*He catches her by the shoulders and turns her face-to-face with him.*] Now tell us whom you did give them to.

RAINA [*succumbing with a shy smile*]: To my chocolate cream soldier.

BLUNTSCHLI [*with a boyish laugh of delight*]: Thatll do. Thank you. [*He looks at his watch and suddenly becomes businesslike.*] Time's up, Major. Youve managed those regiments so well that youre sure to be asked to get rid of some of the infantry of the Timok division. Send them home by way of Lom Palanka. Saranoff: dont get married until I come back: I shall be here punctually at five in the evening on Tuesday fortnight. Gracious ladies [*his heels click*] good evening. [*He makes them a military bow, and goes.*]

SERGIUS. What a man! Is he a man!

For Discussion

1. Describe the character of Bluntschli. Is he the hero? What does Bluntschli mean when he says, "What use are cartridges in battle? I always carry chocolate instead?" What aspects of his character are displayed by this statement?

2. Does Shaw appear to approve or disapprove of Bluntschli's attitude toward war? What does Shaw appear to think of Bluntschli as a man? In what way should the final line of the play be interpreted?

3. How does Raina change during the course of the play? What is her attitude toward Bluntschli at their first meeting? What is her attitude toward him at the end of the play? Try to define the reasons why she ultimately chooses Bluntschli over Sergius.

4. Describe the character of Sergius. Referring to specific scenes in the play, show how Sergius contrasts with Bluntschli. What is Sergius's major problem in life? Why does he find it difficult to be himself? Is Sergius really a brave man, or does he merely behave the way he feels he is expected to behave?

Do answers to the last three questions suggest a criticism of society on Shaw's part? Is Sergius a sympathetic character? In what way is his flirting with Louka a comment on romantic nineteenth-century ideas about love? What kind of person is Louka? In what ways does she contrast with Raina?

5. How does the Petkoffs' attitude toward Bluntschli change during the course of the play? What forces this change? In what way does this change become a social comment by Shaw?

6. Identify the different levels of society represented by the characters.

7. The satirist believes that impassioned sermons and honest pleadings have no effect on man's behavior. He chooses to whip society into good common sense by laughing at it. Explain why *Arms and the Man* might be accurately described as a satirical comedy.

8. Which individual scene most effectively expresses the central meaning of the play? How does it do this?

The Dwarf Trees

SEAMI MOTOKIYO

The nōh *or* nō *plays of Japan (literally: "very accomplished performances") reach back to the fourteenth and fifteenth centuries. Seami Motokiyo, author of* The Dwarf Trees, *lived from 1363 to 1444. The nōh play is one of the most formal and traditional of arts; the secrets and techniques of the actors are passed down in families through many generations. During 600 years there have been few changes in the plays or in the style of their productions. There is little scenery, but the costumes are elaborate and the actors wear wooden masks. There is no attempt at realism; a group of musicians sits at the rear of the stage in full view of the audience.*

Japanese drama does not depend upon the kind of suspense an audience looks for in Western theater. Since the plays have been performed for hundreds of years, the audience probably knows the story before the play begins. The excitement comes from the beauty of the actors' performances. Thus, in The Dwarf Trees, *the audience is not at all surprised to find that a poor wandering priest turns out to be the Emperor of Japan in disguise. This play is typical of the simple legends that form the base of this elaborate and highly traditional theater. It emphasizes the ancient values of Japanese society: loyalty, love, sacrifice, and gratitude.*

Characters

THE EMPEROR OF JAPAN, *disguised as a wandering priest*
TSUNEYO, *a poor man*

TSUNEYO'S WIFE
THE MINISTER OF STATE, and other followers of the Emperor

SCENE ONE

The play takes place in winter: a landscape in a lonely country district. The stage is bare, except for a small hut at the right. A road winds past the hut and leads to the left. It is snowing.

At the beginning, the stage is empty. Then a traveler enters. We can see from his gestures that he is suffering from the cold and that he is lost. The traveler is the Emperor of Japan, disguised as a poor wandering priest.

EMPEROR: I can no longer tell where I have come from, nor where I am going. I am a holy man, wandering through the world, with no home of my own. How cold it is! With this snow falling, I can no longer see the path. I must seek shelter. [*He sees Tsuneyo's house, goes to it, and knocks at the door.*] Is there anyone in this house?

TSUNEYO'S WIFE [*opening the door only a crack*]:   Who is there?

EMPEROR: I am a poor pilgrim, and I am lost. Pray, let me stay here for the night.

WIFE: It is a small thing you ask. But the master of the house, my husband, is away. Only he can invite you in under his roof.

EMPEROR: Then I shall wait for his return.

WIFE: That must be as you please. I will go to the turn of the path and watch for him. When he comes I will tell him that you are here.

Enter Tsuneyo on the other side of the stage, making the gestures of one who shakes snow from his clothes.

TSUNEYO [*to himself*]:   Ah! How the snow falls! Long ago when I lived in the City and served in the forces of the Emperor, how I loved to see it. The snow that falls now is the same that I saw then. But I am old, watching it, and my hair is frost-white. [*He sees his wife coming toward him.*] What is this? Why are you waiting here in the cold in the midst of this snowstorm?

WIFE: A pilgrim has come to our door asking for a night's lodging. When I told him you were not in the house he asked if he might wait until you returned. That is why I am here.

TSUNEYO: Where is this pilgrim now?

WIFE [*leading him back towards the hut where the Emperor is standing*]:   Here he stands!

EMPEROR [*bowing*]:   I am he. Though it is not yet night, how can I find my way in this great storm of snow? I beg you to give me shelter for the night.

TSUNEYO: It is not a great thing that you ask, but I cannot receive you. My house is too poor, and I have no lodging fit for you.

EMPEROR: No, no. I do not care how poor your house is. Allow me to stay here for one night only.

TSUNEYO: I would be glad to ask you to stay, but there is scarcely enough room for my wife and myself. How can we give you lodging? The village of Yamamoto lies only a few miles down the road. You will find a good inn there. You had better start, before night comes down upon you.

EMPEROR: Then you are determined to turn me away?

TSUNEYO: I am sorry, sir, but I cannot invite you to stay in my house. It is too poor for visitors.

EMPEROR [*turning away*]:   Much good it did me to wait for him! I must go my way. [*He continues out along the path.*]

WIFE: Husband, we live here in poverty and ruin because in some former life we did not obey the laws of Heaven. If we turn this pilgrim out into the storm, it will surely bring us ill fortune in our next life. If it is by any means possible for us to shelter him here, please let him stay!

TSUNEYO [*moved by her plea*]:   If that is how you feel, wife, why did you not speak before? He cannot have gone far in this great storm. I shall go after him and bring him back. [*He starts out after the Emperor, calling*] Traveler! Traveler! Hear me! We will give you lodging! Come back! [*There is no answer.*] The snow is falling so thick that he cannot hear me. What a sad plight he is in! Snow covers the path by which he came and new snow covers the path by which he must go. [*He follows the Emperor, and calls again*] Traveler! Come back! We will give you shelter! [*He peers into the distance.*] Look! Look! There he is—he has heard me. He is standing still and shaking the snow from his clothes. Now he is returning.

    The Emperor enters again.

TSUNEYO: Welcome, pilgrim. I was wrong to turn you from my door. Though my house is poor and small, my wife and I rejoice to give you lodging. Come, enter. [*He opens the door of the hut. The Emperor goes in, and Tsuneyo follows him.*]

SCENE TWO

The interior of Tsuneyo's hut.

TSUNEYO [*to his wife*]:   Listen. We have given this traveler lodging, but we have set no food before him. Is there nothing we can give him?

WIFE: We have only a little boiled grain. It is a poor dish, but we can give it to him if he will accept it.

TSUNEYO: I will tell him. [*To the Emperor*] I have given you lodging, traveler, but I have set no food before you. It happens that we have nothing to offer but a little boiled grain. It is coarse food, but pray eat it if you can.

EMPEROR: Coarse food? Not at all! Please give it to me. I shall eat it with pleasure.

TSUNEYO [*to his wife*]:   He says he will take some. Hurry and give it to him.

WIFE: I will do so.

TSUNEYO [*to himself*]:   Long ago when I lived in the City, I never tasted such coarse food as this boiled grain. I read about it in poems and songs about poor peasants. But now my whole life is changed. Now I no longer live in the world. I have retired to this lonely place, and this simple food is all I have.

> Oh, that I might sleep
> And see in my dreams
> Good times that have passed away.
> Such dreams would be a comfort.
> But through my battered walls
> Cold winds from the woods
> Blow sleep away, and with it
> All dreams and remembrances.

As Tsuneyo sings this song, three beautiful miniature trees—each about two feet high —are carried out and set down on the opposite side of the stage.

TSUNEYO: How cold it is! As the night passes, each hour the frost grows keener. Traveler, we have no fuel to light a fire with so that you might sit and warm yourself. Ah, I have thought of something! I have three dwarf trees. I shall cut them down and make a fire of them.

EMPEROR [*surprised*]:   Have you indeed dwarf trees?

TSUNEYO: Yes, years ago I served the Emperor (though I never had the good fortune to see him) and took part in the affairs of the world. In those days I was prosperous and I had a fine collection of trees. But then trouble came upon me. I lost my fancy for raising these beautiful trees and gave them all away. But three of them I kept—plum, cherry, and pine. I brought them with me, and planted them here in this wilderness. Come. [*He leads the Emperor outside the hut to where the three dwarf trees stand.*] Look, there they are, covered with snow. They are precious to me, yet for this night's entertainment, I shall gladly cut them down and set them on fire.

EMPEROR: No, no, you must not do that. I thank you for your kindness, but these trees are all that remain to you of the days when you were prosperous and lived in the City. You need these trees for your pleasure. It is unthinkable that they should be burned.

TSUNEYO: My life is like a dead tree.
              It shoots forth no blossoms.

WIFE: These shrubs, the remains of a former life,
           Are profitless toys. Pilgrim,
           We gladly burn them to keep you warm.

TSUNEYO [*He leaves the hut and walks across the stage to where the dwarf trees stand.*]: I cannot, cannot! Oh, beautiful trees, must I destroy you? You, plum tree, were always the first to send forth your blossoms in the Spring and scent the cold air with flowers. You first shall fall. [*He cuts down the plum tree.*] Now you, pine tree, whom the wind wraps in mist. Now you shall burn like the beacon by a palace gate guarding a king. [*He cuts down the pine tree.*] Cherry tree, each Spring your blossoms were always the last to come forth. I thought you a lonely tree, and I raised you tenderly. Now I am more lonely than you, and you shall blossom only in flames. [*He cuts down the cherry tree.*] Come, let us build our fire. [*Carrying the trees, he returns to the hut.*]

SCENE THREE

Inside the hut. A fire is burning.

EMPEROR: Now that we have a good fire we can forget the cold.

TSUNEYO: If you had not stopped to ask us for shelter, my wife and I would now have no fire to sit by.

EMPEROR: There is something I must ask you. I would like to know to what family my host belongs, and something of his history.

TSUNEYO: I am not of high birth. My family has no famous name.

EMPEROR: Say what you will, I cannot believe that you are a common peasant. Bad luck is not something to be ashamed of. And, after all, your fortune may change. Do not be ashamed to tell me your name.

TSUNEYO: Indeed, I have no reason to conceal it. Know then, that I am Tsuneyo, Lord of Sano, and that I have sunk to such evil days.

EMPEROR: How did it happen, sir, that you fell upon such misery?

TSUNEYO: My relatives stole my land from me. They tricked me and left me to become what I now am.

EMPEROR: Why do you not go up to the Capital and lay your case before the Emperor?

TSUNEYO: It is said that the Emperor cannot be seen. Moreover, they say that he is absent, making a lengthy pilgrimage.

EMPEROR: You are right, I have heard it also.

TSUNEYO: I shall go to the City only if the Emperor is in danger and needs my help. Look, here upon the wall my tall spear hangs ready. Here is my armor hanging beside it. And my horse is tied outside. If at any time there comes news from the city that my Master is in danger,

Rusty though they be,
I shall gird this armor on
And take down this tall spear.
Lean-ribbed though he be,
I shall mount my horse and ride,
Neck by neck with the swiftest,
To enlist in the Emperor's service.

And when the battle begins,
Though the enemy be many,
Yet I shall be the first
To break through their ranks,
Choose one, fight with him, and die.
But here in this wilderness
Another fate awaits me.
Worn out with hunger
I die, useless. Oh, despair, despair!

He buries his face in his hands and his voice sinks.

EMPEROR: Take courage. You shall not end so. [*Rising*] Now it is light. The storm has ended and I must continue my journey. If I live, I shall return to visit you one day.

TSUNEYO: We cannot let you go so soon. At first we were ashamed that you should see the misery of our dwelling.

WIFE: Now we ask you to stay with us awhile.

EMPEROR: Thank you. Do you think that if it were only my own desire I were following, that I would go forth into the snow?

TSUNEYO: After the storm even a clear sky is cold, and tonight—

WIFE: Stay with us one more day.

EMPEROR: My heart remains, but I must leave you.

TSUNEYO and WIFE: Then, farewell.

EMPEROR [*bowing*]: Farewell.

TSUNEYO and WIFE: Come back to us again.

EMPEROR: If one day you should change your mind and come back up to the City, perhaps we shall meet. I am only a humble priest, yet I may be of some help to you. I may be able to bring you before the presence of the Emperor. Do not give up hope. Now I must go my way, though I am sad to leave you.

TSUNEYO: We are sad to lose you from our sight.

They bow in farewell.

SCENE FOUR

Six months later. Tsuneyo is standing outside his hut. His gestures show that he is watching a large number of travelers passing by him on the road.

TSUNEYO [*calling out to the passers-by*]: Hi, you travelers! Is it true that there is a war? Are they raising an army and marching to Kamakura? [*He nods his head as if the unseen travelers answer him. To himself*] So it is true. Barons and Knights from all the Counties of the East are riding to Kamakura to defend the Emperor. What a fine sight it is. They are wearing silver breastplates decorated with bright tassels; their swords and daggers have hilts of gold. Their horses are sleek and well-fed. Even the grooms and pack horses are magnificently appareled.

I am an old warrior. I have nothing left but a rusting sword and broken armor. My horse, too, is old and thin. Yet I cannot stand and watch this army go to the aid of My Lord, the Emperor. I shall join them with horse, sword, and armor that no longer seem worthy of the name.

He goes into the hut and takes down his sword and armor from the wall. He goes outside again and pantomimes the untethering of his horse. He buckles on his armor. Then, as he speaks the following words, he walks across the stage slowly as if proceeding on a journey, miming the action of leading his horse.

TSUNEYO: Let them laugh at me when they see me! I am not a worse man than any of them. Had I a steed to match my heart . . . [*Gesture of cracking a whip.*] Come on, you laggard! Come on, we are falling behind!

He goes out, still leading his horse.

SCENE FIVE

*The throne room in the palace of the Emperor.
The Emperor is seated, wearing magnificent
robes. He claps his hands, and the Minister of
State appears before him.*

MINISTER: I stand before you.

EMPEROR: Have all the armies arrived?

MINISTER: They have all arrived, my Lord.

EMPEROR: Somewhere among them there will
be a Knight in broken armor, carrying a
broken sword and leading an old horse whose
thin ribs show through its flesh. Find him,
and bring him to me.

MINISTER [*bowing*]:   I tremble and obey. [*He
goes out.*]

> *Tsuneyo enters at the other side of the
> stage. The Minister of State approaches
> him.*

MINISTER [*to Tsuneyo*]:   I must speak with
you.

TSUNEYO: What is it?

MINISTER: You are to appear immediately before my Lord.

TSUNEYO: I do not know your lord. Who is
he?

MINISTER: The Emperor of Japan!

TSUNEYO: Is it I you are asking to appear before the Emperor?

MINISTER: Yes, you indeed.

TSUNEYO: It cannot be. You have mistaken me
for another man.

MINISTER: No, it is you I want. I was told to
bring the poorest-looking of all the soldiers.
Come at once.

TSUNEYO: The poorest of all the Emperor's
soldiers?

MINISTER: Yes, truly.

TSUNEYO: Then I am surely the man you seek.
Tell your Lord that I obey.

MINISTER: Follow me.

TSUNEYO: I understand. Too well I understand. One of my enemies has called me a
traitor and I am being led before the throne
to be executed. Well, there is no help for it.
Take me to the Emperor.

*He follows the Minister across the stage to
where the Emperor sits. There are several
richly dressed warriors and courtiers standing
at the Emperor's side. When they see Tsuneyo
they point their fingers at him and burst out
laughing. The Emperor raises his hand for
silence. Tsuneyo bows before the throne.*

TSUNEYO: My Lord, I have come.

EMPEROR: Gentlemen, I bid you bow to this
man, Tsuneyo, Lord of Sano!

*Somewhat bewildered, all the courtiers bow
to Tsuneyo.*

EMPEROR [*to Tsuneyo*]:   Tsuneyo, have you
forgotten the wandering priest whom you
once sheltered in a snowstorm? I see you have
been true to the words you spoke that night:
"If at any time there came news from the City
that my Master is in danger,

> Rusty though they be,
> I shall gird this armor on
> And take down this tall spear.
> Lean-ribbed though he be,
> I shall mount my horse and ride,
> Neck by neck with the swiftest,
> To enlist in the Emperor's service."

Tsuneyo, those were not empty words—you
have come truly and bravely. Know that this
levy of armies was made for only one purpose: to test you and see whether you spoke
true or false.

Now I shall hear the pleas of all the faithful warriors who have obeyed my summons.
And first, in the case of Tsuneyo I make
judgement: To him shall be returned his law-
ful estate—all the land of Sano. Above all else
one thing shall not be forgotten: that in the
great snowstorm he cut down his dwarf trees,
his treasures, and burned them to keep me

warm. And now in gratitude for those three trees—plum, cherry, and pine—I grant him three new estates. One in Kaga, where plums grow; one in Etchū, famous for its cherry trees; one in the pine-covered hills of Kōzuke. He shall hold them forever and leave them to his heirs. [*Handing a scroll to Tsuneyo*] In testimony whereof we give this title deed by our own hand, signed and sealed.

TSUNEYO [*his voice choked with emotion*]: My lord . . . [*He takes the title deeds and bows three times to the Emperor. Addressing the courtiers*] Look, you barons! You laughed at me. Now let your laughter turn to envy.

EMPEROR [*rises from his throne, comes downstage and addresses the audience*]:

Then the warriors took leave of the Emperor
And went their homeward ways.
And among them went Tsuneyo,
Joy breaking upon his brow,
Riding now on a splendid steed.
He returned to the lands torn from him,
Now once again his own.

For Discussion

1. What is the central characteristic of Tsuneyo's personality? Is it possible that the kindness, trust, and loyalty that win him back his title and possessions may have been the cause of his falling into poverty and ruin in the first place? Does Tsuneyo plan to avenge the wrong that has been done to him? What does his wife offer as the reason for their misery?

2. In a sentence or two, try to define the moral of *The Dwarf Trees*. What other fables or fairy tales present the same lesson?

3. Find an explanation of dwarf trees and their cultivation in an encyclopedia. What kind of temperament is necessary for this type of culture? Does the growing of dwarf trees indicate a special attitude toward time on the part of the Japanese? Explain. Why is Tsuneyo's destruction of his dwarf trees considered such a great sacrifice in the play?

4. What is the idea of human justice that the play presents? How does it correspond to or differ from the ideals of justice in the modern world?

5. The traditional setting of a nōh play is extremely simple. A square platform covered by a roof represents a palace, a house, a roadway, or a battlefield. Devise your own production of *The Dwarf Trees*. How much of the traditional staging would you employ? What overall effect would your production try to convey to the audience?

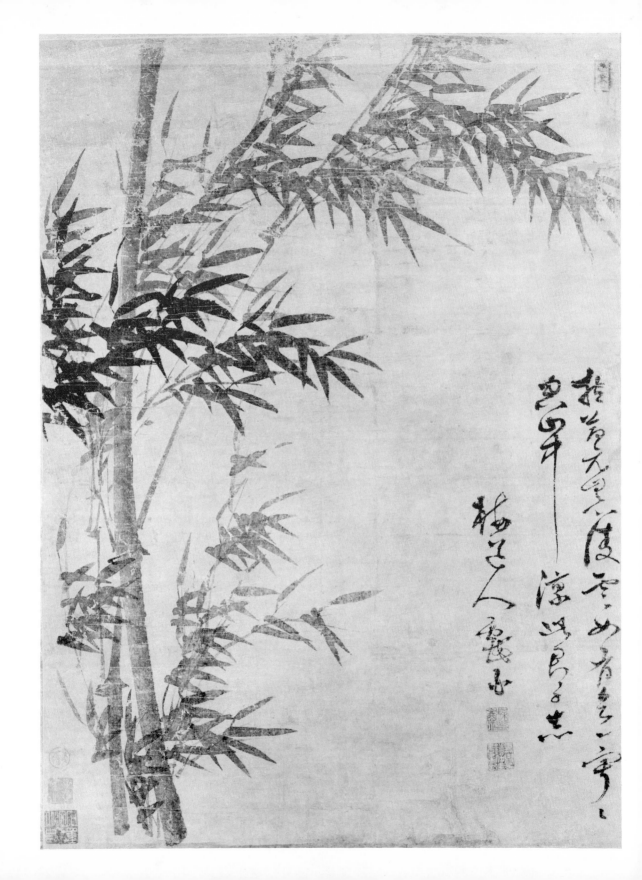

WU CHEN

Bamboo in the Wind

(Museum of Fine Arts.
Boston)

The poet makes things new.

Daily life is a stream of sights, sounds, and impressions. Poetry prevents the

eye and the mind of man from falling into routine. The poet has two

gifts. The first is his capacity for seeing life ever new, ever fresh, and for

finding wonder and beauty in what he sees and feels. The second is his

capacity for finding the right words to communicate his vision to the reader—

words that will keep his vision fresh and alive forever.

Many people have a mistaken idea of poetry. They think of it in terms of delicate songs about flowers or of noble hymns for patriotic occasions. The truth is that the best poetry is about the whole of life. Whatever you are concerned with, poetry is concerned with too.

Of course, not every poem appeals to every reader. Nor should it. Part of the fun of reading is giving in to enthusiasms. Any reader has the right to find one "great" poet exciting and another "great" poet boring. In selecting the following poems, the editors have tried to choose the most exciting poems they could find. At the same time, they have tried to represent the literature of many ages and many nations. For each reader, the best poems in this book are the ones that make *him* see and feel something that is fresh and new.

The poet's most important device is compression. He packs a great deal into a few lines in order to intensify his vision and give it greater power. Look, for example at García Lorca's poem "Gypsy Funeral" (page 221). The material for this poem could have been expanded into a novel: where the gypsy girl was born, how she lived, whom she loved, how she died. Lorca might have told us of his own meetings with the girl, repeated long conversations, reported the attitude of the "nice" people of Spain towards the gypsy way of life, and so forth. Instead, he wrote a funeral lament of fifteen lines. As an experience, it is complete in itself. If you agree with the editors that it is exciting, it is because Lorca has compressed whole lifetimes of feeling into these few lines.

Basic to poetry is metaphor, the poet's way of telling about one thing in terms of another. Comparing things, placing them side by side, forces the reader to see and feel from a fresh point of view. For example, we see the sun in the sky day after day. But do we really *see* it?

How much more vivid and precise the sun becomes when Stephen Crane writes: "The red sun was pasted in the sky like a wafer." A good metaphor is not merely pretty or clever, it is not a decoration plastered across an idea. A good metaphor is welded to the idea it expresses; it is so vital to the idea that it would be impossible to state the idea without it. In "My Fiftieth Year," Yeats says, "My body of a sudden blazed." Literally, this makes no sense; the poet's body was not really shining, was not actually on fire. But he *felt* as if he were blazing, and this choice of metaphor (the comparison to fire) conveys his feeling to the reader.

To compression and metaphor, the poet adds music—the sound that catches his thought and holds it perfectly together. The principal means are meter, rhyme, and repeated sounds. Rhyme is not essential to poetry; classical Greek, Latin, and Japanese poetry does not use rhyme. Classic Chinese poetry, however, does. The rhythm of a poem may be strong and regular (as in Burns's "A Red, Red Rose"), or it may be closer to the rhythm of every day speech (as in Tagore's "The Home" or Cavafy's "Waiting for the Barbarians"). No matter how the devices of poetry are combined, each poem must find its own voice, its own music. Naturally, since many of the poems that follow were written in other languages, the English translations can hope only to suggest the sounds and rhythms of the original poem.

Compression, metaphor, music—these forces operate to give the poem its unity and its uniqueness. Poetry is hard to define, and no two readers may accept precisely the same definition. Yet readers across the centuries have known when they are in the presence of authentic poetry. To a great extent, they have been able to agree upon who the greatest of the poets are.

POEMS ABOUT LOVE

Anne Gregory was the daughter of a friend of the poet's. She appears to have been complaining because people insisted upon praising her beautiful hair rather than herself. In this light-hearted poem, Yeats explains that it is impossible for mere humans to think of Anne's "self" apart from her physical beauty. William Butler Yeats (1865–1939) was the greatest poet of modern Ireland. He was awarded the Nobel Prize in literature in 1923.

For Anne Gregory

WILLIAM BUTLER YEATS

'Never shall a young man,
Thrown into despair
By those great honey-coloured
Ramparts at your ear,
Love you for yourself alone
And not your yellow hair.'

'But I can get a hair-dye
And set such colour there,
Brown, or black, or carrot,
That young men in despair
May love me for myself alone
And not my yellow hair.'

'I heard an old religious man
But yesternight declare
That he had found a text to prove
That only God, my dear,
Could love you for yourself alone
And not your yellow hair.'

Although the poem is light, it is written in a mock-serious tone, as if some weighty point were being discussed. In fact, it does touch upon a serious philosophical question—the gap that exists between human and divine love.

1. "For Anne Gregory" is a dialogue between two speakers. Identify each. Can their personalities be described from what they say? How can the reader tell their relationship? Their relative ages?

2. Explain the last three lines of the poem. Does the speaker intend irony here? Is the girl's yellow hair really a problem, or is it an asset? Did the poet really hear "an old religious man" make the statement in the last stanza, or is it his own invention?

3. In the final stanza the poet presents the yellow hair as a paradox: without it, only God can love her; with it, young men will never love her for herself alone. Is the meaning of the poem restricted only to the people who speak? Suggest general applications of the theme.

———

Japanese poetry is almost always extremely brief. "Pretext" is an exquisite miniature that renews an experience everyone has had at one time or another. Yakamochi lived in the eighth century.

Pretext

YAKAMOCHI

By way of pretext
I said "I will go
And look at
The condition of the bamboo fence";
But it was really to see you!
          [*translated by* ARTHUR WALEY]

The shortness of "Pretext" is an important part of its effect. If the poet had expanded the story, he would have lost the sharp point of his last line.

1. Describe the speaker's personality. Is the poem a confession of deceit? Or is it a way of expressing his love? Is his love passionate? Gentle? Calculating? Indifferent? Why?

2. Does the poem seem to condemn or approve this kind of behavior?

Few lyrics are simpler than Robert Burns's "A Red, Red Rose." For its symbols, the poem mentions only a few universal, elemental things: rose, music, ocean, rocks, time. This simplicity and directness give the poem its feeling of burning sincerity.

A Red, Red Rose

ROBERT BURNS

O my luve is like a red, red rose,
  That's newly sprung in June.
O my luve is like the melodie,
  That's sweetly played in tune.

As fair art thou, my bonny lass,
  So deep in luve am I,
And I will luve thee still, my dear,
  Till a' the seas gang dry.

Till a' the seas gang dry, my dear,
  And the rocks melt wi' the sun!
And I will luve thee still, my dear,
  While the sands o' life shall run.

And fare thee weel, my only luve,
  And fare thee weel a while!
And I will come again, my luve,
  Tho' it were ten thousand mile!

Notice how Burns (1759–1796) suggests the speech of his native Scotland with the use of a few dialect words and contractions.

1. Could "A Red, Red Rose" be set to music easily? What sort of tune would be most effective?

2. Is the lover more interested in the way he feels or in the person who creates this feeling within him? In the first two lines, does the speaker mean

that his sweetheart resembles a rose or that the love he experiences is like the flower? Do roses in bloom last very long? Is the speaker aware of the significance of his comparison? Would the poem be improved or spoiled if the dialect words were changed to standard English?

3. Note that many words and phrases are repeated throughout the poem. What is the effect of this repetition? In most writing, excessive repetition is considered a fault. Why is it justified here?

———————

The traditional Spanish ballad "The Song of the Ships" is a lyrical reflection of the epic struggle between Spaniards and Moors. In 711, a Moslem army invaded and soon conquered most of what is today Spain. It was not until 1492, when the armies of Ferdinand and Isabella conquered Granada, that the Moorish power in Spain was finally crushed. During these wars, many Spanish prisoners were held in North Africa for ransom. In the ballad, a girl urges the warships of Spain to rescue her lover from captivity and bring him back to her.

The Song of the Ships

SPANISH BALLAD

You mariners of Spain
  Bend strongly on your oars,
And bring my love again—
  For he lies among the Moors!

You ships so fairly built
  Like castles on the sea,
O great will be your guilt,
  If you bring him not to me!

———————————————

A RED, RED ROSE: *luve* = love; *bonny* = pretty; *a'* = all; *gang* = go; *wi'* = with; *weel* = well.

The wind is blowing strong,—
　　The breeze will aid your oars;
O swiftly fly along—
　　For he lies among the Moors!

The sweet breeze of the sea
　　Cools every cheek but mine;
Hot is its breath to me,
　　As I gaze upon the brine.

It is a narrow strait—
　　I see the blue hills over;
Your coming I'll await,
　　And thank you for my lover.

To Mary I will pray,
　　While you bend upon your oars;
'Twill be a blessed day
　　You fetch him from the Moors!

Like most ballads, this one was meant to be sung and tells a simple story.

1. Note that the final stanza repeats—in a slightly different form, two lines from earlier stanzas. What is the artistic effect of this double repetition here?

2. What is the "narrow strait" referred to in the fifth stanza?

3. Can you guess the social rank of the woman who speaks? How?

4. What is the primary emotion of the poem? Is it sentimental? Are there modern popular songs that develop this same theme? How do they differ from "The Song of the Ships"?

The lover in Poe's "To Helen" finds a world of permanent, timeless beauty in his lady. To express this timelessness, the poem draws its comparisons from distant, classical ages, "the glory that was Greece, and the grandeur that was Rome."

To Helen

EDGAR ALLAN POE

Helen, thy beauty is to me
　　Like those Nicean barks of yore,
That gently, o'er a perfumed sea,
　　The weary, way-worn wanderer bore
　　To his own native shore.

On desperate seas long wont to roam,
　　Thy hyacinth hair, thy classic face,
Thy Naiad airs have brought me home
　　To the glory that was Greece
　　And the grandeur that was Rome.

Lo! in yon brilliant window-niche
　　How statuelike I see thee stand,
The agate lamp within thy hand!
　　Ah, Psyche, from the regions which
　　Are Holy Land!

Psyche was a maiden beloved by Cupid. It is also the Greek word for "soul" or "mind." Poe is thought to have addressed this poem to Sarah Helen Whitman, a poet, to whom he was briefly engaged.

1. If Poe did indeed write this poem for Sarah Whitman, why did he choose to use her middle name, Helen? Is there a special significance in it?

2. Does the poem give the reader enough information so that he can describe the lady? Or does it merely give an impression of her appearance? How is this impression conveyed?

3. Look up the words "hyacinth" and "hyacinthine" in an unabridged dictionary. What impression do you think Poe intended to convey by the phrase "hyacinth hair"? Do you think he had in mind a color? If not, why? Make the same study of the word "agate."

TO HELEN: *Nicean* = Nicea was an ancient city in Asia Minor; *wont* = accustomed; *Naiad* = the Naiads were water nymphs.

The German poet Heine (1797–1856), sepa-
rated from his beloved, expressed their feelings
in this little fable about two unhappy trees.

Pine Tree and Palm Tree

HEINRICH HEINE

A pine tree stands on a Northern slope,
  Alone, where the cold winds blow.
Sleeping, he is wrapped in a white
  Blanket of ice and snow.

And there he dreams of a palm tree
  That weeps, sad and alone,
On a golden shore, where other winds
  Across the scorched sands moan.

There is a touch of tender comedy in the idea of
two trees in love with each other. In spite of this,
the poem conveys a genuine feeling of longing and
separation. Heine often introduced a bit of irony
into his verse to counteract what might otherwise
be a sentimental thought.

1. If this poem is a fable, does it have a moral?
If so, what is it? If not, what effect does the absence
of a moral give?

2. Why has Heine chosen two trees that are
native to such opposite regions? Would the poem
have the same meaning if both trees grew in the
same forest?

3. Describe a human situation comparable to the
one of the trees. What common truth about life
and love forms the basis of this poem? How does
the poet cast this common truth into a fresh and
unusual perspective?

———————

Shakespeare's sonnets are one of literature's most
lasting monuments in praise of love. "Sonnet 29"
begins with the poet being weighed down by
the frustrations of age, ambition, and envy. The
poem pivots on the words "Haply I think on

thee" and ends with a feeling of exaltation and
serenity.

Sonnet 29

WILLIAM SHAKESPEARE

When, in disgrace with fortune and men's eyes,
I all alone beweep my outcast state,
And trouble deaf heaven with my bootless cries,
And look upon myself, and curse my fate,
Wishing me like to one more rich in hope,
Featured like him, like him with friends pos-
    sessed,
Desiring this man's art and that man's scope,
With what I most enjoy contented least;
Yet in these thoughts myself almost despising,
Haply I think on thee—and then my state,
Like to the lark at break of day arising
From sullen earth, sings hymns at heaven's gate;
For thy sweet love remembered such wealth
    brings
That then I scorn to change my state with kings.

This sonnet is mostly a series of general statements.
They are cast into relief by a single sharp, specific
image: "the lark at break of day arising." This
image reflects the thought and emotion of the en-
tire poem.

1. Why is the image of the lark arising and singing at daybreak appropriate? What is meant by
"sullen earth"? To what state of mind of the poet's
does it correspond?

2. Most sonnets are divided into two sections,
one of eight lines, and one of six. The thought in
the final six-line section usually contrasts with that
in the first eight lines. Does Shakespeare make such
use of the sonnet form in this poem? How?

3. How does the poem show a process of self-
discovery? The sonnet begins with one state of
mind and closes with another. Is the change logical?
Is it convincing?

———————

SONNET 29: *bootless* = useless.

This dramatic poem by the Chinese poet Rihaku (eighth century) takes the form of a letter from a young bride, still in her teens, to her husband, who is absent on business. The story of their childhood friendship, their early marriage, and their separation is sketched in a few lines, as the poem moves effortlessly through time and space. The translation suggests the formality with which a Chinese wife addresses her husband, yet the formal tone does not hide her emotion.

The River-Merchant's Wife: A Letter

RIHAKU

While my hair was still cut straight across my
    forehead
I played about the front gate, pulling flowers.
You came by on bamboo stilts, playing horse,
You walked about my seat, playing with blue
    plums.
And we went on living in the village of Chokan:
Two small people, without dislike or suspicion.

At fourteen I married My Lord you.
I never laughed, being bashful.
Lowering my head, I looked at the wall.
Called to, a thousand times, I never looked back.

At fifteen I stopped scowling,
I desired my dust to be mingled with yours
Forever and forever and forever.
Why should I climb the look out?

At sixteen you departed,
You went into far Ku-to-yen, by the river of
    swirling eddies,
And you have been gone five months.
The monkeys make sorrowful noise overhead.

You dragged your feet when you went out.
By the gate now, the moss is grown, the differ-
    ent mosses,
Too deep to clear them away!
The leaves fall early this autumn, in wind.
The paired butterflies are already yellow with
    August
Over the grass in the West garden;
They hurt me. I grow older.
If you are coming down through the narrows
    of the river Kiang,
Please let me know beforehand,
And I will come out to meet you
                  As far as Cho-fu-Sa.

        [*translated by* EZRA POUND]

Chinese poetry is difficult to translate into English because the grammar of the two languages operates in very different ways. Here the translator gives a sense of the original poem by using short, direct sentences and a large number of simple one-syllable words.

1. How does the young wife change from the time when her hair "was still cut straight" across her forehead until the time when she writes the letter? How long has she known her husband? How old was she when she was married? How old was she when she fell in love with her husband? How old is she as she writes the letter? What details does the poet use to suggest the stages of her maturity?

2. Why has the husband gone away? What lines in the poem suggest his love for his wife?

3. What are some of the pictorial images the poem conveys? Are these images sharp and clear? Are there any parts of the poem which are vague? What are some of the sounds in the poem?

4. Often, the things a person notices reveal a great deal about the way he feels. How does Rihaku use nature to suggest the young wife's emotions? How does she describe each of the following: the mosses, the river, the butterflies, the noise of the monkeys? What is the meaning of each of these descriptions?

The masterpiece of the great Italian poet Dante (1265–1321), is The Divine Comedy, *a long poem telling of a journey from Hell to Purgatory and finally to Heaven. In this sestina the poet tells of his passion for a lady who coldly refuses to return his love. He has traveled up into the hills in order to forget her, but distance does not lessen his suffering. The word "stone" in this poem has a special meaning: the lady's name was Pietra, which means "stone" in Italian. Dante uses it to suggest the hardness of her heart.*

Sestina

DANTE

To the dim light and the large circle of shade
I have clomb, and to the whitening of the hills
There where we see no color in the grass.
Natheless my longing loses not its green,
It has so taken root in the hard stone
Which talks and hears as though it were a lady.

Utterly frozen is this youthful lady
Even as the snow that lies within the shade;
For she is no more moved than is a stone
By the sweet season which makes warm the hills
And alters them afresh from white to green,
Covering their sides again with flowers and grass.

When on her hair she sets a crown of grass
The thought has no more room for other lady;
Because she weaves the yellow with the green
So well that Love sits down there in the shade—
Love who has shut me in among low hills
Faster than between walls of granite-stone.

She is more bright than is a precious stone;
The wound she gives may not be heal'd with grass:
I therefore have fled far o'er plains and hills
For refuge from so dangerous a lady;
But from her sunshine nothing can give shade—
Not any hill, nor wall, nor summer-green.

A while ago, I saw her dress'd in green—
So fair, she might have waken'd in a stone
This love which I do feel even for her shade;
And therefore, as one woos a graceful lady,
I wooed her in a field that was all grass
Girdled about with very lofty hills.

Yet shall the streams turn back and climb the
     hills
Before Love's flame in this damp wood and green
Burn, as it burns within a youthful lady,
For my sake, who would sleep away in stone
My life, or feed like beasts upon the grass,
Only to see her garments cast a shade.

How dark soe'er the hills throw out their shade,
Under her summer-green the beautiful lady
Covers it, like a stone cover'd in grass.

The sestina is an elaborate verse form seldom used by modern poets. Notice that each stanza contains six lines ending in the same series of six words: shade, grass, green, stone, hill, lady. The word ending the last line of each stanza ends the first line of the next stanza, and so on. At the end, all six key words are used within a special three-line stanza, giving a feeling of finality and intensity to the end of the poem.

1. Compare this poem with "A Lover's Complaint" (page 217). What are the differences? Does Dante make something much larger and more serious from his sadness? What is the essential emotion of this poem?

2. Study the use of the color green in the poem. What does it symbolize? With what does it contrast?

3. Using the letters *a* through *f*, make a diagram of the rhyme scheme of the poem. Find the complete pattern within which the words move from one stanza to the next.

SESTINA: *clomb* = climbed; *natheless* = nevertheless; *how dark soe'er* = however dark.

The medieval code of Courtly Love gave rise to many works of literature that celebrated the depths of grief and heights of joy that are a part of most love affairs. This anonymous poem, translated from the Middle English, is a man's song about the unfortunate course his love has taken.

A Lover's Complaint

MIDDLE ENGLISH

O little pretty nightingale,
Among the leaves so green
I would I were with her this night—
   Yet ye know not whom I mean.

The nightingale sits on a branch;
The thorns are sharp and keen.
O comfort me with merry cheer—
   Yet ye know not whom I mean.

A lovely lady she appeared—
The loveliest to be seen.
She spoke to me with words of love.
   Yet ye know not whom I mean.

It did me good to look on her:
Her clothes were all of green.
Away from me her heart she took.
   Yet ye know not whom I mean.

"Lady, pity me!" I cried,
"Who true to you have been.
For I love none but you alone!"
   Yet ye know not whom I mean.

The poem intensifies the lover's loneliness by having him address his lament to a bird rather than to his lady or to another human being.

1. Why does the speaker choose to tell his story to the nightingale? Why not to the owl? The whippoorwill? Another person? Why does he repeat the refrain, "Yet ye know not whom I mean"?

2. Describe what has happened in this love affair.

POEMS ABOUT DEATH

The Greek poet Callimachus lived in Alexandria in Egypt during the fourth century B.C. Hearing of the death of his friend Heraclitus, he wrote this simple, polished poem. In it he insists as men have insisted in all ages, that his friend will live on in memory.

Heraclitus

CALLIMACHUS

They told me, Heraclitus, they told me you
   were dead;
They brought me bitter news to hear and bitter
   tears to shed.
I wept as I remember'd how often you and I
Had tired the sun with talking and sent him
   down the sky.

And now that thou art lying, my dear old
   Carian guest,
A handful of grey ashes, long, long ago at rest,
Still are thy pleasant voices, thy nightingales,
   awake,
For Death, he taketh all away, but them he
   cannot take.
         [*translated by* WILLIAM CORY]

Much of the effect of this epigram comes from the sharp, dramatic contrast between two of its images: "ashes" and "nightingales."

1. A lyric poem might be described as one that tells more about the way the poet feels about a subject than it does about the subject itself. In the light of this definition, how is "Heraclitus" a lyric poem?

2. In a brief essay, support or attack the following proposition: Callimachus' celebration of Heraclitus' immortality is really the poet's own victory over time and death.

HERACLITUS: *Carian* = native of Caria in Asia Minor.

Within the span of his brief life—he died in 1821 at the age of twenty-five—John Keats established himself as one of England's major poets. He wrote this sonnet three years before his death. In it he expressed his fear that life would not give him space enough in which to fulfill his genius.

When I Have Fears

JOHN KEATS

When I have fears that I may cease to be
Before my pen has gleaned my teeming brain,
Before high-pilèd books, in charactry,
Hold like rich garners the full ripened grain;
When I behold, upon the night's starred face,
Huge cloudy symbols of a high romance,
And think that I may never live to trace
Their shadows, with the magic hand of chance;
And when I feel, fair creature of an hour!
That I shall never look upon thee more,
Never have relish in the faery power
Of unreflecting love!—then on the shore
Of the wide world I stand alone, and think
Till Love and Fame to nothingness do sink.

It would be difficult to describe the mood of the last line of this sonnet. It combines personal despair with a kind of acceptance of a larger order in the universe. The poet seems to say, "Although I am sad to think I shall never achieve Love and Fame, what, in fact, do they mean in the light of eternity?"

1. From the evidence of the poem itself, what can be said about the personality of the poet? What is his idea of a rich and full life? Is it a valid one?

2. Describe the main image contained in the first four lines. The key words are "gleaned," "garners," and "grain." What is the image in the last three lines? Does the contrast between the opening and

WHEN I HAVE FEARS: *charactry* = characters, letters; *garner* = granary, a storehouse for grain.

closing images add to the effectiveness of the poem?

3. In this poem, what is Keats's attitude toward life and death?

———————

Death is often portrayed as a skeleton wearing a shroud and carrying a scythe. Here the great German poet Goethe turns Death into the Erl-King, a ghastly crowned figure visible only to the victim he entices to his kingdom. The speaker in the third, fifth, and seventh stanzas is the Erl-King himself.

The Erl-King

WOLFGANG VON GOETHE

O who rides by night thro' the woodland so
    wild?
It is the fond father embracing his child;
And close the boy nestles within his loved arm,
To hold himself fast, and to keep himself warm.

"O father, see yonder! see yonder!" he says;
"My boy, upon what dost thou fearfully gaze?"
"O 'tis the Erl-King with his crown and his
    shroud."
"No, my son, it is but a dark wreath of the
    cloud."

"O come and go with me, thou loveliest child;
By many a gay sport shall thy time be beguiled;
My mother keeps for thee full many a fair toy,
And many a fine flower shall she pluck for my
    boy."

"O father, my father, and did you not hear
The Erl-King whisper so low in my ear?"
"Be still, my heart's darling—my child, be at
    ease;
It was but the wild blast as it sung thro' the
    trees."

"O wilt thou go with me, thou loveliest boy?
My daughter shall tend thee with care and with
    joy;
She shall bear thee so lightly thro' wet and thro'
    wild,
And press thee, and kiss thee, and sing to my
    child."

"O father, my father, and saw you not plain
The Erl-King's pale daughter glide past thro'
    the rain?"
"O yes, my loved treasure, I knew it full soon;
It was the gray willow that danced to the moon."

"O come and go with me, no longer delay,
Or else, silly child, I will drag thee away."
"O father! O father! now, now, keep your hold,
The Erl-King has seized me—his grasp is so
    cold!"

Sore trembled the father; he spurr'd thro' the
    wild,
Clasping close to his bosom his shuddering child;
He reaches his dwelling in doubt and in dread
But, clasp'd to his bosom, the infant was dead.

        [*translated by* SIR WALTER SCOTT]

*Johann Wolfgang von Goethe (1749–1832) is to
German literature what Shakespeare is to the literature of England. His towering masterpiece is the
long poetic drama* Faust.

1. Does the father hear the Erl-King's voice?
Why? Does he suspect that something is wrong?
How does he reveal this suspicion? In what way
does he try to defeat the power of the Erl-King?

2. What are the three arguments the Erl-King
gives to the child? What does the last of these arguments reveal about the Erl-King's true nature?

3. How does the physical setting of the poem add
dramatic power to the theme?

4. Describe the Erl-King in the poem. Is he
proud? Does he abuse his power? What attitude
toward Death does the poem contain?

*Catullus' brother died in Asia Minor, far from
Rome. The poet made the long journey to his
brother's burial place, bearing symbolic gifts as
a final tribute. "On the Burial of His Brother"
may be thought of as an inscription for a
monument.*

On the Burial of His Brother

CATULLUS

By ways remote and distant waters sped,
    Brother, to thy sad graveside am I come,
That I may give the last gift to the dead,
    And vainly parley with thine ashes dumb;
Since She who now bestows and now denies
    Hath ta'en thee, hopeless brother, from mine
      eyes.
But lo! these gifts, the heirlooms of past years,
    Are made sad things to grace thy coffin-shell;
Take them, all drenchèd with a brother's tears,
    and, brother, for all time, hail and farewell.

        [*translated by* AUBREY BEARDSLEY]

*This verse was written in Latin during the 1st
century B.C. In its brevity and polished grace it is
typical of those the ancient Greeks and Romans
composed in memory of the dead. For other examples, see "Heraclitus" (page 217), "Inscription
for the Grave of a Dog" (page 228), and "The Inscription at Thermopylae" (page 237).*

1. Who is meant by "She who now bestows and
now denies"? Does this reference suggest a philosophical background for the poem?

2. What sort of tributes and gifts are suggested
by the phrase "heirlooms of past years"? What effect is gained by leaving the gifts unspecified?

3. What is the effect of the final three words of
the poem? Is there an element of surprise in the
combination of these words? Explain. Are these
words well placed at the very end of the poem?
Why?

There are men who work all their lives to amass possessions and who then die before they have a chance to enjoy the benefits of their labors. "You Will Die" is Confucius' advice to a man who has surrounded himself with more material wealth than he can ever use.

You Will Die

CONFUCIUS

You have coats and robes,
But you do not trail them;
You have chariots and horses
But you do not ride them.
By and by you will die,
And another will enjoy them.

You have courtyards and halls,
But they are not sprinkled and swept;
You have bells and drums,
But they are not struck.
By and by you will die,
And another will possess them.

You have wine and food;
Why not play daily on your lute,
That you may enjoy yourself now
And lengthen your days?
By and by you will die,
And another will take your place.

[*translated by* H. A. GILES]

Confucius, the great Chinese philosopher, lived from about 551 to 479 B.C. His philosophy concerns the establishment of peace and order in the individual, the family, and the state. His sayings are among the noblest ever recorded.

1. Is the meaning of this poem restricted only to the Chinese of Confucius' day? To what modern instances does the moral of this poem apply? In our own society, are there areas where we have worked so hard to make life enjoyable that we have forgotten how to enjoy living?

2. Why does Confucius tell the man that he will lengthen his days by enjoying himself now? Is there any medical basis to this advice? Explain.

3. Why does Confucius repeat that another will come to possess and enjoy the man's possessions and eventually take his place? In a brief essay, defend or attack the following proposition: It is foolish for a man to work for the benefit and comfort of those who come after him.

Federico García Lorca (1899–1936) is widely considered the greatest twentieth-century poet of the Spanish language. His best poems have roots in the traditional songs of Spain, and were meant to be read aloud. If you are familiar with flamenco music, you will have some idea of how the following three poems—"Gypsy Funeral" in particular—are meant to sound. Lorca also wrote plays which have been performed in all parts of the world. His plays, like his poetry, reflect the themes of violence and death which are so much a part of the temperament and literature of Spain.

In "Rider's Song" the speaker sees death ahead on the road to Córdoba, but with wild acceptance he goes on towards his destiny instead of attempting an escape. "Gypsy Funeral" is a lament as well as a tribute to the passion which the dead gypsy girl embodied. In "The Balcony" the poet expresses his intense love of life by asking that, after his death, the doors to the balcony be left open so that the life of the world may continue to enter his room.

Three Poems

FEDERICO GARCIA LORCA

RIDER'S SONG

Córdoba.
Distant. Alone.
Black my pony, big the moon,
Olives in my saddlebag.
I know the roads, and yet
I shall not get to Córdoba.

Across the plain, beneath the wind,
Black my pony, red the moon,
Death stands and watches as I come,
Watches from the towers of Córdoba.

Ay! How long the road goes on!
Ay! How brave my pony is!
Ay! Death lies in wait for me
Before I get to Córdoba.

Córdoba.
Distant. Alone.

GYPSY FUNERAL

Ay! you fierce gypsy!
Yayay! fierce gypsy girl!

There were no "nice" girls
at your funeral.
None of those who wear
white mantillas on fair days,
and cut off their beautiful curls
to toss at Christ's coffin.
Those at your funeral
were sinister people who carry
their hearts in their heads.
They followed your body
crying through the streets.

Ay! you fierce gypsy!
Yayay! fierce gypsy girl!

THE BALCONY

And if I die
leave the balcony open!

A small boy eating an orange
(can be seen from my balcony).

They are harvesting the wheat
(you can hear from my balcony).

If I die
leave the balcony open!

*Córdoba is a city in the South of Spain; the accent
is placed on the first syllable. "Gypsy Funeral"
mentions the girls who "cut off their beautiful
curls / to toss at Christ's coffin." The reference is
to a Spanish custom in which girls, as a gesture of
sorrow and penitence, cut off their curls and throw
them at a symbolic coffin carried through the
streets in the processions of Holy Week.*

   1. "Rider's Song" suggests a story, but who the
rider is, why he is riding towards Córdoba, and
what kind of death awaits him, these are left deliberately vague. Would the poem be improved
if these "story" elements were more clearly defined?
Or would it then become a different kind of poem?

   2. In "Gypsy Funeral" what does the poet mean
by "nice" girls? What is his attitude toward them?
The poem contrasts two ways of life. What are
they? Which way does the poet prefer? What does
he mean by "people who carry/their hearts in their
heads"?

   3. In Spanish houses most rooms open onto bal-
conies that overlook the street or countryside. Although "The Balcony" concerns death, the effect
it produces is of an intense relish for life. How do
the details—a boy eating an orange and the sound
of the harvesters—contribute to the poem?

POEMS ABOUT NATURE

The poet often finds himself reflected in nature. The way he looks at earth, sky, and sea turns them into an expression of his own attitudes and emotions. Shakespeare's Hamlet describes the world as "an unweeded garden that grows to seed." In doing so, Hamlet reveals more about his own troubles than he does about the world. "June Nights" evokes the sights, sounds, and odors of a summer night in the country. The poet's own inner peace is mirrored in the surrounding landscape.

June Nights

VICTOR HUGO

In summer, when the daylight's gone, the fields,
Covered with blossoms, scent the air for miles
    around.
We sleep, but in a half sleep of transparent
    dreams,
Eyes shut, ears half opened to the summer's
    sound.

Pure are the stars, then; and the dark is sweet:
A faint half daylight stains the eternal dome,
And gentle dawn, waiting for her hour to come,
All night below the sky's edge seems to roam.

Victor Hugo (1802–1885), author of Les Misérables *and* The Hunchback of Notre Dame, *was also one of the leading Romantic poets of France. "June Nights" is simpler than much of his verse. The poem produces a definite sense of the mixture of night and day, light and dark.*

1. What effect does Hugo make by repeating the word "half"? How does it combine with the words "faint" and "transparent"?

2. The poem contains an example of personification. Identify it. Does this personification contribute anything to the poem considered as a whole?

In "Yellow Spring" the eye becomes the queen of the senses. A whole springtime countryside arises in the Spanish poet's words.

Yellow Spring

JUAN RAMÓN JIMÉNEZ

April came, filled
with yellow flowers:
the brook was yellow,
hedges and hillside were yellow,
the children's graveyard,
and the garden where love once dwelt.

  The sun anointed the world in yellow;
its fallen light
warmed golden lilies
in its golden waters,
and yellow butterflies
hung above yellow roses!

  Yellow garlands climbed the trees;
the day became a kind of grace
perfumed with gold, in the midst
of a gold awakening of life.
God was opening, among the bones of the dead,
his hands, filled with yellow.

Jiménez's hypnotic repetition of the words "yellow" and "gold" turn the poem into an almost magic ritual or incantation.

1. Does the poet concern himself only with the beauty of new life and growth? Where in the poem does he recognize the presence of death? Does this give the poem a more realistic attitude toward existence? Or does it make the poem morbid? Explain.

2. How does yellow characterize spring? Is there an element of surprise in the use of yellow and gold for this purpose? Why?

3. What is the one instance where the poem appeals to a sense other than sight?

4. In a paragraph, explain your interpretation of the last two lines.

In Robert Browning's poetic play Pippa Passes, *the child Pippa roams the countryside, pleased with the world and all humanity. Older people, caught up in greed, envy, and passion, watch Pippa as she goes by. Her shining innocence reforms them. This is the song she sings as she skips along.*

Song

ROBERT BROWNING

The year's at the spring
And day's at the morn;
Morning's at seven;
The hillside's dew-pearled;
The lark's on the wing;
The snail's on the thorn:
God's in his heaven—
All's right with world!

In any work of literature, each statement must be looked at in its context. It would be unfair to say, reading this "Song," that Browning's own philosophy of life is summed up by the words "all's right with the world." In fact, Browning saw much that was wrong with the world. A song such as this is the lyrical expression of a way of feeling, not a pronouncement about life.

1. What is the design of the poem? How does it progress from the general to the particular? What is the rhyme scheme? Show how the first six lines prepare for the last two.

2. In a brief essay, defend or disagree with this proposition: The philosophy of life expressed in Browning's poem is too simple.

———————

William Wordsworth (1770–1850) was not the first poet to write about nature, but he was the first major poet to make the beauty of nature a central subject of his poems. In this sonnet he complains of modern man's separation from nature. Too often, he says, we give up our natural heritage to pursue material things that are temporary and worthless.

The World Is Too Much with Us

WILLIAM WORDSWORTH

The world is too much with us; late and soon,
Getting and spending, we lay waste our powers:
Little we see in Nature that is ours;
We have given our hearts away, a sordid boon!
The Sea that bares her bosom to the moon;
The winds that will be howling at all hours
And are up-gathered now like sleeping flowers;
For this, for everything, we are out of tune;
It moves us not.—Great God! I'd rather be
A pagan suckled in a creed outworn;
So might I, standing on this pleasant lea,
Have glimpses that would make me less forlorn;
Have sight of Proteus rising from the sea;
Or hear old Triton blow his wreathèd horn.

Proteus and Triton are figures from Greek legend. Proteus was the old man of the sea; he tended the herds of seals that belonged to the king of the sea, Poseidon. Triton was Poseidon's son, a merman (half man, half fish) who lived in the sea and carried a trumpet made from a conch shell.

1. Is the speaker of this poem angry? Why? With whom and what is he disturbed? What has made him "forlorn"?

2. What is meant by "we are out of tune"?

3. Is the way of life the poet advocates possible in the modern world?

4. Does the poet, in the last two lines, literally wish to see Proteus rising from the sea and to hear Triton's horn? What is he really asking for? Why does he mention the two legendary figures here?

———————

THE WORLD IS TOO MUCH WITH US: *boon* = gift.

Robert Frost's "Stopping by Woods on a Snowy Evening" is often cited as one of the finest lyrics in the English language. Simple and direct, it communicates its idea with precision and grace. The reader's imagination, however, is provoked to consider many levels of meaning.

Stopping by Woods on a Snowy Evening

ROBERT FROST

Whose woods these are I think I know.
His house is in the village though;
He will not see me stopping here
To watch his woods fill up with snow.

My little horse must think it queer
To stop without a farmhouse near
Between the woods and frozen lake
The darkest evening of the year.

He gives his harness bells a shake
To ask if there is some mistake.
The only other sound's the sweep
Of easy wind and downy flake.

The woods are lovely, dark and deep.
But I have promises to keep,
And miles to go before I sleep,
And miles to go before I sleep.

The rhyme scheme of Frost's poem helps bind the four stanzas together. Note that the rhyme of the third line in each stanza becomes the main rhyme of the next stanza.

1. How does the rhyme scheme of the last stanza differ from the others? What is the effect produced?

2. Repetition is a device for making emphasis. Why is the last line repeated? What effect does it give? Would it be fair to state that the line has a slightly different meaning each time? If so, how do these meanings differ?

3. Does the poem present a sharp, clear picture? What indicates the period of the action of the poem?

4. Explain in your own words the meaning or meanings you find in the last stanza.

————

The English Romantic poet Shelley (1792–1822) distorts nature in this poem to fit his own pain and grief. The storm really reflects the spiritual strife within the speaker.

A Dirge

PERCY BYSSHE SHELLEY

Rough wind, that moanest loud
  Grief too sad for song;
Wild wind, when sullen cloud
  Knells all the night long;
Sad storm, whose tears are vain,
Bare woods, whose branches strain,
Deep caves and dreary main,
  Wail, for the world's wrong!

The design of this "Dirge" is a simple one: the first seven lines build to the climax of a final line which explains what has gone before.

1. Show how the poem is based on the personification of natural forces.

2. Is it possible to tell the cause of the poet's despair? Is this cause deliberately left vague? Why?

3. What attitude towards the "world's wrong" is suggested by the fifth line?

————

DIRGE: *knells* = tolls, like a bell ringing for the dead; *main* = ocean.

Japanese haiku poetry has become increasingly popular in recent years among English-speaking people. The form is a strict one: a haiku usually contains exactly seventeen syllables. The syllables are divided into three lines: five in the first, seven in the second and five in the third. (In translations of Japanese haiku, and in haiku composed in English, a few syllables more or less do not matter. The 5-7-5 syllable pattern does not suit the structure of English.)

A haiku is based on a sharp impression of nature: tree, mountain, animal, insect, pond, snow, and so forth. It often contains a contrast of opposites: small against large (as in "The Great Statue of Buddha"); silence against sound (as in "By the Old Pond"); hot against cold, dry against wet (as in "Heat"); or presence against absence ("Cherry Trees").

Six Japanese Haiku

CHERRY TREES

They blossom, and then
    we gaze, and then the blooms
        scatter, and then . . .
                        ONITSURA (*1660–1738*)

THE GREAT STATUE OF BUDDHA

Out from the hollow
    of Great Buddha's nose—
        comes a swallow.
                        ISSA (*1762–1826*)

THE NEW MOON

Just three days old,
    the moon, and it's all warped and bent!
        How keen the cold!
                        ISSA

AUTUMN

On a withered branch
    a crow has settled—
        autumn nightfall.
                        BASHŌ (*1644–1694*)

BY THE OLD POND

Old pond—
    and a frog-jump-in
        water-sound.
                        BASHŌ

HEAT

The summer river:
    although there is a bridge, my horse
        goes through the water.
                        SHIKI

[*translated by* HAROLD G. HENDERSON]

The reader may be interested to see the way in which a haiku operates in Japanese. Here is one of the above poems reproduced in Japanese, with a literal English translation beneath each word. The poem is "The New Moon":

Mikazuki   / wa   / soru   / zo / samusa
Three-day-moon / as-for / be-curved / ! / cold
          / wa   / saekaeru
          / as-for / is-very-strong

For a more detailed description of just how haiku are written, and what they mean, see Harold G. Henderson's An Introduction to Haiku, *Doubleday & Company, Inc., Anchor Books.*

1. Identify the pairs of opposites in the six haiku above. Explain how each intensifies the other.

2. Each haiku is in itself an image. Describe the picture formed by each. What do all six poems have in common?

3. Attempt writing haiku of your own, using natural objects familiar to you. Writers of modern haiku do not limit themselves to nature in the sense of trees, ponds, and animals. They include anything that stirs their imagination: a jet plane, a necktie, a piece of wrapping paper, the fragmented image on a television screen, and so forth.

POEMS ABOUT ANIMALS

The snake is one creature men do not look to for companionship. Its name alone is enough to send a chill down the spine of most people. In this poem, Emily Dickinson writes of the sensations that attend a sudden meeting with this "narrow fellow."

The Snake

EMILY DICKINSON

A narrow fellow in the grass
Occasionally rides;
You may have met him–did you not?
His notice instant is.

The grass divides as with a comb,
A spotted shaft is seen;
And then it closes at your feet
And opens further on.

He likes a boggy acre,
A floor too cool for corn,
Yet when a boy, and barefoot,
I more than once, at noon,

Have passed, I thought, a whiplash
Unbraiding in the sun—
When stooping to secure it,
It wrinkled, and was gone.

Several of nature's people
I know, and they know me;
I feel for them a transport
Of cordiality;

But never met this fellow,
Attended or alone,
Without a tighter breathing,
And zero at the bone.

Note that Emily Dickinson never uses the word "snake" in the poem. The titles which are usually printed over her poems are the work of her editors —she used no titles in her own manuscripts. As she left the poem to us, the reader was meant to decipher the subject from her indirect description.

1. What are the synonyms for "snake" used in the poem? Do these synonyms deepen the reader's natural loathing for snakes? Or do they try to make the snake seem less alarming? Try to define the precise attitude these synonyms produce in the reader.

2. By what means does Emily Dickinson convey her own experience of the snake to the reader? Does the word "barefoot" in this context produce a definite sensation? Is it appropriate?

———————

The monkey cage is usually the most crowded attraction at any zoo, perhaps because of all the animals the monkey is the most immediate mirror of man. Here are the worst human characteristics—greed, deceit, distrust, cowardice, foolishness—turned to comedy. In this poem, the Russian poet Khodasevich (1886–1939) reverses the usual concept of the monkey. In a casual meeting with a traveling monkey, he finds a reflection of nobler human qualities—dignity, grace, and gratitude.

The Monkey

VLADISLAV KHODASEVICH

The day was hot. The forests were on fire.
Time dragged. Behind the country house next
    door
A cock was crowing. The gate swung behind
    me.
There on a bench, leaning against the fence,
A wandering Serb, lean, swarthy, had dozed off.

A heavy cross, fashioned of silver, hung
On his half-naked breast, down which great
    drops
Of sweat were rolling. On the fence, close by,
A small red-skirted monkey crouched, and
    chewed
The dusty leaves of lilac overhead.
A leather collar on a heavy chain
That pulled her back pressed hard against her
    throat.
The Serb, roused by my step, awoke and wiped
His sweat, and begged some water for the crea-
    ture.
He tasted it, to test how cold it was,
Then placed the saucer on the bench. At once
The monkey, wetting eager fingers, seized
The saucer in both hands. She leaned her elbows
Upon the bench, and crouching thus, she drank.
Her chin was almost resting on the boards,
And her back arched above her half-bald head.
Even so Darius, centuries ago,
Fleeing the phalanxes of Alexander,
Must have leaned to a puddle in the road.
When she had drunk her water, casually
The monkey brushed the saucer off the bench,
And standing up, with an immortal gesture
She offered me her small black horny hand
The moisture had left cool. . . .
Though I have pressed the hands of lovely
    women,
Of poets, and of men who led a nation,
Yet there was not one hand among them all
Had such a noble shape. Not any hand
Ever touched mine in such full comradeship!
I swear by God that no one ever looked
Into my eyes so wisely and so deeply;
Her soft gaze pierced me. That indigent creature
Revived for me the sweetest lore bequeathed
By far antiquity to human hearts.
And in that moment life appeared so full,
It seemed to me the sun and moon, the waves
Of all the seas, the winds, the heavenly spheres,
Were choiring together, organ music
That rang as wonderfully in my ears
As in the days beyond man's memory.

And then the Serb, knuckling his tambourine,
Went off, the monkey perched on his left
    shoulder:
A maharajah on an elephant.
And in the heavens, wreathed in opal smoke,
A swollen, raspberry-colored sun was hanging.
Heat, with no hope of thunder, lay upon
The wheat fields that were wilting in the blaze.
That was the very day war was declared.

[*translated by* BABETTE DEUTSCH]

"The Monkey" takes the form of an anecdote. One of the devices Khodasevich uses is to contrast the monkey with the Serb who owns her. The man seems sweaty, lifeless, dull. The monkey is alert, quick, intelligent. The poet is not interested in the Serb, but fascinated by the monkey. He compares the man to an elephant. He compares the monkey to both a King and a maharajah, as well as to lovely ladies, poets, and the leaders of nations.

1. Socrates, the Greek philosopher, once said, "The unexamined life is not worth living." How is this poem an "examination of life"? Does the poet's penetrating examination make the experience richer?

2. Why does the Serb test the water's tempera-ture before he gives it to the monkey? In the days of Kings, a monarch employed a taster to protect him against the danger of poison in his food. What is suggested by the Serb's becoming the "taster" for the monkey?

3. How does the poet's attitude toward the monkey show his attitude toward mankind? What is that attitude? What, in the poet's view, does man lack that the monkey possesses?

4. What unexpected meaning does the last line give to the rest of the poem? How does it make a comment on the poet's experience with the monkey? Would you say that the poem reveals an attitude toward war? Explain.

THE MONKEY: *Darius* = Darius III, King of ancient Persia, who fled before the armies of Alexander The Great; *indigent* = poor, needy; *war* = the First World War.

A dog's capacity for loyalty has made him a favorite companion of man. This verse is a moving tribute to the hunting dog who had been the poet's companion on many expeditions.

Inscription for the Grave of a Dog

SIMONIDES

Beneath this mound, my hound, my faithful huntress,
Rest by a hearth whose flames forever burn.
The hills around recall your barking valor;
The beasts we hunted fear, still, your return.

The Greek poet Simonides (556?–468? B.C.) won special fame as the author of funeral tributes. This verse is an example of his best qualities: it is dignified, but not pompous, and it conveys emotion without being sentimental.

1. What qualities of the dog does the poet praise in this epitaph? How does the poet make the grave an extension of the setting the dog knew when alive?
2. Does the poet reveal his feelings for the dog? How? What were they?

——————

The state of captivity often crushes the dignity of a being meant to be free in nature. Here Baudelaire (1821–1867), one of the great poets of the French language, describes the capture of a majestic bird by the crew of a ship. Deprived of its power to fly, the bird becomes a ludicrous freak.

The Albatross

CHARLES BAUDELAIRE

Sometimes, to entertain themselves, the men of
    the crew
Lure upon the deck an unlucky albatross, one
    of those vast
Birds of the sea that follow unwearied the
    voyage through,
Flying in slow and elegant circles above the
    mast.

No sooner have they disentangled him from
    their nets
Than this aerial colossus, shorn of his pride,
Goes hobbling pitiably across the planks and
    lets
His great wings hang like heavy, useless oars
    at his side.

How droll is the poor floundering creature,
    how limp and weak—
He, but a moment past so lordly, flying in
    state!
They tease him: One of them tries to stick a
    pipe in his beak;
Another mimics with laughter his odd lurch-
    ing gait.

The Poet is like that wild inheritor of the
    cloud,
A rider of storms, above the range of arrows
    and slings;
Exiled on earth, at bay amid the jeering crowd,
He cannot walk for his unmanageable wings.

[*translated by* GEORGE DILLON]

Baudelaire wrote the first three stanzas as a separate poem. Years later, he added the final stanza comparing poets (including himself) to the wounded bird, and society to the jeering sailors.

1. Why do the men trap the albatross? How do they turn it into a comic figure? How does the poet criticize the men without stating his disapproval directly?

2. Why is the albatross a good choice of a bird in this poem? Why would the penguin be a poor one?

3. Is the comparison in the last stanza a good one? Should the poet soar above the clouds, or should he mingle with the crowd on earth? Would the poem be improved if the last stanza were omitted?

These five brief poems give delicate insights into animal life familiar to the Japanese. For comments on the form of the haiku see page 225.

Five Japanese Haiku

THE MONKEY'S RAINCOAT

The first cold showers pour.
Even the monkey seems to want
a little coat of straw.

BASHŌ

THE MOURNFUL CHIRPING

Eaten by the cat!
Perhaps the cricket's widow
may be wailing that!

KIKAKU (*1661–1707*)

THE WHALE

A whale!
Down it goes, and more and more
up goes its tail!

BUSON (*1715–1783*)

IN THE HOUSE

At the butterflies
the caged bird gazes, envying—
just watch its eyes!

ISSA

THE SNAKE

A snake! Though it passes,
eyes that had glared at me
stay in the grasses.

KYOSHI (*1874–1959*)

[*translated by* HAROLD G. HENDERSON]

These five haiku about animals are simpler and more direct than the six nature haiku printed on page 225. Because they are not so complicated, it is harder to say exactly what are the "opposites" in them. "The Monkey's Raincoat" contrasts the shivering of the animal with his ordinary high spirits. In "The Mournful Chirping" a new interpretation of the cricket's song occurs to the poet. "The Whale" is a study in motion: up and down. "In the House" contrasts freedom with captivity, stillness with motion. In "The Snake" the opposites, as in "The Cherry Trees" on page 225, are presence and absence.

1. Compare "The Monkey's Raincoat" with Khodasevich's "The Monkey" (page 226).

2. Compare "The Snake" with Emily Dickinson's poem of the same name (page 226).

3. Write some haiku on two or three animals you have observed.

For thousands of years, the fables of Aesop have provided a comment on the folly of human behavior. "The Fox and the Crow" has always been a favorite.

The Fox and the Crow

LA FONTAINE

A crow, perched debonairly on a branch,
  Was holding a cheese he'd found—by chance.
Along came a fox. He sniffed that cheese,
  And he spoke to its owner in words like these:

"Good morning, good morning, dear Brother
    Crow!
  My, you look fine! I've never seen you so—
So—*handsome*. Yes! I mean every word of it!
  And your lovely voice! Won't you sing a
    bit?"

The crow was enchanted—he could see no
    choice
  But give the fox a sample of his voice.
He opened his beak, and—cheese, goodbye!
  The fox grabbed it up without batting an eye.

Said the fox: "As a payment for what you've
    lost
  I'll give you a lesson worth twice the cost:
Flattery's a game for two, my dear,
  One to talk—and another to hear."

*Jean de la Fontaine (1621–1695) rewrote many
of Aesop's fables in polished French verse. But La
Fontaine was more than a translator; he gave his
animals characteristics of the Frenchmen of his
time. His versions of the fables add a sharpness all
his own.*

  1. In a sentence, state the moral of this story.
Does it still apply?
  2. Why is the crow a good choice for the fox's
victim? Would a lark serve as effectively? An
owl? Why? What is the characteristic of the crow
that makes his surrender to flattery so funny?
  3. A poet's attitude toward his subject creates
the mood of a poem. What is the mood of "The
Fox and the Crow"?

POEMS OF DELIGHT

*It is not necessary to travel widely to experience
the thrill of discovery. John Keats's sonnet cap-
tures a moment of revelation and joy that came
to him as he read John Chapman's translation of
Homer's epic poems.*

On First Looking into Chapman's Homer

JOHN KEATS

Much have I travell'd in the realms of gold,
  And many goodly states and kingdoms seen;
  Round many western islands have I been
Which bards in fealty to Apollo hold.
Oft one of wide expanse had I been told
  That deep-brow'd Homer ruled as his de-
    mesne:
  Yet did I never breathe its pure serene
Till I heard Chapman speak out loud and bold.

Then felt I like some watcher of the skies
  When a new planet swims into his ken;
Or like stout Cortez when with eagle eyes
  He stared at the Pacific—and all his men
Look'd at each other with a wild surmise—
  Silent, upon a peak in Darien.

*Keats's sonnet is one of the most famous in Eng-
lish. It also contains one of the most famous literary
"boners": it was, of course, Balboa rather than
Cortez who first saw the Pacific Ocean.*

  1. What does the poet mean when he says that
he has "travell'd in the realm of gold"? What
sort of man is he? Is he an astronomer? An explorer? What are his interests?
  2. In the final six lines, Keats makes two comparisons to his own experience. What are these

ON FIRST LOOKING INTO CHAPMAN'S HOMER: *fealty* =
loyalty, reverence; *demesne* = kingdom; *ken* =
sight.

comparisons? Are they effective? Why does he not choose another reading experience?

3. Compare this poem with Keats's other sonnet, "When I Have Fears" (page 218). Together, what do they tell us about the poet?

Rafu, the girl in this anonymous Chinese poem, is like the girl in Yeats's "For Anne Gregory" (page 211). Wherever she goes, her beauty becomes a source of delight to others.

A Ballad of the Mulberry Road

CHINESE

The sun rises in south east corner of things
To look on the tall house of the Shin
For they have a daughter named Rafu, (pretty girl).
She made the name for herself: "Gauze Veil,"
For she feeds mulberries to silkworms.
She gets them by the south wall of the town.
With green strings she makes the warp of her basket,
She makes the shoulder-straps of her basket from the boughs of Katsura,
And she piles her hair up on the left side of her head-piece.

Her earrings are made of pearl,
Her underskirt is of green pattern-silk,
Her overskirt is the same silk dyed in purple,
And when men going by look on Rafu
    They set down their burdens,
They stand and twirl their moustaches.

       [*translated by* EZRA POUND]

The method of this poem lies in the accumulation of detail. The reader can use these details to build a personal experience. The poet does not allow his own feelings to interfere directly, but he clearly shows the delight of the men who "stand and twirl their moustaches."

1. Is it possible to tell the relationship of the poet to the girl? Do you feel that he is older than the girl or of the same age?

2. Explain the effect of the final image of the poem—that of the men setting down their burdens to stand and twirl their moustaches.

3. Do the details in "A Ballad of the Mulberry Road" make the girl Rafu seem a unique person?

Sometimes happiness comes to a man for no apparent reason. Such a moment of illumination is recounted by the great Irish poet Yeats.

My Fiftieth Year

WILLIAM BUTLER YEATS

My fiftieth year had come and gone,
I sat, a solitary man,
In a crowded London shop,
An open book and empty cup
On the marble table-top.

While on the shop and street I gazed
My body of a sudden blazed;
And twenty minutes more or less
It seemed, so great my happiness,
That I was blessèd and could bless.

There is a sharp contrast between the first and second stanzas. At the beginning Yeats emphasizes his age and his loneliness. The shop itself is an ordinary, everyday place. This dull background in the first stanza makes the blaze of happiness stand out more sharply in the second.

1. What action of the poet's causes the sudden blaze of happiness? Is there any significance in the fact that he is gazing at the shop and street rather than at his book?

2. Is the meaning of this poem limited only to older people or to those who fear old age? Explain.

3. Why does the poet say that his "body" blazed rather than his "mind"? Explain carefully the last line of the poem.

Everyday life, to the alert eye and ear, can be a source of excitement and delight. Sarojini Naidu's "Street Cries" reflects the poet's pleasure in the sights and sounds of an Indian town.

Street Cries

SAROJINI NAIDU

When dawn's first cymbals beat upon the sky,
Rousing the world to labor's various cry,
To tend the flock, to bind the mellowing grain,
From ardent toil to forge a little gain,
And fasting men go forth on hurrying feet,
Buy bread, buy bread, rings down the eager
    street.

When the earth falters and the waters swoon
With the implacable radiance of noon,
And in dim shelters koels hush their notes,
And the faint, thirsting blood in languid throats
Craves liquid succor from the cruel heat,
Buy fruit, buy fruit, steals down the panting
    street.

When twilight twinkling o'er the gay bazaars,
Unfurls a sudden canopy of stars,
When lutes are strung and fragrant torches lit
On white roof terraces where lovers sit
Drinking together of life's poignant sweet,
Buy flowers, buy flowers, floats down the sing-
    ing street.

The poem's structure follows the rhythm of the day. The first stanza takes place at dawn, the second at noon, the last at evening.

1. From the poem itself, can you tell the climate of the town that is the poem's subject? What sort of people live here? What are their occupations? Is this an industrial center?

2. Does the poet seem in any way dissatisfied with the way of life he describes? Is there any protest here against social injustice?

STREET CRIES: *koel* = the cuckoo of India.

In this poem, Carl Sandburg communicates his relish for one of the most important parts of American popular culture—jazz. He evokes the rhythms, the sounds, and the images that the sounds suggest.

Jazz Fantasia

CARL SANDBURG

Drum on your drums, batter on your banjoes,
sob on the long cool winding saxophones.
Go to it, O jazzmen.

Sling your knuckles on the bottoms of the happy
tin pans, let your trombones ooze, and go husha-
husha-hush with the slippery sand-paper.

Moan like an autumn wind high in the lonesome
treetops, moan soft like you wanted somebody
terrible, cry like a racing car slipping away from
a motorcycle cop, bang-bang! you jazzmen,
bang altogether drums, traps, banjoes, horns,
tin cans—make two people fight on top of a
stairway and scratch each other's eyes in a
clinch tumbling down the stairs.

Can the rough stuff . . . now a Mississippi
steamboat pushes up the night river with a
hoo-hoo-hoo-oo . . . and the green lanterns
calling to the high soft stars . . . a red moon
rides on the humps of the low river hills . . . go
to it, O jazzmen.

Sandburg does not merely talk about jazz music. He makes the poem itself a piece of jazz by duplicating the sounds of the music in his verse.

1. Diction in poetry refers to the type of word the poet selects to suggest his meaning. How does the diction of "Jazz Fantasia" differ from the diction of the other poems in this book? Is the use of phrases such as these justified in poetry: "Go to it," "sling your knuckles," "can the rough stuff," "clinch"? Do they add to the effectiveness of this poem?

POEMS OF REGRET

In "My Heart's in the Highlands," Robert Burns sings of his longing for his native Scotland.

My Heart's in the Highlands

ROBERT BURNS

Farewell to the Highlands, farewell to the
    North,
The birthplace of valor, the country of worth;
Wherever I wander, wherever I rove,
The hills of the Highlands forever I love.

  My heart's in the Highlands, my heart is not
    here;
  My heart's in the Highlands, a-chasing the
    deer;
  A-chasing the wild deer, and following the
    roe,
  My heart's in the Highlands wherever I go.

Farewell to the mountains, high-covered with
    snow;
Farewell to the straths and green valleys below;
Farewell to the forests and wild-hanging woods,
Farewell to the torrents and loud-pouring floods.

  My heart's in the Highlands, my heart is not
    here;
  My heart's in the Highlands, a-chasing the
    deer;
  A-chasing the wild deer, and following the
    roe,
  My heart's in the Highlands wherever I go.

MY HEART'S IN THE HIGHLANDS: *straths* = flatlands
along a river.

In this poem (unlike "A Red, Red Rose" on page 212) Burns uses no dialect words. The lilt of a Scottish tune, however, can still be heard. In fact, Burns wrote most of his poems to fit the traditional melodies of Scotland.

1. Show how the poem is related to a specific background. Does this strongly local feeling make the emotion less universal?
2. What features of his homeland does the poet miss most? What does this show about him?

A deep sense of regret for things done and for things not done permeates this elegy by the English poet Charles Lamb.

The Old Familiar Faces

CHARLES LAMB

I have had playmates, I have had companions,
In my days of childhood, in my joyful school-
    days,
All, all are gone, the old familiar faces.

I have been laughing, I have been carousing,
Drinking late, sitting late, with my bosom
    cronies,
All, all are gone, the old familiar faces.

I loved a love once, fairest among women;
Closed are her doors on me, I must not see her—
All, all are gone, the old familiar faces.

I have a friend, a kinder friend has no man;
Like an ingrate, I left my friend abruptly;
Left him, to muse on the old familiar faces.

Ghost-like I paced round the haunts of my child-
    hood.
Earth seemed a desert I was bound to traverse,
Seeking to find the old familiar faces.

Friend of my bosom, thou more than a brother,
Why wert not thou born in my father's dwell-
    ing?
So might we talk of the old familiar faces—

How some they have died, and some they have
    left me,
And some are taken from me; all are departed;
All, all are gone, the old familiar faces.

*The vanished past is the subject of Lamb's poem.
Instead of yearning for it as Burns does, Lamb accepts the fact that the past is the past.*

1. To whom is the poem addressed? Is this person mentioned at more than one point? What does
the relationship of this person to Charles Lamb
tell us about the poet?
2. The German writer Novalis said that "character is fate." How does "The Old Familiar Faces"
supply an example of this?

————————

*The parting of friends is a theme many poets
have used in their verse. The Chinese poet
Rihaku supplies a fresh, vivid picture for this
familiar emotion.*

Taking Leave of a Friend

RIHAKU

Blue mountains to the north of the walls,
White river winding about them;
Here we must make separation
And go out through a thousand miles of dead
    grass.

Mind like a floating wide cloud,
Sunset like the parting of old acquaintances
Who bow over their clasped hands at a distance.
Our horses neigh to each other
            As we are departing.
                    [*translated by* EZRA POUND]

*The last two lines of the poem are a good example
of the way in which Chinese poets present abstract
emotion in specific terms. The two friends are
already too far from each other to speak: they
can only bow. The sharp sound of the horses'
neighing is really an extension of the voices of the
two friends themselves.*

1. Does the poem present a sharp picture? What
is meant by "a thousand miles of dead grass"?
2. How is nature used to express the feelings of
the poet?
3. Sentimentality may be described as emotion
which is excessive for any situation. Is this poem
sentimental? Explain your answer.

————————

*The Irish poet Yeats wrote this lively paraphrase
of a Japanese poem.*

Imitated from the Japanese

WILLIAM BUTLER YEATS

A most astonishing thing—
Seventy years have I lived;

(Hurrah for the flowers of Spring,
For Spring is here again.)

Seventy years have I lived
No ragged beggar-man,
Seventy years have I lived,
Seventy years man and boy,
And never have I danced for joy.

*The old man in the poem strongly regrets that
he has never "danced for joy." On the other hand,
the rhythms of the poem are bright, and the old*

man seems delighted with the spring and with the fact that he has lived so long.

1. What is the "astonishing thing" referred to in the first line?

2. What do the words "no ragged beggar-man" contribute to the poem?

———————

François Villon, the medieval French poet, lived violently and died mysteriously. He was a student and scholar, but he also lived in the underworld of Paris. There is good evidence that Villon was a thief and that at one time he was sentenced to death on the gallows. In this ballad he speaks as if he were one of a group of six criminals who have died by hanging. Looking back on a life that has gone astray, he sincerely begs pity and pardon from both man and God.

Ballad of the Hanged Men

FRANÇOIS VILLON

Brother men that after us shall be,
   Let not your hearts be hard to us:
If you take pity on our misery,
   God shall in time to you be piteous.
   Look at us six that hang here thus,
Observe the flesh we so much cherished,
How it is eaten by the birds, and perished—
   Dust and ashes starting to take its place.
Mock not at us that now so feeble be,
   But pray God pardon us out of His grace.

Listen, we pray you, and look not in scorn,
   Though it is just that we are cast to die:
For neither you nor any man is born
   Who keeps his wisdom with him constantly.
   Be you then merciful and cry
To Mary's Son that is all piteous
That He with mercy take our stain from us,
   And save us from Hell's fiery place.
We are but dead: let no soul now deny
   To pray God pardon us out of His grace.

We are washed clean by rain down from the
      skies;
   The sun has scorched us black and bare;
Ravens and crows have pecked our eyes
   And feathered their nests with our beards and
      hair.
   Hanging, tossing here and there,
This way and that, at the wind's will,
Not for a moment is my body still—
   And the birds are busy about my face.
Live not as we! Fare not as we fare!
   Pray God pardon us out of His grace!

ENVOI

Prince Jesus, Master of all, to Thee
We pray Hell gain no mastery
   Upon us, and that we avoid that place.
Brother men, that after us shall be,
   Pray God pardon us out of His grace.

Sometimes the word "ballad" refers to a simple story poem or to a poem that can be sung. Here, it refers to an elaborate and strict form developed by the troubadors. The last line of each stanza is the same, with very slight variations, and acts as a refrain. The last six lines are an "envoi" in which the poet directly addresses his Prince or the lady he loves. Here, most appropriate for this poem, it is not an earthly but a heavenly Prince whom the poet addresses in the final lines.

1. Does the speaker blame society for his death? Do he and his companions blame themselves? What reason do they give for their deaths on the gallows? What identification do they make with the rest of humanity?

2. Why do these criminals feel that they are not beyond redemption?

3. The poem vividly describes the medieval practice of allowing the bodies of executed victims to remain hanging in public as a lesson to others. Does the poet seem to approve or disapprove of this practice? Or does he seem to take it for granted?

POEMS ABOUT WAR

One of the greatest of the classic Chinese poets, Li Po, lived some time during the Sung period (618–954). In this poem he protests the slaughter that men do in the name of an ideal.

The Nefarious War

LI PO

Last year we fought by the head-stream of the
    So-kan,
This year we are fighting on the Tsung-ho
    road.
We have washed our armor in the waves of the
    Chiao-chi lake,
We have pastured our horses on Tien-shan's
    snowy slopes.
The long, long war goes on ten thousand miles
    from home,
Our three armies are worn and grown old.

The barbarian does man-slaughter for plowing;
On his yellow sand-plains nothing has been seen
    but blanched skulls and bones.
Where the Chin emperor built the walls against
    the Tartars,
There the defenders of Han are burning beacon
    fires.
The beacon fires burn and never go out,
There is no end to war!—

In the battlefield men grapple each other and
    die;
The horses of the vanquished utter lamentable
    cries to heaven,
While ravens and kites peck at human entrails,

Carry them up in their flight, and hang them
    on the branches of dead trees.
So, men are scattered and smeared over the
    desert grass,
And the generals have accomplished nothing.

Oh, nefarious war! I see why arms
Were so seldom used by the benign sovereigns.

           [*translated by* SHIGEYOSHI OBATA]

Li Po lived at least 1500 years after Bunno, the author of "The Song of the Bowmen of Shu." Yet the war he describes here might be the same war as in Bunno's poem. The whole history of China may be viewed as a struggle between those emperors ("the benign sovereigns") who worked for peace, order, and justice, and those who allowed their nation to suffer under disorder and war.

    1. Compare the attitude toward war in this poem with that in "The Inscription at Thermopylae" (page 237).
    2. Compare Li Po's attitude toward militarism with that of Bunno in "Song of the Bowmen of Shu." Which poet is the angrier?
    3. Who are the "we" who are the speakers of this poem?
    4. What comment on the whole poem is made by the last two lines?

THE NEFARIOUS WAR: *kite* = a bird similar to the hawk.

When Xerxes invaded Greece with an overwhelming Persian army (480 B.C.), Leonidas and three hundred men from Sparta successfully repelled the attack for three days in the narrow pass at Thermopylae. There they perished. This inscription was written to be engraved on the monument erected as a tribute to their courage and loyalty.

The Inscription at Thermopylae

Traveler, if you get to Sparta, say:
Here, obedient to their command, we lie.

This Greek epigram has long been famous as an example of how much meaning and emotion can be packed into a few words.

1. What is the primary virtue celebrated by this inscription?

2. What attitude toward war is implied in this poem? Is it an attitude men still hold today? Give some examples from recent history that parallel the events at Thermopolae.

3. Does the poem take into account the tragic side of war as well as its glories?

———————

One theme runs through these poems on the subject of war: that war is evil and unproductive. The Chinese poet Bunno, who lived about a thousand years before the Christian era, writes of two emotions familiar to all soldiers: boredom and discontent with the "brass hats."

Song of the Bowmen of Shu

BUNNO

Here we are, picking the first fern-shoots
And saying: When shall we get back to our
  country?
Here we are because we have the Ken-nin for
  our foemen,
We have no comfort because of these Mongols.
We grub the soft fern-shoots,
When anyone says "Return," the others are full
  of sorrow.

Sorrowful minds, sorrow is strong, we are
  hungry and thirsty.
Our defence is not yet made sure, no one can let
  his friend return.
We grub the old fern-stalks.
We say: Will we be let to go back in October?
There is no ease in royal affairs, we have no
  comfort.
Our sorrow is bitter, but we would not return
  to our country.
What flower has come into blossom?
Whose chariot? The General's.
Horses, his horses even, are tired. They were
  strong.
We have no rest, three battles a month.
By heaven, his horses are tired.
The generals are on them, the soldiers are by
  them.
The horses are well trained, the generals have
  ivory arrows and quivers ornamented with
  fish-skin.
The enemy is swift, we must be careful.
When we set out, the willows were drooping
  with spring,
We come back in the snow,
We go slowly, we are hungry and thirsty,
Our mind is full of sorrow, who will know of
  our grief?

[*translated by* EZRA POUND]

The bowmen (archers) of Shu were waging an endless expeditionary campaign against invading Mongol forces. The horses of the generals are used as an objective symbol of the footsoldiers themselves—well trained but tired.

1. How does the poet represent the passage of time? How does the reader know that this has been a long campaign? What sort of war is this? Is it a war which arrives at decisive moments?

2. What do the complaining bowmen long for most? What is their attitude toward the war they are fighting? Toward their own leaders?

3. What is meant by the line, "What flower has come into blossom"? Is it ironic?

The Irish flyer in this poem served in the Royal Air Force during the First World War. These were the years when the Irish people were engaged in a bitter struggle for independence from England. It is for this reason that the speaker of the poem, the pilot, declares, "Those that I guard I do not love." Why then does a man risk his life for a cause he does not believe in? Can danger itself give meaning to life? In the poem, the airman resolves this problem in a dramatic way.

An Irish Airman Foresees His Death

WILLIAM BUTLER YEATS

I know that I shall meet my fate
Somewhere among the clouds above;
Those that I fight I do not hate,
Those that I guard I do not love;
My country is Kiltartan Cross,
My countrymen Kiltartan's poor,
No likely end could bring them loss
Or leave them happier than before.
Nor law, nor duty bade me fight,
Nor public men, nor cheering crowds,
A lonely impulse of delight
Drove to this tumult in the clouds;
I balanced all, brought all to mind,
The years to come seemed waste of breath,
A waste of breath the years behind
In balance with this life, this death.

The Kiltartan Cross referred to in the poem is the airman's native village in Ireland.

1. What is the airman's attitude toward the enemy? Is it any different from his attitude toward those on whose side he is fighting? What will be the effect of victory on the pilot's own people, "Kiltartan's poor"? What effect will defeat have on them?

2. Discuss the airman's attitude toward his own past and future. What motive drives him to the "tumult in the clouds"?

3. What effect does the poet obtain by repeating the phrase "Waste of breath" and the word "balance"?

4. There are two ideas of "death" in the poem: one expressed in the title and the other in the last line. Discuss the difference between these two meanings. Try to define exactly what the airman means by "this life, this death" in the final line.

This short poem by the Chinese poet Li I (827?) is not a haiku, but it has the same effect of producing a sharp moment of revelation. War's cold, hardship, and violence contrast with a moment of tender beauty as the moon rises above the desert.

With the Army on the North Frontier

LI I

It snowed soon after the cold sea wind came;
The flutes blew all the time, and the roads were
     hard.
There were three hundred thousand soldiers on
     the desert.
Suddenly they all turned and looked at the
     moon.

The size of the army—three hundred thousand soldiers—is probably exaggerated by the poet. The exaggeration, however, produces a moment of poetic truth: a vast number of individuals united by a single emotion.

1. There are several sets of contrasts, or "opposites," in this poem. Identify as many as possible.

2. What attitude toward war is implied by this poem? How is this attitude communicated?

This anonymous Danish ballad reflects the values of medieval knighthood and the practice of jousting. The poem tells of the death of a hero, Sir Oluf, in combat with a mysterious knight dressed in magical armor.

The Elected Knight

MEDIEVAL DANISH

Sir Oluf he rideth over the plain,
    Full seven miles broad and seven miles wide;
But never, ah! never, can meet with the man
    A tilt with him dare ride.

He saw under the hill-side
    A knight full well equipped;
His steel was black, his helm was barred;
    He was riding at full speed.

He wore upon his spurs
    Twelve little golden birds;
Anon in eddies the wild wind blew,
    And there sat all the birds and sang.

He wore upon his mail
    Twelve little golden wheels;
Anon in eddies the wild wind blew,
    And round and round the wheels they flew.

He wore before his breast
    A lance that was poised in rest,
And it was sharper than diamond-stone;
    It made Sir Oluf's heart to groan.

He wore upon his helm
    A wreath of ruddy gold;
And that gave him the Maidens Three,
    The youngest was fair to behold.

Sir Oluf questioned the knight eftsoon
    If he were come from heaven down;
"Art thou Christ of Heaven?" quoth he,
    "So will I yield me unto thee."

"I am not Christ the Great,
    Thou shalt not yield thee yet;
I am an Unknown Knight,
    Three modest Maidens have me bedight."

"Art thou a knight elected?
    And have three maidens thee bedight?
So shalt thou ride a tilt this day,
    For all the maidens' honor!"

The first tilt they together rode,
    They put their steeds to the test;
The second tilt they together rode,
    They proved their manhood best.

The third tilt they together rode,
    Neither of them would yield;
The fourth tilt they together rode,
    They both fell on the field.

Now lie the lords upon the plain,
    And their blood runs unto death;
Now sit the Maidens in the high tower,
    The youngest sorrows till death.

[*translated by* HENRY WADSWORTH LONGFELLOW]

Medieval literature made extensive use of symbols, and the meanings of many of these symbols are lost to modern readers. In "The Elected Knight," for example, we can only guess at the symbolic importance of the twelve golden birds, the twelve golden wheels, and the three maidens.

1. Why do you think Sir Oluf asks the Elected Knight if he is "Christ of Heaven"?

2. In the poem, is one of the knights presented as the hero and the other as the villain? Or is the reader meant to be equally sympathetic toward both?

3. From your knowledge of other ancient ballads, tell what characteristics of the ballad form are shown in "The Elected Knight."

THE ELECTED KNIGHT: *tilt* = jousting contest; *helm* = helmet; *anon* = soon, then; *eftsoon* = then or afterwards; *bedight* = equipped.

Since Homer's time, at least, poets have lamented the destruction of young men in battle. Arthur Rimbaud here makes this common tragedy more vivid by surrounding the victim with a quiet, beautiful countryside.

The Sleeper of the Valley

ARTHUR RIMBAUD

There's a green hollow where a river sings
Silvering the torn grass in its glittering flight,
And where the sun from the proud mountain flings
Fire—and the little valley brims with light.

A soldier young, with open mouth, bare head,
Sleeps with his neck in dewy watercress,
Under the sky and on the grass his bed,
Pale in the deep green and the light's excess.

He sleeps amid the iris and his smile
Is like a sick child's slumbering for a while.
Nature, in thy warm lap his chilled limbs hide!

The perfume does not thrill him from his rest.
He sleeps in sunshine, hand upon his breast,
Tranquil—with two red holes in his right side.

[*translated by* LUDWIG LEWISOHN]

Arthur Rimbaud (1854–1891) was one of the most amazing geniuses of literature. He is one of the very greatest and most original of French poets. Although he lived thirty-seven years, he wrote all of his verse before he reached the age of twenty.

1. What line tells the reader that the young sleeper has been killed in battle? Is it a surprise?

2. What is the season of the year in this poem? How can you tell? What is meant by the "perfume" in the third line from the end?

3. Identify the elements that are contrasted in the final line.

POEMS ON THE CONDUCT OF LIFE

This epigram protesting against materialism is as meaningful today as when the Persian poet wrote it in the thirteenth century.

Advice

SAADI

If you lose all your worldly goods,
And only have two loaves of bread—
Sell one of them: take what you get,
And buy some flowers for your soul instead.

Another work by Saadi, "The Legend of the King and the Peasant," appears on page 465.

1. Why does the poet select bread as the last possession a man would have?

2. Describe the poet's ideal of happiness. How does he feel about poverty? Does he believe it necessary to be poor in order to achieve true happiness? Explain.

3. Could this philosophy be applied in the modern world? Compare the philosophy of the poem with that expressed in Tolstoy's "Conversation among Wealthy People" (page 480).

―――――

The speaker of "Life Is a Dream" is Segismundo, who has lived since childhood in a prison in the wilderness, unaware of the fact that he is a prince. Suddenly, he is brought to a castle, told that he is a prince, and given rich robes to wear. Then, just as suddenly, he finds himself back in his prison. Now he wonders if all that happened to him was only a dream. Possibly—for life itself is nothing but a dream.

Life Is a Dream

CALDERÓN DE LA BARCA

How strange—a world where life itself's a
    dream!
Experience has taught me that the man who
    lives
Dreams, and goes on dreaming 'till he wakes.
The king is only dreaming he's a king:
He goes on making laws with an imagined
    power,
Until the winds have carried off his praises
(Which were only borrowed) and Death turns
    him to ashes.
Why, then, do men wish power? Since they
    know
That they must wake up to a dream of death?
The rich man's only dreaming that he's rich—
And it's a dream that brings him care and worry.
The poor man's only dreaming that he's hungry.
The man who has luck dreams; the man of action
Dreams; and those who harm the lives of others
    dream.
So in this whole wide world everyone's dream-
    ing,
Whatever he is: but no one understands it.
Right now I dream I'm lying here in chains:
A while ago I dreamed that I enjoyed
A life more pleasing. And what is life? Frenzy!
What is life? Illusion! Shadow! Fiction!
The good in life is little. Life is a dream,
And dreams themselves are only parts of dreams.

Calderón's play Life Is a Dream *(1635) is as well
known to Spanish-speaking people as is* Hamlet
*to English and American readers. This speech of
Segismundo's is as famous as Hamlet's "To be or
not to be."*

1. This speech is delivered by a man who is
in chains and wearing ragged clothes. Would a man
who enjoys prosperity and happiness find it easy
to agree that "life is a dream"?

2. In a brief essay, defend or disagree with the
philosophy put forth in this speech.

*On the threshold of the greatest part of his
career, John Milton suffered an incurable blindness. His faith and will were strong, however,
and he went on to compose his great epic,*
Paradise Lost, *by dictating to his daughters.*

On His Blindness

JOHN MILTON

When I consider how my light is spent
Ere half my days, in this dark world and wide,
And that one talent which is death to hide
Lodged with me useless, though my soul more
    bent
To serve therewith my Maker, and present
My true account, lest He returning chide;
"Doth God exact day labor, light denied?"
I fondly ask. But Patience, to prevent
That murmur, soon replies, "God doth not need
Either man's work or his own gifts. Who best
Bear his mild yoke, they serve him best. His state
Is kingly: thousands at his bidding speed,
And post o'er land and ocean without rest;
They also serve who only stand and wait."

*There are two references to the Gospel in this
poem. The word "talent" in the third line refers
to the parable of the talents (Matthew 25:15–30)
in which a servant was condemned for burying his
one talent (a coin) in the earth. Milton uses the
word "talent" in two senses: the biblical coin and
our modern meaning of ability and skill. The other
Gospel reference is in the words "his mild yoke."
Jesus said (Matthew 11:29–30), "My yoke is easy."*

1. Half of this sonnet is a question and half is
the answer. Who states the question? Who gives
the answer?

2. What does the poet believe that God expects
of him? What is the "one talent" that he names?
Why would it be "death" to hide this talent?

3. Describe the poet's problem. What does the
last line of the poem mean? How does it resolve
the poet's problem?

ON HIS BLINDNESS: *fondly* = foolishly; *thousands* =
the angels.

Wordsworth believed that there was a divine innocence in childhood. The loss of this innocence with age is a corruption against which man should struggle. "My Heart Leaps Up" is the poetic cry of a man who has discovered this truth.

My Heart Leaps Up

WILLIAM WORDSWORTH

My heart leaps up when I behold
A rainbow in the sky.
So was it when my life began;
So is it now I am a man,
So be it when I shall grow old,
  Or let me die!
The child is father of the man;
And I would wish my days to be
Bound each to each by natural piety.

The last line expresses the hope that the poet will feel the sacred influences of nature when he is old just as strongly as when he was a child.

  1. Explain the line, "The child is father of the man."

  2. Do the first two lines of the poem indicate that the poet has been able to live his belief? How?

  3. How does the poet feel about change? What lines reveal his attitude? Why should the poet wish his days to be "bound" to each other?

———————

In this poem, Pasternak compares himself to Shakespeare's Hamlet—a man suffering from his own indecision and from the fact that he is isolated from the rest of the world. He also compares his suffering to that of Jesus in the garden of Gethsemane.

Hamlet

BORIS PASTERNAK

The plaudits slowly die away.
Again I come upon the stage.
I strain to hear in dying echoes
The fate that waits our present age.

Through thousands of binoculars
The night of darkness stares at me.
If possible, O Abba, Father,
Then take away this cup from me.

I love Thy stern design, and I am
Content to act this role of woe.
But there's another play on stage;
Then spare me now, and let me go.

The acts and parts are planned with care;
The end, foredoomed. I stand alone.
The Pharisees exult. How hard
This life, and long my way of stone.

[*translated by* EUGENE M. KAYDEN]

Boris Pasternak (1890–1960) is considered one of the greatest modern poets. In 1957, he was awarded the Nobel Prize for his novel Dr. Zhivago. *The book exposed the brutality and stupidity that were a part of the Russian revolution, and the Soviet government refused to allow it to be published in Russia. Because of pressures brought by the government, Pasternak had to refuse the Nobel award.*

  1. What view of the future does the poem give? What will be the poet's own part in this future? Is he a man of action?

  2. At what point does the poet switch from comparing himself to Hamlet and begin to compare himself with Christ? Who were the Pharisees? Who are the Pharisees of the modern world? Why do they jeer at the poet?

  3. What causes the speaker's suffering? What resolution of this suffering does he see for himself? Does he see any?

In "The Home" Tagore describes the sunset over a landscape in his native India. The poet is alone, the earth is bare, darkness is coming. Suddenly the sound of a boy's voice rises through the darkness. The boy is unaware that anyone is listening, and for this very reason, his song becomes an important message to the poet.

The Home

RABINDRANATH TAGORE

I paced alone on the road across the field while the sunset was hiding its last gold like a miser.

The daylight sank deeper and deeper into the darkness, and the widowed land, whose harvest had been reaped, lay silent.

Suddenly a boy's shrill voice rose into the sky. He traversed the dark unseen, leaving the track of his song across the hush of the evening.

His village home lay there at the end of the waste land, beyond the sugar-cane field, hidden among the shadows of the banana and the slender areca palm, the coconut, and the dark green jack-fruit trees.

I stopped for a moment in my lonely way under the starlight, and saw spread before me the darkened earth surrounding with her arms countless homes furnished with cradles and beds, mothers' hearts and evening lamps, and young lives glad with a gladness that knows nothing of its value for the world.

"The Home" is not written in metrical verse. That is, its rhythm depends upon long cadences and phrasings. In choosing this form for many of his poems, Tagore may have been influenced by the American poet Walt Whitman.

1. How does the fact that the gladness "knows nothing of its value for the world" actually make it more valuable? Are the final phrases of the poem a good description of the boy's song?

2. What is the significance to the poem of the phrase "lonely way"?

3. What is the effect of the word "shrill"? Why does Tagore not choose the word "beautiful" to describe the boy's voice?

The subject of this sonnet is really an abstract idea, the refusal of a man to accept Divine Grace. Lope de Vega makes it dramatic and exciting by presenting a sharp visual image—Christ standing outside the poet's gate like a beggar in the cold. The final lines are dramatized as a debate between the poet's soul and his guardian angel.

Tomorrow

LOPE DE VEGA

What had I, Lord, to offer, that with such care
You sought my friendship? and for my sake did
    wait,
Covered with dew, standing outside my gate
Passing the long, black nights of Winter there?

Strange was my madness, that I did not greet
Your blest approach. Heaven to me is lost
If with ingratitude's unkindly frost
I've chilled the bleeding wounds upon your feet!

Often my guardian angel gently cried:
"Soul, from thy window look, and thou shalt
    see
How He persists to call and wait for thee."
And often, to that angel's voice of sorrow,
"Tomorrow He may enter," I replied;
Then, when tomorrow came, said, "No—
    tomorrow!"

Lope de Vega (1562–1635) is one of the towering figures of Spanish literature and best known as a dramatist. At great speed, he wrote hundreds of plays, sacred, comic, and tragic. His lyrical poems, however, are also of great importance. Late in life, he joined a religious order.

1. Judging from this poem, what is Lope de Vega's concept of the Divinity?

2. What kind of person is the speaker of this poem? Is his action of refusal—in spite of the fact that he knows he is wrong—believable?

3. How is the speaker of this poem like the speaker of F. R. Scott's "Bangkok" (below)?

———————

Bangkok, capital of Thailand, is an ancient city famous for the beauty of its Buddhist temples. The modern Canadian poet F. R. Scott describes his experience during a visit to such a temple.

Bangkok

F. R. SCOTT

Deep in the brown bosom
Where all the temples rose
I wandered in a land
That I had never owned
With millions all around.

I had been here before
But never to this place
Which seemed so nearly home
Yet was so far away
I was not here at all.

There was a central mound
That took away my breath
So steep it was and round
So sudden by my side
So Asia all beyond.

And when I came inside
I had to walk barefoot
For this was holy ground
Where I was being taught
To worship on a mat.

A great white wind arose
And shakes of temple bells
Descended from the eaves
To make this gold and brown
One continent of love.

And only my own lack
Of love within the core
Sealed up my temple door
Made it too hard to break
And forced me to turn back.

The subject of the poem is a conflict of cultures within an individual. Conditioned to one way of life and to one faith, the poet finds it impossible to enter another.

1. What words describe the interior of the temple? What is the meaning of the word "love" as used in this poem? What kind of love does the poet mean?

2. In the second stanza, what does the poet mean when he says, "I had been here before, / But never to this place"? How is this possible?

3. What is the reason the poet gives for his inability to join the "continent of love" he finds within the temple? In the third line from the end, what does the word "temple" refer to?

———————

A. M. Klein describes a visit to an Indian reservation in his native Canada. He contrasts his boyhood concept of the noble, graceful Indian with the reality he sees before him. These pale Indians are no longer vital, exciting; they are "fauna in a museum." Their own culture is dead, preserved on a reservation as an amusement for the tourists ("the pious prosperous ghosts") who come to buy baskets, blankets, and other relics of the past.

Indian Reservation: Caughnawaga

A. M. KLEIN

Where are the braves, the faces like autumn
  fruit,
who stared at the child from the coloured
  frontispiece?
And the monosyllabic chief who spoke with his
  throat?
Where are the tribes, the feathered bestiaries?—
Rank Aesop's animals erect and red,
with fur on their names to make all live things
  kin—
Chief Running Deer, Black Bear, Old Buffalo
  Head?

Childhood, that wished me Indian, hoped that
one afterschool I'd leave the classroom chalk,
the varnish smell, the watered dust of the street,
to join the clean outdoors and the Iroquois track.
Childhood; but always,—as on a calendar,—
there stood that chief, with arms akimbo,
  waiting
the runaway mascot paddling to his shore.

With what strange moccasin stealth that scene
  is changed!
With French names, without paint, in overalls,
their bronze, like their nobility expunged,—
the men. Beneath their alimentary shawls
sit like black tents their squaws; while for the
  tourist's
brown pennies scattered at the old church door,
the ragged papooses jump, and bite the dust.

Their past is sold in a shop: the beaded shoes,
the sweetgrass basket, the curio Indian,
burnt wood and gaudy cloth and inch-canoes—
trophies and scalpings for a traveller's den.
Sometimes, it's true, they dance, but for a bribe;
after a deal don the bedraggled feather
and welcome a white mayor to the tribe.

This is a grassy ghetto, and no home.
And these are fauna in a museum kept.
The better hunters have prevailed. The game,
losing its blood, now makes these grounds its
  crypt.
The animals pale, the shine of the fur is lost,
bleached are their living bones. About them
  watch
as through a mist, the pious prosperous ghosts.

*This poem is not a difficult one, if read with close
attention. Like much modern poetry (like poetry
of all ages, for that matter) it contains some phrases
which are so compressed in meaning that the reader
must "decipher" them. The structure of the poem
is as follows: the first two stanzas present the
writer's romantic boyhood ideas about Indians; the
second two stanzas give a picture of the reality he
finds on a modern Indian reservation; in the last
stanza he reflects upon the meaning of his experience.*

1. Who is "the child" in the first stanza? What is
the deeper meaning in the fact that the Indians
were once named after animals?

2. The second stanza presents the writer's childhood fantasy. Explain the phrase, "Childhood, that
wished me Indian."

3. Much of the population of Canada is of French
ancestry. The Indians have dropped their tribal
names for modern French ones. Explain the line,
"their bronze, like their nobility expunged."

4. The phrase "alimentary shawls" is particularly
compressed. The shawls are alimentary (food-giv-
ing, nourishing) because their sale to tourists supplies the Indians with a living. What is the irony
of the phrase "bite the dust"? Explain the meaning
of "inch-canoes."

5. What is meant by "a grassy ghetto"? Who are
the "better hunters"? Who are "the game" and the
"animals"? In what sense are the white tourists, the
"prosperous ghosts," pious?

INDIAN RESERVATION: CAUGHNAWAGA: *bestiaries* =
books of tales about animals; *ghetto* = an area in
which members of a racial group are segregated.

Poetry often conveys its emotion and its meaning through the use of symbols. A specific moment or gesture, a single object, is made to stand for something larger. In the following poem a man closes a window. The poet dramatizes this simple, common action, making it a symbol of a way of life.

The Window

JAIME TORRES BODET

You closed the window. And it was the world,
the world that wanted to enter, all at once,
the world that gave that great shout,
that great, deep, rough cry
you did not want to hear—and now
will never call to you again as it called today,
asking your mercy!

The whole of life was in that cry:
the wind, the sea, the land
with its poles and its tropics,
the unreachable skies,
the ripened grain in the resounding wheat field,
the thick heat above the wine presses,
dawn on the mountains, shadowy woods,
parched lips stuck together longing for
cool water condensed in pools,
and all pleasures, all sufferings,
all loves, all hates,
were in this day, anxiously
asking your mercy . . .

But you were afraid of life.
And you remained alone,
behind the closed and silent window,
not understanding that the world calls to a man
only once that way, and with that kind of cry,
with that great, rough, hoarse cry!

Jaime Torres Bodet (1902–   ) is one of Mexico's most distinguished writers. He has published poems, criticisms, and essays on philosophy and politics. He has also served as his country's Minister of Education.

1. Who is the "you" in the poem? What can the reader tell of the relation between the poet and the man he speaks to?

2. Tell in your own words what the closing of the window stands for.

3. There are other symbols in the poem. Identify some of them and discuss their use.

In Rilke's "Autumn" the falling of the dried leaves starts the poet thinking about the fact that all life must come to an end. There is a sadness in the rhythms of this poem, but it ends with an expression of faith.

Autumn

RAINER MARIA RILKE

The dry leaves fall, as if from far away,
fall from distant gardens in the skies,
fall with an air of resignation.

And in the night this heavy Earth falls down,
down from the stars, into a loneliness.

All of us fall. This hand must fall.
And look around you: it will all go the same
        way.

Yet there is One who holds all falling things,
gently, eternally, within His hands.

Rainer Maria Rilke (1875–1926) was born in Prague. He lived a cosmopolitan life, wandering throughout Europe, finally to die in Switzerland. Rilke's literary language was German. Many readers consider him the greatest modern poet of that language. His "Solemn Hour" appears on page 446.

1. Why is the word "fall" repeated so often throughout the poem? Is the word "fall" used in more than one sense? Explain.

2. Explain the phrase "an air of resignation." In line seven, to what does the word "all" refer?

3. What is the mood of "Autumn"?

POEMS OF COMEDY AND SATIRE

The brief, neatly turned epigram was a favorite verse form of the classic Greek and Roman writers. In fact, as is the case with haiku in Japan, epigrams were composed by most literate people, not by professional poets only. There are several examples of serious epigrams in this book, among them "The Inscription at Thermopylae" (page 237) and "Inscription for the Grave of a Dog" (page 228). Epigrams were also used as political and personal satire. One way of getting back at your enemy was to write a nasty little verse about one of his weaknesses— and then let it circulate throughout the town.

Two Epigrams

MARTIAL

A HINTED WISH

You told me, Maro, whilst you live
You'd not a single penny give,
But that, whene'er you chanced to die,
You'd leave a handsome legacy:
You must be mad beyond redress,
If my next wish you cannot guess!

[*translated by* SAMUEL JOHNSON]

BOUGHT LOCKS

The golden hair that Gulla wears
  Is hers: who would have thought it?
She swears 'tis hers, and true she swears,
  For I know where she bought it.

[*translated by* SIR JOHN HARINGTON]

Martial (c40–c104), the Latin poet, was born in Spain during the days when Spain was part of the Roman Empire. Most of his mature life, however, was spent at Rome. He is the master of the kind of comic epigram that turns into a whiplash in its final line.

1. Satire is said to have a healthy aim: correcting human foibles through laughter. How does this statement apply to these two epigrams? What human characteristics does each poem satirize?

2. Show how Martial uses "logic" as the basis of the comedy in his two verses.

———————

Using the symbols of fire and ice, the great New England poet considers the opposites of love and hate, and makes a wry comment on human nature.

Fire and Ice

ROBERT FROST

Some say the world will end in fire,
Some say in ice.
From what I've tasted of desire
I hold with those who favor fire.
But if it had to perish twice,
I think I know enough of hate
To say that for destruction ice
Is also great
And would suffice.

Frost has treated a serious subject in a lighthearted way. The length of the lines is irregular, and the rhymes are unexpected. In contrast to its grim subject, the sound of the poem is something like a children's jingle or nursery rhyme.

1. How do fire and ice themselves make a comment on the emotions they stand for?

2. Is the poem intended as a serious comment on the end of the world? If not, what is its real subject?

A young girl of ancient China, plucking plums from a tree, becomes more and more concerned as the plums disappear and no one comes to ask for her hand. Centuries have passed, but girls have not yet stopped worrying over this weighty matter.

Anxiety of a Young Girl to Get Married

CHINESE

Ripe, the plums fall from the bough;
Only seven-tenths left there now!
Ye whose hearts on me are set,
Now the time is fortunate!

Ripe, the plums fall from the bough;
Only three-tenths left there now!
Ye who wish my love to gain
Will not now apply in vain!

No more plums upon the bough!
All are in my basket now!
Ye who me with ardor seek,
Need the word but freely speak!

[*translated by* JAMES LEGGE]

The light tone of the poem assures the reader that the young girl really has little to worry about.

   1. What season of the year is suggested? How is it related to the theme of the poem?
   2. Of what is the plum tree a symbol in the young girl's mind? Explain.
   3. Where is the humor in this poem? Is the situation funny from the girl's point of view? Why then should it be amusing to the reader?

The story of Richard Cory is a reminder that envy and admiration should not be too freely indulged.

Richard Cory

EDWIN ARLINGTON ROBINSON

Whenever Richard Cory went downtown,
  We people on the pavement looked at him:
He was a gentleman from sole to crown,
  Clean favored, and imperially slim.

And he was always quietly arrayed,
  And he was always human when he talked;
But still he fluttered pulses when he said,
  "Good-morning," and he glittered when he
    walked.

And he was rich—yes, richer than a king—
  And admirably schooled in every grace:
In fine, we thought that he was everything
  To make us wish that we were in his place.

So on we worked, and waited for the light,
  And went without the meat, and cursed the
    bread;
And Richard Cory, one calm summer night,
  Went home and put a bullet through his head.

The satire in this poem is aimed both at Richard Cory and at the townspeople (the "we" of the poem). Of Richard Cory we know little: that he was rich and that he had beautiful clothes and manners. We also discover that, for all his aristocratic surface, he did not have the inner strength to face life. The townspeople are satirized for their willingness to accept Richard Cory's glittering surface as "everything," and to debase themselves before him.

1. Does the last line of the poem come as a surprise? Why? Has it been prepared for in any way?

2. The reason why Richard Cory kills himself is not given. Why is the reason not important to the meaning of the poem?

3. Irony is saying one thing and meaning something else. In what ways are the following words and phrases ironic: "crown," "imperially," "arrayed," "he was always human when he talked," "glittered," "one calm summer night"?

———

Writers of all nations have traditionally made sport of country bumpkins, like this bewildered Arab, who find themselves confused by the size and bustle of the big city. Jami was a Persian poet of the fifteenth century. The translator, Edward Fitzgerald, is best known for his version of the Rubaiyat of Omar Khayyam.

The Bewildered Arab

JAMI

From the solitary desert
Up to Baghdad came a simple
  Arab; there amid the rout
Grew bewildered of the countless
People, hither, thither, running
Coming, going, meeting, parting,
Clamor, clatter, and confusion,
  All about him and about.

Travel-wearied, hubbub-dizzy,
  Would the simple Arab fain
Get to sleep—"but then, on waking,
  How," quoth he, "amid so many
Waking, know myself again?"

So to make the matter certain
Strung a gourd about his ankle,
And, into a corner creeping,
Baghdad and himself and people
  Soon were blotted from his brain.

But one that heard him and divined
His purpose, slyly crept behind;
From the sleeper's ankle clipping,
  Round his own the pumpkin tied,
  And laid him down to sleep beside.

By and by the Arab, waking,
Looks directly for his signal—
Sees it on another's ankle
Cries aloud, "Oh, good-for-nothing
  Rascal to perplex me so!
That by you I am bewildered,
  Whether I be I or no!
If I—the pumpkin why on you?
If you—then where am I, and who?"

    [*translated by* EDWARD FITZGERALD]

Although this poem is meant as fun, it is based on a serious philosophical question: how does a man know who and what he is? How do we establish our own "identity"?

1. Give other examples of stories, plays, comic strips, and so forth, which find comedy in the situation of the country boy in the big city.

2. Is the bewildered Arab stupid? What drives him to his sudden concern over preserving his identity?

3. How is the Arab's confusion a parody of logic?

Like "The Bewildered Arab" this poem by W. H. Auden concerns the loss of human identity. "The Bewildered Arab" is a gently comic poem. "The Unknown Citizen" is deadly serious in its intent. Auden satirizes a mechanical attitude toward man which is a very real force in the modern world.

The Unknown Citizen
JS/07/M/378

THIS MARBLE MONUMENT IS
ERECTED BY THE STATE

W. H. AUDEN

He was found by the Bureau of Statistics to be
One against whom there was no official com-
    plaint,
And all the reports on his conduct agree
That, in the modern sense of an old-fashioned
    word, he was a saint,
For in everything he did he served the Greater
    Community.
Except for the war till the day he retired
He worked in the factory and never got fired,
But satisfied his employers, Fudge Motors Inc.
Yet he wasn't a scab or odd in his views,
For his Union reports that he paid his dues,
(Our report on his Union shows it was sound)
And our Social Psychology workers found
That he was popular with his mates and liked a
    drink.
The Press are convinced that he bought a paper
    every day
And that his reactions to poetry were normal in
    every way.
Policies taken out in his name prove that he was
    was fully insured,
And his Health Card shows he was once in
    hospital but left it cured.

Both Producers Research and High-Grade Liv-
    ing declare
He was fully sensible to the advantages of the
    Installment Plan
And had everything necessary to the Modern
    Man,
A gramophone, a radio, a car, and a frigidaire.
Our researchers into public opinion are content
That he held the proper opinions for the time of
    year.
When there was peace, he was for peace; when
    there was war, he went.
He was married and added five children to the
    population,
Which our Eugenists say was the right number
    for a parent of his generation,
And our teachers report that he never interfered
    with their education.
Was he free? Was he happy? The question is
    absurd:
Had anything been wrong, we certainly should
    have heard.

Notice the use of capital letters for satirical effect. Ordinarily such words as "press," "health card," "installment plan," "greater community," and "modern man" would be written with small letters. The capitals show that these ideas have become institutionalized—that they have come to have an importance of their own which overshadows the importance of the individual.

1. Who is the speaker of this poem? What is his attitude toward a good and full life? What lines show this attitude? What is Auden's own concept of the things most important to man? How does he communicate it?

2. Does the poet suggest that the information about the Unknown Citizen is accurate? How might it be misleading?

3. Why, in the poem, has "saint" become an old-fashioned word?

4. List examples of irony in this poem. In what sense is the whole poem—as a document—ironic?

Like "The Unknown Citizen," "Waiting for the Barbarians" is a bitter comment on the State. Auden's poem sees the State as a perfect, mechanical monster. In Cavafy's poem, the State is crumbling and weak, suffering from moral collapse.

Waiting for the Barbarians

C. F. CAVAFY

"What are we waiting for,
All of us gathered together like this in the
    Square?"

"The Barbarians are due to arrive today."

"Why is the Senate at a standstill?
Why do the Senators sit without making laws?"

"Because the Barbarians are coming today.
What laws would the Senate pass now?
When the Barbarians get here *they* will make the
    laws."

"Why has our Emperor sat since dawn
Solemnly enthroned at the City gates,
And wearing his crown?"

"That's because the Barbarians are on their way.
The Emperor is ready to receive their chief,
And has even had a scroll prepared
Conferring honors and titles upon him."

"Why have our two consuls and our praetors
    come forth
In their heavily embroidered scarlet togas?
And why are they decked with amethyst brace-
    lets,
And rings sparkling with emeralds?
Why do they carry their choicest staffs
So finely carved?"

"Oh, that's all for the Barbarians, coming today;
Costly things like these will dazzle Barbarians."

"And why are our gifted orators
Not holding forth with their usual eloquence?"

"Because the Barbarians are coming today,
And *they* won't value long speeches or fine
    rhetoric."

"Now why, so suddenly, this commotion and
    concern?
How troubled the faces have become!
Why are streets and squares emptying so fast,
And why does everyone head for home, looking
    so sombre?"

"It's because night is falling,
And the Barbarians have not come.
Some folk just in from the frontiers say
That now there aren't any Barbarians any more."

*   *   *

"So now what will become of us, without
    Barbarians?
For they were, after all, a kind of solution."

[*translated by* MARGUERITE YOURCENAR
and GRACE FRICK]

C. F. Cavafy is one of the leading twentieth-century poets of Greece. "Waiting for the Barbarians" is not descriptive of any specific moment in history. In general, it suggests the collapse of the Roman Empire. Its true subject is the parallel it draws between ancient and modern times.

1. The poem is a conversation between two speakers. Who are they? What is the difference between them?

2. The citizens of the city in this poem feel both admiration and contempt for the barbarians. Which lines show their admiration? What qualities of the barbarians do they admire? In what respects do they feel themselves superior to the barbarians?

3. How is it possible that "there aren't any Barbarians any more"? Why are the citizens disappointed at this news? To what problems would the barbarians have been a solution?

4. The mention of scrolls and togas clearly place the poem in an ancient setting. In what sense is this poem a comment on modern times?

PETER BREUGHEL THE ELDER

Ships

(The Metropolitan Museum
of Art, Rogers Fund)

UNIT 6: ADVENTURE AROUND THE WORLD

Life is the ultimate adventure.

And, as we see in the poetry of Emily Dickinson or in the writings of Helen
Keller, it is not necessary to travel in space or to the bottom of the ocean
to find wonder and drama. Observation and imagination can discover sur-
prises and hidden meanings in the world close by.

Still, there comes at times an overpowering longing for distant horizons.
We turn to literature that tells of experiences in strange lands where, perhaps,

physical danger sharpens the senses and intensifies each moment. Men and women who follow tides, jungle paths, and airstreams become the heroes and heroines of the epic of man's quest for thrills and knowledge. Accounts of their exploits tell us something of the reasons that compel individuals to test their courage by exposing themselves to violent hazards and even to death.

From Ernst Udet's chivalric air duel with the French ace Georges Guynemer to Jacques-Yves Cousteau's bold familiarity with sharks beneath the surface of the Mediterranean Sea, the following selections offer the reader glimpses into the thoughts, feelings, and observations of men who have hovered for a moment at the edge of the precipice dividing life from death. Through an awareness of the states of mind of men under stress, we arrive at conclusions that help us understand ourselves. We may not confront real bullets from an enemy machine gun, nor face the jaws of sharks, yet we love to have our imaginations stirred by the accounts of men who do. Symbolically, we participate in exciting events that would otherwise remain dim and remote.

The literature of adventure undoubtedly stretches backward in time far beyond the invention of writing. Men preserved in oral literature, as they still do in many parts of the world, legends of the heroic exploits of their ancestors. Homer's two epics, *The Iliad* and *The Odyssey*, had been repeated around campfires and in the great halls of palaces for centuries before they were ever written down. *The Odyssey*, from which one episode has been taken for this volume, is the classic adventure. The hero leaves the safety of his home to participate in a heroic exploit—the Trojan War. Through strength and cleverness, and with the aid of the gods, he conquers his enemies. But he must undergo many trials and sufferings on land and sea, and overcome them all as he overcomes the Cyclops, before he is allowed to return to his own home and a peaceful life.

Writers of adventure stories, both true and fictional, provide their readers with thrills. But thrill seeking is not the basic reason why tales of adventure have made up so large a part of the literature of the world. Adventure stories are tales of man's courage, endurance, and imagination. Through them we discover our own moral and physical possibilities.

Of the adventurers whose tales are told in this unit, none were reckless thrill seekers. Many had sound scientific purposes for risking their lives and fortunes. Thor Heyderdahl, aboard the *Kon-Tiki*, was first an anthropologist and second an adventuring sailor. Jacques-Yves Cousteau took chances with his own life far below the sea as a means of gathering information which could not have been obtained by other methods. Tenzing Norgay on the top of Mount Everest and Roald Amundsen in the polar regions pushed themselves to the limits of endurance in order to report the facts about places where no man had ever set foot. Sherlock Holmes's adventure is one of the mind: he matches wits with a master criminal. Louis Slotin was also an adventurer of the mind, even though he had to sacrifice his life for science.

The tales of these explorers, scientists, and warriors all point to the fact that the greatest adventurers are those with a serious purpose.

The Spirit of Adventure

THEODORE ROOSEVELT

Theodore Roosevelt's ideal adventurer is a man, alone against the elements, who actively challenges all the dangers that nature can offer. In a way this is a restatement of the medieval legends—the inspiration of Don Quixote—in which the knight, pure in heart, set out to test himself against the dragons and giants and temptations of the world. Like the knight of the myth, Roosevelt's adventurer must be worthy of the nobility of his quest. He must be strong and daring to reap the spiritual rewards of his enterprise. In this expression of the philosophy of adventure, Roosevelt asserts that the greatest joy comes to the man who has the courage to make the greatest demands on experience.

THE MAN should have youth and strength who seeks adventure in the wide, waste spaces of the earth, in the marshes, and among the vast mountain masses, in the northern forests, amid the steaming jungles of the tropics, or on the deserts of sand or of snow. He must long greatly for the lonely winds that blow across the wilderness, and for sunrise and sunset over the rim of the empty world. His heart must thrill for the saddle and not for the hearthstone. He must be helmsman and chief, the cragsman, the rifleman, the boat steerer. He must be the wielder of ax and of paddle, the rider of fiery horses, the master of the craft that leaps through white water. His eye must be true and quick, his hand steady and strong. His heart must never fail nor his head grow bewildered, whether he face brute and human foes, or the frowning strength of hostile nature, or the awful fear that grips those who are lost in trackless lands. Wearing toil and hardship shall be his; thirst and famine he shall face, and burning fever. Death shall come to greet him with poison fang or poison arrow, in shape of charging beast or of scaly things that lurk in lake and river; it shall lie in wait for him among untrodden forests, in the swirl of wild waters, and in the blast of snow blizzard or thunder-shattered hurricane.

THEODORE ROOSEVELT (1858–1919), who led the historic Rough Riders on the cavalry charge up San Juan Hill during the Spanish-American War and who later became the twenty-sixth President of the United States, was a man of many accomplishments. He wrote well, and his books, Ranch Life and the Hunting Trail, African Game Trails, and the four-volume The Winning of the West, still attract readers. He rode, hunted, explored, fished, climbed mountains, boxed, wrestled, studied, and engaged in politics—and did all these things with enormous zest. During his administration, he encouraged the "muck-raking" campaign that exposed corruption in city and state government. He inaugurated the first of our conservation laws, fought to break big-business monopolies, and worked to establish the Pure Food and Drug Act as law. Roosevelt's foreign policy was partly summed up in his expression, "Speak softly, but carry a big stick." Masculine aggressiveness characterized everything he did or thought. Yet he received the Nobel Prize for Peace in 1905 for his role in negotiating an end to the Russo-Japanese War.

Not many men with wisdom make such a life their permanent and serious occupation. Those whose tasks lie along other lines can lead it for but a few years. For them it must normally come in the hardy vigor of their youth, before the beat of the blood has grown sluggish in their veins.

Nevertheless, older men also can find joy in such a life, although in their case it must be led only on the outskirts of adventure, and although the part they play therein must be that of the onlooker rather than that of the doer. The feats of prowess are for others. It is for other men to face the peril of unknown lands, to master unbroken horses, and to hold their own among their fellows with bodies of supple strength. But much, very much, remains for the man who has "warmed both hands before the fire of life," and who, although he loves the great cities, loves even more the fenceless grassland and the forest-clad hills.

The grandest scenery of the world is his to look at if he chooses; and he can witness the strange ways of tribes who have survived into an alien age from an immemorial past, tribes whose priests dance in honor of the serpent and worship the spirits of the wolf and the bear. Far and wide, all the continents are open to him as they never were to any of his forefathers; the Nile and the Paraguay are easy of access, and the borderland between savagery and civilization; and the veil of the past has been lifted so that he can dimly see how, in time immeasurably remote, his ancestors—no less remote—led furtive lives among uncouth and terrible beasts, whose kind has perished utterly from the face of the earth. He will take books with him as he journeys; for the keenest enjoyment of the wilderness is reserved for him who enjoys also the garnered wisdom of the present and the past. He will take pleasure in the companionship of the men in the open; in South America, the daring and reckless horseman who guard the herds of the grazing country, and the dark-skinned paddlers who guide their clumsy dug-outs down the dangerous equatorial rivers; the white and red and half-breed hunters of the Rockies, and of the Canadian woodland; and in Africa the faithful black gunbearers who have stood steadily at his elbow when the lion came on with coughing grunts, or when the huge mass of the charging elephant burst asunder the vine-tangled branches.

The beauty and charm of the wilderness are his for the asking, for the edges of the wilderness lie close beside the beaten roads of present travel. He can see the red splendor of desert sunsets, and the unearthly glory of the after-

Theodore Roosevelt with his Rough Riders on San Juan Hill

glow on the battlements of desolate mountains. In sapphire gulfs of ocean he can visit islets, above which the wings of myriads of sea fowl make a kind of shifting cuneiform script in the air. He can ride along the brink of the stupendous cliff-walled canyon, where eagles soar below him, and cougars make their lairs on the ledges and harry the big-horned sheep. He can journey through the northern forests, the home of the giant moose, the forests of fragrant and murmuring life in summer, the iron-bound and melancholy forests of winter.

The joy of living is his who has the heart to demand it.

For Discussion

1. What are the qualifications that Roosevelt demands of the real adventurer? What are the qualities of a man not suited for adventure? Do you agree? Explain.

2. Do you think that Roosevelt considered the possibility that women might choose to become adventurers? Why?

3. Find examples from the literature of adventure that apply to Roosevelt's doctrine? Are there examples that contradict the principles of this selection?

4. How much of Theodore Roosevelt's character appears in the writing of this selection? When he writes, "His heart must thrill for the saddle and not for hearthstone," does he consider all kinds of adventurers? How do you think Roosevelt feels toward the man who explores the mysterious paths of the human mind? Would he consider Albert Einstein an adventurer? Would you? Why?

5. In a paragraph or two, write your own philosophy of adventure. How does it differ from Theodore Roosevelt's? What does your philosophy of adventure reveal about yourself?

Adventure of the Cyclops

HOMER

Odysseus is a hero of heroes. The anger of the gods has pursued him since he led the men who slipped from their hiding place within the famous wooden horse to attack the Trojans while they slept. His journey home has become a nightmare of destruction as the gods devise ingenious ways to stop his progress. His comrades die along the way. But Odysseus' strength and courage and cunning combine to oppose the forces that work to destroy him. In this selection from Book IX of The Odyssey, *Odysseus' boats run aground on the island of the Cyclops. The fierce hostility of these one-eyed giants leads to grim consequences. But Odysseus' resourcefulness guides him toward the exploitation of his enemy's weakness, and he executes a spectacular escape. For three thousand years, the tale of the Cyclops has been a classic in the literature of adventure.*

And now we came unto the land
Where dwell the Cyclops—arrogant
And lawless beings, who, with trust
In the undying gods, plough not
Nor plant with hands a single plant.
Yet crops spring up for them unsown
On fields untended—wheat and barley
And vines that bear full-clustered grapes
To make them wine. The rain of Zeus
Still brings increase in all. These men
Have neither meeting-place for council
Nor settled laws. They live apart
On lofty mountain ridges, dwelling
In hollow caverns. Each makes laws
For wife and child, and gives no heed
To any save himself.

                There lies,
Facing the Cyclops' land, an island,
Sheltering the haven's outer side,
Not near, nor yet far out.

                Thither we sailed
Seeking the land. Surely it was
Some god that gave us guidance thither
Through the dense night, for we could see
Nothing before our eyes: the mist
Shut close about the ships; no moon
Showed forth in heaven, for clouds enclosed it.
So no man with his eyes beheld
That isle or saw the long seas rolling
Against the land till we had beached
Our well-benched ships.

We drew our ships
Forth on the sands and lowered sail,
And we ourselves went up beyond
The breaking of the seas, and there
We fell asleep, and lay awaiting
The sacred dawn.

But when the dawn
Came, early-born and rosy-fingered,
We went forth, roaming through the island,
Gazing in wonder.

Now we looked
And saw not far away the mainland
Where dwelt the Cyclops. And we saw
Smoke rise, and heard the speech of men
And bleat of sheep and goats. Then came
The setting of the sun and darkness;
And there we slept beside the breakers.
But when the earliest dawn appeared
Rose-fingered, then I called together
My men and spoke to all:

"Rest here,
Dear comrades, while with my own ship
And my own men I go to learn
What men these are—if wild and cruel
And ignorant of right, or kind
To every stranger and with hearts
That fear the gods."

I spoke and went
Aboard my ship and bade my men
Embark and loose the cables. Quickly
They came aboard and sat them down
Each in his place and smote with oars
The whitening sea.

Now when we reached
That land that lay hard by, we saw
Upon its utmost point a cave
Close to the sea: high-roofed it was,
With laurel overhung, and many
The flocks of sheep and goats that there
Found shelter in the night. Around it
A courtyard lay, high-walled with stones
Set deep in earth, with lofty pines
And high-leaved oaks.

Within this lair
A man was wont to sleep, a monster
Who grazed his sheep far off, alone,
Nor ever mingled with his kind,
But lonely dwelt—lawless and evil.
And marvellously was he shapen—
This monstrous being, not like mortals
That live by bread, but like a peak
That rising rough with woods stands forth
Apart from other hills.

And I
Now bade my trusty men to bide
Close by the ship and guard the ship,
But twelve I chose, the best of all,
And we set forth.

I bore with me
A goatskin filled with dark sweet wine,
Which Maron, priest of Phœbus, gave me
Sweet and unmixed, a drink for gods.
Not one of all his slaves or servants
Might taste that wine at home, save only
Himself, his wife, and the good matron
Who had his house in charge. Whenever
They drank that red wine, honey-sweet,
He took one cup, no more, and served it
Mingled with water twenty times
The measure of the wine; and yet
Up from the mixing-bowl there rose
Rare scent and sweetness, till no man
Could find it easy to refrain
From drinking of that wine. I filled
A great skin with this, and I bore it
As I set forth, and bore besides
Food in a leathern sack. For now
My fearless heart foresaw a meeting
With a strange man of monstrous might—
A savage, scornful of the gods
And of man's law.

Straightway we reached
His cave and entered, but we found not
The man within. For far away
He herded, while they grazed at pasture,
His goodly flock. So on we passed
Far into that great cave and marvelled
At all we saw within. Here stood

*"Some three thousand years ago, there
came into being two great poems,
perhaps the two greatest poems in the
world. We do not know who wrote
them. We call their author Homer, but
we do not know whether this name
denotes one man or several men. It
stands, like the x in algebra, for the
unknown author.*

*"Perhaps one supreme poet brought
together and tinged with his personality
a group of poems composed by lesser
bards. Perhaps one inspired poet wrote
the greater part of these poems and
others later added other scenes and
stories, copying his tone and manner.
It is hardly possible that these poems
as they stand can be the work of one
poet. It seems equally unlikely that
accident or evolution could have built
up, out of the work of independent
poets, two works so sustained in spirit,
so symmetrical in design. Throughout
both, one finds evidence of one creating
or dominating mind. This mind we
call Homer."* *

Crates heaped with cheese and here were pens
Crowded with lambs and kids; all these
Were penned in pens apart; in one
Were kept the eldest, in another,
The younger; in a third, the youngest;
And all the well-wrought vessels used
For milking—pails and bowls—stood full,
Brimming with whey.

> And now my men
Besought me eagerly to carry
The cheeses thence, and come again
And loose the kids and lambs and drive them
In haste to our swift ship, then sail

Away o'er the salt sea. But this
I would not grant, though better far
Had I but done so! For I hoped
To look upon this man—he might
Give gifts of friendship. But, alas,
When he appeared, he was to bring
My poor men little joy!

> So there
We kindled fire and of that cheese
We made an offering, and ate
Ourselves thereof, and sat and waited
Until at last he entered, driving
His flock before him.

> He bore in
Dry wood to cook his meal, a load
Of wondrous weight, and down he flung it
Within the cave, with such a crash
We cowered back with fear and crouched
In the cave's corner. Then he drove
Into that spacious cave the sheep
That he must milk, and left the others—
The rams and goats—without, to roam
The high-walled court.

> Then in its place
He set the massive rock that closed
The doorway of the cave: he raised it
Lightly aloft, a weight so vast
That never two and twenty wagons,
Four-wheeled and firmly built, might stir it
From where it lay on earth—so great
That towering crag was that he set
To close his door.

> Now sat he down
And milked his sheep and bleating goats
All in due order, and he set
Her young by each. Half the white milk
He curdled and then gathered it
And set it by in wicker baskets;
And half he left there in the bowls
That he might sup thereon. And now,
When he had labored busily
And finished every task, he stayed
And kindled up the fire and saw us
And asked us:

> "Strangers, who are you,

---

* Herbert Bates, introduction to *The Odyssey of Homer*, translated into English verse by Herbert Bates, McGraw-Hill Book Company, Inc., New York, 1929.

And whence do you come sailing hither
Over the sea's wet ways? What errand
Can bring you hither? Or perchance
You wander purposeless, like robbers
Who rove the seas and venture life
To bring to strangers in far lands
An evil fortune."
                              So he spoke,
And at his words our hearts within us
Were crushed and broken, for we feared
The man's deep voice and monstrous body.
Yet I spoke up and answered, saying:
"We are Achæans come from Troy;
We wander blown by every wind
Over the sea's great gulf, still striving
To reach our homes, yet ever go
On alien ways, by paths we never
Have willed to travel—so it pleases
Zeus to decree. We boast we once
Were warriors under Atreus' son,
Great Agamemnon, he whose fame
Is highest under heaven—so great
A city [1] he laid low, so many
The men he slew there. Now we come
Hither before your knees to pray you
Give welcome to your guests and grant us
Such gifts as guests should have. Respect,
O mighty one, the gods, for we
Are suppliants, and Zeus avenges
The suppliant and stranger: he
Is god of strangers, watching over
Each worthy wanderer."
                              So I spoke,
And pitiless of heart, he answered:
"Stranger, you either are a fool
Or come from a far land, to bid me
Fear or beware the gods! We Cyclops
Fear not your ægis-wielding Zeus
Nor any god above. For we
Are mightier far than they. I would not
Show mercy to your men or you
To shun the wrath of Zeus, nay, never
Unless my own heart bade. But come,

Tell me, where left you your good ship
When you came hither? Was it near
Or at the land's far end? Nay, tell me,
For I would know."
                              So asked he, striving
To trap the truth from me, but caught not
My tried mind unaware. So thus
With crafty words I spoke:
                              "The god
Who shakes the earth, Poseidon, broke
My ship asunder, for he drove her
Upon the cliffs that line your land
And dashed her on the rocks. A tempest
Had blown us in from sea and I
And these my comrades here but barely
Escaped sheer death."
                              So I replied.
He, cruel-hearted, made no answer,
But springing up, reached forth his hands
And seized my comrades. Two at once
He snatched up in his grasp and dashed them
To earth like helpless puppies. Forth
The brains flowed, moistening the ground.
Then limb from limb he tore their bodies
And made his meal, devouring them
Savagely as a lion bred
Among the mountains. Naught of them
He left uneaten—flesh or entrails
Or marrowy bones. And we cried out
In lamentation and uplifted
Our hands to Zeus, to see a deed
So horrible. Numb terror laid
Hold on our hearts.
                              And now the Cyclops,
When he had filled that monstrous belly
With flesh of men, and followed this
With draughts of unmixed milk, lay stretched
Full length upon the cavern floor
Among his flock.
                              And now I formed
This plan within my daring heart—
To venture nearer and to draw
My keen sword from my thigh and thrust it
Deep in his breast, straight to the spot
Where lay his liver, feeling first

---

[1] *city* Troy.

To seek the place; and yet a thought
Withheld me, for we all, each man,
Must then have met sheer death; for never
Could our strength stir from that high door
The massive stone he set there. So
Lamenting there we sat and waited
The sacred dawn.

                  And when the dawn
Came, rosy-fingered, then once more
He kindled fire and milked his flock
Of wondrous sheep, in order due,
Setting her young by each; and now
When he had labored busily
And finished every task, he seized
Once more upon two men and made
His morning meal. And after this,
His breakfast done, he drove away
His goodly flock, moving with ease
The mighty door-stone thence, then set it
In place as lightly as a man
Would set the lid upon a quiver.
So with a mighty whoop the Cyclops
Went driving his fat flock away
Off to the mountains.

                  There he left me
Pondering evil—how I best
Might find revenge, if but Athene
Would hear my prayer. And this plan seemed
Best to my mind at last:

                  There lay
Close by the pens, a mighty staff
Cut by the Cyclops. Olive wood
It was, still green, for he had cut it
To use when it had dried: it seemed,
As we stood gazing, the great mast
Of some broad ship of twenty oars,
Laden with cargo, a black ship
That sails the great gulf of the sea,
So long and thick it seemed. So there
I took my stand by it and cut
A fathom's length away, and this
I gave my men and bade them shape it,
They made it smooth, while I stood by
And brought it to a point and charred it
In glowing fire; and then I took it

And hid it in the dung that lay
In heaps about the cave.

                  I bade then
My company cast lots to see
Which men of them would dare to join me
And lift that stake and bore it deep
Into his eye when gentle slumber
Should come upon him. And the lot
Fell on the four I should have chosen,
And I myself became the fifth
To share the venture.

                  And now came
The Cyclops home at evening, herding
His well-fleeced flocks. Straightway he drove
Into that cavern, one and all,
His goodly flocks, nor left he any
In the wide court without. He felt,
Perhaps, some sense of coming evil;
Perhaps some god had warned him. Next
He set in place the massive door-stone,
Lifting it lightly, and sat down
And milked his sheep and bleating goats
All in due order, and he set
Her young by each; and when at last
With busy labor he had finished
His every task, then once again
He seized on two of my companions
And made his evening meal.

                  And now
I stood before him, and thus spoke,
The while I held forth in my hands
An ivy bowl, filled with dark wine:
"Here, Cyclops, take this wine, and drink
After your feast of human flesh,
And learn how good a drink we kept
Hidden within our ship. I brought it
An offering to you, in hope
You might have pity on my sorrows
And help me home. But you, alas,
In rage exceed all patience! Madman!
How shall there ever come hereafter
Another stranger here to seek you
From any land on earth, if you
Thus scorn all human laws!"

                  So said I.

He took the wine and drank it. Vastly
That sweet drink pleased him. And again
He begged of me:
                              "In goodness give me
Yet more, I pray. And tell me now
Your name, and quickly! I will give you
A gift to make your heart rejoice.
Indeed the Cyclops' fertile fields
Yield noble wine from mighty clusters,
And Zeus sends rain to speed their growing,
But this you give me is a cup
Of nectar and ambrosia mingled."
So spoke he, and once more I bore him
That glowing wine. Aye, thrice I bore it
And gave it him, and thrice in folly
He drained it off. Then when the wine
Had stolen round his wits, I spoke
And said in honeyed words:
                              "O Cyclops,
You ask my far-famed name, and this
I now will tell you. Give me therefore
The stranger's gift, as you have promised.
My name is Noman; aye, and Noman
My father and my mother called me
And all my comrades."
                              So I spoke,
And he with cruel heart replied:
"Noman, of all his company,
I shall eat last; and all the others
I'll eat before him. This shall be
My gift to you—my guest."
                              So spoke he,
Then down he sank and on his back
Lay flat, his thick neck bent aside,
And from his throat there poured forth wine
And fragments of men's flesh, for drunken
With wine, he vomited.

                    And now
Deep under heaped-up coals I thrust
That stake till it grew hot, and stirred
The courage of my men with speech
Lest one of them should shrink with fear
And fail my need.
                    And now that stake

Of olive wood, green as it was,
Was ready to burst forth in flame,
All glowing with fierce heat. I drew it
Forth from the fire, while round about me
My men stood ready. Then—for surely
Some god had breathed into our hearts
High courage—they laid hold upon
That sharpened olive stake and thrust it
Deep in his eye, the while above them
I leaned upon its top and turned it
As one who with an auger bores
A great ship timber. Those below him
Twist it by thongs on either side,
And still it ever turns unceasing.
So holding that huge stake of wood
Deep in his eye, we kept it turning.
Round that hot brand, forth poured the blood;
And round it all his brows and lashes
Were singed off by the blast that came
Out of that burning eye. Its roots
Seethed in the fire. As when a smith
Dips a great axe or adze in water
To temper it, and loud it hisses—
For so steel gets its strength—even so
His eye hissed round that olive stake.
And loud his cry and terrible
Till the rocks echoed and we fled
Away in fear. Then from his eye
He wrenched away that stake, thick clotted
With his own blood and raging hurled it
Out of his hands. Then loud he shouted
To all the Cyclops who dwelt round him
In caves upon the windy heights.

They heard his shout and straggling gathered,
One here, one there, from every side,
And standing all about his cave
They asked what grieved him.
                              "What can ail you,
O Polyphemus, that so loudly
You cry out in the heavenly night
And keep us sleepless? Is some man,
Some mortal, driving off your flocks
Against your will; or is some man
Now slaying you by force or cunning?"

Homer. *There are no portraits of the poet dating
from his own time. This marble bust, done centuries later, is an imaginative projection by a
Roman sculptor.*

And thus in answer from his cave
Spoke mighty Polyphemus:
                             "Friends,
Noman is slaying me by cunning,
Nor uses force at all!"
                      And they
With wing'd words thus replied:
                            "Since no man
Now does you violence, while you
Are there alone, this illness sent
By mighty Zeus, no man may shun
In any way. But pray you now
To your great father, Lord Poseidon." [2]

  [2] *Poseidon* The god of the sea. He was the father
and protector of the Cyclops.

So said they and then went their way.
And in my heart I laughed to think
How with that name and my shrewd plan
I had deceived them.
                          But the Cyclops,
Groaning in agony and anguish,
Went groping with his hands, and lifted
The great rock from the door and there
He sat athwart the doorway, stretching
His hands, to catch, if it might be,
Any who sought to pass the door
Among the sheep; for in his heart
He hoped that I might prove so foolish
As thus to venture. But I still
Sat planning how to bring this peril
To a good end and win us all—
My men and me—escape. Full many
The plan and trick I fashioned, striving
For life itself, for great the peril
And close at hand. And at the last
This, as I deemed, was of them all
The wisest plan.
                      There in the cave
Were well-grown rams of thickest wool,
Fair beasts and great, and dark of fleece.
These silently I bound together
With twisted willow withes, whereon
The Cyclops slept, that savage monster
Who knew no law nor right. I bound them
By three together and the midmost
Bore under him a man; the others,
One on each side, were to conceal
And save my comrades: so there went
A man to each three sheep. And I,
Myself, now seized upon a ram,
The best of all that flock, and grasped
His back from underneath, and lay
Beneath his shaggy belly; there
Twisting my fingers deep within
That wondrous fleece, I hung, face upward,
With steadfast heart. And so, lamenting,
We waited sacred dawn.
                          And now,
When earliest dawn came rosy-fingered,
Then forth the rams went to the pasture,

But all the unmilked ewes went bleating
About their pens with swollen udders.
Their lord, though torn by cruel pain,
Yet, ere each ram passed, made him stand
And felt along his back. He guessed not
In his dull mind, that there beneath
Those fleecy breasts, were bound my men.

Now to the door, last of them all,
The great ram slowly came, weighed down
With heavy fleece and with the burden
Of me and my shrewd plans. Upon him
The mighty Polyphemus then
Laid searching hands, and said:
                                        "Dear ram,
Why do you cross the cave so slowly,
Last of the flock? Till now, you never
Lagged thus, but ever first of all
Sped forth with mighty strides to crop
The soft bloom of the grass, and ever
Were first to reach the running waters,
And first, when evening came, to long
To turn back home. And yet you now
Come last of all. Surely you sorrow
Over your lord's lost eye! A villain
Has quenched its sight—he and his crew
Of wretched fellows, mastering
My wits with wine, this fellow Noman!
Not yet, I say, has he escaped
The death that waits him. Would but you
Could know my thought and had the power
To speak in words and let me know
Where he is skulking from my wrath!
For I should smite him down and dash
His brains about the cave—here, there,
Aye, on the ground! By such a deed
My heart might find some ease from all
The evils that this worthless Noman
Has brought upon me."
                              So he spoke,
And sent the ram forth through the doorway.

And now, when we were safe outside
That cavern and its yard, I loosed
My grip upon the great ram's fleece

And then unbound my men in turn,
Setting them free. And then in haste
We drove that flock before us—sheep
Most rich in fat, most long of stride—
And yet we often turned our heads
To glance behind us ere we came
Safe to our ship. Welcome indeed
We were to our dear comrades, snatched
From death itself; and yet they wept
Lamenting those we lost. But this
I would not suffer, but forbade,
With lifted brows, all lamentation,
And bade them quickly bear aboard
Into the ship those many sheep
So fine of fleece, and sail away
Across the salt sea waves. And they
Went then aboard and took their seats
Each in his place, and smote with oars
The whitening sea.
                          And now, when yet
A shout might reach the land, I called
To Cyclops, taunting him:
                                  "O Cyclops,
You were not, then, to find that man
A helpless weakling—him whose men
You ate there in your hollow cave
With might and cruel strength. For surely
These evil deeds of yours are doomed
To overtake you. O mad fool
Who felt no shame, but must devour
Your guests in your own home! May Zeus
And all the other gods send vengeance
Upon you for such deeds!"
                                    So spoke I,
And he in heart grew angrier yet
And tearing off a hill's great summit,
He hurled it. And it fell beyond
Our dark-bowed ship: the sea surged high
As that great rock crashed down. A wave
Came rolling back, a mighty billow
Out of the deep, and swept our ship
In toward the land. Swiftly I grasped
A great pole in my hands and thrust
The ship from shore and bade my men,
Nodding my brows, fall to and pull

Their best upon the oars and flee
Out of that danger; and they all
Bent to their oars.
                                  But when we now
Were twice as far from shore as we
Had been before, once more I called
Unto the Cyclops:
                                  "If, O Cyclops,
A mortal man shall ever ask you
How it befell your eye was blinded
So hideously, then answer thus:
It was Odysseus blinded you,
Taker of Troy, Laërtes' son,
Who dwells in Ithaca."
                                  So spoke I,
And with a groan he spoke and answered:
"Alas, for now are come upon me
The ancient oracles. A prophet
Once dwelt here, a great man and good,
And he foretold me everything
That time should bring to pass—that I
Should lose my sight here at the hand
Of one Odysseus. But I ever
Watched for the coming of a man
Tall, handsome, armed with wondrous strength;
And now this little worthless fellow
Has robbed me of my eye by craft,
First mastering me with wine. Yet now
Come hither, O Odysseus, come!
For I would give my guest his gifts
And would implore the far-famed god
Who shakes the shores to give you help
Upon your way. I am his son:
He owns himself my father. He,
And he alone, can make me whole
If so he will, but this no other
Can do, no other of the gods
On high or mortal men who perish."

So spoke he and I answered thus:
"Would I could be as sure that I
Could strip you bare of soul and being,
And send you to Death's house, as I
Am sure of this:—that none shall ever

Restore your eye, not even he [3]
Who makes earth tremble!"
                                  So I spoke,
And he with hands upraised in prayer
To starry heaven, thus besought
The lord Poseidon:
                                  "Hear me now,
Thou dark-haired god who mak'st earth tremble!
If I be verily thy son
And thou wilt own thyself my father,
Grant that Odysseus, he who took
The towers of Troy, come never home.
Yet, should it be his fate to see
His friends once more and come at last
To his good house and native land,
Late may he come, in evil fortune,
With loss of all his men, and borne
Within a stranger's ship, and meet
In his own home affliction."
                                                          So
He spoke in prayer, and to his words
The dark-haired god gave ear.
                                                          Once more
He stooped and lifted up a rock
Far greater than before, and swung it
And summoned all his monstrous strength
And hurled it. And it fell behind
Our dark-bowed ship and barely missed
The rudder's end. Up surged the sea
As that huge rock came down: the wave
Drove us upon our way and toward
The farther shore.
                                  And so we came
Back to the isle where our good ships
Were lying side by side, and here
Beside them sat our comrades weeping
And watching for our coming. Quickly
We drew our ship ashore, far up
Beyond the breaking of the seas,
And brought, then, out our hollow ship,
The Cyclops' sheep ashore and justly
Divided all that no man lacked

---

[3] *he* Poseidon.

His equal portion. To myself
In special honor as my share
Out of that flock, my mailed companions
Gave the great ram. And there I slew him
Upon the shore, burning the thighs
In offering to cloud-hidden Zeus,
Great son of Cronus, lord of all.
He heeded not my offering
But planned instead that all should perish—
All my good ships and all my comrades
Trusted and true.
                    So all that day
Until the sun went down, we sat

And feasted there on meat in plenty
And pleasant wine; and when the sun
Went down and darkness came upon us,
There slept we by the breaking sea.
But when the earliest dawn appeared
Rose-fingered, then I roused my men
And bade embark and loose the cables.
Then quickly they embarked and took
Their seats upon the thwarts, in order,
And smote with oars the whitening sea.
So sailed we on with aching hearts,
Glad we were saved from death, yet sad
To think how our dear comrades perished.

For Discussion

1. How does Odysseus take advantage of Polyphemus' greed and isolation? Is Polyphemus an easy victim for Odysseus' shrewdness? What are the Cyclops's qualities that Odysseus could never overcome? Illustrate.

2. What kind of man is Odysseus? What are his heroic characteristics? Can you find any weaknesses in him? Give examples and explain.

3. Many younger readers criticize *The Odyssey* because it involves sorceresses, giants, and monsters that do not exist. They object that it is not "realistic." Is this criticism valid? Explain. Can you name any modern stories that include creatures that are unknown in the world we can see? Can you suggest reasons why authors use such weird and imaginative creations?

4. Discuss this selection as an example of the art of storytelling. How does it sustain the reader's interest? Is the narrative simple or difficult to understand? Do you think that the story suggests a larger meaning? What is it?

5. Can you find any qualities in the Cyclops that can be explained as exaggerations of human tendencies? What are they?

Kon-Tiki

THOR HEYERDAHL

In April of 1947, anthropologist Thor Heyerdahl and five companions set sail from Callao, Peru, upon a huge balsa-wood raft, the Kon-Tiki. *They wanted to test the possibility that the natives of Polynesia originally had come from South America, navigating unbelievable distances of the Pacific in primitive craft. The daring and ingenuity of these scientists brought to light many facts about the sea that otherwise might have remained unknown. Their voyage became one of the great adventures of modern times. Thor Heyerdahl writes about it with both the sensitivity of an artist and the curiosity and precision of a scientist. The reader of this essay finds himself deeply involved with the dangers and poetry of a lonely raft that drifts with the currents and winds of the Pacific Ocean. This essay is Heyerdahl's original account of his voyage. It is preceded by a "Foreword" by the editors of* Natural History, *the magazine in which it first appeared.*

FOREWORD

By the Editors of *Natural History*

Authorities generally agree that the ancestors of the American Indians came from Asia by way of the Aleutian Islands or Bering Strait. The earliest of these people may have come as much as twenty thousand to forty thousand years ago. But up to fifteen hundred years ago the vast island domain of the Central Pacific known as Polynesia apparently remained uninhabited. There seem to have been two migrations into these islands, one perhaps around A.D. 500 and the other around A.D. 1000.

The question of where these Polynesian people came from has long occupied the attention of anthropologists. Obviously they must have come from either Asia or America. Almost all specialists in this field of science have considered it more likely that they came from Asia.

The present article is written by a man who, after several years of study including approximately a year in Polynesia, a year among the Indians of the Northwest Coast, and many months in South America, became convinced that the Polynesians came from the American side of the Pacific. So firmly did certain cultural similarities lead him to this theory that he resolved to duplicate this long voyage from Peru to Polynesia with the same primitive equipment that the Peruvians are known to have had prior to the first European contacts. The present article is the story of this voyage.

Neither the author nor the editor would have felt it within the scope of this article to present or evaluate the various complex arguments bearing on this migration riddle. The author has assembled his own arguments in a sizeable book, and there they will be judged by scholars on their own merit. Here we have opportunity to see, as if at firsthand, the actual problems that would have been met by a group of prehistoric Peruvians if they embarked or were cast adrift on one of their large rafts. As such, the voyage of Mr. Heyerdahl and his five companions provides new information on one of the significant aspects of this question, and it can be considered one of the most enterprising expeditions of recent years.

USUALLY MEN who have embarked on an ocean raft in modern times have been shipwrecked sailors whose sole desire was to escape the perils of the open sea and reach the nearest coast. But this was not the case in April of last year, when the tugboat *Guardian Rio* towed a clumsy raft away from the sheltered docks of the Peruvian port of Callao and left it adrift well outside the harbor entrance. The six of us that were left aboard the raft were filled with one single hope—that the wind and current would push our primitive craft far away from the South American mainland and right into the wide-open span of the vast Pacific Ocean.

Our purpose was not to flee the Republic of Peru. Leading officials of many nations had bidden us hearty farewell at the dock as the Peruvian Navy tugged us to our point of departure. Nor did we possess any desire to establish a world record in hazardous ocean drift. Yet the betting went high at the docks when we left.

Some claimed that we would be picked up off the coast in a few days or would never be seen again. The nine logs of porous balsa wood upon which we floated were too fragile and would break asunder in the heavy coastal swells,

or they would at least be waterlogged and sink underneath us far short of the halfway mark to Polynesia, whose nearest islands lay some four thousand miles from Peru. With a foot and a half of freeboard at the highest section of the bamboo deck, and with an open bamboo hut with thatched roof as our only shelter, we would be at the constant mercy of the waves and the weather and be lost in the first storm.

Others claimed that ropes were no good in the tropic sun and in the sea water and that the complete absence of nails, pegs, and wire in our raft would allow it to tear to pieces as soon as the constant movements of the logs started to chafe the hemp-rope lashings. And if a balsa-wood raft, against all the warnings of the experts, should prove to be seaworthy, it would still not be navigable with its clumsy, square sail and primitive steering oar. How, then, could we possibly expect to hit one of the tiny, far-flung islands? The distance ahead was twice the journey of Columbus and the clumsy raft not even comparable.

All these sinister but well-meant warnings were haunting my mind the first night after the last smoke of the tugboat had dissolved behind the horizon. When I was relieved from watch and tried to sleep, I realized how everything was in motion, not so much the pitching and rolling, as the restlessly undulating movement of the bamboo matting on which we lay on top of the great logs. Each time the stern was lifted by the seas, I saw dancing black hills of water, silhouetted against the stars as they chased along both sides of our raft, with whitecaps hissing at us as they passed. I listened to the squeaking and gnawing of a hundred ropes and the splashing and hammering of water everywhere. At regular intervals heavy seas thundered on board astern, but I noticed with comfort how the water, after whirling up to the waists of the two steersmen, instantly dwindled by falling between the open logs or over the sides of the raft. The seas fell in a pit before they could reach the unprotected bamboo hut lashed on deck a few feet from the stern. Therefore, we struggled to hold the stern to the weather and never let the seas in from the sides.

Gradually I felt happy and proud of our peculiar craft. But I could not quite get away from the complaining music of all the light and heavy ropes as everything aboard moved slowly up and down and even sideways as far as the ropes would permit.

What would the future bring us? How would the raft behave after a week, a month, or perhaps a year at sea?

I was not a sailor, and only one of my companions was experienced in handling an ordinary boat at sea. I had not been able, word by word, to answer the pessimistic warnings of naval authorities and other experts before we put out to sea. I was, nevertheless, firmly convinced that our raft could float across the ocean and bring us safely to some distant Polynesian shore. The secret of my stubborn confidence was that I felt certain that this same ocean route had been covered before by prehistoric men on the very same type of craft.

Already in 1937, after leaving the University of Oslo, I had made a zoological-ethnological survey on the lonely Marquesas Islands in the Southeast Pacific. What I found led me to suspect that an influence from early Central or South America had somehow preceded the present Polynesian culture in this area. It is well known that a number of striking similarities in the culture of South America and Polynesia have been noted. These include two of the important cultivated plants—the sweet potato and the bottle gourd—and many cultural features. The theory has therefore frequently been advanced—and again as frequently rejected—that there must have been a prehistoric contact between these two areas.

There can be no possibility of any land bridge having existed in human times, for a comparative study of the animal life of Polynesia proves its hoary isolation. The island people, when first discovered by Europeans, possessed good seagoing canoes, whereas the natives of Peru had only clumsy balsa rafts for their coastal navigation. Because of this, it has usually been assumed by the few who believe there was a cultural transfer that the South American cultures were influenced by the island people rather than vice versa. This view has never been fully accepted and is even doubted by competent scholars of the present day. It is too obvious that some of the Peruvian constructions, artifacts, and food plants in question date from an earlier period in America than A.D. 500, which is commonly accepted, through comparative genealogy, as the approximate date when the first Polynesians spread into the East Pacific.

Thus I had found myself inescapably drawn toward the alternative theory to explain the striking parallels between Peru and Polynesia—namely, that an offshoot from the amazing cultures of early Peru drifted, intentionally or otherwise, into the Pacific.

I was instantly met by one killing argument: How could the Peruvians have covered the thousands of miles of intermediate ocean when their only means of navigation in prehistoric times was an open balsa raft?

To me, there was only one satisfactory answer, and that was to build such a balsa raft and see if it could survive this journey.

I selected five dependable men who volunteered to join me on the experimental voyage. One of them, Herman Watzinger, was a technical engineer, and he directed the building of the balsa raft, guided by detailed accounts and sketches left in the earliest records after the conquest of Peru. First we had to get into the heart of the Ecuadorian jungle to find present-day balsa trees that would match the dimensions of the prehistoric rafts. We cut down nine giant trees, and floated on them down a jungle river to the Pacific coast. With the blessings of the President of Peru and his Naval Minister, the prehistoric type of craft was built in the main naval harbor of Callao under our own supervision.

The nine balsa logs were lashed together side by side with many separate pieces of hemp rope. The bow of the raft took an organ-pipe design, with the longest log in the middle measuring forty-five feet and projecting beyond the others both in the front and in the stern. In the stern it supported a big chunk of balsa holding tholepins for the steering oar. Of the two-foot cross section of these logs, more than half was submerged in the water, but nine smaller crossbeams of light balsa covered with bamboo lifted the highest portion of the deck (including the floor of the open hut upon which we slept) eighteen inches above the sea. The little plaited bamboo hut with thatched roof; two hardwood masts side by side, with a square sail; five centerboards two feet wide and six feet deep, inserted at irregular intervals between the logs; and a long wooden steering oar astern completed our replica of the colorful prehistoric craft.

We named our raft *Kon-Tiki* in honor of the mythical sun king who the Incas claim built the enormous stone constructions near Lake Titicaca[1] before he was defeated in war by local tribes. After the defeat, according to legend, he fled with his light-colored people down to the coast and then westward into the Pacific Ocean, never again to return to Peru. Throughout the Polynesian islands, Tiki is remembered as the mythical hero who was first in the line of aboriginal chiefs to settle the islands and to claim direct descent from the sun. The Peruvian prefix "Kon" means Sun.

The six of us went aboard on April 28 and were left at the mercy of the elements in the old Inca fishing grounds outside the port of Callao. Our ages ranged from twenty-five to thirty-two. Herman Watzinger, second-in-command, was in charge of testing and hydrographic

[1] *Lake Titicaca* On the boundaries of Peru and Bolivia.

and meteorologic measurements. Erik Hesselberg, an artist, was responsible for plotting our drift. Our radio operators were Knut Haugland and Torstein Raaby, both famous for their sabotage activities during World War II (instrumental, respectively, in the important sabotage of the German Heavy-Water Plant and the battleship *Tirpitz*). Bengt Danielsson, lonely Swede on our Norwegian expedition, was an ethnologist from the University of Upsala who joined us in South America after an expedition in the jungles of Brazil.

Our voyage would carry us through a vast span of ocean that was very little known, since it was outside all the usual shipping lines. We had therefore been requested to make continuous observations and transfer them via the amateur radio network to the United States Weather Bureau. But unless we should use the radio for calling help, it would not alter the primitive conditions of our experiment in any way.

The first weeks at sea were hard. One man was seasick for several days and confined to the hut; consequently, with the ocean breaking over us, two of us at a time constantly had to battle with the clumsy steering oar, trying to hold our stern against the short, racing seas of the Humboldt Current. We were soon caught by the offshore trade winds and were then only able to sail before the wind. We now realized that we had cut all our bridges and that there was no road back to the coast.

We had been at sea only a couple of days when an airplane flew out to bring us a last farewell. We never saw the plane (our horizons were narrowly fenced in with watery hills on all sides), nor did they see us, but we spoke to them for several hours with our little radio.

After the first weeks we came into calmer seas with long, rolling swells. The great blue ocean was dotted with whitecaps, and trade wind clouds drifted across the blue sky. We had soft days with swimming and rest, and we

The Kon-Tiki *being towed on a trial run off the coast of Peru*

traveled along in comfort. Our drift turned from northwest to west as we left the green and cold Humboldt Current and entered the blue and increasingly warm South Equatorial Current. We made as much progress as seventy-two miles in one day, with a daily average of forty-two miles for the entire voyage. The surface drift exceeded the current drift and occasionally blew us out of the main sweep of the central current.

We found little wearing on the ropes and learned the reason why. The balsa was too soft to chafe them. In case of friction, a rope would soon work itself into the waterlogged surface of the balsa logs and thus remain protected. It was more discomforting to observe that splinters cut from the surface of the logs had become waterlogged and sank when thrown overboard. It had been common opinion in Peru that the logs would be completely submerged before we sighted the islands.

Archaeologists no longer doubt that the prehistoric Peruvians used sails. Not only are there good historical descriptions of rafts equipped with sails, but centerboards of late pre-European date have been found. Our testings with centerboards clearly proved that they are useless on a raft if it is merely paddled or carried along by the current.

The first real excitement we ran into after entering the South Equatorial Current was the largest monster of the seas—the rare but famous whale shark. Accompanied by a shoal of pilot fish, this giant among all fishes slowly caught up with us from astern, and the water splashed around its enormous, white-speckled back as though on a small reef. The fish bumped into the steering oar and placed its huge, frog-like head, with tiny eyes and a five-foot mouth, right up against the raft. The whale shark has been measured to a length of forty-five feet and undoubtedly grows larger. We would never have dared such an estimate, but while the head appeared on one side of the raft, the tail simultaneously appeared on the other.

The whale shark kept us company for several hours, and the excitement on board was great, with everybody prepared with spears, hand harpoons, and motion picture camera. The peaceful visit ended when the excited navigator ran his harpoon with all his strength down between his legs and into the cartilaginous head of the monster. During the terrific commotion the whale shark dived, broke the harpoon, snapped the rope, and disappeared.

Only at one other time were we visited by what we suspected to be whale sharks. It was during a fairly calm night when three immensely large and phosphorescent bodies swam in circles under us. But occasionally we ran into schools of whales. The huge, snorting animals rolled right up beside us without the slightest fear. They could have splintered our raft with a single blow of their mighty tails, but after an exhibition of their swimming ability, they left us behind.

Some six hundred miles southwest of the Galápagos we were twice visited by giant sea turtles. One was under constant attack by a dozen furious dolphins which tried to snap at the turtle's neck and fins. After sighting the raft, the turtle made its way right up to our side but swam away as soon as it saw us. Three of of our men, equipped with rope, pursued the turtle in a tiny, inflatable rubber float, but our visitor escaped while the bewildered dolphins concentrated all their attention on the bouncing little float.

Weather permitting, we often got into our rubber float, two or three at a time, and took a "vacation" from our sturdy log raft to study our craft from a distance. We could imagine the sight that early Peruvian seafarers must have had when they sailed their flotillas of rafts side by side along the coast—or into the ocean like Inca Tupac Yupanqui, who according to

legend discovered some East Pacific islands before the Spanish Conquest. Particularly at night, we experienced an unforgettable sight. Night-black seas, billowing on all sides, and twinkling stars formed our entire world.

The year 1947—A.D. or B.C.—what did it mean? We were at least alive. Time had little meaning; we were lost in the endless dark. Ahead of us *Kon-Tiki* rose and then sank between the seas. In moonlight there was an unbelievable atmosphere around the raft. The huge, wet logs fringed with seaweed, the square contour of the sail, the bushy jungle hut with a petrol lamp astern looked like something cut from a fairy tale rather than from reality . . . Now and then the raft would disappear entirely behind the black sea; then, with water pouring from the logs, it would rise high to be silhouetted against the stars.

Although we spent 101 days and nights drifting on our raft, we never sighted a ship or any floating debris left by mankind. If a ship had crossed our path during an average day at sea, it would have found us slowly dancing up and down over great rolling swells dotted with minor waves that were stirred up by the trade winds, which constantly blow from the New World into the island domain. A tanned and bearded man, devoid of clothing, would have been sighted at the stern of the raft, either desperately struggling with the ropes of a long steering oar or, if the wind were steady, sitting and dozing in the sun. Bengt would be found on his stomach in the doorway of the hut reading one of his seventy-three sociological books. Herman would be seen busily occupied anywhere, at the top of the mast, underneath the logs, or running around with instruments to measure wind and water. Knut and Torstein were always struggling with the weather-beaten radio sets, repairing damage and sending out reports at night to the amateur stations that could hear our signals. Erik was always mending sail and splicing rope and sketching fishes and bearded men alike. And each noon he grabbed his sextant and gazed at the sun to determine how far we had moved since the day before. As to myself, I was writing logs, collecting plankton for food experimentation, and fishing or filming.

The day started with a glorious sunrise over the sea, the cook being relieved by the last night watchman to collect the flying fish that had flown on board during the night. These were fried on a small primus stove and devoured at the edge of the raft after a quick morning dip in the sea. Extra flying fish were used as bait for the great colorful dolphin fish that followed the raft day in and day out across the ocean. Dolphins that we did not eat were used as bait for the great sharks that calmly swam around us day and night. When the sea was high, we could see them sideways as though through a perpendicular glass wall raised high above the level of the raft. Then the raft tipped up and let the water and the slowly moving sharks pass beneath us. They never seemed treacherous except when we cleaned fish, and they scented blood. Then they would wake up in a fury. Yet we never quite trusted them, and in one day we pulled aboard nine six- to ten-foot sharks just to dispose of their intimate company.

When we slid the sharks up onto our shallow and slippery logs, the remoras, clinging to the sharks' skin by suction, would jump off and attach themselves to the side of the raft; and the pilot fish, having lost their king and master, would find a substitute in *Kon-Tiki*, joining us in nice formation before the bow or between the centerboards. If a big blue shark passed, they would occasionally follow him away, but more than forty of them tailed us right across the ocean until our raft was shattered on the reef.

Although we carried our rations lashed to the logs beneath the bamboo deck, it was still of great importance to me to find out whether primitive man, accustomed to hardship as he was, would have been able to renew his supply of food and water on such a long-lasting drift.

The answer was affirmative. After the fourth day at sea, there was not a single day throughout the journey when we were not accompanied by numbers of dolphin fish. They kept to the side of the raft or beneath us and could be fished, speared, or hooked whenever we desired. Edible barnacles and seaweeds grew all over the huge logs and could be picked like garden greens. And they often housed tiny, edible pelagic crabs or very small fishes. A dozen or more flying fish, often accompanied by baby squids, came aboard almost every night, sailing through the air in schools right above the surface if pursued by dolphins or sharks. Twice in mid-ocean on dark nights, a long snakelike fish with huge eyes and carnivorous jaws jumped right into our sleeping bags inside the bamboo hut and caused a great commotion. It was probably the *Gempylus*, which was seen this way by man for the first time, only a couple of skeletons having previously been found on South American shores. Soaked shark meat, delicious bonito, and yellow-fin tuna completed our seafood menu and made it clear enough that early, hardy raftsmen were not menaced by hunger.

We carried two hundred coconuts and samples of the Peruvian sweet potato and gourd, which were important food plants that the aborigines of Peru shared with those of Polynesia. Those not eaten en route were successfully planted upon our arrival on the islands, to prove that they could be carried on a raft without loss of germinating power. These prehistoric food plants could never have drifted across the ocean without the aid and care of human hands, and the aboriginal name for sweet potato was *Kumara*—both in Peru and on the Polynesian islands.

The early raftsmen along the dry South American coast carried their water supply in gourds or pottery containers and in huge canes of bamboo with the joints pierced out. Left in the shade underneath the bamboo deck, where they were constantly washed by the seas, we found that our plain Peruvian spring water was preserved for more than two months before the first samples began to rot. At that time we had already entered a part of the ocean where drizzles were frequent and rains occasional, and we were able to collect sufficient rain water for our daily needs. We consumed a ton of water on the journey, along with more than ample rations, and the buoyancy of the balsa logs would have permitted us to double our water supply in easily stored bamboo canes under the deck. With the warm climate creating a demand for salt, we could mix up to 40 per cent of sea water with our drinking water without evil effects. Like our early predecessors and many sailors shipwrecked during the war, we found several simple methods of abstracting the thirst-quenching juice from raw fish, a supply that never ran short.

In this way, with the days full of testings and practical experiments, we found ourselves carried across the ocean bit by bit. By the forty-fifth day we had drifted from the seventy-eighth meridian to the one hundred-eighth and were exactly halfway to the first islands. During those days we were more than two thousand miles away from the nearest shore in any direction. When the ocean was smoothly rolling, we could leave our raft in the little float and row away into the blue space between eternal sea and sky. As we watched our grotesque craft growing smaller and smaller in the distance, an oppressive sense of loneliness came over us. It was as though we were suspended in space, like disembodied spirits. When we rowed back to our distant raft, we felt a strange feeling of relief and were happy to crawl on board our precious, weather-beaten logs and find shade from the glaring sun inside the bamboo hut. The now familiar scent of bamboo and thatched roof made us feel that we were back in our earthly home again, inside a jungle dwelling that was far away from the limitless sea.

We enjoyed our evening meals as the glorious sun sank into the sea before our bow, while sky and water became a dream of colors. Small, striped pilot fish would rush to the surface to snap at our crumbs, and they were occasionally followed by a lazy shark, like kittens by a bulldog.

As darkness came we would light our petrol lamp, and Erik would fetch his guitar. Then merry song and music from the raft spread with the dim light over the nearest waves of a trackless, endless ocean. We would soon roll up on the bamboo matting inside the hut, leaving the watchman alone with the stars and the steering oar.

We hit two storms when we approached the end of the journey. The first lasted one day and the second five. With sail down and ropes shrieking, *Kon-Tiki* rode the breaking ocean like a duck. A raft in high seas with wet and slippery logs and no railing requires careful stepping. The second storm had just begun when Herman went overboard. When visible again, he was seen struggling behind the stern. He struck for the blade of the steering oar, but a strong wind pushed us ahead, and he missed. We could not turn our raft around to go back a single inch. There was no possibility of even stopping our stubborn craft in its reckless trek to the west. The airy float would blow like a feather ahead of the raft if put to sea in such a wind. We threw out a life belt, once, twice, but it blew right back on board. We became desperate as Herman, our best swimmer, was left farther and farther behind. With a line in one hand Knut leaped into the sea, and slowly the two friends worked their way toward each other. Thirty yards behind the raft they joined hands, and the four of us on board pulled them in.

We had a green parrot as ship's pet. It was a perfect sailor and a joyous companion, until a big sea stole it on the sixtieth day.

At the end of the third month, we were constantly visited by Polynesian frigate birds and boobies in increasing numbers. Then we sighted a rising cumulo-nimbus cloud, revealing the existence of some hidden, sun-baked isle beneath the western horizon. We steered for the cloud as best we could, and as the golden sun rose from the sea on the ninety-third day, the blue haze of land was outlined against a reddish sky. We were passing the tiny atoll of Pukapuka, but wind and current would not permit us to turn around. We had covered four thousand miles of ocean heading west, and yet we could not force ourselves four miles to the east to reach the island. More than ever was this a plain and unmistakable lesson, stressing the fact that in this ocean a drifting craft and a natural migration would inevitably be pushed to the west. And it was with strange feelings that we sat quietly down on our raft and saw the little, solid speck of land—the first and only for twelve weeks—slide away on our port stern. For a moment the wind carried a mild whiff of verdant tropical foliage and smoky native household odors, and we filled our salty lungs before the fata morgana [2]—the mirage of our hopes—sank into the sea.

On the ninety-seventh day another island grew up out of the ocean, straight ahead of us in line with the bow. As we approached, we saw from the top of the mast that a roaring reef was twisted like a submerged snake all around the island, blocking the approach to the palm-clad beaches behind. All day long we struggled in the current alongside the island to keep clear of the boiling reef and yet be close enough to attempt a landfall wherever an opening might be seen.

Late in the afternoon we sighted the first natives on a beach, and we hoisted all our flags in joy. A great commotion was seen on the beach, and shortly after, the first Polynesians in small outrigger canoes slid through a passage in the reef and swarmed aboard the *Kon-Tiki*. A strong wind blew up, and our ocean raft

struggled away from land as the sun went down in the sea. There was a desperate fight against the elements, in which we were assisted by all the friendly natives who were able to get out and join us in the open sea. As the dark night engulfed the island and the sea, a great campfire was lit on shore to show us the direction of the entrance through the reef. But the wind increased its grip, and won another battle. When the glare of the great fire dwindled like a spark in the distance and the roar of the reef was no longer heard, our excited native friends jumped into their canoes to return to their homes on Angatau for fear of drifting with some crazy strangers into the open sea. And we drifted farther into the heart of the Tuamotu, or Dangerous Archipelago.

One night an unusual motion of the raft awakened me, and I suspected land ahead. Next morning, our one hundred-first at sea, we were alarmed by the watchman on the top of the mast, who had sighted an enormous reef that spanned the entire horizon ahead of us. It was the treacherous twenty-mile reef of Raroia Atoll. With white spray shooting high into the air, the surf battered the endless reef in fury.

As we rode directly into this boiling inferno, we had three hours to prepare for all eventualities. We lowered the sail and threw out an improvised anchor on a long rope that kept sliding along the bottom. We carried valuable cargo into the hut and lashed it fast in watertight bags. We cut off all ropes holding the centerboards in position and pulled them up to get a shallow draft. With shoes on for the first time in one hundred days, we concentrated on the last order: Hang on—hang onto the raft whatever happens!

The first walls of thundering water broke down upon us from above as soon as our logs ran against the solid coral reef. Tons of crashing water tore up the deck, flattened the hut, broke the hardwood mast like a match, and splintered the steering oar and stern crossbeam, while we

---

[2] *fata morgana*   A mirage.

were thrown in and dragged out, thrown in and dragged out, by the furious ocean. During these minutes, when we cramped every existing muscle to withhold the deadly grasp of the passing seas, we made up for all the leisure of the average ocean day. I felt the last of my strength giving away when a wave larger than the others lifted *Kon-Tiki* free of the water and tossed us high up on the reef. Other waves pushed us closer to shore, until we could jump off the raft and wade the shallow coral reef to a tiny, uninhabited coconut island. Never did any tiny piece of land embody paradise so perfectly to me as this verdant, palm-clad isle with its white and shiny beach facing a crystal-clear lagoon, calm as green glass.

A week later we were found by natives who had detected from another island six miles across the lagoon the drift wreckage and the light from our campfire. And about the same time *Kon-Tiki* was carried by high seas right across the solid reef and left becalmed inside the lagoon. The nine main logs that had carried us 4,300 miles across the ocean in 101 days were still intact, and after an unforgettable two-week Polynesian welcome party on lonely Raroia, our battered raft was towed to Tahiti by the French Government schooner *Tamara*, which was sent expressly to pick us up.

We shall never forget the welcome on these Polynesian islands.

From Tahiti the *Kon-Tiki* was carried as deck cargo back to the Norwegian Museum of Navigation in Oslo.

For Discussion

1. In what ways could Thor Heyerdahl's expedition be compared with Christopher Columbus's voyage across the Atlantic Ocean? In what ways does it differ? Do you feel that both faced equal dangers? Which of the two would you name the more courageous? Why?

2. List some of the dangers over which the men on the raft had no control. What were the threats to safety that they managed to eliminate? In what ways can you explain the voyage of the *Kon-Tiki* as a symbolic representation of man's journey through life?

3. What were some of the sea creatures that the *Kon-Tiki* met? Were the men on the raft terrified of these creatures? What was Heyerdahl's attitude toward the sharks that followed the raft?

4. How effectively do you think the voyage of the *Kon-Tiki* proves Thor Heyerdahl's theory of the origin of the inhabitants of Polynesia? Did the success of the voyage scientifically prove that this was the way people once reached these islands? Upon what evidence does Heyerdahl connect Polynesia with South America? Do you feel that this is enough proof?

5. Imagine that you are a member of the crew of the *Kon-Tiki*. Write an account of a day's experiences on board, perhaps in the form of a letter or diary entry.

The Adventure of the Bruce-Partington Plans

SIR ARTHUR CONAN DOYLE

The narrow face shadowed by the peak of the deer stalker's cap, the meerschaum pipe gripped in the straight, humorless mouth, and the narrowed eyes peering for clues through the magnifying glass are characteristics that identify the most famous of all fictional detectives, Sherlock Holmes. His mind interweaves shreds of evidence until they fit together into a net that traps the criminal. Then, with his friend Dr. Watson, Holmes returns to his rooms in Baker Street to pursue intellectual hobbies that would challenge the powers of scholars. "The Adventure of the Bruce-Partington Plans" is a story of espionage and murder in which the theft of submarine plans endangers Britain's security as a nation. Holmes and his partner carefully reconstruct the crime in a fashion that has been often imitated but never surpassed by later fictional detectives.

IN THE third week of November, in the year 1895, a dense yellow fog settled down upon London. From the Monday to the Thursday I doubt whether it was ever possible from our windows in Baker Street to see the loom of the opposite houses. The first day Holmes had spent in cross-indexing his huge book of references. The second and third had been patiently occupied upon a subject which he had recently made his hobby—the music of the Middle Ages. But when, for the fourth time, after pushing back our chairs from breakfast we saw the greasy, heavy brown swirl still drifting past us and condensing in oily drops upon the window-panes, my comrade's impatient and active nature could endure this drab existence no longer. He paced restlessly about our sitting-room in a fever of suppressed energy, biting his nails, tapping the furniture, and chafing against inaction.

"Nothing of interest in the paper, Watson?" he said.

I was aware that by anything of interest, Holmes meant anything of criminal interest.

There was the news of a revolution, of a possible war, and of an impending change of government; but these did not come within the horizon of my companion. I could see nothing recorded in the shape of crime which was not commonplace and futile. Holmes groaned and resumed his restless meanderings.

"The London criminal is certainly a dull fellow," said he in the querulous voice of the sportsman whose game has failed him. "Look out of this window, Watson. See how the figures loom up, are dimly seen, and then blend once more into the cloud-bank. The thief or the murderer could roam London on such a day as the tiger does the jungle, unseen until he pounces, and then evident only to his victim."

"There have," said I, "been numerous petty thefts."

Holmes snorted his contempt.

"This great and sombre stage is set for something more worthy than that," said he. "It is fortunate for this community that I am not a criminal."

"It is, indeed!" said I heartily.

"Suppose that I were Brooks or Woodhouse, or any of the fifty men who have good reason for taking my life, how long could I survive against my own pursuit? A summons, a bogus appointment, and all would be over. It is well they don't have days of fog in the Latin countries—the countries of assassination. By Jove! here comes something at last to break our dead monotony."

It was the maid with a telegram. Holmes tore it open and burst out laughing.

"Well, well! What next?" said he "Brother Mycroft is coming round."

"Why not?" I asked.

"Why not? It is as if you met a tram-car coming down a country lane. Mycroft has his rails and he runs on them. His Pall Mall lodgings, the Diogenes Club, Whitehall—that is his cycle. Once, and only once, he has been here. What upheaval can possibly have derailed him?"

"Does he not explain?"

Holmes handed me his brother's telegram.

Must see you over Cadogan West. Coming at once.

                                        Mycroft

"Cadogan West? I have heard the name."

"It recalls nothing to my mind. But that Mycroft should break out in this erratic fashion! A planet might as well leave its orbit. By the way, do you know what Mycroft is?"

I had some vague recollection of an explanation at the time of the Adventure of the Greek Interpreter.

"You told me that he had some small office under the British government."

Holmes chuckled.

"I did not know you quite so well in those days. One has to be discreet when one talks of high matters of state. You are right in thinking that he is under the British government. You would also be right in a sense if you said that occasionally he *is* the British government."

"My dear Holmes!"

"I thought I might surprise you. Mycroft draws four hundred and fifty pounds a year, remains a subordinate, has no ambitions of any kind, will receive neither honour nor title, but remains the most indispensable man in the country."

"But how?"

"Well, his position is unique. He has made it for himself. There has never been anything like it before, nor will be again. He has the tidiest and most orderly brain, with the greatest capacity for storing facts, of any man living. The same great powers which I have turned to the detection of crime he has used for this particular business. The conclusions of every department are passed to him, and he is the central exchange, the clearing-house, which makes out the balance. All other men are specialists, but his specialism is omniscience. We will suppose that a minister needs information as to a point which involves the Navy, India, Canada and the bimetallic question;[1] he could get his separate advices from various departments upon

[1] *bimetallic question* An important monetary problem in the 19th century.

SIR ARTHUR CONAN DOYLE (*1859–1930*)
*began his career not as a writer but as
a physician. His interest in the analytical
capacities of the human mind led him
to write* A Study in Scarlet, *the first
of the Sherlock Holmes books, in 1887.
Gradually, he abandoned the practice
of medicine to devote all his time to
the writing of fiction. Soon his
memorable team of Sherlock Holmes
and Dr. Watson, like a modern Don
Quixote and Sancho Panza, became
familiar to millions of readers. With a
nimble mind that closely resembles the
keen, jigsaw intelligence of Edgar Allan
Poe's creation,* Auguste Dupin *of* The
Murders in the Rue Morgue, *Sherlock
Holmes outwits the cleverest of murder-
ers and thieves, while Dr. Watson
looks on with bumbling awe and mild
confusion in story after story. Once,
Doyle tried to "kill off" his most famous
creation, but public demand was such
that Holmes had to be revived. Doyle
left behind a body of written work
which each generation rediscovers with
delight. Some of his most popular books
are* The Sign of the Four (*1889*), The
Adventures of Sherlock Holmes (*1891*),
and The Hound of the Baskervilles
(*1902*).

———————————————

each, but only Mycroft can focus them all, and
say offhand how each factor would affect the
other. They began by using him as a short-cut, a
convenience; now he has made himself an essential. In that great brain of his everything is
pigeon-holed and can be handed out in an instant. Again and again his word has decided the
national policy. He lives in it. He thinks of
nothing else save when, as an intellectual exercise, he unbends if I call upon him and ask him
to advise me on one of my little problems. But
Jupiter is descending to-day. What on earth can
it mean? Who is Cadogan West, and what is he
to Mycroft?"

"I have it," I cried, and plunged among the
litter of papers upon the sofa. "Yes, yes, here
he is, sure enough! Cadogan West was the
young man who was found dead on the Underground on Tuesday morning."

Holmes sat up at attention, his pipe halfway
to his lips.

"This must be serious, Watson. A death
which has caused my brother to alter his habits
can be no ordinary one. What in the world
can he have to do with it? The case was feature-
less as I remember it. The young man had apparently fallen out of the train and killed himself. He had not been robbed, and there was no
particular reason to suspect violence. Is that not
so?"

"There has been an inquest," said I, "and a
good many fresh facts have come out. Looked
at more closely, I should certainly say that it
was a curious case."

"Judging by its effect upon my brother, I
should think it must be a most extraordinary
one." He snuggled down in his armchair. "Now,
Watson, let us have the facts."

"The man's name was Arthur Cadogan West.
He was twenty-seven years of age, unmarried,
and a clerk at Woolwich Arsenal."

"Government employ. Behold the link with
brother Mycroft!"

"He left Woolwich suddenly on Monday
night. Was last seen by his fiancée, Miss Violet
Westbury, whom he left abruptly in the fog
about 7:30 that evening. There was no quarrel
between them and she can give no motive for
his action. The next thing heard of him was
when his dead body was discovered by a plate-
layer named Mason, just outside Aldgate Station
on the Underground system [2] in London."

"When?"

"The body was found at six on the Tuesday
morning. It was lying wide of the metals upon
the left hand of the track as one goes eastward,
at a point close to the station, where the line
emerges from the tunnel in which it runs. The

———————————————

[2] *Underground system*   The subway.

head was badly crushed—an injury which might well have been caused by a fall from the train. The body could only have come on the line in that way. Had it been carried down from any neighbouring street, it must have passed the station barriers, where a collector is always standing. This point seems absolutely certain."

"Very good. The case is definite enough. The man, dead or alive, either fell or was precipitated from a train. So much is clear to me. Continue."

"The trains which traverse the lines of rail beside which the body was found are those which run from west to east, some being purely Metropolitan, and some from Willesden and outlying junctions. It can be stated for certain that this young man, when he met his death, was travelling in this direction at some late hour of the night, but at what point he entered the train it is impossible to state."

"His ticket, of course, would show that."

"There was no ticket in his pockets."

"No ticket! Dear me, Watson, this is really very singular. According to my experience it is not possible to reach the platform of a Metropolitan train without exhibiting one's ticket. Presumably, then, the young man had one. Was it taken from him in order to conceal the station from which he came? It is possible. Or did he drop it in the carriage? That also is possible. But the point is of curious interest. I understand that there was no sign of robbery?"

"Apparently not. There is a list here of his possessions. His purse contained two pounds fifteen. He had also a check-book on the Woolwich branch of the Capital and Counties Bank. Through this his identity was established. There were also two dress-circle tickets for the Woolwich Theatre, dated for that very evening. Also a small packet of technical papers."

Holmes gave an exclamation of satisfaction.

"There we have it at last, Watson! British government—Woolwich. Arsenal—technical papers—Brother Mycroft, the chain is complete. But here he comes, if I am not mistaken, to speak for himself."

A moment later the tall and portly form of Mycroft Holmes was ushered into the room. Heavily built and massive, there was a suggestion of uncouth physical inertia in the figure, but above this unwieldy frame there was perched a head so masterful in its brow, so alert in its steel-grey, deep-set eyes, so firm in its lips, and so subtle in its play of expression, that after the first glance one forgot the gross body and remembered only the dominant mind.

At his heels came our old friend Lestrade, of Scotland Yard—thin and austere. The gravity of both their faces foretold some weighty quest. The detective shook hands without a word. Mycroft Holmes struggled out of his overcoat and subsided into an armchair.

"A most annoying business, Sherlock," said he. "I extremely dislike altering my habits, but the powers that be would take no denial. In the present state of Siam it is most awkward that I should be away from the office. But it is a real crisis. I have never seen the Prime Minister so upset. As to the Admiralty—it is buzzing like an overturned beehive. Have you read up the case?"

"We have just done so. What were the technical papers?"

"Ah, there's the point! Fortunately, it has not come out. The press would be furious if it did. The papers which this wretched youth had in his pocket were the plans of the Bruce-Partington submarine."

Mycroft Holmes spoke with a solemnity which showed his sense of the importance of the subject. His brother and I sat expectant.

"Surely you have heard of it? I thought everyone had heard of it."

"Only as a name."

"Its importance can hardly be exaggerated. It has been the most jealously guarded of all government secrets. You may take it from me that naval warfare becomes impossible within the radius of a Bruce-Partington's operation. Two years ago a very large sum was smuggled through the Estimates and was expended in acquiring a monopoly of the invention. Every effort has been made to keep the secret. The plans, which are exceedingly intricate, comprising some thirty separate patents, each essential to the working of the whole, are kept in an elaborate safe in a confidential office adjoining the arsenal, with burglar-proof doors and windows. Under no conceivable circumstances were the plans to be taken from the office. If the chief constructor of the Navy desired to consult them, even he was forced to go to the Woolwich office for the purpose. And yet here we find them in the pockets of a dead junior clerk in the heart of London. From an official point of view it's simply awful."

"But you have recovered them?"

"No, Sherlock, no! That's the pinch. We have not. Ten papers were taken from Woolwich. There were seven in the pockets of Cadogan West. The three most essential are gone—stolen, vanished. You must drop everything, Sherlock. Never mind your usual petty puzzles of the police-court. It's a vital international problem that you have to solve. Why did Cadogan West take the papers, where are the missing ones, how did he die, how came his body where it was found, how can the evil be set right? Find an answer to all these questions, and you will have done good service for your country."

"Why do you not solve it yourself, Mycroft? You can see as far as I."

"Possibly, Sherlock. But it is a question of getting details. Give me your details, and from an armchair I will return you an excellent expert opinion. But to run here and run there, to cross-question railway guards, and lie on my face with a lens to my eye—it is not my *métier*. No, you are the one man who can clear the matter up. If you have a fancy to see your name in the next honours list—"

My friend smiled and shook his head.

"I play the game for the game's own sake," said he. "But the problem certainly presents some points of interest, and I shall be very pleased to look into it. Some more facts, please."

"I have jotted down the more essential ones upon this sheet of paper, together with a few addresses which you will find of service. The actual official guardian of the papers is the famous government expert, Sir James Walter, whose decorations and sub-titles fill two lines of a book of reference. He has grown grey in the service, is a gentleman, a favoured guest in the most exalted houses, and, above all, a man whose patriotism is beyond suspicion. He is one of two who have a key of the safe. I may add that the papers were undoubtedly in the office during working hours on Monday, and that Sir James left for London about three o'clock taking his key with him. He was at the house of Admiral Sinclair at Barclay Square during the whole of the evening when this incident occurred."

"Has the fact been verified?"

"Yes; his brother, Colonel Valentine Walter, has testified to his departure from Woolwich, and Admiral Sinclair to his arrival in London; so Sir James is no longer a direct factor in the problem."

"Who was the other man with a key?"

"The senior clerk and draughtsman, Mr. Sidney Johnson. He is a man of forty, married, with five children. He is a silent, morose man, but he has, on the whole, an excellent record in the public service. He is unpopular with his colleagues, but a hard worker. According to his own account, corroborated only by the word of his wife, he was at home the whole of Monday evening after office hours, and his key has never left the watchchain upon which it hangs."

"Tell us about Cadogan West."

"He has been ten years in the service and has done good work. He has the reputation of being hot-headed and impetuous, but a straight, honest man. We have nothing against him. He was next Sidney Johnson in the office. His duties brought him into daily, personal contact with the plans. No one else had the handling of them."

"Who locked the plans up that night?"

"Mr. Sidney Johnson, the senior clerk."

"Well, it is surely perfectly clear who took them away. They are actually found upon the person of this junior clerk, Cadogan West. That seems final, does it not?"

"It does, Sherlock, and yet it leaves so much unexplained. In the first place, why did he take them?"

"I presume they were of value?"

"He could have got several thousands for them very easily."

"Can you suggest any possible motive for taking the papers to London except to sell them?"

"No, I cannot."

"Then we must take that as our working hypothesis. Young West took the papers. Now this could only be done by having a false key—"

"Several false keys. He had to open the building and the room."

"He had, then, several false keys. He took the papers to London to sell the secret, intending, no doubt, to have the plans themselves back in the safe next morning before they were missed. While in London on this treasonable mission he met his end."

"How?"

"We will suppose that he was travelling back to Woolwich when he was killed and thrown out of the compartment."

"Aldgate, where the body was found, is considerably past the station for London Bridge, which would be his route to Woolwich."

"Many circumstances could be imagined under which he would pass London Bridge. There was someone in the carriage, for example, with whom he was having an absorbing interview. This interview led to a violent scene in which he lost his life. Possibly he tried to leave the carriage, fell out on the line, and so met his end. The other closed the door. There was a thick fog, and nothing could be seen."

"No better explanation can be given with our present knowledge; and yet consider, Sherlock, how much you leave untouched. We will sup-pose, for argument's sake, that young Cadogan West *had* determined to convey these papers to London. He would naturally have made an appointment with the foreign agent and kept his evening clear. Instead of that he took two tickets for the theatre, escorted his fiancée halfway there, and then suddenly disappeared."

"A blind," said Lestrade, who had sat listening with some impatience to the conversation.

"A very singular one. That is objection No. 1. Objection No. 2: We will suppose that he reaches London and sees the foreign agent. He must bring back the papers before morning or the loss will be discovered. He took away ten. Only seven were in his pocket. What had become of the other three? He certainly would not leave them of his own free will. Then, again, where is the price of his treason? One would have expected to find a large sum of money in his pocket."

"It seems to me perfectly clear," said Lestrade. "I have no doubt at all as to what occurred. He took the papers to sell them. He saw the agent. They could not agree as to price. He started home again, but the agent went with him. In the train the agent murdered him, took the more essential papers, and threw his body from the carriage. That would account for everything, would it not?"

"Why had he no ticket?"

"The ticket would have shown which station was nearest the agent's house. Therefore he took it from the murdered man's pocket."

"Good, Lestrade, very good," said Holmes. "Your theory holds together. But if this is true, then the case is at an end. On the one hand, the traitor is dead. On the other, the plans of the Bruce-Partington submarine are presumably already on the Continent. What is there for us to do?"

"To act, Sherlock—to act!" cried Mycroft, springing to his feet. "All my instincts are against this explanation. Use your powers! Go to the scene of the crime! See the people concerned! Leave no stone unturned! In all your career you have never had so great a chance of serving your country."

"Well, well!" said Holmes, shrugging his shoulders. "Come, Watson! And you, Lestrade, could you favour us with your company for an hour or two? We will begin our investigation by a visit to Aldgate Station. Good-bye, Mycroft. I shall let you have a report before evening, but I warn you in advance that you have little to expect."

An hour later Holmes, Lestrade and I stood upon the Underground railroad at the point where it emerges from the tunnel immediately before Aldgate Station. A courteous red-faced old gentleman represented the railway company.

"This is where the young man's body lay," said he, indicating a spot about three feet from the metals. "It could not have fallen from above, for these, as you see, are all blank walls. Therefore, it could only have come from a train, and that train, so far as we can trace it, must have passed about midnight on Monday."

"Have the carriages been examined for any sign of violence?"

"There are no such signs, and no ticket has been found."

"No record of a door being found open?"

"None."

"We have had some fresh evidence this morning," said Lestrade. "A passenger who passed Aldgate in an ordinary Metropolitan train about 11:40 on Monday night declares that he heard a heavy thud, as of a body striking the line, just before the train reached the station. There was dense fog, however, and nothing could be seen. He made no report of it at the time. Why, whatever is the matter with Mr. Holmes?"

My friend was standing with an expression of strained intensity upon his face, staring at the railway metals where they curved out of the tunnel. Aldgate is a junction, and there was a network of points.[3] On these his eager, questioning eyes were fixed, and I saw on his keen, alert face that tightening of the lips, that quiver of the nostrils, and concentration of the heavy, tufted brows which I knew so well.

"Points," he muttered; "the points."

"What of it? What do you mean?"

"I suppose there are no great number of points on a system such as this?"

"No; there are very few."

"And a curve, too. Points, and a curve. By Jove! if it were only so."

"What is it, Mr. Holmes? Have you a clue?"

"An idea—an indication, no more. But the case certainly grows in interest. Unique, perfectly unique, and yet why not? I do not see any indications of bleeding on the line."

"There were hardly any."

"But I understand that there was a considerable wound."

"The bone was crushed, but there was no great external injury."

"And yet one would have expected some bleeding. Would it be possible for me to inspect the train which contained the passenger who heard the thud of a fall in the fog?"

"I fear not, Mr. Holmes. The train has been broken up before now, and the carriages redistributed."

"I can assure you, Mr. Holmes," said Lestrade, "that every carriage has been carefully examined. I saw to it myself."

It was one of my friend's most obvious weaknesses that he was impatient with less alert intelligences than his own.

"Very likely," said he, turning away. "As it happens, it was not the carriages which I desired to examine. Watson, we have done all we can here. We need not trouble you any further, Mr. Lestrade. I think our investigations must now carry us to Woolwich."

At London Bridge, Holmes wrote a telegram to his brother, which he handed to me before dispatching it. It ran thus:

See some light in the darkness, but it may possibly flicker out. Meanwhile, please send by

---

[3] *points*   Railroad switches.

messenger, to await return at Baker Street, a complete list of all foreign spies or international agents known to be in England, with full address.

SHERLOCK

"That should be helpful Watson," he remarked as we took our seats in the Woolwich train. "We certainly owe brother Mycroft a debt for having introduced us to what promises to be a really very remarkable case."

His eager face still wore that expression of intense and high-strung energy, which showed me that some novel and suggestive circumstance had opened up a stimulating line of thought. See the foxhound with hanging ears and drooping tail as it lolls about the kennels, and compare it with the same hound as, with gleaming eyes and straining muscles, it runs upon a breast-high scent—such was the change in Holmes since the morning. He was a different man from the limp and lounging figure in the mouse-coloured dressing-gown who had prowled so restlessly only a few hours before round the fog-girt room.

"There is material here. There is scope," said he. "I am dull indeed not to have understood its possibilities."

"Even now they are dark to me."

"The end is dark to me also, but I have hold of one idea which may lead us far. The man met his death elsewhere, and his body was on the *roof* of a carriage."

"On the roof!"

"Remarkable, is it not? But consider the facts. Is it a coincidence that it is found at the very point where the train pitches and sways as it comes round on the points? Is not that the place where an object upon the roof might be expected to fall off? The points would affect no object inside the train. Either the body fell from the roof, or a very curious coincidence has occurred. But now consider the question of the blood. Of course, there was no bleeding on the line if the body had bled elsewhere. Each fact is suggestive in itself. Together they have a cumulative force."

"And the ticket, too!" I cried.

"Exactly. We could not explain the absence of a ticket. This would explain it. Everything fits together."

"But suppose it were so, we are still as far as ever from unravelling the mystery of his death. Indeed, it becomes not simpler but stranger."

"Perhaps," said Holmes thoughtfully, "perhaps." He relapsed into a silent reverie, which lasted until the slow train drew up at last in Woolwich Station. There he called a cab and drew Mycroft's paper from his pocket.

"We have quite a little round of afternoon calls to make," said he. "I think that Sir James Walter claims our first attention."

The house of the famous official was a fine villa with green lawns stretching down to the Thames. As we reached it the fog was lifting, and a thin, watery sunshine was breaking through. A butler answered our ring.

"Sir James, sir?" said he with solemn face. "Sir James died this morning."

"Good heavens!" cried Holmes in amazement. "How did he die?"

"Perhaps you would care to step in, sir, and see his brother, Colonel Valentine?"

"Yes, we had best do so."

We were ushered into a dim-lit drawing-room, where an instant later we were joined by a very tall, handsome, light-bearded man of fifty, the younger brother of the dead scientist. His wild eyes, stained cheeks, and unkempt hair all spoke of the sudden blow which had fallen upon the household. He was hardly articulate as he spoke of it.

"It was this horrible scandal," said he. "My brother, Sir James, was a man of very sensitive honour, and he could not survive such an affair. It broke his heart. He was always so proud of the efficiency of his department, and this was a crushing blow."

"We had hoped that he might have given us some indications which would have helped us to clear the matter up."

"I assure you that it was all a mystery to

him as it is to you and to all of us. He had already put all his knowledge at the disposal of the police. Naturally he had no doubt that Cadogan West was guilty. But all the rest was inconceivable."

"You cannot throw any new light upon the affair?"

"I know nothing myself save what I have read or heard. I have no desire to be discourteous, but you can understand, Mr. Holmes, that we are much disturbed at present, and I must ask you to hasten this interview to an end."

"This is indeed an unexpected development," said my friend when we had regained the cab. "I wonder if the death was natural, or whether the poor old fellow killed himself! If the latter, may it be taken as some sign of self-reproach for duty neglected? We must leave that question to the future. Now we shall turn to the Cadogan Wests."

A small but well-kept house in the outskirts of the town sheltered the bereaved mother. The old lady was too dazed with grief to be of any use to us, but at her side was a white-faced young lady, who introduced herself as Miss Violet Westbury, the fiancée of the dead man, and the last to see him upon that fatal night.

"I cannot explain it, Mr. Holmes," she said. "I have not shut an eye since the tragedy, thinking, thinking, thinking, night and day, what the true meaning of it can be. Arthur was the most single-minded, chivalrous, patriotic man upon earth. He would have cut his right hand off before he would sell a State secret confided to his keeping. It is absurd, impossible, preposterous to anyone who knew him."

"But the facts, Miss Westbury?"

"Yes, yes; I admit I cannot explain them."

"Was he in any want of money?"

"No; his needs were very simple and his salary ample. He had saved a few hundreds, and we were to marry at the New Year."

"No signs of any mental excitement? Come, Miss Westbury, be absolutely frank with us."

The quick eye of my companion had noted some change in her manner. She coloured and hesitated.

"Yes," she said at last, "I had a feeling that there was something on his mind."

"For long?"

"Only for the last week or so. He was thoughtful and worried. Once I pressed him about it. He admitted that there was something, and that it was concerned with his official life. 'It is too serious for me to speak about, even to you,' said he. I could get nothing more."

Holmes looked grave.

"Go on, Miss Westbury. Even if it seems to tell against him, go on. We cannot say what it may lead to."

"Indeed, I have nothing more to tell. Once or twice it seemed to me that he was on the point of telling me something. He spoke one evening of the importance of the secret, and I have some recollection that he said that no doubt foreign spies would pay a great deal to have it."

My friend's face grew graver still.

"Anything else?"

"He said that we were slack about such matters—that it would be easy for a traitor to get the plans."

"Was it only recently that he made such remarks?"

"Yes, quite recently."

"Now tell us of that last evening."

"We were to go to the theatre. The fog was so thick that a cab was useless. We walked, and our way took us close to the office. Suddenly he darted away into the fog."

"Without a word?"

"He gave an exclamation; that was all. I waited but he never returned. Then I walked home. Next morning, after the office opened, they came to inquire. About twelve o'clock we heard the terrible news. Oh, Mr. Holmes, if you could only, only save his honour! It was so much to him."

Holmes shook his head sadly.

"Come, Watson," said he, "our ways lie elsewhere. Our next station must be the office from which the papers were taken.

"It was black enough before against this young man, but our inquiries make it blacker," he remarked as the cab lumbered off. "His coming marriage gives a motive for the crime. He naturally wanted money. The idea was in his head, since he spoke about it. He nearly made the girl an accomplice in the treason by telling her his plans. It is all very bad."

"But surely, Holmes, character goes for something? Then, again, why should he leave the girl in the street and dart away to commit a felony?"

"Exactly! There are certainly objections. But it is a formidable case which they have to meet."

Mr. Sidney Johnson, the senior clerk, met us at the office and received us with that respect which my companion's card always commanded. He was a thin, gruff, bespectacled man of middle age, his cheeks haggard, and his hands twitching from the nervous strain to which he had been subjected.

"It is bad, Mr. Holmes, very bad! Have you heard of the death of the chief?"

"We have just come from his house."

"The place is disorganized. The chief dead, Cadogan West dead, our papers stolen. And yet, when we closed our door on Monday evening, we were as efficient an office as any in the government service. Good God, it's dreadful to think of! That West, of all men, should have done such a thing!"

"You are sure of his guilt, then?"

"I can see no other way out of it. And yet I would have trusted him as I trust myself."

"At what hour was the office closed on Monday?"

"At five."

"Did you close it?"

"I am always the last man out."

"Where were the plans?"

"In that safe. I put them there myself."

"Is there no watchman to the building?"

"There is, but he has other departments to look after as well. He is an old soldier and a most trustworthy man. He saw nothing that evening. Of course the fog was very thick."

"Suppose that Cadogan West wished to make his way into the building after hours; he would need three keys, would he not, before he could reach the papers?"

"Yes, he would. The key of the outer door, the key of the office, and the key of the safe."

"Only Sir James Walter and you had those keys?"

"I had no keys of the doors—only of the safe."

"Was Sir James a man who was orderly in his habits?"

"Yes, I think he was. I know that so far as those three keys are concerned he kept them on the same ring. I have often seen them there."

"And that ring went with him to London?"

"He said so."

"And your key never left your possession?"

"Never."

"Then West, if he is the culprit, must have had a duplicate. And yet none was found upon his body. One other point: if a clerk in this office desired to sell the plans, would it not be simpler to copy the plans for himself than to take the originals, as was actually done?"

"It would take considerable technical knowledge to copy the plans in an effective way."

"But I suppose either Sir James, or you, or West had that technical knowledge?"

"No doubt we had, but I beg you won't try to drag me into the matter, Mr. Holmes. What is the use of our speculating in this way when the original plans were actually found on West?"

"Well, it is certainly singular that he should run the risk of taking originals if he could safely have taken copies, which would have equally served his turn."

"Singular, no doubt—and yet he did so."

"Every inquiry in this case reveals something inexplicable. Now there are three papers still missing. They are, as I understand, the vital ones."

"Yes, that is so."

"Do you mean to say that anyone holding these three papers, and without the seven others, could construct a Bruce-Partington submarine?"

"I reported to that effect to the Admiralty. But to-day I have been over the drawings again, and I am not so sure of it. The double valves with the automatic self-adjusting slots are drawn in one of the papers which have been returned. Until the foreigners had invented that for themselves they could not make the boat. Of course they might soon get over the difficulty."

"But the three missing drawings are the most important?"

"Undoubtedly."

"I think, with your permission, I will now take a stroll round the premises. I do not recall any other question which I desired to ask."

He examined the lock of the safe, the door of the room, and finally the iron shutters of the window. It was only when we were on the lawn outside that his interest was strongly excited. There was a laurel bush outside the window, and several of the branches bore signs of having been twisted or snapped. He examined them carefully with his lens, and then some dim and vague marks upon the earth beneath. Finally he asked the chief clerk to close the iron shutters, and he pointed out to me that they hardly met in the centre, and that it would be possible for anyone outside to see what was going on within the room.

"The indications are ruined by the three days' delay. They may mean something or nothing. Well, Watson, I do not think that Woolwich can help us further. It is a small crop which we have gathered. Let us see if we can do better in London."

Yet we added one more sheaf to our harvest before we left Woolwich Station. The clerk in the ticket office was able to say with confidence that he saw Cadogan West—whom he knew well by sight—upon the Monday night, and that he went to London by the 8:15 to London Bridge. He was alone and took a single third-class ticket. The clerk was struck at the time by his excited and nervous manner. So shaky was he that he could hardly pick up his change, and the clerk had helped him with it. A reference to the timetable showed that the 8:15 was the first train which it was possible for West to take after he had left the lady about 7:30.

"Let us reconstruct, Watson," said Holmes after half an hour of silence. "I am not aware that in all our joint researches we have ever had a case which was more difficult to get at. Every fresh advance which we make only reveals a fresh ridge beyond. And yet we have surely made some appreciable progress.

"The effect of our inquiries at Woolwich has in the main been against young Cadogan West; but the indications at the window would lend themselves to a more favourable hypothesis. Let us suppose, for example, that he had been approached by some foreign agent. It might have been done under such pledges as would have prevented him from speaking of it, and yet would have affected his thoughts in the direction indicated by his remarks to his fiancée. Very good. We will now suppose that as he went to the theatre with the young lady he suddenly, in the fog, caught a glimpse of this same agent going in the direction of the office. He was an impetuous man, quick in his decisions. Everything gave way to his duty. He followed the man, reached the window, saw the abstraction of the documents, and pursued the thief. In this way we get over the objection that no one would take originals when he could make copies. This outsider had to take originals. So far it holds together."

"What is the next step?"

"Then we come into difficulties. One would imagine that under such circumstances the first act of young Cadogan West would be to seize the villain and raise the alarm. Why did he not do so? Could it have been an official superior who took the papers? That would explain West's conduct. Or could the thief have given West the slip in the fog, and West started at once to London to head him off from his own rooms, presuming that he knew where the rooms were? The call must have been very pressing, since he left his girl standing in the fog, and made no effort to communicate with her. Our scent runs cold here, and there is a vast gap between either hypothesis and the laying of West's body, with seven papers in his pocket, on the roof of a Metropolitan train. My instinct now is to work from the other end. If Mycroft has given us the list of addresses we may be able to pick our man and follow two tracks instead of one."

Surely enough, a note awaited us at Baker Street. A government messenger had brought it post-haste. Holmes glanced at it and threw it over to me.

There are numerous small fry, but few who would handle so big an affair. The only men worth considering are Adolph Meyer, of 13 Great George Street, Westminister; Louis La Rothière, of Campden Mansions, Notting Hill; and Hugo Oberstein, 13 Caulfield Gardens, Kensington. The latter was known to be in town on Monday and is now reported as having left. Glad to hear you have seen some light. The Cabinet awaits your final report with the utmost anxiety. Urgent representations have arrived from the very highest quarter. The whole force of the State is at your back if you should need it.

Mycroft

"I'm afraid," said Holmes, smiling, "that all the queen's horses and all the queen's men cannot avail in this matter." He had spread out his big map of London and leaned eagerly over it. "Well, well," said he presently with an exclamation of satisfaction, "things are turning a little in our direction at last. Why, Watson, I do honestly believe that we are going to pull it off, after all." He slapped me on the shoulder with a sudden burst of hilarity. "I am going out now. It is only a reconnaissance. I will do nothing serious without my trusted comrade and biographer at my elbow. Do you stay here, and the odds are that you will see me again in an hour or two. If time hangs heavy get foolscap and a pen, and begin your narrative of how we saved the State."

I felt some reflection of his elation in my own mind, for I knew well that he would not depart so far from his usual austerity of demeanour unless there was good cause for exultation. All the long November evening I waited, filled with impatience for his return. At last, shortly after nine o'clock, there arrived a messenger with a note:

Am dining at Goldini's Restaurant, Gloucester Road, Kensington. Please come at once and join me there. Bring with you a jimmy, a dark lantern, a chisel, and a revolver.

S. H.

It was a nice equipment for a respectable citizen to carry through the dim, fog-draped streets. I stowed them all discreetly away in my overcoat and drove straight to the address given. There sat my friend at a little round table near the door of the garish Italian restaurant.

"Have you had something to eat? Then join me in a coffee and curaçao.[4] Try one of the proprietor's cigars. They are less poisonous than one would expect. Have you the tools?"

"They are here, in my overcoat."

"Excellent. Let me give you a short sketch of what I have done, with some indication of what we are about to do. Now it must be evident to you, Watson, that this young man's body was *placed* on the roof of the train. That was clear from the instant that I determined the fact that it was from the roof, and not from a carriage, that he had fallen."

"Could it not have been dropped from a bridge?"

[4] *curaçao* A sweet drink made from oranges grown in Curaçao.

"I should say it was impossible. If you examine the roofs you will find that they are slightly rounded, and there is no railing round them. Therefore, we can say for certain that young Cadogan West was placed on it."

"How could he be placed there?"

"That was the question which we had to answer. There is only one possible way. You are aware that the Underground runs clear of tunnels at some points in the West End. I had a vague memory that as I have travelled by it I have occasionally seen windows just above my head. Now, suppose that a train halted under such a window, would there be any difficulty in laying a body upon the roof?"

"It seems most improbable."

"We must fall back upon the old axiom that when all other contingencies fail, whatever remains, however improbable, must be the truth. Here all other contingencies *have* failed. When I found that the leading international agent, who had just left London, lived in a row of houses which abutted upon the Underground. I was so pleased that you were a little astonished at my sudden frivolity."

"Oh, that was it, was it?"

"Yes, that was it. Mr. Hugo Oberstein, of 13 Caulfield Gardens, had become my objective. I began my operations at Gloucester Road Station, where a very helpful official walked with me along the track and allowed me to satisfy myself not only that the back-stair windows of Caulfield Gardens open on the line but the even more essential fact that, owing to the intersection of one of the larger railways, the Underground trains are frequently held motionless for some minutes at that very spot."

"Splendid, Holmes! You have got it!"

"So far—so far, Watson. We advance, but the goal is afar. Well, having seen the back of Caulfield Gardens, I visited the front and satisfied myself that the bird was indeed flown. It is a considerable house, unfurnished, so far as I could judge, in the upper rooms. Oberstein

lived there with a single valet, who was probably a confederate entirely in his confidence. We must bear in mind that Oberstein has gone to the Continent to dispose of his booty, but not with any idea of flight; for he had no reason to fear a warrant, and the idea of an amateur domiciliary visit would certainly never occur to him. Yet that is precisely what we are about to make."

"Could we not get a warrant and legalize it?"

"Hardly on the evidence."

"What can we hope to do?"

"We cannot tell what correspondence may be there."

"I don't like it, Holmes."

"My dear fellow, you shall keep watch in the street. I'll do the criminal part. It's not a time to stick at trifles. Think of Mycroft's note, of the Admiralty, the Cabinet, the exalted person who waits for news. We are bound to go."

My answer was to rise from the table.

"You are right, Holmes. We are bound to go."

He sprang up and shook me by the hand.

"I knew you would not shrink at the last," said he, and for a moment I saw something in his eyes which was nearer to tenderness than I had ever seen. The next instant he was his masterful, practical self once more.

"It is nearly half a mile, but there is no hurry. Let us walk," said he. "Don't drop the instruments, I beg. Your arrest as a suspicious character would be a most unfortunate complication."

Caulfield Gardens was one of those lines of flat-faced, pillared and porticoed houses which are so prominent a product of the middle Victorian epoch in the West End of London. Next door there appeared to be a children's party, for the merry buzz of young voices and the clatter of a piano resounded through the night. The fog still hung about and screened us with its friendly shade. Holmes had lit his lantern and flashed it upon the massive door.

"This is a serious proposition," said he. "It is certainly bolted as well as locked. We would do better in the area. There is an excellent arch-way down yonder in case a too zealous police-man should intrude. Give me a hand, Watson, and I'll do the same for you."

A minute later we were both in the area. Hardly had we reached the dark shadows be-fore the step of the policeman was heard in the fog above. As its soft rhythm died away, Holmes set to work upon the lower door. I saw him stoop and strain until with a sharp crash it flew open. We sprang through into the dark passage, closing the area door behind us. Holmes led the way up the curving, uncarpeted stair. His little fan of yellow light shone upon a low window.

"Here we are, Watson—this must be the one." He threw it open, and as he did so there was a low, harsh murmur, growing steadily into a loud roar as a train dashed past us in the dark-ness. Holmes swept his light along the window-sill. It was thickly coated with soot from the passing engines, but the black surface was blurred and rubbed in places.

"You can see where they rested the body. Halloa, Watson! what is this? There can be no doubt that it is a blood mark." He was pointing to faint discolourations along the woodwork of the window. "Here it is on the stone of the stair also. The demonstration is complete. Let us stay here until a train stops."

We had not long to wait. The very next train roared from the tunnel as before, but slowed in the open, and then, with a creaking of brakes, pulled up immediately beneath us. It was not four feet from the window-ledge to the roof of the carriages. Holmes softly closed the window.

"So far we are justified," said he. "What do you think of it, Watson?"

"A masterpiece. You have never risen to a greater height."

"I cannot agree with you there. From the moment that I conceived the idea of the body being upon the roof, which surely was not a very abstruse one, all the rest was inevitable. If it were not for the grave interests involved

the affair up to this point would be insignificant. Our difficulties are still before us. But perhaps we may find something here which may help us."

We had ascended the kitchen stair and entered the suite of rooms upon the first floor. One was a dining-room, severely furnished and contain-ing nothing of interest. A second was a bed-room, which also drew blank. The remaining room appeared more promising, and my com-panion settled down to a systematic examina-tion. It was littered with books and papers, and was evidently used as a study. Swiftly and methodically Holmes turned over the contents of drawer after drawer and cupboard after cup-board, but no gleam of success came to brighten his austere face. At the end of an hour he was no further than when he started.

"The cunning dog has covered his tracks," said he. "He has left nothing to incriminate him. His dangerous correspondence has been de-stroyed or removed. This is our last chance."

It was a small tin cash-box which stood upon the writing-desk. Holmes pried it open with his chisel. Several rolls of paper were within, covered with figures and calculations, without any note to show to what they referred. The recurring words, "water pressure" and "pres-sure to the square inch" suggested some possible relation to a submarine. Holmes tossed them all impatiently aside. There only remained an envelope with some small newspaper slips inside it. He shook them out on the table, and at once I saw by his eager face that his hopes had been raised.

"What's this, Watson? Eh? What's this? Record of a series of messages in the advertise-ments of a paper. *Daily Telegraph* agony col-umn [5] by the print and paper. Right-hand top corner of a page. No dates—but messages ar-range themselves. This must be the first:

[5] *agony column* British colloquial term for the column where personal notices are printed in the classi-fied advertisements section of a newspaper.

"Hoped to hear sooner. Terms agreed to. Write fully to address given on card.

PIERROT

"Next comes:

"Too complex for description. Must have full report. Stuff awaits you when goods delivered.

PIERROT

"Then comes:

"Matter presses. Must withdraw offer unless contract completed. Make appointment by letter. Will confirm by advertisement.

PIERROT

"Finally:

"Monday night after nine. Two taps. Only ourselves. Do not be so suspicious. Payment in hard cash when goods delivered.

PIERROT

"A fairly complete record, Watson! If we could only get at the man at the other end!" He sat lost in thought, tapping his fingers on the table. Finally he sprang to his feet.

"Well, perhaps it won't be so difficult, after all. There is nothing more to be done here, Watson. I think we might drive round to the offices of the *Daily Telegraph*, and so bring a good day's work to a conclusion."

Mycroft Holmes and Lestrade had come round by appointment after breakfast next day and Sherlock Holmes had recounted to them our proceedings of the day before. The professional shook his head over our confessed burglary.

"We can't do these things in the force, Mr. Holmes," said he. "No wonder you get results that are beyond us. But some of these days you'll go too far, and you'll find yourself and your friend in trouble."

"For England, home and beauty—eh, Watson? Martyrs on the altar of our country. But what do you think of it, Mycroft?"

"Excellent, Sherlock! Admirable! But what use will you make of it?"

Holmes picked up the *Daily Telegraph* which lay upon the table.

"Have you seen Pierrot's advertisement to-day?"

"What? Another one?"

"Yes, here it is:

"To-night. Same hour. Same place. Two taps. Most vitally important. Your own safety at stake.

PIERROT"

"By George!" cried Lestrade. "If he answers that we've got him!"

"That was my idea when I put it in. I think if you could both make it convenient to come with us about eight o'clock to Caulfield Gardens we might possibly get a little nearer to a solution."

One of the most remarkable characteristics of Sherlock Holmes was his power of throwing his brain out of action and switching all his thoughts on to lighter things whenever he had convinced himself that he could no longer work to advantage. I remember that during the whole of that memorable day he lost himself in a monograph which he had undertaken upon the Polyphonic Motets of Lassus.[6] For my own part I had none of this power of detachment, and the day, in consequence, appeared to be interminable. The great national importance of the issue, the suspense in high quarters, the direct nature of the experiment which we were trying—all combined to work upon my nerve. It was a relief to me when at last, after a light dinner, we set out upon our expedition. Lestrade and Mycroft met us by appointment at the outside of Gloucester Road Station. The area door of Oberstein's house had been left open the night before, and it was necessary for me, as

[6] *Lassus* Orlando Lassus (1520?–1594), a Flemish composer.

And it did! It is a matter of history—that secret history of a nation which is often so much more intimate and interesting than its public chronicles—that Oberstein, eager to complete the coup of his lifetime, came to the lure and was safely engulfed for fifteen years in a British prison. In his trunk were found the invaluable Bruce-Partington plans, which he had put up for auction in all the naval centres of Europe.

Colonel Walter died in prison towards the end of the second year of his sentence. As to Holmes, he returned refreshed to his monograph upon the Polyphonic Motets of Lassus, which has since been printed for private circulation, and is said by experts to be the last word upon the subject. Some weeks afterwards I learned incidentally that my friend spent a day at Windsor,[9] whence he returned with a remarkably fine emerald tie-pin. When I asked him if he had bought it, he answered that it was a present from a certain gracious lady in whose interests he had once been fortunate enough to carry out a small commission. He said no more; but I fancy that I could guess at that lady's august name, and I have little doubt that the emerald pin will forever recall to my friend's memory the adventure of the Bruce-Partington plans.

For Discussion

1. Apart from his uncanny ability to find meaning in the slightest bits of evidence, what kind of man is Sherlock Holmes? What are his major interests? Does he track down criminals because of his profound sense of justice? Is he an affectionate man? How does his appearance reflect his character?

2. Is Dr. Watson similar in temperament to Sherlock Holmes? In what ways does he differ?

3. In this story, Sir Arthur Conan Doyle presents the reader with the same facts that Sherlock Holmes uses to solve the case. Do you think that a reader would be able to deduce the right conclusion if the author withheld the climax of the story?

Why? What advantage does Sherlock Holmes have that the reader does not?

4. Compare some modern fictional detectives from books or television programs with Sherlock Holmes. In what ways do they differ? How are they alike?

5. Can you describe Sherlock Holmes's method of analysis? How does he arrive at the conclusion that Cadogan West's body fell from the roof of the train rather than from inside as a passenger? What are the central clues of the case from which the rest of the reconstruction follows logically?

---

[9] *Windsor* Windsor castle, Queen Victoria's home.

Shark Close-ups

JACQUES-YVES COUSTEAU

*The first of the skin divers, Jacques-Yves Cousteau, was not a pleasure
seeker. Here, in his own words, are the practical reasons behind the
adventure of "Shark Close-ups":*

*"Since ancient times lonely men have tried to penetrate the sea. Sir
Robert H. Davis has found records in each flourishing age of men who
tried to make underwater breathing apparatus, most of them on
swimming or free-walking principles. There are Assyrian bas-reliefs
of men attempting impossible submersions while sucking on goatskin
bellows. Leonardo da Vinci doodled several impractical ideas for diving
lungs. Fevered Elizabethan craftsmen tinkered with leather suits
for diving. . . . Obviously man has to enter the sea. There is no choice
in the matter. The human population is increasing so rapidly and land
resources are being depleted at such a rate, that we must take
sustenance from the great cornucopia. . . ."*

ON A goggle dive at Djerba Island off Tunisia in
1939 I met sharks underwater for the first time.
They were magnificent gun-metal creatures,
eight feet long, that swam in pairs behind their
servant remoras.[1] I was uneasy with fear, but I
calmed somewhat when I saw the reaction of
my diving companion, Simone. She was scared.
The sharks passed on haughtily.

The Djerba sharks were entered in a shark
casebook I kept religiously until we went to the
Red Sea in 1951, where sharks appeared in such
numbers that my census lost value. From the
data, covering over a hundred shark encounters
with many varieties, I can offer two conclusions:
the better acquainted we become with sharks,
the less we know them, and one can never tell
what a shark is going to do.

Man is separated from the shark by an abyss
of time. The fish still lives in the late Mesozoic,
when the rocks were made: it has changed but
little in perhaps three hundred million years.
Across the gulf of ages, which evolved other
marine creatures, the relentless, indestructible
shark has come without need of evolution, the
oldest killer, armed for the fray of existence in
the beginning.

---

[1] *remora* A fish which attaches itself to other fish.

One sunny day in the open sea between the islands of Boavista and Maio, in the Cape Verde group, a long Atlantic swell beat on an exposed reef and sent walls of flume high into the air. Such a sight is the dread of hydrographers, who mark it off sternly to warn the mariner. But the *Élie Monnier* was attracted to such spots. We anchored by the dangerous reef to dive from the steeply rolling deck into the wild sea. Where there is a reef, there is abundant life.

Small sharks came when we [2] dropped anchor. The crew broke out tuna hooks and took ten of them in as many minutes. When we went overside for a camera dive, there were only two sharks left in the water. Under the racing swell we watched them strike the hooks and thrash their way through the surface. Down in the reef we found the savage population of the open ocean, including some extremely large nurse sharks, a class that is not supposed to be harmful to man. We saw three sharks sleeping in rocky caverns. The camera demanded lively sharks. Dumas and Tailliez swam into the caves and pulled their tails to wake them. The sharks came out and vanished into the blue, playing their bit parts competently.

We saw a fifteen-foot nurse shark. I summoned Didi and conveyed to him in sign language that he would be permitted to relax our neutrality toward sharks and take a crack at this one with his super-harpoon gun. It had a six-foot spear with an explosive head and three hundred pounds of traction in its elastic bands. Dumas fired straight down at a distance of twelve feet. The four-pound harpoon struck the shark's head and, two seconds later, the harpoon tip exploded. We were severely shaken. There was some pain involved.

The shark continued to swim away, imperturbably, with the spear sticking from its head like a flagstaff. After a few strokes the harpoon shaft fell to the bottom and the shark moved on. We swam after it as fast as we could to see what would happen. The shark showed every sign of normal movement, accelerated gradually and vanished. The only conclusion we could draw was that the harpoon went clear through the head and exploded externally, because no internal organ could survive a blast that nearly incapacitated us six harpoon lengths away. Even so, taking such a burst a few inches from the head demonstrated the extraordinary vitality of sharks.

One day we were finishing a movie sequence on trigger fish when Dumas and I were galvanized with ice-cold terror. It is a reaction unpleasant enough on land, and very lonely in the water. What we saw made us feel that naked men really do not belong under the sea.

At a distance of forty feet there appeared from the gray haze the lead-white bulk of a twenty-five-foot *Carcharodon carcharias*, the only shark species that all specialists agree is a confirmed maneater. Dumas, my bodyguard, closed in beside me. The brute was swimming lazily. In that moment I thought that at least he would have a bellyache on our three-cylinder lungs.

Then, the shark saw us. His reaction was the last conceivable one. In pure fright, the monster voided a cloud of excrement and departed at an incredible speed.

Dumas and I looked at each other and burst into nervous laughter. The self-confidence we gained that day led us to a foolish negligence. We abandoned the bodyguard system and all measures of safety. Further meetings with sharp-nosed sharks, tiger sharks, mackerel sharks, and ground sharks, inflated our sense of shark mastery. They all ran from us. After several weeks in the Cape Verdes, we were ready to state flatly that all sharks were cowards. They were so pusillanimous they wouldn't hold still to be filmed.

---

[2] *we* The author's companions on his expedition aboard the *Élie Monnier* were Frédéric Dumas ("Didi") and Phillippe Tailliez.

. . . I heard shouts from the deck, "Whales!" A herd of sluggish bottlenosed whales surrounded the *Élie Monnier.*

In the clear water we studied the big dark forms. Their heads were round and glossy with bulbous foreheads, the "bottle" which gives them their name. When a whale broke the surface, it spouted and the rest of the body followed softly, stretching in relaxation. The whale's lips were curved in a fixed smile with tiny eyes close to the tucks of the lips, a roguish visage for such a formidable creature. Dumas skinned down to the harpoon platform under the bow while I stuck a film magazine in the underwater camera. The whales were back from a dive. One emerged twelve feet from Dumas. He threw the harpoon with all his might. The shaft struck near the pectoral fin and blood started. The animal sounded in an easy rhythm and we paid out a hundred yards of harpoon line, tied to a heavy gray buoy. The buoy was swept away in the water—the whale was well hooked. The other whales lay unperturbed around the *Élie Monnier.*

We saw Dumas's harpoon sticking out of the water; then it, the whale and buoy disappeared. Dumas climbed the mast with binoculars. I kept the ship among the whales, thinking they would not abandon a wounded comrade. Time passed.

Libera, the keen-eyed radio man, spotted the buoy and there was the whale, seemingly unhurt, with the harpoon protruding like a toothpick. Dumas hit the whale twice with dum-dum bullets.[3] Red water washed on the backs of the faithful herd, as it gathered around the stricken one. We struggled for an hour to pick up the buoy and tie the harpoon line to the *Élie Monnier.*

A relatively small bottlenosed whale, heavily wounded, was tethered to the ship. We were out of sight of land, with fifteen hundred fathoms of water under the keel, and the whale herd diving and spouting around the ship. Tailliez and I

entered the water to follow the harpoon line to the agonized animal.

The water was an exceptional clear turquoise blue. We followed the line a few feet under the surface, and came upon the whale. Thin streams of blood jetted horizontally from the bullet holes. I swam toward three other bottlenoses. As I neared them, they turned up their flukes and sounded. It was the first time I had been underwater to actually see them diving and I understood the old whaler's word "sound." They did not dive obliquely as porpoises often do. They sped straight down, perfectly vertical. I followed them down a hundred feet. A fifteen-foot shark passed way below me, probably attracted by the whale's blood. Beyond sight was the deep scattering layer; down there a herd of leviathans [4] grazed; more sharks roamed. Above in the sun's silvery light was Tailliez and a big whale dying. Reluctantly I returned to the ship.

Back on deck I changed into another lung and strapped a tablet of cupric acetate on an ankle and one on my belt. When this chemical dissolves in water it is supposed to repulse sharks. Dumas was to pass a noose over the whale's tail, while I filmed. Just after we went under he saw a big shark, but it was gone before I answered his shout. We swam under the keel of the ship and located the harpoon line.

A few lengths down the line in a depth of fifteen feet we sighted an eight-foot shark of a species we had never before seen. He was impressively neat, light gray, sleek, a real collector's item. A ten-inch fish with vertical black-and-white stripes accompanied him a few inches above his back, one of the famous pilot fish. We boldly swam toward the shark, confident that he would run as all the others had. He did not retreat. We drew within ten feet of him, and saw all around the shark an escort of tiny striped pilots three or four inches long.

They were not following him; they seemed

[3] *dum-dum bullets* Soft-nosed bullets which expand when they hit an object.

[4] *leviathan* Biblical term for ocean monsters.

"Across the gulf of ages, which evolved other marine creatures, the relentless, indestructible shark has come without need of evolution, the oldest killer . . ."

part of him. A thumbnail of a pilot fish wriggled just ahead of the shark's snout, miraculously staying in place as the beast advanced. He probably found there a compressibility wave that held him. If he tumbled out of it, he would be hopelessly left behind. It was some time before we realized that the shark and his courtiers were not scared of us.

Sea legends hold that the shark has poor eyesight and pilot fish guide him to the prey, in order to take crumbs from his table. Scientists today tend to pooh-pooh the attribution of the pilot as a seeing-eye dog, although dissection has

confirmed the low vision of sharks. Our experiences lead us to believe they probably see as well as we do.

The handsome gray was not apprehensive. I was happy to have such an opportunity to film a shark, although, as the first wonder passed, a sense of danger came to our hearts. Shark and company slowly circled us. I became the film director, making signs to Dumas, who was co-starred with the shark. Dumas obligingly swam in front of the beast and along behind it. He lingered at the tail and reached out his hand. He grasped the tip of the caudal fin, undecided about giving it a good pull. That would break the dreamy rhythm and make a good shot, but it might also bring the teeth snapping back at him. Dumas released the tail and pursued the shark round and round. I was whirling in the center of the game, busy framing Dumas. He was swimming as hard as he could to keep up with the almost motionless animal. The shark made no hostile move nor did he flee, but his hard little eyes were on us.

I tried to identify the species. In outline and marking he resembled no shark we had seen or studied.

The shark had gradually led us down to sixty feet. Dumas pointed down. From the visibility limit of the abyss, two more sharks climbed toward us. They were fifteen-footers, slender, steel-blue animals with a more savage appearance. They leveled off below us. They carried no pilot fish.

Our old friend, the gray shark, was getting closer to us, tightening his slowly revolving cordon. But he still seemed manageable. He turned reliably in his clockwise prowl and the pilots held their stations. The blue pair from the abyss hung back, leaving the affair to the first comer. We revolved inside the ring, watching the gray, and tried to keep the blues located at the same time. We never found them in the same place twice.

Below the blue sharks there appeared great tunas with long fins. Perhaps they had been there since the beginning, but it was the first time we noticed them. Above us flying fish gamboled, adding a discordant touch of gaiety to what was becoming a tragedy for us. Dumas and I ransacked our memories for advices on how to frighten off sharks. *"Gesticulate wildly," said a lifeguard.* We flailed our arms. The gray did not falter. *"Give 'em a flood of bubbles," said a helmet diver.* Dumas waited until the shark had reached his nearest point and released a heavy exhalation. The shark did not react. *"Shout as loud as you can," said Hans Hass.* We hooted until our voices cracked. The shark

appeared deaf. *"Cupric acetate tablets fastened to leg and belt will keep sharks away if you go into the drink," said an Air Force briefing officer.* Our friend swam through the copper-stained water without a wink. His cold, tranquil eye appraised us. He seemed to know what he wanted, and he was in no hurry.

A small dreadful thing occurred. The tiny pilot fish on the shark's snout tumbled off his station and wriggled to Dumas. It was a long journey for the little fellow, quite long enough for us to speculate on his purpose. The mite butterflied in front of Dumas's mask. Dumas shook his head as if to dodge a mosquito. The little pilot fluttered happily, moving with the mask, inside which Dumas focused in cross-eyed agony.

Instinctively I felt my comrade move close to me, and I saw his hand held out clutching his belt knife. Beyond the camera and the knife, the gray shark retreated some distance, turned, and glided at us head-on.

We did not believe in knifing sharks, but the final moment had come, when knife and camera were all we had. I had my hand on the camera button and it was running, without my knowledge that I was filming the oncoming beast. The flat snout grew larger and there was only the head. I was flooded with anger. With all my strength I thrust the camera and banged his muzzle. I felt the wash of a heavy body flashing past and the shark was twelve feet away, circling us as slowly as before, unharmed and expressionless. I thought, *Why doesn't he go to the whale? The nice juicy whale. What did we ever do to him?*

The blue sharks now climbed up and joined us. Dumas and I decided to take a chance on the surface. We swam up and thrust our masks out of the water. The *Élie Monnier* was three hundred yards away, under the wind. We waved wildly and saw no reply from the ship. We believed that floating on the surface with one's head out of the water is the classic method of being eaten away. Hanging there, one's legs could be plucked like bananas. I looked down. The three sharks were rising toward us in a concerted attack.

We dived and faced them. The sharks resumed the circling maneuver. As long as we were a fathom or two down, they hesitated to approach. It would have been an excellent idea for us to navigate toward the ship. However, without landmarks, or a wrist compass, we could not follow course.

Dumas and I took a position with each man's head watching the other man's flippers, in the theory that the sharks preferred to strike at feet. Dumas made quick spurts to the surface to wave his arms for a few seconds. We evolved a system of taking turns for brief appeals on the surface, while the low man pulled his knees up against his chest and watched the sharks. A blue closed in on Dumas's feet while he was above. I yelled. Dumas turned over and resolutely faced the shark. The beast broke off and went back to the circle. When we went up to look we were dizzy and disoriented from spinning around underwater, and had to revolve our heads like a lighthouse beacon to find the *Élie Monnier*. We saw no evidence that our shipmates had spied us.

We were nearing exhaustion, and cold was claiming the outer layers of our bodies. I reckoned we had been down over a half hour. Any moment we expected the constriction of air in our mouthpieces, a sign that the air supply nears exhaustion. When it came, we would reach behind our backs and turn the emergency supply valve. There was five minutes' worth of air in the emergency ration. When that was gone, we could abandon our mouthpieces and make mask dives, holding our breath. That would quicken the pace, redouble the drain on our strength, and leave us facing tireless, indestructible creatures that never needed breath. The movements of the sharks grew agitated. They ran around us, working all their strong propulsive fins, turned down and disappeared. We could not believe it. Dumas and I stared at each other. A shadow

fell across us. We looked up and saw the hull of the *Élie Monnier's* launch. Our mates had seen our signals and had located our bubbles. The sharks ran when they saw the launch.

We flopped into the boat, weak and shaken. The crew were as distraught as we were. The ship had lost sight of our bubbles and drifted away. We could not believe what they told us; we had been in the water only twenty minutes. The camera was jammed by contact with the shark's nose.

On board the *Élie Monnier*, Dumas grabbed a rifle and jumped into the small boat to visit the whale. He found it faintly alive. We saw a brown body separate from the whale and speed away, a shark. Dumas rowed around to the whale's head and gave the *coup de grâce*, point-blank with a dum-dum bullet. The head sank with the mouth open, streaming bubbles from the blowhole. Sharks twisted in the red water, striking furiously at the whale. Dumas plunged his hands in the red froth and fastened a noose to the tail, which is what he had started out to do when we were diverted by our friend.

We hoisted the whale aboard and were impressed by the moon-shaped shark bites. The inch-thick leather of the whale had been scooped out cleanly, without rips, ten or fifteen pounds of blubber at a bite. The sharks had waited until we were cheated away from them before they struck the easy prey.

Standing for Dakar we met a porpoise herd. Dumas harpooned one in the back. It swam like a dog on a tether, surrounded by the pack. The mammals demonstrated a decided sense of solidarity. Save that the whale was now a porpoise, Dumas and Tailliez dived into a re-enactment of the previous drama. This time the dinghy carefully followed their air bubbles.

I watched the porpoise swimming on its leash like a bait goat a lion hunter has tied to a stake. The sharks went for the porpoise. It was cruelty to an animal but we were involved with a serious study of sharks, and had to carry it out. The sharks circled the porpoise as they had circled us. We stood on deck remarking on the cowardice of sharks, beasts as powerful as anything on earth, indifferent to pain, and splendidly equipped as killers. Yet the brutes timidly waited to attack. Attack was too good a word for them. The porpoise had no weapons and he was dying in a circle of bullies.

At nightfall Dumas sent a *coup de grâce* into the porpoise. When it was dead, a shark passed closely by the mammal, and left entrails in the water. The other sharks passed across the porpoise, muddying the sea with blood. There was no striking and biting. The sharks spooned away the solid flesh like warm butter, without interrupting their speed.

Sharks have never attacked us with resolution, unless the overtures of our friend and the two blues may be called pressing an attack. Without being at all certain, we suppose that sharks more boldly strike objects floating on the surface. It is there that the beast finds its usual meals, sick or injured fish and garbage thrown from ships. The sharks we have met took a long time surveying submerged men. A diver is an animal they may sense to be dangerous. Aqualung bubbles may also be a deterrent.

After seeing sharks swim on unshaken with harpoons through the head, deep spear gashes on the body and even after sharp explosions near their brains, we place no reliance in knives as defensive arms. We believe better protection is our "shark billy," a stout wooden staff four feet long, studded with nail tips at the business end. It is employed, somewhat in the manner of the lion tamer's chair, by thrusting the studs into the hide of an approaching shark. The nails keep the billy from sliding off the slippery leather, but do not penetrate far enough to irritate the animal. The diver may thus hold a shark at his proper distance. We carried shark billies on wrist thongs during hundreds of dives in the Red Sea, where sharks were commonplace. We have never had occasion to apply the billy, and it may prove to be merely another theoretical defense against the creature which has eluded man's understanding.

For Discussion

1. Does Jacques-Yves Cousteau come to a definite conclusion about the behavior of sharks? What is it? Do you feel that it is an inference that derives logically from the facts of his experience? Give reasons for your answer.

2. Why has the shark as a species escaped the changes of evolution that affect other creatures of the land and sea? What are the features that suit the shark for survival?

3. Would you classify Jacques-Yves Cousteau as a scientist or as an adventurer or as both? In what ways is he a scientist? In what ways an adventurer?

4. Of what use to civilization are Jacques-Yves Cousteau's observations on the habits of the shark? Do you think that knowledge of the life that exists in the depths of the ocean is as important to us as knowledge about outer space?

5. Although Jacques-Yves Cousteau's account of the shark remains mostly objective, are there instances of self-revelation from which the reader can derive the character of the author? Does he have a sense of humor? Give illustrations. Does he take unnecessary risks? Does he conduct his study of sharks methodically, or does he follow his whims? What other characteristics can you find?

The Dream Comes True

TENZING NORGAY AND JAMES RAMSEY ULLMAN

*On May 29, 1953, a British expedition led by Sir John Hunt
successfully reached the summit of Mount Everest, the world's highest
peak, in the Himalayas. The two men who actually made the complete
ascent were Edmund Hillary, a New Zealand beekeeper, and Tenzing
Norgay, a Sherpa mountain guide. Sir John Hunt in his book* The
Conquest of Everest *praises Tenzing Norgay's role in the marvelous
achievement of conquering the mountain that had beaten back all
previous attempts to reach the top. In this selection Tenzing Norgay
gives his account of the triumphant climax of the climb. Born in the
village of Tami, Nepal, in 1914, he ran away from home in 1935 to
become a porter on a British mountain-climbing party. With the
years his skill increased until his reputation was worldwide, and great
climbers sought his assistance. His accomplishment with Edmund
Hillary won him the George Medal. "The Dream Comes True" is
the thrilling account of the last stages of an accomplishment of which
generations of mountain climbers had dreamed.*

WHEN IT first grew light it was still blowing, but by eight o'clock the wind had dropped. We looked at each other and nodded. We would make our try.

But a bad thing had happened during the night: Pemba had been sick. And it was clear that he could not go higher. Now, only Ang Nyima was left of the original Sherpa[1] team

of three. This meant that the rest of us would all have to carry heavier loads, which would make our going slower and harder; but there was nothing we could do about it. A little before nine Lowe, Gregory and Ang Nyima started off, each of them carrying more than forty pounds and breathing oxygen, and about an hour later Hillary and I followed, with fifty pounds apiece. The idea of this was that our support party would do the slow hard work of cutting steps in the ice, and then we would be able to follow at our own pace, without tiring ourselves. . . . Or maybe I should say without tiring ourselves *too much*.

[1] *Sherpa* The Sherpas are a Tibetan tribe living in the foothills of the Himalaya mountains who serve as guides to climbing expeditions. Tenzing Norgay, a citizen of Nepal, is himself a member of the Sherpa tribe.

We crossed the frozen rocks of the col.[2] Then we went up the snow-slope beyond and a long couloir, or gully, leading toward the southeast ridge. As had been planned, the fine steps cut by the others made the going easier for us, and by the time they reached the foot of the ridge—about noon—we had caught up with them. Then slowly we went on up the ridge. It was quite steep, but not too narrow, with rock that sloped upward and gave a good foothold, if you were careful about the loose snow that lay over it. We came to the highest point that Colonel Hunt and Da Namgyal had reached two days before, and there in the snow were the tent, food and oxygen tanks which they had left for us. These now we had to add to our own loads, and from there on we were carrying weights of up to sixty pounds.

The ridge grew steeper, and our pace was now very slow. Then the snow became thicker, covering the rocks deeply, and it was necessary to cut steps again. Most of the time Lowe did this, leading the way with his swinging ax, while the rest of us followed. But by two in the afternoon all of us, with our great loads, were beginning to get tired, and it was agreed that we must soon find a camping place.

"Hey, where are you leading us to?" asked Lowe and Gregory. "We have to go down."

"It can't be far now," I said. "Only five minutes."

But still we climbed, still we didn't get there. And I kept saying, "Only five minutes . . . Only five minutes."

"Yes, but how many five minutes are there?" Ang Nyima asked in disgust.

Then at last we got there. It was a partly level spot in the snow, down a little from the exposed ridge and in the shelter of a rocky cliff; and there we dropped our loads. With a quick "Good-by—good luck," Lowe, Gregory and Ang Nyima started down for the col, and Hillary and I were left alone. It was then the

middle of the afternoon, and we were at a height of about 27,900 feet. The summit of Lhotse, the fourth-highest peak in the world, at which we had looked up every day during the long expedition, was now below us. Over to the southeast, Makalu [3] was below us. Everything we could see for hundreds of miles was below us, except only the top of Kangchenjunga,[3] far to the east—and the white ridge climbing on above us into the sky.

We started pitching the highest camp that has ever been made. And it took us almost until dark. First we chopped away at the ice to try to make our sleeping place a little more level. Then we struggled with frozen ropes and canvas and tied the ropes around oxygen cylinders to hold them down. Everything took five times as long as it would have in a place where there was enough air to breathe; but at last we got the tent up, and when we crawled in it was not too bad. There was only a light wind, and inside it was not too cold to take off our gloves. Hillary checked the oxygen sets, while I got our little stove going and made warm coffee and lemon juice. Our thirst was terrible, and we drank them down like two camels. Later we had some soup, sardines, biscuits and canned fruit, but the fruit was frozen so hard we had first to thaw it out over the stove.

We had managed to flatten out the rocks and ice under the tent, but not all at one level. Half the floor was about a foot higher than the other half, and now Hillary spread his sleeping bag on the upper shelf and I put mine on the lower. When we were in them each of us rolled over close against the canvas, so that the weight of our bodies would help hold it in place. Mostly the wind was still not too bad, but sometimes great gusts would come out of nowhere and the tent would seem ready to fly away. Lying in the dark, we talked of our plans for the next day. Then, breathing the "night oxygen," we tried to sleep. Even in our

---

[2] *col* A mountain pass.

[3] *Makalu, Kangchenjunga* Other peaks.

eiderdown bags we both wore all our clothes, and I kept on my Swiss reindeer boots. At night most climbers take off their boots, because they believe this helps the circulation in the feet; but at high altitudes I myself prefer to keep them on. Hillary, on the other hand, took his off and laid them next to his sleeping bag.

The hours passed. I dozed and woke, dozed and woke. And each time I woke, I listened. By midnight there was no wind at all. "God is good to us," I thought. "Chomolungma is good to us." The only sound was that of our own breathing as we sucked at our oxygen.

At about three-thirty in the morning we began to stir. I got the stove going and boiled snow for lemon juice and coffee, and we ate a little of the food left over from the night before. There was still no wind. When, a while later, we opened the tent-flap, everything was clear and quiet in the early morning light. It was then that I pointed down and showed Hillary the tiny dot that was the Thyangboche Monastery, 16,000 feet below. "God of my father and mother," I prayed in my heart, "be good to me now—today."

But the first thing that happened was a bad thing. Hillary's boots, lying all night outside his sleeping bag, had frozen, and now they were like two lumps of black iron. For a whole hour we had to hold them over the stove, pulling and kneading them, until the tent was full of the smell of scorched leather and we were both panting as if we were already climbing the peak. Hillary was very upset, both at the delay and at the danger to his feet. "I'm afraid I may get frostbitten, like Lambert," [4] he said. But at last the boots were soft enough for him to put on, and then we prepared the rest of our gear. For this last day's climbing I was

dressed in all sorts of clothes that came from many places. My boots, as I have said, were Swiss; my windjacket and various other items had been issued by the British. But the socks I was wearing had been knitted by Ang Lahmu. My sweater had been given me by Mrs. Henderson of the Himalayan Club. My wool helmet was the old one that had been left to me by Earl Denman. And, most important of all, the red scarf around my neck was Raymond Lambert's. At the end of the fall expedition he had given it to me and smiled and said, "Here, maybe you can use it sometime."

At six-thirty, when we crawled from the tent, it was still clear and windless. We had pulled three pairs of gloves onto our hands—silk, wool and windproof; and now we fastened our crampons to our boots and onto our backs slung the forty pounds of oxygen apparatus that would be the whole load for each of us during the climb. Around my ax were still the four flags, tightly wrapped. And in the pocket of my jacket was a small red-and-blue pencil.

"All ready?"

"*Ah chah*. Ready."

And off we went.

Hillary's boots were still stiff, and his feet cold, so he asked me to take the lead. And for a while that is how we went on the rope—up from the campsite to the southeast ridge and then on along the ridge toward the south summit. By now Hillary's feet were feeling better, so we changed places on the rope; and we kept doing this from then on, with first one of us leading the way and then the other, in order to share the work of kicking and chopping.

Up until now the climbing—if not the weather—had been much the same as I remembered from the year before: along the steep broken ridge, with a rock precipice on the left and snow cornices hiding another precipice on the right. But now, just below the south summit, the ridge broadened out into a sort of snow face, so that the steepness was not so much to the sides as straight behind us, and

---

[4] *Raymond Lambert* Swiss mountaineer whom Tenzing had accompanied on an earlier, and unsuccessful, ascent of Everest.

we were climbing up an almost vertical white wall. The worst part of it was that the snow was not firm, but kept sliding down, sliding down—and we with it—until I thought, "Next time it will keep sliding, and we will go all the way to the bottom of the mountain." For me this was the one really bad place on the whole climb, because it was not only a matter of what you yourself did, but what the snow under you did, and this you could not control. It was one of the most dangerous places I had ever been on a mountain. Even now, when I think of it, I can still feel as I felt then, and the hair almost stands up on the back of my hands.

At last we got up it, though, and at nine o'clock we were on the south summit. For ten minutes we rested there, looking up at what was still ahead. There was not much further to go—only about 300 feet of ridge—but it was narrower and steeper than it had been below, and, though not impossible-looking, would certainly not be easy. On the left, as before, was the precipice falling away to the Western Cwm, 8,000 feet below, where we could now see the tiny dots that were the tents of Camp Four. And on the right were still the snow cornices, hanging out over a 10,000-foot drop to the Kangshung Glacier. If we were to get to the top it would have to be along a narrow, twisting line between precipice and cornices: never too far to the left, never too far to the right—or it would be the end of us.

One thing we had eagerly been waiting for happened on the south summit. Almost at the same moment we each came to the end of the first of our two bottles of oxygen, and now we were able to dump them here, which reduced the weight we were carrying from forty to only twenty pounds. Also, as we left the south summit, another good thing happened. We found that the snow beyond it was firm and sound. This could make all the difference on the stretch that we still had to go.

"Everything all right?"

"*Ah chah*. All right."

From the south summit we first had to go down a little. Then up, up, up. All the time the danger was that the snow would slip, or that we would get too far out on a cornice that would then break away; so we moved just one at a time, taking turns going ahead, while the second one wrapped the rope around his ax and fixed the ax in the snow as an anchor. The weather was still fine. We were not too tired. But every so often, as had happened all the way, we would have trouble breathing and have to stop and clear away the ice that kept forming in the tubes of our oxygen sets. In regard to this, I must say in all honesty that I do not think Hillary is quite fair in the story he later told, indicating that I had more trouble than he with breathing and that without his help I might have been in serious difficulty. In my opinion our difficulties were about the same—and luckily never too great—and we each helped and were helped by the other in equal measure.

Anyhow, after each short stop we kept going, twisting always higher along the ridge between the cornices and the precipices. And at last we came to what might be the last big obstacle below the top. This was a cliff of rock rising straight up out of the ridge and blocking it off, and we had already known about it from aerial photographs and from seeing it through binoculars from Thyangboche. Now it was a question of how to get over or around it, and we could find only one possible way. This was along a steep, narrow gap between one side of the rock and the inner side of an adjoining cornice, and Hillary, now going first, worked his way up it, slowly and carefully, to a sort of platform above. While climbing, he had to press backwards with his feet against the cornice, and I belayed him from below as strongly as I could, for there was great danger of the ice giving way. Luckily, however, it did not. Hillary got up safely to the top of the rock and then held the rope while I came after.

Here again I must be honest and say that I

do not feel his account, as told in *The Conquest of Everest*, is wholly accurate. For one thing, he has written that this gap up the rock wall was about forty feet high, but in my judgment it was little more than fifteen. Also, he gives the impression that it was only he who really climbed it on his own, and that he then practically pulled me, so that I "finally collapsed exhausted at the top, like a giant fish when it has just been hauled from the sea after a terrible struggle." Since then I have heard plenty about that "fish," and I admit I do not like it. For it is the plain truth that no one pulled or hauled me up the gap. I climbed it myself, just as Hillary had done; and if he was protecting me with the rope while I was doing it, this was no more than I had done for him. In speaking of this I must make one thing very plain. Hillary is my friend. He is a fine climber and a fine man, and I am proud to have gone with him to the top of Everest. But I do feel that in his story of our final climb he is not quite fair to me; that all the way through he indicates that when things went well it was his doing and when things went badly it was mine. For this is simply not true. Nowhere do I make the suggestion that I could have climbed Everest by myself; and I do not think Hillary should suggest that he could have, or that I could not have done it without his help. All the way up and down we helped, and were helped by, each other—and that was the way it should be. But we were not leader and led. We were partners.

On top of the rock cliff we rested again. Certainly, after the climb up the gap we were both a bit breathless, but after some slow pulls at the oxygen I am feeling fine. I look up; the top is very close now; and my heart thumps with excitement and joy. Then we are on our way again. Climbing again. There are still the cornices on our right and the precipice on our left, but the ridge is now less steep. It is only a row of snowy humps, one beyond the other, one higher than the other. But we are still afraid of the cornices and, instead of following the

ridge all the way, cut over to the left, where there is now a long snow slope above the precipice. About a hundred feet below the top we come to the highest bare rocks. There is enough almost level space here for two tents, and I wonder if men will ever camp in this place, so near the summit of the earth. I pick up two small stones and put them in my pocket to bring back to the world below. Then the rocks, too, are beneath us. We are back among the snowy humps. They are curving off to the right, and each time we pass one I wonder, "Is the next the last one? Is the next the last?" Finally we reach a place where we can see past the humps, and beyond them is the great open sky and brown plains. We are looking down the far side of the mountain upon Tibet. Ahead of us now is only one more hump—the last hump. It is not a pinnacle. The way to it is an easy snow slope, wide enough for two men to go side by side. About thirty feet away we stop for a minute and look up. Then we go on. . . .

I have thought much about what I will say now: of how Hillary and I reached the summit of Everest. Later, when we came down from the mountain, there was much foolish talk about who got there first. Some said it was I, some Hillary. Some that only one of us got there— or neither. Still others that one of us had to drag the other up. All this was nonsense. And in Katmandu,[5] to put a stop to such talk, Hillary and I signed a statement in which we said, "we reached the summit almost together." We hoped this would be the end of it. But it was not the end. People kept on asking questions and making up stories. They pointed to the "almost" and said, "What does that mean?" Mountaineers understand that there is no sense to such a question; that when two men are on the same rope they are *together*, and that is all there is to it. But other people did not understand. In India and Nepal, I am sorry to

[5] *Katmandu* Capital of Nepal.

Tenzing Norgay climbing in the Himalayas

say, there has been great pressure on me to say that I reached the summit before Hillary. And all over the world I am asked, "Who got there first? Who got there first?"

Again I say: it is a foolish question. The answer means nothing. And yet it is a question that has been asked so often—that has caused so much talk and doubt and misunderstanding—that I feel, after long thought, that the answer should be given. As will be clear, it is not for my own sake that I give it. Nor is it for Hillary's. It is for the sake of Everest—the prestige of Everest—and for the generations who will come after us. "Why," they will say, "should there be a mystery to this thing? Is there something to be ashamed of? To be hidden? Why can we not know the truth?" . . . Very well: now they will know the truth. Everest is too great, too precious, for anything but the truth.

A little below the summit Hillary and I stopped. We looked up. Then we went on. The rope that joined us was thirty feet long, but I held most of it in loops in my hand, so that there was only about six feet between us. I was

not thinking of "first" and "second." I did not say to myself, "There is a golden apple up there. I will push Hillary aside and run for it." We went on slowly, steadily. And then we were there. Hillary stepped on top first. And I stepped up after him.

So there it is: the answer to the "great mystery." And if, after all the talk and argument, the answer seems quiet and simple, I can only say that that is as it should be. Many of my own people, I know, will be disappointed at it. They have given a great and false importance to the idea that it must be I who was "first." These people have been good and wonderful to me, and I owe them much. But I owe more to Everest—and to the truth. If it is a discredit to me that I was a step behind Hillary, then I must live with that discredit. But I do not think it was that. Nor do I think that, in the end, it will bring discredit on me that I tell the story. Over and over again I have asked myself, "What will future generations think of us if we allow the facts of our achievement to stay shrouded in mystery? Will they not feel ashamed of us—two comrades in life and death— who have something to hide from the world?" And each time I asked it the answer was the same: "Only the truth is good enough for the future. Only the truth is good enough for Everest."

Now the truth is told. And I am ready to be judged by it.

We stepped up. We were there. The dream had come true. . . .

What we did first was what all climbers do when they reach the top of their mountain. We shook hands. But this was not enough for Everest. I waved my arms in the air and then threw them around Hillary, and we thumped each other on the back until, even with the oxygen, we were almost breathless. Then we looked around. It was eleven-thirty in the morning, the sun was shining, and the sky was the deepest blue I have ever seen. Only a gentle breeze was blowing, coming from the direction of Tibet, and the plume of snow that always blows from Everest's summit was very small. Looking down the far side of the mountain, I could see all the familiar landmarks from the earlier expeditions. Then, turning, I looked down the long way we ourselves had come: past the south summit, the long ridge, the South Col; onto the Western Cwm, the icefall, the Khumbu Glacier; all the way down to Thyangboche and on to the valleys and hills of my homeland.

Beyond them, and around us on every side, were the great Himalayas, stretching away through Nepal and Tibet. For the closer peaks—giants like Lhotse, Nuptse and Makalu—you now had to look sharply downward to see their summits. And farther away, the whole sweep of the greatest range on earth—even Kangchenjunga itself—seemed only like little bumps under the spreading sky. It was such a sight as I had never seen before and would never see again: wild, wonderful and terrible. But terror was not what I felt. I loved the mountains too well for that. I loved Everest too well. At that great moment for which I had waited all my life my mountain did not seem to me a lifeless thing of rock and ice, but warm and friendly and living. She was a mother hen, and the other mountains were chicks under her wings. I too, I felt, had only to spread my own wings to cover and shelter the brood that I loved.

We turned off our oxygen. Even there on top of the world it was possible to live without it, so long as we were not exerting ourselves. We cleared away the ice that had formed on our masks, and I popped a bit of sweet into my mouth. Then we replaced the masks. But we did not turn on the oxygen again until we were ready to leave the top. Hillary took out his camera, which he had been carrying under his clothing to keep it from freezing, and I unwound the four flags from around my ax. They were tied together on a string, which was fastened to the blade of the ax, and now I held the ax up and Hillary took my picture. Actually he took three, and I think it was lucky,

in those difficult conditions, that one came out so well. The order of the flags from top to bottom was United Nations, British, Nepalese, Indian; and the same sort of people who have made trouble in other ways have tried to find political meaning in this too. All I can say is that on Everest I was not thinking about politics. If I had been, I suppose I would have put the Indian or Nepalese flag highest—though that in itself would have been a bad problem for me. As it is, I am glad that the UN flag was on top. For I like to think that our victory was not only for ourselves—not only for our own nations—but for all men everywhere.

I motioned to Hillary that I would now take his picture. But for some reason he shook his head; he did not want it. Instead, he began taking more pictures himself, around and down on all sides of the peak, and meanwhile I did another thing that had to be done on the top of our mountain. From my pocket I took the package of sweets I had been carrying. I took the little red-and-blue pencil that my daughter Nima had given me. And scraping a hollow in the snow, I laid them there. Seeing what I was doing. Hillary handed me a small cloth cat, black and with white eyes, that Hunt had given him as a mascot, and I put this beside them. In his story of our climb Hillary says it was a crucifix that Hunt gave him and that he left it on top; but if this was so I did not see it. He gave me only the cloth cat. All I laid in the snow was the cat, the pencil and the sweets. "At home," I thought, "we offer sweets to those who are near and dear to us. Everest has always been dear to me, and now it is near too." As I covered up the offerings I said a silent prayer. And I gave my thanks. Seven times I had come to the mountain of my dream, and on this, the seventh, with God's help, the dream had come true.

"*Thuji chey, Chomolungma*. I am grateful. . . ."

We had now been on top almost fifteen minutes. It was time to go. Needing my ax for the descent, I could not leave it there with the flags; so I untied the string that held them, spread the flags across the summit, and buried the ends of the string as deeply as I could in the snow. A few days later planes of the Indian Air Force flew around the peak, making photographs, but the fliers reported they could see nothing that had been left there. Perhaps they were too far off. Or perhaps the wind had blown the flags away. I do not know.

Before starting down we looked around once more. Had Mallory and Irvine reached the top before they died? Could there be any sign of them? We looked, but we could see nothing. Still they were in my thoughts, and I am sure in Hillary's too. All those who had gone before us were in my thoughts—sahibs [6] and Sherpas, English and Swiss—all the great climbers, the brave men, who for thirty-three years had dreamed and challenged, fought and failed on this mountain, and whose efforts and knowledge and experience had made our victory possible. Our companions below were in my thoughts, for without them, too—without their help and sacrifice—we could never have been where we were that day. And closest of all was one figure, one companion: Lambert. He was so near, so real to me, that he did not seem to be in my thoughts at all, but actually standing there beside me. Any moment now I would turn and see his big bear face grinning at me. I would hear his voice saying, "Ça va bien, Tenzing. Ça va bien!" [7]

Well, at least his red scarf was there. I pulled it more tightly around my throat. "When I get back home," I told myself, "I will send it to him." And I did.

Since the climbing of Everest all sorts of questions have been put to me, and not all of them have been political. From the people of the East there have been many that have to do with religion and the supernatural. "Was the Lord Buddha [8] on the top?" I have been asked.

Or, "Did you see the Lord Siva?" [8] From many sides, among the devout and orthodox, there has been great pressure upon me to say that I had some vision or revelation. But here again—even though it may be disappointing to many—I can tell only the truth; and this is no, that on top of Everest I did not see anything supernatural or feel anything superhuman. What I felt was a great closeness to God, and that was enough for me. In my deepest heart I thanked God. And as we turned to leave the summit I prayed to Him for something very real and very practical: that, having given us our victory, he would get us down off the mountain alive.

We turned on our oxygen sets. We started off. And though we were anxious to get down as quickly as possible, we went slowly and carefully, because we knew that we were more tired than before, that our reactions were less sure, and that most accidents on mountains happen when men are tired and careless on the way down. Kick-step, kick-step we went in the steep snow, mostly using the track we had made on the climb up. When we got to the rocky cliff and the gap beside it we got down with little trouble. In fact I just let go and jumped for part of the way. Then we were on the ridge again, kicking and sliding, and in an hour we had reached the south summit. Through this part of the descent Hillary went first and I second, holding the rope tight when there was any danger. And though we were both tired, we were not exhausted. The thing that bothered us most was thirst; for the water in our flasks had frozen, and to have eaten snow would have only made it worse for our mouths and throats.

At the south summit we rested a little. Then came the steep snow wall just below it, and, even more than on the way up, it was dangerous and terrifying. In front of me Hillary was at

---

[6] *sahibs* The Europeans who had led previous attempts to climb Everest.

[7] *Ça va bien"* French: "It's going well."

[8] *Lord Buddha, Lord Siva* Gautama Buddha, who lived about 500 years before Christ, was an Indian prince and philosopher who founded the Buddhist religion, of which the Sherpas are members. Siva is one of the chief Buddhist divinities.

the same time trying to go down and to hold himself back, and his knees were so bent that his buttocks often touched the snow. Above him, I was every moment gripping the rope and bracing myself in case he should slip, for beneath him here was nothing but the Kangshung Glacier, 10,000 feet below. In the end, though, we got down all right. Now the worst was behind us. A little farther on we picked up the two oxygen bottles that had been left by Bourdillon and Evans; and the timing of this was just right, because our own supply was now almost gone. At about two o'clock we reached the high tent, where we stopped and rested again and I heated some sweet lemon juice over the stove. This was the first drink we had had for hours, and it was like new life pouring down into our bodies.

Then we went on down from Camp Nine. Along the ridge, past the old Swiss tent, down the big couloir of the snow slope that led to the South Col. We were sometimes able to use our old steps, but in other places the wind had wiped them out, and it was so steep that, even with our crampons, we had to cut new holds to keep from sliding off. Here we changed places, and I went first on the rope, hacking and chopping for what seemed like days instead of hours. But by now we could see the tents on the col and little moving dots around them. Slowly the tents and the dots grew bigger. And then at last we came down onto the easier snow, just above the col, and George Lowe, in the lead of those below, came up to meet us. He threw his arms around us, gave us hot coffee to drink, and then, with the help of the others, led us down to the camp.

Gregory had descended earlier that day. But Noyce had come up with the Sherpa, Pasang Phutar, and they and Lowe did everything possible to make us warm and comfortable. Lowe had given us coffee. Now Noyce brought us tea. And he must have been excited and tipped the stove while he was making it, for it was full of kerosene; but it didn't matter—it didn't matter at all—and I thought, as I was drinking it: "It tastes as sweet as buttered milk, because it is mixed with love and kindness." The others were asking us questions, of course. But just then we could answer only a few. We had to rest. It was getting dark and cold, and we crept into our sleeping bags—Hillary in one tent with Lowe and Noyce and I in another with Pasang. I lay still, with my "night oxygen," and tried to sleep. I felt *ah chah*—O.K. But tired. It was hard to think or feel anything.

"The real happiness," I thought, "will come later."

For Discussion

1. What kind of man is Tenzing Norgay? Do you think that he longs for fame? Does he regard Mount Everest as simply a mountain? How do you account for his attitude?

2. In the sentence, "Certainly, after the climb up the gap we were both a bit breathless, but after some slow pulls at the oxygen I am feeling fine," the verb tense changes from the past to the present, and the passage that follows remains in the present. Can you suggest reasons for this sudden shift? What is the effect?

3. Norgay digresses to explain why it is not important who reached the top of the mountain first. Do you agree with him, or do you feel that for the future, the record must be accurate?

4. From this selection can you gather convincing evidence to prove that mountain climbing is a test of the body and spirit that, when successful, becomes both a physical and spiritual triumph?

5. Would you classify Tenzing Norgay as a true adventurer or simply as a guide who earns a living climbing mountains? Explain your answer.

The Strange Death of Louis Slotin

STEWART ALSOP AND RALPH E. LAPP

Man's ingenuity in harnessing the raw forces of nature sometimes creates new problems and dangers. Electricity, which men manufacture, brings power and light; yet direct contact with its current can kill. So with nuclear energy. Atomic fission has already brought a major breakthrough in technological progress, but the grim presence of deadly radioactivity hangs over civilization like a death's head. Louis Slotin was an early atomic scientist, working on the famous Manhattan Project. His daring and sacrifice are a testimonial to the dedication of scientists and to the fact that the laboratory can be as dangerous and adventurous as jungle, mountain, sky, or sea.

DR. LOUIS SLOTIN, a young and brilliant atomic scientist, began to die at precisely twenty minutes past three o'clock, on the afternoon of May 21, 1946. The story of how he began to die, and of what happened afterward—which can only now be fully told—is in some ways a rather horrible story. Yet, if only because it helps strip the mystery from the most terrifying effect of atomic weapons—the invisible killer, nuclear radiation—Louis Slotin's story is worth telling all the same.

The place where Louis Slotin began to die was a laboratory in a canyon near Los Alamos, the war-built town in New Mexico where the world's first atomic bomb was made. A few minutes after he began to die, Doctor Slotin, with the precision of a trained scientist, drew a careful chart of this laboratory, showing the exact location of its occupants at the time. From this chart, and from the accounts of those who were present and survived, it is possible to reconstruct the scene accurately.

Visualize, then, a large, oblong, white-painted room, unfurnished except for a metal desk near the center, and a table against one wall, bearing the complicated equipment of the atom-bomb-maker's trade. The spring sunshine floods obliquely through the single large window. There are eight people in the room. Their silence is broken only by the staccato clicking of a Geiger counter, as all attention is focused on a short figure standing over the metal desk.

This is Louis Slotin, thirty-four years old, five feet six inches in height, slender, wiry, his face heavily bronzed by the New Mexico sun, his black hair already graying a little at the temples. He is wearing an open sports shirt, a rather gaudy Mexican belt and khaki trousers tucked into cowboy boots. Through thick, horn-rimmed spectacles—which betray the scientist and the intellectual, despite the cowboy boots—he is peering intently at certain objects on the desk.

These are two hollow, silvery-gray half globes of metal, which Slotin is deliberately manipulating closer to each other, using an ordinary screw driver as a lever. These hunks of metal are the guts of an atomic bomb.

Standing behind Slotin is a fellow scientist—Scientist X, we shall call him—a quiet-mannered, pleasant-faced man, also thirty-four years old. Scientist X has his hand resting casually on Slotin's shoulder, and he is leaning forward with intense interest—he has never seen this experiment before.

The six other people in the room are laboratory assistants, technicians and others gathered more or less by chance to watch the experiment. Two are standing in front of the desk, at a distance of about six feet. The four others are grouped behind the desk, at a distance of eight feet or more. The scene is a casual one. Like Slotin, the others are dressed informally, in open shirts or sweaters. Slotin himself appears confident, almost gay. He loves this experiment—"tickling the dragon's tail," he calls it—and he has already performed it at least forty times. Even so, there is a certain tension in the room. Those present are aware that manipulating the guts of an atomic bomb is no child's play.

Slotin has his ear cocked to the click of the Geiger counter, and he also glances frequently at an instrument called a "neutron monitor," which is recording on a roll of paper, in a thin, wavy line of red ink, the radiation emitted by the lumps of metal. As Slotin slowly moves the lumps, the red line staggers upward and the Geiger counter clicks erratically, always a little faster, like a deranged clock.

Suddenly the Geiger counter begins to click insanely, and then stops dead. All in a moment, the people in the room sense rather than see a strange blue glow, stronger than the spring sunlight. Instantly, Slotin throws himself forward, thrusting the half globes of deadly metal apart with his naked hands. Then he stands up, his face a chalky white beneath the tan.

In a concerted, instinctive, almost somnambulistic movement, the eight people file quickly from the room, without speaking. Some of them are aware of a dry, prickly, sour sensation on their tongues—a sign of excessive radiation. Some of them are no doubt also aware of a little flicker of fear in their hearts. Yet aside from the sour taste, they feel nothing else at all—not even Louis Slotin, who has already begun to die.

To understand what happened, and why, and what it means, it is necessary to know something about Louis Slotin, and the reason he tickled the dragon's tail. The bare facts of Slotin's thirty-four years can be quickly recited.

He was born, Louis Alexander Slotin, in 1912, of prosperous Jewish parents in Winnipeg, Canada. At the tender age of fifteen, he entered Winnipeg's University of Manitoba, and received his master-of-science degree at the equally tender age of twenty-one. He studied physics for four years at the University of London, and got his Ph.D. in 1936.

In 1937 he was in Chicago, apparently on his way home to Winnipeg, when he ran into Prof. William D. Harkins, pioneer atomic chemist of the University of Chicago. Harkins remarked that he badly needed an assistant for cyclotron work, but he had no money to pay an assistant. Slotin immediately went to work for nothing a week—a salary for which he worked for almost two years.

His work at Chicago University led him directly into the Manhattan District, the super-secret wartime atomic project. He worked for

STEWART ALSOP (*1914–*   ) *is an editor and journalist who specializes in political affairs.* RALPH E. LAPP (*1917–*   ) *is a leading American nuclear scientist. During the Second World War he worked on the Manhattan Project which developed the first atomic bomb.*

a time in Chicago, then at Indiana University, and later at Oak Ridge. In late 1943, Slotin came to Los Alamos, when the job of actually putting the atomic bomb together was started, and there he began to tickle the dragon's tail.

So much for the bare facts. The bare facts, of course, do not answer the question: What kind of man was Louis Alexander Slotin?

"No man," John Donne wrote, "is an island unto himself." Yet Louis Slotin was more nearly an island unto himself than most men. He was extraordinarily reserved. "Louis was a sweet kind of guy," one of his former colleagues has remarked, "but no one ever got to know him really well."

Even so, certain well-marked characteristics of the man emerge through the mists of time. In the first place, Slotin was a brave man—but brave in an odd sort of way. "Slotin had a positive hankering for danger," another of those who knew him says. "He seemed to be suffering from some sort of inner tension, and he was always very quiet. But he was downright gay when he was doing something dangerous."

This hankering for danger led Slotin to pester the Manhattan District authorities to allow him to accompany the first atomic bombs to their Japanese targets, as a scientific observer. When the authorities refused, Slotin was deeply depressed for weeks. And the same strange hankering no doubt also led Slotin to become the Manhattan District's chief practitioner of the art of tickling the dragon's tail.

This experiment, it must be understood, was not a kind of scientific Russian roulette which Slotin and the other young physicists at Los Alamos thought up to relieve their boredom. It was a vitally important experiment, absolutely essential to the bomb-making process—and, indeed, it is still essential today.

Fissionable material—uranium 235 and plutonium—is queer stuff. Below a certain size and weight, a lump of this very heavy, greasy-gray metal is no more dangerous than a lump of lead. But it has one special characteristic which may one day destroy civilization as we know it. For if a certain amount of this metal is brought together all in one place, a chain reaction starts within the mass of metal. It is the chain reaction, of course, which lends to the atomic bomb the power to blast and sear a whole city. The amount of the metal required for the chain reaction to start is called a "critical mass"—a "crit," to use the physicists' shorthand.

But how much is a crit? There were and are ways of calculating theoretically the amount of fissionable material required to form a critical mass. But such calculations can never be wholly precise. Moreover, in order to achieve "optimum efficiency"—for which read killing power —in an atomic bomb, the size of the crit had to be determined—and still must—under various conditions.

Even today, for reasons of security, it is necessary to be a little imprecise about the experiment which Louis Slotin performed that May day in 1946—and which his successors are still performing under very different conditions. But it can be said, accurately though unscientifically, that the idea was to shove together lumps of fissionable material in such quantities, and in such a geometric relationship to each other, that the whole amount *just* went critical. In other words, a chain reaction was permitted to begin—thus establishing the crit—but it was stopped before the material became dangerously overcritical. The problem, of course, was to know when to stop.

No one at Los Alamos had any illusions about the danger involved. There was, to be sure, no danger that Los Alamos might be blown off the face of the map if something went wrong. In order to generate true explosive power, the critical mass must somehow be held together by an outside force—this is called "maintaining assembly." Otherwise the power of the chain reaction automatically "disassembles the crit." In the meantime, however, if a true chain reaction is permitted really to get under way, the critical mass of fissionable material becomes briefly but intensely radioactive. It sends out precisely the same lethal radioactive rays as an atomic bomb does when it explodes over a city.

Slotin particularly had good reason to be aware of this danger. Before the day when Slotin tickled the dragon's tail for the last time, at least three people at Los Alamos had fallen victim to the invisible killer. One of these was Slotin's friend and laboratory assistant, Harry Daglian. Slotin spent many hours at his assistant's bedside, during the month that it took Daglian to die.

Particularly after Daglian died, those in authority at Los Alamos worried about the radiation danger. One Nobel Prize winner told Slotin, "I predict you won't last a year if you keep on doing that experiment." But Slotin happily carried on.

"Sure, it's dangerous," Slotin remarked to one colleague, "but it has to be that way." One suspects that Slotin, perhaps unconsciously, wanted it to be that way.

Ironically, on May 21, 1946, Slotin was performing his beloved experiment for what he knew to be the last time. For more than two years he had performed the experiment again and again in different ways and under various conditions. He was particularly proud of the fact that he had been chosen to test the criticality of the world's first atomic bomb—he cherished the receipt for this bomb which he got when he returned it to be exploded at Alamogordo, after having tickled its tail. Now he had been ordered to Bikini, to participate in the bomb tests there. He was eager to be off—

when final orders came to perform the experiment just once more, for the benefit of Scientist X. So Slotin tickled the dragon's tail just once more—and the dragon lashed back to destroy him.

What went wrong? Part of the answer may no doubt be found in Slotin's hankering for danger—such a man may always be tempted to go too far. But part of the answer is also certainly found in the fact that Slotin, at the age of thirty-four, was already an old-fashioned scientist.

Slotin received his whole training as a physicist in the '30's, before the time when national survival depended on the special skills of his kind. It was quite typical of those days that a brilliantly qualified physicist like Slotin should work for nothing a year. In the '30's physicists led a hand-to-mouth existence, dependent for their equipment, their experiments and their livelihood, not on an anxious and munificent Government, but on the sometimes capricious generosity of a few great universities.

In those years physicists learned to perform their experiments with whatever came to hand —even an ordinary screw driver. This cavalier attitude carried over into the well-financed period of the Manhattan District, and men like Slotin had a certain pride in their own casual approach to the great and mysterious forces locked up in matter. After Daglian died, for example, a rather simple spring-actuated safety device was designed, to push the lumps of fissionable material apart as soon as they threatened to become dangerously radioactive.

Slotin would have none of it. He had, he said proudly, "a feeling for the experiment," and besides, he argued, such devices would cause accidents rather than prevent them—the experimenter would come to rely on the safety devices rather than on his own judgment.

Certain photographs which the Atomic Energy Commission recently released provide a striking contrast between present and past. These pictures show two insanely complicated "critical assembly machines"—one is rather coyly called "Topsy" and the other "Godiva" because the assembly is allowed to become only "barely" critical. There is another photograph, of the remote-control panel used to work these machines. It is straight out of George Orwell's "1984"[1]—complete with levers, knobs, three television screens and a blond lady in an aseptic white blouse. The blond lady is, according to the AEC release, "controlling the assembly of Godiva"—at a distance of a quarter of a mile.

In other words, the blond lady is manipulating the guts of an atomic bomb, just as Louis Slotin was doing that day in May when the nuclear age was still young. But in his case, the deadly stuff was right under his nose, and he had no levers, no knobs, no television screens, no remote-control panels. He had his Geiger counter, his neutron monitor, his skill and experience— and his screw driver.

There is no doubt about what happened that day in May or about when it happened. The record of the neutron monitor which Slotin used has been preserved. A thin red-ink line mounts gradually across the paper, showing the amount of radiation emitted by the lumps of metal at each given moment. At precisely 3:20 P.M., the line simply disappears. At this precise point the radiation became so intense that the instrument was forced right off scale.

As for why it happened, no one, not even Slotin himself, was entirely sure. The experiment was almost finished—it was a matter of manipulating one last piece of metal an eighth of an inch from the rest of the assembly. "When the point of criticality was almost reached," one of those present writes, "the piece somehow slipped and the gap was closed." The "somehow" is still unexplained. But the best explanation combines the overconfidence of an overbrave man with Slotin's casual use of an ordinary

screw driver to lever the deadly hunks of metal. In a word, the screw driver slipped.

At any rate, Slotin knew instantly what had happened, and his reaction was instantaneous. When he lunged forword and pulled the chunks of metal apart, he "disassembled the critical mass." If he had not done so, if he had instantly ducked away from the table, he might conceivably have saved himself. It is far more probable that he would have condemned others in the room to death.

"It is unquestionably true," Scientist X has written, "that I and perhaps others of those present owe our lives to his action. I do not know whether this is heroism or not. I suspect that Louis would have objected to such a term."

To understand the meaning of Slotin's action, it is necessary to understand something of the nature of the invisible killer. The gamma rays emitted by a chain reaction penetrate into the body of anyone sufficiently exposed, and kill individual cells deep within the body. A grim peculiarity of radiation injury is that there is a latent period before this killing of the cells becomes apparent. This is because the cells do not die until the periodic cell division—a process which is going on all the time in everyone's body—takes place. Thus in a sense, radiation injury is the opposite of cancer. Cancer kills when the cells divide and reproduce themselves too rapidly. Nuclear radiation kills when the cells fail to divide and do not reproduce themselves at all.

But, even more than in the case of cancer, it is important for all of us who live in the age of nuclear war to understand that nuclear radiation need not be fatal. Everything depends on the size of the "dose." The "dose" is measured in r's, or roentgens, of radiation. When a person receives a radiation injury, the first thing the doctors want to know is whether he has received "LD/50." This is medical shorthand for a "median lethal dose," which causes a 50 per cent average death rate.

---

[1] "1984" George Orwell's satirical novel presents a vision of a mechanized and totalitarian future.

LD/50 has never been precisely determined, simply because there have not been many human guinea pigs on whom to test the human body's resistance to radiation injury. At the time of the accident, it was thought that LD/50 was in the neighborhood of 400 roentgens. The best estimates now place LD/50 at 525 roentgens, plus or minus 75.

The number of roentgens of radiation a person receives depends principally on the power of the radiation source and the time of exposure. When Slotin lunged forward to disperse the critical assembly and break the chain reaction, he sharply reduced the danger to the other people in the room, by reducing both the power of the radiation and the time of exposure of the others. He also, of course, exposed himself to actual physical contact with the lumps of fissionable material at the very moment the chain reaction was taking place.

Within an hour of the accident, all the eight people in the laboratory were taken to the Los Alamos hospital—a temporary, wartime, shack-like, wooden structure—and placed under close observation. Other than Scientist X, the man who had been closest to Slotin was an unmarried fifty-four-year-old technician, who was standing about six feet in front of the metal desk. He was kept in the hospital for two weeks, and he showed certain symptoms of radiation injury, including measurable radio-sodium and radio-phosphorus in his urine. But he felt quite well —and six weeks later this man, who was something of an athlete, was happily hiking six miles in one day without ill effect.

Others who were standing somewhat farther away had even less reason to complain, although everyone in the room had taken a dose of radiation. So much nonsense has been spread abroad about the silent nuclear killer that many people have come to feel that it is absolutely lethal at almost any range. Actually, the athletic technician took a dose of about 100 roentgens, according to later calculations—the same dose he would

have taken if he had been wholly exposed to the radiation effect of a modern, 100-kiloton atom bomb exploding at a distance of 6500 feet.

Despite the technician's rapid and complete recovery, a dose of 100 roentgens is no laughing matter. If Slotin had not reacted so quickly, if the technician had been exposed a little longer, the technician would certainly have suffered as Scientist X suffered—and he might well have died.

Scientist X, remember, was standing with his hand on Louis Slotin's shoulder, watching intently the experiment which he himself would have to perform later, when the accident happened. According to later calculations, he took a dose of about 180 roentgens. This is still well under LD/50, but it is nevertheless in the danger area. It is the same dose he would have taken if he had been about 6000 feet from a modern atomic bomb, only a few hundred feet less than the athletic technician. Where nuclear radiation is concerned, short distances can make an enormous difference.

A courageous and unexcitable man by nature, Scientist X was calm and made no complaints when he was admitted to the hospital. Shortly after being admitted, he vomited once. The feeling of nausea passed away in about ten hours, leaving Scientist X feeling weak and tired, with little appetite, but otherwise well enough. He continued thus for about five days. On the fifth day the delayed effect of the gamma rays on his cell tissue began to make itself felt. His temperature climbed close to 103 degrees, and two blood transfusions were required. For some time he felt terribly drowsy and highly irritable, but his temperature fell gradually, and after the fifteenth day he was well enough to be sent home to rest.

But the gamma rays were not yet through with him. He had lost ten pounds, and for some weeks he tired very easily, and spent upward of sixteen hours in bed each day. On the seventeenth day after the accident an unpleasant experience, which Scientist X had known enough to expect, began. On that day the skin on his left temple and on the left side of his head—which had been most exposed—began to feel sensitive. In the two following days this sensitive feeling increased to the point of acute pain. On the twentieth day Scientist X was combing his hair, and found large tufts coming out in the comb.

Thereafter, his hair came out easily by the handful. He lost almost all the hair on the left side of his head, and his beard also stopped growing over most of his left cheek. But the point to emphasize is that such symptoms were wholly temporary.

The only permanent aftereffect which Scientist X has suffered is a moderate radiation cataract in the left eye, which reduces his vision from 20/20 to 20/40. The fact that he has suffered no other ill effect is underscored by his brilliant subsequent contributions to our atomic-energy program, notably in the development of that most terrible of weapons, the hydrogen bomb.

In short, a man can survive even a vicious attack by the silent radiation killer on his living cell tissue. But Scientist X unquestionably had a close brush with death. Of Louis Slotin, to whom, as he says, he owes his life, Scientist X has written:

"I can perhaps tell you as much about his personality and character as I could in very many words if I merely quote to you his first statement to me when we were alone together in a hospital room. He said, 'I'm sorry I got you into this. I am afraid I have less than a fifty-fifty chance of living. I hope you have better than that.' My own estimate of our chances coincided pretty well with his. I felt I had a pretty good chance. I only hoped he had."

For some days there seemed reason for hope. Slotin vomited twice before he got to the hospital, and in the first twelve hours thereafter he continued to vomit repeatedly. But he, too, like Scientist X, recovered from his initial nausea,

and his only other immediate general symptoms were a slight temperature and feeling of tiredness.

His hands, of course, had taken a terrible dose, since he had used them to shove the metal apart and break the chain reaction. Within three hours Slotin's left hand became very red, swollen and bluish under the nails. Twenty-eight hours after the accident this hand began to blister painfully, and the symptoms spread to his right hand and both arms. From this time on, both arms were packed in ice, to reduce the swelling and the pain. His lower abdomen also became red and tender, and this spread gradually and became more intense.

Yet aside from these local symptoms, Slotin's general condition seemed greatly to improve after the first twenty-four hours. What had happened quickly became known throughout the Manhattan District, and everything possible was done to help him. No fewer than ten doctors were called in to consult on his case. Maj. Gen. Leslie Groves wrote to him: "I have nothing but admiration for your heroic actions. . . . Your quick reactions and disregard for the danger to yourself undoubtedly prevented a much more serious accident."

Groves' letter cheered Slotin, and he was cheered more when Groves ordered a special Army plane to bring his mother and father from Winnipeg to his bedside. When they arrived, they found their son normal, composed and even downright cheerful, despite the pain in his arms. When friends and colleagues came to visit him, he would introduce them to his parents, and then ask, half jokingly, the crucial question: "Well, what's the dose?"

For five days no one knew. But on the fifth day the answer became tragically obvious—the dose was more than LD/50. That morning Slotin had a new complaint—his tongue was sore opposite a tooth which had a gold inlay. The doctors found a small whitish ulceration on his tongue, and immediately suspected the cause. The gold in his tooth was heavily radioactive.

The inlay was capped with gold foil and the pain eased. But this was a bad sign.

There was a worse sign on the same day, when Anna May Dickey, then a nurse in the Los Alamos hospital, took Slotin's blood count. When she looked at the results, she began to weep. She knew the meaning of the sudden, precipitous fall in the leucocyte, or whitebloodcell, count. The silent killer was at work on Louis Slotin's blood, and the lifesaving white cells were failing to reproduce themselves.

On this same day Slotin's pulse rate rose very rapidly. Thereafter he could eat nothing, and visibly lost weight. On the seventh day his mind began to fail, and he had long periods of mental confusion, in which he could not recognize his parents or colleagues. Gradually, he sank into a coma. Early in the morning of the ninth day, May 30, 1946, Louis Slotin quietly died.

That is about the end of Louis Slotin's story. His parents flew back to Winnipeg with his corpse, and scientists and others from all over the United States and Canada attended his funeral. His parents offered a last sacrifice to the cause of science, when they permitted an autopsy to be performed on his body, although this was against the tenets of their religion. It was later estimated, according to the Atomic Energy Commission's recently declassified report on his case, that Slotin had taken about 880 roentgens of nuclear radiation. This was as though he had been fully exposed to the explosion of a modern atomic bomb at a distance of 4800 feet. Nothing could have saved him.

Louis Slotin was not a great or famous man, and he has been in his grave now for almost eight years. Yet his story has seemed worth telling, and not only because nuclear radiation, which kills without being seen or felt, is more terrifying than need be, just because it is so mysterious. It has seemed worth telling also because it is a story of human bravery and sacrifice, qualities which may yet save a civilization threatened with destruction by the very weapons Louis Slotin helped to make.

For Discussion

1. A major change in the life of man usually gives birth to a new language to express new objects and concepts. "GI," "bazooka," "jeep," "paratrooper," and "snafu" are a few of the terms that originated during the Second World War. List some of the terms that have roots in atomic research and development. Do you find these terms used often in newscasts and conversation? With how many were you familiar before you read this selection? What are some recognizable features of these words?

2. Would you say that Louis Slotin was a brave man or simply a reckless one? Would you say that he was a martyr to science or merely a victim of his own carelessness? Explain.

3. What did the atomic scientists learn about radioactivity from the Los Alamos accident that cost Louis Slotin his life? In what ways did this knowledge help them to make changes in the future handling of radioactive materials?

4. Jesus, in John 15:13, says, "Greater love hath no man than this, that a man lay down his life for his friends." Is this noble ideal part of the theme of this selection? Do you feel that the other men in the laboratory at the time of the accident owe their lives to Louis Slotin's quick action? Can you recall situations from life or literature where men have sacrificed their own lives to protect those around them? Name some.

5. Uranium is a radioactive substance that, in its ordinary state, slowly releases energy until time has reduced it to inert matter. This process takes many thousands of years and is so gradual that it has no harmful effect upon plants or creatures. How does this selection show the problems that come about when man disturbs the natural order of things? Can you give illustrations of other human discoveries or scientific developments that have created similar problems?

A Duel with Guynemer

ERNST UDET

Ernst Udet won his fame as a German ace during the First World War. An ace was a pilot who had single-handedly downed five enemy aircraft, and Udet far surpassed this number. The appearance of his plane would send less-experienced enemy pilots racing behind their own lines for protection. In airplanes made of wood and covered with a canvas fabric, these First World War pilots, in a game where death claimed the careless and untalented, carried on a tradition that had roots in the chivalry originated by the knights of the Middle Ages. German pilots would challenge French, American, or British airmen of outstanding ability to single combat, while the guns below remained silent for the duration of the contest. Wearing no parachute and often depending upon luck to keep their temperamental airplanes aloft, the pilots of both sides faced death daily, and many of them perished in flames or bullet-riddled plunges to earth. In this selection from his book Ace of the Black Cross, *Ernst Udet reveals the thoughts and feelings of a pilot who recognizes his opponent's superiority and who, when his own guns fail him, appears to face certain death.*

JAGDSTAFFEL [1] 15, which had been formed from the old single-seater fighter command at Habsheim, now consisted of four machines, three acting sergeant-majors and myself, the flight-commander. We generally flew alone.

There was a good deal of activity along the fronts, and it was rumored that a big offensive was being prepared on the other side. Every day we saw long rows of captive balloons, which, against the summer sky, looked like a string of oversize sausages. These balloons annoyed us and we decided that something would have to be done about them.

So one morning I started out early, at a time when I should have the sun at my back as I made my dive at the enemy balloon. I flew very

---

[1] *Jagdstaffel* Fighter squadron.

320

*A German fighter plane over
Flanders in the First World
War*

high, higher, I think, than I had ever flown before. The altimeter showed fifteen thousand feet, the air was thin, and it was very cold.

The world below me looked like a huge aquarium. Above Lierval, where Reinhold had fallen, I sighted a hostile machine. From the distance it looked like a minute water beetle.

Then, from the west, a small object rapidly approached. Small and black at first, it quickly grew in size and soon I recognized it as a Spad, an enemy fighter on the lookout for trouble-seekers like myself. I braced myself in my cockpit, for I knew that there was going to be a fight.

We met at the same altitude. As the sun caught it, I saw that the other man's machine was painted light brown. Soon we were circling round each other playing for an opening. From below we probably looked like two great birds of prey indulging in springtime frolics, but we knew that it was a game of death. The first man to get behind the other's back was the winner. In the single-seater fighters you could only shoot forward, and if your opponent got on your tail you were lost.

Sometimes we passed so near to each other that I could see every detail of my opponent's face—that is, all that was visible of it below his helmet. On the machine's side there was a stork and two words painted in white. The fifth time that he flew past me—so close that I could feel the draft of his propeller—I managed to spell out a word: *"V-i-e-u-x."* And *"Vieux Charles"* [2] was Guynemer's insignia.

And, indeed, there could only have been one Frenchman who handled a machine with the skill that he showed. He was the man who, like all really dangerous beasts of prey, always hunted alone. Guynemer it was who made a practice of diving at his victims from out of the sun, destroying them in a few seconds. In this way he had shot down my friend Puz. He had

[2] *"Vieux Charles"* French: "old Charles."

some thirty victories to his credit, and I knew that I was in for the fight of my life.

I threw a half-loop, with the object of getting at him from above, but immediately he grasped my purpose, and half rolled out of the way. I tried another maneuver, but again Guynemer forestalled me and the jockeying for position continued.

Once, as I was coming out of a turn, he had the advantage of me for a few seconds, and a regular hailstorm of bullets rattled against the wings of my plane.

I tried every trick that I knew—turns, loops, rolls, and sideslips—but he followed each movement with lightning speed and gradually I began to realize that he was more than a match for me. Not only had he a better machine, but the man in it was the superior duelist. But I had to fight on, to turn away would be fatal.

I went into a steep turn, and for a moment I had him at the end of my sights. I pressed the trigger . . . there was no response . . . my gun had jammed!

Holding the stick in my left hand, I hammered at the gun with my right. But my efforts to clear the stoppage were unavailing.

For a moment I considered the possibility of escaping by diving away from him. But with such an opponent that would have been inviting disaster. In a few seconds he would have been on my tail, and could have shot me down with the utmost ease.

We still flew in circles round each other. It was a wonderful flying experience—if one could forget that one's life was at stake. I have never had to deal with a more skillful opponent, and for a while I completely forgot that he was Guynemer, my enemy. It seemed to me, rather, that I was having some practice over the aerodrome with an old friend. This feeling, however, did not last for very long.

For eight minutes we had been flying round each other in circles, and they were the longest eight minutes that I have ever experienced.

Suddenly Guynemer looped, and flew on his back over my head. At that moment I relinquished hold of the stick, and hammered with both hands at the M.G. It was a primitive remedy, but it sometimes worked.

Guynemer had observed my actions and now knew that I was his helpless victim.

He again passed close over my head, flying almost on his back. And then, to my great surprise, he raised his arm and waved to me. Immediately afterwards he dived away towards the west, in the direction of his own lines.

I flew back home, stupefied.

There are some people who believe that Guynemer himself had a machine-gun stoppage at the same time. Others claim that he feared that I, in desperation, might ram him in the air. I do not believe any of them. Rather do I believe that Guynemer gave proof that even in modern warfare there is still something left of the knightly chivalry of bygone days. And, accordingly, I lay this belated wreath on Guynemer's unknown grave.

For Discussion

1. Is Ernst Udet's attitude toward Guynemer truly warlike? What criterion does he use to evaluate Guynemer's character? Does Udet hate Guynemer for having shot down his friend Puz? How can you explain his attitude?

2. In what ways has aerial combat changed since the first World War? Do modern fighter pilots fly alone? With supersonic jet planes in conflict, do you think this sort of situation could repeat itself? Why?

3. From what Ernst Udet writes and from the way he writes it, can you guess what kind of man he is? Is he a savage fighter determined to win for Germany at all costs? Is he without fear? Does he

have an affection for his fallen comrades and does he attribute their doom to the viciousness of the enemy? Does he seem dedicated to avenge their deaths? Does he love flying? Is he brave?

4. What is Udet's attitude toward death? What evidence can you gather from this account to support your judgment?

5. Why does Udet prefer to believe that Guynemer's gallantry springs from reasons other than a machine-gun stoppage or the fear of getting rammed? Do you think that the spirit of chivalry was a stronger bond in uniting these pilots as brave men than the power of war that acted to separate them as enemies? Explain.

How I Became an Explorer

ROALD AMUNDSEN

Roald Amundsen (1872–1928) spent his youth dreaming of the day when he would be able to embark on daring explorations. Born in the village of Norge in southeast Norway, he led an uneventful childhood. Although he yearned to investigate the barren North, he followed the advice of his mother and studied medicine. But in 1894, shortly after her death, he went to sea. In 1903, aboard the forty-seven ton sloop Gjoa, *he led an expedition through the Northwest Passage and successfully fixed the position of the magnetic North Pole. His next major expedition found him on the ship* Fram, *and he became the first man to reach the South Pole. Accompanied by Lincoln Ellsworth in the semirigid dirigible* Norge, *he flew over the North Pole. On May 24, 1928, the polar explorer General Nobile crashed in his airship* Italia. *Roald Amundsen volunteered to conduct a search. His plane, on the way from Bergen to Spitzenbergen, disappeared. No trace of Amundsen has ever been found. In this selection we see the tenacity of purpose that drove young Roald Amundsen to become one of the world's greatest explorers, and that also brought about his death.*

HOW DID I happen to become an explorer? It did not just happen, for my career has been a steady progress toward a definite goal since I was fifteen years of age. Whatever I have accomplished in exploration has been the result of life-long planning, painstaking preparation, and the hardest kind of conscientious work.

I was born a few miles south of Oslo in Norway, and when I was three months of age my parents removed to the capital, where I was reared and educated. I passed without incident through the usual educational routine of Norway, which is divided into a primary school for the ages of six to nine, a "gymnasium" for the ages of nine to fifteen, and college from the age of fifteen to eighteen. My father died when I was fourteen, and my older brothers went out into the world to care for themselves. I was thus left at home alone with my mother, by whom I was directed toward a course to prepare me to practice medicine. This ambition, however—which originated with her and for which I never shared her enthusiasm—was never to be realized. When I was fifteen years old, the works of Sir John Franklin, the great British explorer, fell into my hands. I read them with a fervid fascination which has shaped the whole course of my life. Of all the brave Britishers who for four hundred years had given freely of their treasure, courage, and enterprise to dauntless but unsuccessful attempts to negotiate the Northwest Passage, none was braver than Sir John Franklin.[1] His description of the return from one of his expeditions thrilled me as nothing I had ever read before. He told how for three weeks he and his little band had battled with the ice and storms, with no food to eat except a few bones found at a deserted Indian camp, and how before they finally returned to the outpost of civilization they were reduced to eating their own boot leather to keep themselves alive.

Strangely enough the thing in Sir John's narrative that appealed to me most strongly was the sufferings he and his men endured. A strange ambition burned within me to endure those same sufferings. Perhaps the idealism of youth, which often takes a turn toward martyrdom, found its crusade in me in the form of Arctic exploration. I, too, would suffer in a cause—not in the blazing desert on the way to Jerusalem, but in the frozen North on the way to new knowledge in the unpierced unknown.

In any event, Sir John's descriptions decided me upon my career. Secretly—because I would never have dared to mention the idea to my mother, who I knew would be unsympathetic —I irretrievably decided to be an Arctic explorer.

More than that, I began at once to fit myself for this career. In Norway, in those days, there were no organized athletic sports as there are now everywhere. The only sports at all were football and skiing. Although I did not like football, I went in for it as part of the task of training my body to endure hardship. But to skiing I took with perfect naturalness and intense enthusiasm. At every opportunity of freedom from school, from November to April, I went out in the open, exploring the hills and mountains which rise in every direction around Oslo, increasing my skill in traversing ice and snow and hardening my muscles for the coming great adventure.

In those days, houses were kept tightly closed in winter, so I was regarded as an innovator and something of a freak because I insisted on sleeping with my bedroom windows wide open, even in the bitterest weather. My mother anxiously expostulated with me about this practice. To her I explained that I liked fresh air, but of course it was really a part of my conscientious hardening process.

At eighteen I graduated from the college, and, in pursuance of my mother's ambition for me, entered the university, taking up the medical course. Like all fond mothers, mine believed that I was a paragon of industry, but the truth is that I was a worse than indifferent student. Her death two years later, in my twenty-first year, saved her from the sad discovery which she otherwise would have made, that my own ambitions lay in another direction and that I had made but poor progress in realizing hers. With enormous relief, I soon left the university, to throw myself wholeheartedly into the dream of my life.

Before I could realize it, however, I had to discharge the duty of all young men in Norway, of performing my tour of military service. Military service in Norway occupies only a few weeks of the year, so I had plenty of time to carry on my own course of special training for my future career of explorer. One incident of this training very nearly wrote "finis" to my life, and involved dangers and hardships fully as severe as any I was destined ever to encounter in the polar regions.

This adventure happened in my twenty-second year. It was in an effort to achieve a sort of

[1] *Sir John Franklin* Explorer who, in 1845, sailed in search of the Northwest Passage. He perished in the Arctic.

Arctic passage not many miles from Oslo itself. To the west of the capital there rises a line of steep mountainsides surmounted by a plateau of about six-thousand-feet elevation. This plateau extends westward nearly to the coast of Norway, in the neighborhood of Bergen, and is marked on that side by an even more abrupt descent—so difficult, in fact, that only two safe trails down its side exist. In summer the plateau was frequented only by Lapp herdsmen pasturing their nomadic herds of reindeer. No farmers lived there, so the only building of any sort in many miles was a hut erected by these herdsmen for shelter from cold rainstorms in the fall of the year. In the winter, the Lapps descended to the valleys, and the plateau was deserted. There was no record of any person having ever crossed the plateau in winter, from the mountain farm called Mogen on the east to the farm called Garen on the west coast. I determined to make this crossing.

Choosing a single companion, I proposed that we make the venture together. He agreed, and we left Oslo during the Christmas holidays. We made our way rapidly over the snow on our skis to the little farm called Mogen. Here we stopped at the last farmhouse that we expected to see on the whole trip. It was a tiny affair of only one room in which were crowded an old man and his wife and their two married sons —six people in all. They were, of course, of the simplest peasant type. There were no tourists in those days in any season of the year, so that our descent upon them would have been a surprise at any time. Coming as we did in the dead of winter, they were doubly astonished. We had no difficulty in persuading them to allow us to stay overnight with them. They were hospitable folk and made room for us on the floor near the fireplace, where we rolled ourselves up in in our reindeer sleeping bags and slept very comfortably.

On the morrow, however, it was snowing, and this storm turned out to be a regular blizzard. It lasted for eight days, and we spent the whole of this time in the farmhouse.

Of course, our hosts were curious to know what errand could have brought us to their remote home. When we told them our plan to ascend to the plateau and cross it to the coast, they were first incredulous and then greatly alarmed for our safety. All three of the men were familiar with the plateau and joined in earnestly warning us not to attempt to cross it in winter. It had never been done, and they were sure it could not be done. Nevertheless, we were determined to push on and attempt it, so on the ninth day they accompanied us to the foot of the plateau at the head of their valley and showed us the best way to ascend. They bade us good-by sadly, and we understood that they feared they would never see us again.

Of course, we were lighthearted about the enterprise. To us it seemed simple enough. The plateau was only about seventy-two miles wide, and with our skill on skis and any decent luck with the weather, we counted at most on two days to make the crossing. Our equipment for the venture was based upon this theory, and accordingly was of the sketchiest character. Besides our skis and ski sticks, we each had a reindeer sleeping bag that we carried on our backs. We took no tent. Each of us had a small bag containing our provisions and a small alcohol lamp. This bag was rolled inside the sleeping bag. Our provisions consisted of a few crackers, some bars of chocolate, and a little butter—at the best scant rations for perhaps eight days. We had a pocket compass and a map of the region printed on paper.

We had no difficulty in ascending to the plateau. It was not a perfectly level plain that we found, but, for the practical purpose of travel, it might as well have been, for it offered no distinguishing landmarks to guide our course. There was nothing to be seen but an endless succession of small and indistinct hills.

We set our course by the compass. Our destination for our first day's travel was the herder's hut which was about in the middle of the plateau. At that time of the year in Norway, the daylight is little better than twilight, but with our compass we had no difficulty in getting along, and early in the evening we found the hut.

Our elation at this discovery was rather short-lived, for we found that the door and window of the hut had been nailed up and the top of the chimney covered over with heavy boards. We were pretty well tired with our day's exertions, the wind had started to blow again, and the thermometer was about ten degrees Fahrenheit below zero. With these handicaps, it was the hardest kind of work to get into the hut and later to clamber onto the roof and clear the top of the chimney so that we could start a fire. Both of us got our fingers badly frostbitten, and my companion, for some weeks after, was in grave danger of losing one of his.

We had the good fortune to find firewood stacked up in the hut. It took us some time, however, to make it of any use to us—if you have ever tried to build an open fire under a cold chimney with the thermometer below zero, you will understand the difficulty we had in getting a draft going. The cold air settles down on your fire like a blanket, and you have to get a pretty brisk blaze going before the heat displaces the column of cold air in the flue. Meanwhile, of course, in our efforts to do this, we had filled the little hut with smoke that got

into our eyes and throats and caused us much discomfort.

We felt pretty good after we had the fire blazing and had eaten a supper. At length, we rolled up in our sleeping bags in the bunks on the opposite wall and slept very comfortably.

In the morning, we found that our troubles had only begun. The wind of the night before was still blowing, and it was now snowing heavily. The storm was so severe that it would obviously be folly to venture out in it. We therefore settled down to sit the storm out before the fireplace. Further exploration of the hut revealed another bit of good luck—it disclosed a small sack of rye flour that had been left behind by some herdsman. As we now realized that our own provisions must be husbanded, we made a thin porridge of this flour, which we cooked in an iron kettle over the open fire. We spent two days in the hut, and the only food we took in that time was this weak porridge. At best, it was not very nourishing, and neither was it palatable.

On the third day, the storm had somewhat abated, and we decided to resume our march westward toward Garen. We now had to set our course very carefully, as there were only two places on the west coast at which a descent

Roald Amundsen with a dog team on one of his Polar expeditions

from the plateau was at all possible, and as these places were several miles apart, we had now definitely to choose one of them and reject the other. Having made this choice we set forward.

We had not gone far before it started snowing again and the weather grew milder. We had frequently to consult the map to take our bearings, and the wet snow falling on the flimsy paper soon reduced it to pulp. After that, we had to proceed as best we could by the compass alone.

Night overtook us before we reached the edge of the plateau and, of course, there was nothing to do but to camp where it found us, out in the open. That night nearly finished us. When we had unrolled our sleeping bags, we took out our provision bags and laid them at our feet. Alongside them we set up our ski sticks as markers to indicate in the morning where the bags were if the overnight snow should cover them. We spent the night in extreme discomfort. The soft snow had melted on our clothing and had saturated it with moisture. When we got into our sleeping bags, the heat of our bodies turned enough of this moisture into steam so that it permeated the inside of the sleeping bags as well. It was a wretched experience. Worse yet, it turned cold again in the night. I woke up in the darkness feeling half frozen, and was so uncomfortable that I could not go back to sleep. It finally occurred to me that, if I got up and drank some of the alcohol out of the lamp in my provision bag, it would restore my circulation. I climbed out of the sleeping bag and felt around in the dark until I got hold of my ski stick, and then I clawed about for my provision bag. To my astonishment and chagrin, it was not to be found. When morning broke, we both resumed the search and could find neither of the bags. To this day I have not been able to make a reasonable conjecture that would explain what became of them. There was, however, no doubt of the fact—they were gone.

Our plight now was worse than uncomfortable, it was extremely dangerous. Unless we could speedily reach shelter and food, we should certainly freeze to death. With this alarming situation confronting us, we headed west again in hopes of reaching the edge of the plateau before night fell.

Luck was still against us. It soon began to snow so heavily that we could not see our way more than a few feet ahead. We decided now that the only thing to do was to turn around and try to make our way east across the plateau to our starting point. We made a few miles on this new course when night again overtook us.

Again the night was wet. We were drenched, and our bags were still heavy with moisture. Snow was still falling. When night came on, we had reached a small peak that thrust up out of the plateau. We sought out its lee side, figuring that we might be reasonably comfortable if we could keep out of the wind. We found that it did make a good deal of difference. I decided to improve even on that. I dug into the snow and made myself a small cave not much larger than my body, and into the cave I climbed head first and pulled my bag in after me. I soon congratulated myself on this idea, for I escaped altogether the gusts of wind outside.

In the night, the weather turned cold suddenly. The wet snow had settled down on me in my cave and over its entrance at my feet. When the temperature dropped, it froze. In the middle of the night I woke up. I was lying on my back with my right wrist across my eyes and the palm of my hand up—as one often sleeps to keep the morning light out of his eyes. My muscles felt cramped and I made the instinctive move to change my position. I could not move an inch. I was practically frozen inside a solid block of ice! I struggled desperately to free myself, but without the slightest effect. I shouted to my companion. Of course he could not hear.

I was now stricken with horror. In my panic, I naturally thought he likewise had been frozen in the wet snow that had fallen in the night and that he was in a like predicament with me. Unless a thaw immediately set in, we should both soon freeze to death in our ghastly coffins of ice.

My shouts quickly died away, as I found it impossible to breathe deeply. I realized that I must keep quiet or I would suffocate. I do not know whether it was the heaviness of the little air I had to breathe, or what was the reason, but I soon dropped off into either sleep or unconsciousness. When I came to I could hear faint sounds. My companion, after all, had not been imprisoned. Probably the only reason he had not emulated my example and built himself a cave the night before was that he was too tired, and from exhaustion too indifferent, to go to the trouble. In any event, his failure to do so saved both our lives. When he awakened and looked about, he found himself alone in an ocean of snow. He called to me, and I did not answer. Then he began a frantic search for some trace that would show him where I had gone. There was only one, and providentially his eye fell upon it—a few hairs of the reindeer skin of my sleeping bag were visible in the snow. At once he began digging with his hands and ski stick to extricate me from my prison. It took him three hours to dig me out.

Both of us were now getting pretty weak. It was still night when he got me out, but we were too much upset to think of trying to rest further. Though it was still dark, the sky was clear and we were able to set a course and travel by the stars. We had been going two hours, with my companion in the lead, when suddenly he disappeared as if the earth had swallowed him up. Instinctively, I realized that he had gone over a precipice, and, instinctively, I acted instantly to save myself. I threw myself flat on the ground. A moment later, I heard his voice calling up, "Don't move. I have dropped over a precipice." He had indeed fallen about thirty feet. Fortunately, he had landed on his back, so that the sleeping bag which he carried as a pack on his shoulders had broken the force of the fall and he did not suffer more than a severe shaking up. Naturally, we did not attempt to go farther until daylight. Then we plowed ahead on our seemingly hopeless travels.

We had now been four days without food of any sort, and the two days before that our diet of weak rye porridge had not been much better, so far as sustenance was concerned. We were getting nearly exhausted. The only thing that had saved us from collapse was our ability to get drinking water. On the plateau were numerous little lakes connected by small streams, and at these streams we had been able to keep our stomachs filled with water, and this saved us from the extreme effects of starvation.

At nightfall we came upon a little shanty filled with hay. There were ski tracks around the shanty. This discovery renewed our courage and proved that we were certainly back near civilization. It gave us hope, that, if we could keep ourselves going, on the morrow we might find food and shelter. The hay offered us a luxurious bed, and we spent the night burrowed into the heart of it.

The next morning I turned out to explore our surroundings. My companion was now so exhausted and dispirited that he seemed unequal to the effort and I left him in the haymow while I followed the ski tracks. After an hour's trudging, I saw a man in the distance. I surmised correctly that he was a peasant farmer making the morning rounds of the snares he had set for ptarmigan.[2] I called loudly to him. He gave a startled look and, to my dismay, proceeded to run as fast as he could away from me. These lonely peasants are a superstitious folk. While they are courageous enough in the presence of real danger, they suffer many terrors of their own creation. Doubtless his first impression of me was of a ghostly apparition haunting the uninhabited plateau.

I called again and threw my whole soul into the cry. My tone must have conveyed my desperation, for the man stopped running and, after some hesitation, came back to meet me. I explained our plight and asked him where we were. I had a little difficulty in understanding his explanation, and even when I did, could hardly believe my senses, for it showed that we

[2] *ptarmigan*   A kind of game bird.

were now not more than an hour's travel from the farmhouse above Mogen from which, eight days before, we had started on our misadventure.

Heartened by this information, I hurried back for my companion. The news put fresh vigor in him, too, and soon, with no great trouble, we made our way down the little valley to the familiar farmhouse. We knocked at the door, were invited to enter, and went in. I was puzzled at our reception—until later I saw myself in the mirror. In the single room of the farmhouse the women were busy at their spinning and the men at wood-carving. They looked up hospitably, but merely greeted us with a brief "How do you do," in an entirely impersonal and inquiring manner. It was soon apparent that they did not recognize us. Little wonder, as I later realized, for our scraggly beards had grown, our eyes were gaunt and hollow, our cheeks were sunken, and the ruddy glow of color had changed to a ghastly greenish yellow. We were a truly awful spectacle. Our hosts at first would not believe us when we explained that we were the two young fellows who had left them eight days earlier. They could see no resemblance to their former guests in the gaunt specters before them. At length we convinced them, and they showed us every kindness. We spent a couple of days with them, eating and sleeping until our strength returned, and then, with many expressions of gratitude, we took our leave of them and made our way safe into Oslo.

The sequel of the story I did not myself learn until a year later, when I discovered it was known that the farmer who owned Garen, on the westernly edge of the plateau at the head of the trail we had intended to descend, had come out of his house one morning and found ski tracks within a few yards of his doorway coming from the east and not from the west. He could not credit his eyes, because he knew no one had ever come that way in the winter, nor did he believe it was possible. Those tracks could have been none other than ours, for the date also matched.

Think of it! We had been unknowingly within a hundred yards of our destination and had turned back to recross the plateau after being within ten minutes' walk of a safe haven on its western edge!

As I said when I started to describe this adventure, it involved as many hardships and dangers as anything I later encountered in my polar expeditions. It was a part of my preliminary training for my polar career. The training proved severer than the experience for which it was a preparation and it well-nigh ended the career before it began.

For Discussion

1. To what does Amundsen attribute his success as an explorer? Do you believe that early determination and persistent preparation are the only ways of insuring success in later life?

2. Explain what Amundsen means when he writes, "Perhaps the idealism of youth, which often takes a turn toward martyrdom, found its crusade in me in the form of Arctic exploration." Do you agree? Why does he compare his desire to trek through frozen wastes to a crusade?

3. What lesson does Amundsen learn from this youthful expedition that might have proved useful in his later serious trips to the Poles? Was this a silly thing to do? Can you make suggestions about supplies and procedure that would lessen the risks of such an attempt?

4. What did this reckless expedition prove to the young Amundsen? Does he attempt to enlist the reader's sympathy for the physical hardships he endures on this trip? Do you feel that he deserves all the suffering he receives because he acts rashly?

5. Do you feel that if both Amundsen and his friend had died, their daring attempt would have been considered a senseless waste? Explain.

By the Waters of Babylon

STEPHEN VINCENT BENÉT

*The coming of nuclear warfare has made it possible for man to bring
about the destruction of civilization. In an age when whole nations
may be reduced quickly to rubble, the human race must learn morally
to keep pace with its own technical skills. In this story, Stephen
Vincent Benét portrays an imaginative journey into a great, empty
city that, out of the gathering wilderness, thrust its wreckage—a
brooding monument to man's folly.*

THE NORTH and the west and the south are good
hunting ground, but it is forbidden to go east.
It is forbidden to go to any of the Dead Places
except to search for metal and then he who
touches the metal must be a priest or the son of
a priest. Afterwards, both the man and the metal
must be purified. These are the rules and the
laws; they are well made. It is forbidden to
cross the great river and look upon the place
that was the Place of the Gods—this is most
strictly forbidden. We do not even say its
name though we know its name. It is there that
spirits live, and demons—it is there that there
are the ashes of the Great Burning. These things
are forbidden—they have been forbidden since
the beginning of time.

My father is a priest; I am the son of a priest.
I have been in the Dead Places near us, with my
father—at first, I was afraid. When my father
went into the house to search for the metal, I
stood by the door and my heart felt small and
weak. It was a dead man's house, a spirit house.
It did not have the smell of man, though there
were old bones in a corner. But it is not fitting

that a priest's son should show fear. I looked
at the bones in the shadow and kept my voice
still.

Then my father came out with the metal—a
good, strong piece. He looked at me with both
eyes but I had not run away. He gave me the
metal to hold—I took it and did not die. So he
knew that I was truly his son and would be a
priest in my time. That was when I was very
young—nevertheless my brothers would not
have done it, though they are good hunters.
After that, they gave me the good piece of
meat and the warm corner by the fire. My father
watched over me—he was glad that I should be
a priest. But when I boasted or wept without a
reason, he punished me more strictly than my
brothers. That was right.

After a time, I myself was allowed to go into
the dead houses and search for metal. So I
learned the ways of those houses—and if I saw
bones, I was no longer afraid. The bones are
light and old—sometimes they will fall into dust
if you touch them. But that is a great sin.

I was taught the chants and the spells—I was

330

taught how to stop the running of blood from a wound and many secrets. A priest must know many secrets—that was what my father said. If the hunters think we do all things by chants and spells, they may believe so—it does not hurt them. I was taught how to read in the old books and how to make the old writings—that was hard and took a long time. My knowledge made me happy—it was like a fire in my heart. Most of all, I liked to hear of the Old Days and the stories of the gods. I asked myself many questions that I could not answer, but it was good to ask them. At night, I would lie awake and listen to the wind—it seemed to me that it was the voice of the gods as they flew through the air.

We are not ignorant like the Forest People —our women spin wool on the wheel, our priests wear a white robe. We do not eat grubs from the tree, we have not forgotten the old writings, although they are hard to understand. Nevertheless, my knowledge and my lack of knowledge burned in me—I wished to know more. When I was a man at last, I came to my father and said, "It is time for me to go on my journey. Give me your leave."

He looked at me for a long time, stroking his beard, then he said at last, "Yes. It is time." That night, in the house of the priesthood, I asked for and received purification. My body hurt but my spirit was a cool stone. It was my father himself who questioned me about my dreams.

He bade me look into the smoke of the fire and see—I saw and told what I saw. It was what I have always seen—a river, and, beyond it, a great Dead Place and in it the gods walking. I have always thought about that. His eyes were stern when I told him—he was no longer my father but a priest. He said, "This is a strong dream."

"It is mine," I said, while the smoke waved and my head felt light. They were singing the Star song in the outer chamber and it was like the buzzing of bees in my head.

He asked me how the gods were dressed and I told him how they were dressed. We know how they were dressed from the book, but I saw them as if they were before me. When I had finished, he threw the sticks three times and studied them as they fell.

"This is a very strong dream," he said. "It may eat you up."

"I am not afraid," I said and looked at him with both eyes. My voice sounded thin in my ears but that was because of the smoke.

He touched me on the breast and the forehead. He gave me the bow and the three arrows.

"Take them," he said. "It is forbidden to travel east. It is forbidden to cross the river. It is forbidden to go to the Place of the Gods. All these things are forbidden."

"All these things are forbidden," I said, but it was my voice that spoke and not my spirit. He looked at me again.

"My son," he said. "Once I had young dreams. If your dreams do not eat you up, you may be a great priest. If they eat you, you are still my son. Now go on your journey."

I went fasting, as is the law. My body hurt but not my heart. When the dawn came, I was out of sight of the village. I prayed and purified myself, waiting for a sign. The sign was an eagle. It flew east.

Sometimes signs are sent by bad spirits. I waited again on the flat rock, fasting, taking no food. I was very still—I could feel the sky above me and the earth beneath. I waited till the sun was beginning to sink. Then three deer passed in the valley, going east—they did not wind me or see me. There was a white fawn with them— a very great sign.

I followed them, at a distance, waiting for what would happen. My heart was troubled about going east, yet I knew that I must go. My head hummed with my fasting—I did not even see the panther spring upon the white fawn. But, before I knew it, the bow was in my hand. I shouted and the panther lifted his head from the fawn. It is not easy to kill a

STEPHEN VINCENT BENÉT (*1898–1943*)
was one of the most popular American
writers of his time. Many of his works,
such as "The Devil and Daniel Webster"
and "John Brown's Body," have become
modern classics.

panther with one arrow but the arrow went through his eye and into his brain. He died as he tried to spring—he rolled over, tearing at the ground. Then I knew I was meant to go east— I knew that was my journey. When the night came, I made my fire and roasted meat.

It is eight suns' journey to the east and a man passes by many Dead Places. The Forest People are afraid of them but I am not. Once I made my fire on the edge of a Dead Place at night and, next morning, in the dead house, I found a good knife, little rusted. That was small to what came afterward but it made my heart feel big. Always when I looked for game, it was in front of my arrow, and twice I passed hunting parties of the Forest People without their knowing. So I knew my magic was strong and my journey clean, in spite of the law.

Toward the setting of the eighth sun, I came to the banks of the great river. It was half-a-day's journey after I had left the god-road— we do not use the god-roads now for they are falling apart into great blocks of stone, and the forest is safer going. A long way off, I had seen the water through trees but the trees were thick. At last, I came out upon an open place at the top of a cliff. There was the great river below, like a giant in the sun. It is very long, very wide. It could eat all the streams we know and still be thirsty. Its name is Ou-dis-sun, the Sacred, the Long. No man of my tribe had seen it, not even my father, the priest. It was magic and I prayed.

Then I raised my eyes and looked south. It was there, the Place of the Gods.

How can I tell what it was like—you do not know. It was there, in the red light, and they were too big to be houses. It was there with the red light upon it, mighty and ruined. I knew that in another moment the gods would see me. I covered my eyes with my hands and crept back into the forest.

Surely, that was enough to do, and live. Surely it was enough to spend the night upon the cliff. The Forest People themselves do not come near. Yet, all through the night, I knew that I should have to cross the river and walk in the places of the gods, although the gods ate me up. My magic did not help me at all and yet there was a fire in my bowels, a fire in my mind. When the sun rose, I thought, "My journey has been clean. Now I will go home from my journey." But, even as I thought so, I knew I could not. If I went to the place of the gods, I would surely die, but, if I did not go, I could never be at peace with my spirit again. It is better to lose one's life than one's spirit, if one is a priest and the son of a priest.

Nevertheless, as I made the raft, the tears ran out of my eyes. The Forest People could have killed me without fight, if they had come upon me then, but they did not come. When the raft was made, I said the sayings for the dead and painted myself for death. My heart was cold as a frog and my knees like water, but the burning in my mind would not let me have peace. As I pushed the raft from the shore, I began my death song—I had the right. It was a fine song.

"I am John, son of John," I sang. "My people are the Hill People. They are the men.
I go into the Dead Places but I am not slain.
I take the metal from the Dead Places but I am not blasted.
I travel upon the god-roads and am not afraid. E-yah! I have killed the panther, I have killed the fawn!
E-yah! I have come to the great river. No man has come there before.
It is forbidden to go east, but I have gone, forbidden to go on the great river, but I am there.
Open your hearts, you spirits, and hear my song.

Now I go to the place of the gods, I shall not
   return.
My body is painted for death and my limbs
   weak, but my heart is big as I go to the place
   of the gods!"

All the same, when I came to the Place of
the Gods, I was afraid, afraid. The current of
the great river is very strong—it gripped my
raft with its hands. That was magic, for the
river itself is wide and calm. I could feel evil
spirits about me, in the bright morning; I could
feel their breath on my neck as I was swept
down the stream. Never have I been so much
alone—I tried to think of my knowledge, but it
was a squirrels' heap of winter nuts. There was
no strength in my knowledge any more and I
felt small and naked as a new-hatched bird—
alone upon the great river, the servant of the
gods.

Yet, after a while, my eyes were opened and
I saw. I saw both banks of the river—I saw
that once there had been god-roads across it,
though now they were broken and fallen like
broken vines. Very great they were, and wonderful and broken—broken in the time of the
Great Burning when the fire fell out of the sky.
And always the current took me nearer to the
Place of the Gods, and the huge ruins rose before my eyes.

I do not know the customs of rivers—we are
the People of the Hills. I tried to guide my
raft with the pole but it spun around. I thought
the river meant to take me past the Place of
the Gods and out into the Bitter Water of the
legends. I grew angry then—my heart felt
strong. I said aloud, "I am a priest and the son
of a priest!" The gods heard me—they showed
me how to paddle with the pole on one side
of the raft. The current changed itself—I drew
near to the Place of the Gods.

When I was very near, my raft struck and
turned over. I can swim in our lakes—I swam
to the shore. There was a great spike of rusted
metal sticking out into the river—I hauled
myself up upon it and sat there, panting. I

had saved my bow and two arrows and the
knife I found in the Dead Place but that was all.
My raft went whirling downstream toward the
Bitter Water. I looked after it, and thought
if it had trod me under, at least I would be
safely dead. Nevertheless, when I had dried my
bow-string and re-strung it, I walked forward
to the Place of the Gods.

It felt like ground underfoot; it did not burn
me. It is not true what some of the tales say,
that the ground there burns forever, for I have
been there. Here and there were the marks and
stains of the Great Burning, on the ruins, that
is true. But they were old marks and old stains.
It is not true either, what some of our priests
say, that it is an island covered with fogs and
enchantments. It is not. It is a great Dead Place—
greater than any Dead Place we know. Everywhere in it there are god-roads, though most
are cracked and broken. Everywhere there are
the ruins of the high towers of the gods.

How shall I tell what I saw? I went carefully,
my strung bow in my hand, my skin ready for
danger. There should have been the wailings of
spirits and the shrieks of demons, but there were
not. It was very silent and sunny where I had
landed—the wind and the rain and the birds
that drop seeds had done their work—the grass
grew in the cracks of the broken stone. It is a
fair island—no wonder the gods built there. If
I had come there, a god, I also would have built.

How shall I tell what I saw? The towers are
not all broken—here and there one still stands,
like a great tree in a forest, and the birds nest
high. But the towers themselves look blind, for
the gods are gone. I saw a fish-hawk, catching
fish in the river. I saw a little dance of white
butterflies over a great heap of broken stones
and columns. I went there and looked about
me—there was a carved stone with cut-letters,
broken in half. I can read letters but I could
not understand these. They said UBTREAS.
There was also the shattered image of a man or
a god. It had been made of white stone and he
wore his hair tied back like a woman's. His
name was ASHING, as I read on the cracked

half of a stone. I thought it wise to pray to ASHING, though I do not know that god.

How shall I tell what I saw? There was no smell of man left, on stone or metal. Nor were there many trees in that wilderness of stone. There are many pigeons, nesting and dropping in the towers—the gods must have loved them, or, perhaps, they used them for sacrifices. There are wild cats that roam the god-roads, green-eyed, unafraid of man. At night they wail like demons but they are not demons. The wild dogs are more dangerous, for they hunt in a pack, but them I did not meet till later. Everywhere there are the carved stones, carved with magical numbers or words.

I went North—I did not try to hide myself. When a god or a demon saw me, then I would die, but meanwhile I was no longer afraid. My hunger for knowledge burned in me—there was so much that I could not understand. After awhile, I knew that my belly was hungry. I could have hunted for my meat, but I did not hunt. It is known that the gods did not hunt as we do—they got their food from enchanted boxes and jars. Sometimes these are still found in the Dead Places—once, when I was a child and foolish, I opened such a jar and tasted it and found the food sweet. But my father found out and punished me for it strictly, for, often, that food is death. Now, though, I had long gone past what was forbidden, and I entered the likeliest towers, looking for the food of the gods.

I found it at last in the ruins of a great temple in the mid-city. A mighty temple it must have been, for the roof was painted like the sky at night with its stars—that much I could see, though the colors were faint and dim. I went down into great caves and tunnels—perhaps they kept their slaves there. But when I started to climb down, I heard the squeaking of rats, so I did not go—rats are unclean, and there must have been many tribes of them, from the squeaking. But near there, I found food, in the heart of a ruin, behind a door that still opened. I ate

only the fruits from the jars—they had a very sweet taste. There was drink, too, in bottles of glass—the drink of the gods was strong and made my head swim. After I had eaten and drunk, I slept on the top of a stone, my bow at my side.

When I woke, the sun was low. Looking down from where I lay, I saw a dog sitting on his haunches. His tongue was hanging out of his mouth; he looked as if he were laughing. He was a big dog, with a grey-brown coat, as big as a wolf. I sprang up and shouted at him but he did not move—he just sat there as if he were laughing. I did not like that. When I reached for a stone to throw, he moved swiftly out of the way of the stone. He was not afraid of me; he looked at me as if I were meat. No doubt I could have killed him with an arrow, but I did not know if there were others. Moreover, night was falling.

I looked about me—not far away there was a great, broken god-road, leading North. The towers were high enough, but not so high, and while many of the dead-houses were wrecked, there were some that stood. I went toward this god-road, keeping to heights of the ruins, while the dog followed. When I had reached the god-road, I saw that there were others behind him. If I had slept later, they would have come upon me asleep and torn out my throat. As it was, they were sure enough of me; they did not hurry. When I went into the dead-house, they kept watch at the entrance—doubtless they thought they would have a fine hunt. But a dog cannot open a door and I knew, from the books, that the gods did not like to live on the ground but on high.

I had just found a door I could open when the dogs decided to rush. Ha! They were surprised when I shut the door in their faces—it was a good door, of strong metal. I could hear their foolish baying beyond it but I did not stop to answer them. I was in darkness—found stairs and climbed. There were many stairs, turning around till my head was dizzy. At the top was another door—I found the knob and opened it. I was in a long small chamber—on one side of it was a bronze door that could not be opened, for it had no handle. Perhaps there was a magic word to open it but I did not have the word. I turned to the door in the opposite side of the wall. The lock of it was broken and I opened it and went in.

Within, there was a place of great riches. The god who lived there must have been a powerful god. The first room was a small ante-room—I waited there for some time, telling the spirits of the place that I came in peace and not as a robber. When it seemed to me that they had had time to hear me, I went on. Ah, what riches! Few, even, of the windows had been broken—it was all as it had been. The great windows that looked over the city had not been broken at all though they were dusty and streaked with many years. There were coverings on the floors, the colors not greatly faded, and the chairs were soft and deep. There were pictures upon the walls, very strange, very wonderful—I remember one of a bunch of flowers in a jar—if you came close to it, you could see nothing but bits of color, but if you stood away from it, the flowers might have been picked yesterday. It made my heart feel strange to look at this picture—and to look at the figure of a bird, in some hard clay, on a table and see it so like our birds. Everywhere there were books and writings, many in tongues that I could not read. The god who lived there must have been a wise god and full of knowledge. I felt I had right there, as I sought knowledge also.

Nevertheless, it was strange. There was a washing-place but no water—perhaps the gods washed in air. There was a cooking-place but no wood, and though there was a machine to cook food, there was no place to put fire in it. Nor were there candles or lamps—there were things that looked like lamps but they had neither oil nor wick. All these things were magic, but I touched them and lived—the magic had gone out of them. Let me tell one thing to show. In the washing-place, a thing said "Hot" but it was not hot to the touch—another thing said "Cold" but it was not cold. This must have been a strong magic but the magic was gone. I do not understand—they had ways—I wish that I knew.

It was close and dry and dusty in their house of the gods. I have said the magic was gone but that is not true—it had gone from the magic things but it had not gone from the place. I felt the spirits about me, weighing upon me. Nor had I ever slept in a Dead Place before—and yet, tonight, I must sleep there. When I thought of it, my tongue felt dry in my throat, in spite of my wish for knowledge. Almost I would have gone down again and faced the dogs, but I did not.

I had not gone through all the rooms when the darkness fell. When it fell, I went back to the big room looking over the city and made fire. There was a place to make fire and a box with wood in it, though I do not think they cooked there. I wrapped myself in a floor-covering and slept in front of the fire—I was very tired.

Now I tell what is very strong magic. I woke in the midst of the night. When I woke, the fire had gone out and I was cold. It seemed to me that all around me there were whisperings and voices. I closed my eyes to shut them out. Some will say that I slept again, but I do not think that I slept. I could feel the spirits drawing my spirit out of my body as a fish is drawn on a line.

Why should I lie about it? I am a priest and the son of a priest. If there are spirits, as they say, in the small Dead Places near us, what spirits must there not be in that great Place of the Gods? And would not they wish to speak? After such long years? I know that I felt myself drawn as a fish is drawn on a line. I had stepped out of my body—I could see my body asleep in front of the cold fire, but it was not I. I was drawn to look out upon the city of the gods.

It should have been dark, for it was night, but it was not dark. Everywhere there were lights—lines of light—circles and blurs of light—ten thousand torches would not have been the same. The sky itself was alight—you could barely see the stars for the glow in the sky. I thought to myself "This is strong magic" and trembled. There was a roaring in my ears like the rushing of rivers. Then my eyes grew used to the light and my ears to the sound. I knew that I was seeing the city as it had been when the gods were alive.

That was a sight indeed—yes, that was a sight: I could not have seen it in the body—my body would have died. Everywhere went the gods, on foot and in chariots—there were gods beyond number and counting and their chariots blocked the streets. They had turned night to day for their pleasure—they did not sleep with the sun. The noise of their coming and going was the noise of many waters. It was magic what they could do—it was magic what they did.

I looked out of another window—the great vines of their bridges were mended and the god-roads went East and West. Restless, restless, were the gods and always in motion! They burrowed tunnels under rivers—they flew in the air. With unbelievable tools they did giant works—no part of the earth was safe from them, for, if they wished for a thing, they summoned it from the other side of the world. And always, as they labored and rested, as they feasted and made love, there was a drum in their ears—the pulse of the giant city, beating and beating like a man's heart.

Were they happy? What is happiness to the gods? They were great, they were mighty, they were wonderful and terrible. As I looked upon them and their magic, I felt like a child—but a little more, it seemed to me, and they would pull down the moon from the sky. I saw them with wisdom beyond wisdom and knowledge beyond knowledge. And yet not all they did was well done—even I could see that—and yet their wisdom could not but grow until all was peace.

Then I saw their fate come upon them and that was terrible past speech. It came upon them as they walked the streets of their city. I have been in the fights with the Forest People—I have seen men die. But this was not like that. When gods war with gods, they use weapons we do not know. It was fire falling out of the sky and a mist that poisoned. It was the time of the Great Burning and the Destruction. They ran about like ants in the streets of their city—poor gods, poor gods! Then the towers began to fall. A few escaped—yes, a few. The legends tell it. But, even after the city had become a Dead Place, for many years the poison was still in the ground. I saw it happen, I saw the last of them die. It was darkness over the broken city and I wept.

All this, I saw. I saw it as I have told it, though not in the body. When I woke in the morning, I was hungry, but I did not think first of my hunger for my heart was perplexed and confused. I knew the reason for the Dead Places but I did not see why it had happened. It seemed to me it should not have happened, with all the magic they had. I went through the house looking for an answer. There was so much in the house I could not understand—and yet I am a priest and the son of a priest. It was like being on one side of the great river, at night, with no light to show the way.

Then I saw the dead god. He was sitting in his chair, by the window, in a room I had not entered before and, for the first moment, I thought that he was alive. Then I saw the skin on the back of his hand—it was like dry leather. The room was shut, hot and dry—no doubt that had kept him as he was. At first I was afraid to approach him—then the fear left me. He was sitting looking out over the city—he was dressed in the clothes of the gods. His age was neither young nor old—I could not tell his age. But there was wisdom in his face and great sadness. You could see that he would have not run away. He had sat at his window, watching his city die—then he himself had died. But it is better to lose one's life than one's spirit—and you could see from the face that his spirit had not been lost. I knew, that, if I touched him, he would fall into dust—and yet, there was something unconquered in the face.

That is all of my story, for then I knew he was a man—I knew then that they had been men, neither gods nor demons. It is a great knowledge, hard to tell and believe. They were men—they went a dark road, but they were men. I had no fear after that—I had no fear going home, though twice I fought off the dogs and once I was hunted for two days by the Forest People. When I saw my father again, I prayed and was purified. He touched my lips and my breast, he said, "You went away a boy. You come back a man and a priest." I said, "Father, they were men! I have been in the Place of the Gods and seen it! Now slay me, if it is the law—but still I know they were men."

He looked at me out of both eyes. He said, "The law is not always the same shape—you have done what you have done. I could not have done it in my time, but you come after me. Tell!"

I told and he listened. After that, I wished to tell all the people but he showed me otherwise. He said, "Truth is a hard deer to hunt. If you eat too much truth at once, you may die of the truth. It was not idly that our fathers forbade the Dead Places." He was right—it is better the truth should come little by little. I have learned that, being a priest. Perhaps, in the old days, they ate knowledge too fast.

Nevertheless, we make a beginning. It is not for the metal alone we go to the Dead Places now—there are the books and the writings. They are hard to learn. And the magic tools are broken—but we can look at them and wonder. At least, we make a beginning. And, when I am chief priest we shall go beyond the great river. We shall go to the Place of the Gods—the place new-york—not one man but a company. We shall look for the images of the gods and find the god ASHING and the others—the gods Licoln and Biltmore and Moses. But they were men who built the city, not gods or demons. They were men. I remember the dead man's face. They were men who were here before us. We must build again.

For Discussion

1. Why do the narrator and his people worship the former inhabitants of the city as gods? Why are only priests and priests' sons allowed to touch the metals in the ruins? Can you find an irony in this worship? Do these simple people consider godlike those same qualities that were instrumental in bringing about the destruction of the city?

2. From small bits of evidence, do you think you can identify the city of this story? Name the river? Can you offer the reason why the current changes during the narrator's crossing? Who is the god ASHING?

3. When the narrator escapes the dog pack, he enters rooms which he describes as "a place of great riches." From his description, do you feel that it is a lavish apartment? Where is the narrator when he says that he is in a temple that has great caves and tunnels? Can you name other architectural structures of a city that might suggest temples or shrines to a primitive mind?

4. What effect does the discovery that these were men, not gods, have upon the narrator? Why does he feel he ought to be punished for his knowledge? Does what he learn on his journey to the Place of the Gods change his life? In what way?

5. Can you see in the men alive on earth the seeds of destruction that brought about the ruin of the once powerful cities? What can you predict as an ultimate consequence of the animosity that exists between the forest people and the narrator's people? Do the primitive people seem to be following the same path that the destroyed civilization followed? Can you find a double meaning in the last line of the story, "We must build again"?

ycpolinh q̃ mexica

UNIT 7: MEETINGS OF CULTURES

Culture is more than art and

literature, more than the refinement of taste. The culture of a race or of a nation embraces the entire body of its beliefs, language, social forms, and material goods. The culture of the United States includes our houses and public buildings, the songs we sing, the patterns of logic and intuition that make up the way we think—in short, everything that goes to shape our collective behavior.

Climate, terrain, and history have important effects on the intellectual and emotional temperament of any group of people. The differences that have come to exist between societies are vast. Moreover, men usually distrust and show hostility to cultural patterns that differ from their own. One society, using its own code for a standard, comes to judge another society as "inferior." Men tend to make easy generalizations about others—to say that the Germans are "methodical," or that the English "have no sense of humor." Some Europeans think that all Americans are typified by the aggressively rich tourist wearing a loud tie and bustling from one historic monument to the next taking snapshots. Often, it is easier to accept those oversimplifications than to make a sincere effort to understand the complicated background, language, and values that shape another's culture.

Travel in the modern world is faster and less expensive than it has ever been before. More than ever, men and women of differing cultures come in contact with each other. The following selections examine representative "meetings of cultures." What kinds of conflicts arise? How are they resolved? Are they always resolved happily? Or have they sometimes tragic results? These stories and essays suggest that there is no simple formula to unite men of many faiths, languages, and customs. Only a wide and sympathetic understanding, free of prejudice and based upon knowledge, can help men of differing traditions to live together harmoniously.

The stories and articles in this unit often recognize an unpleasant fact: that the world we live in is not one of complete harmony. The brotherhood of man is an ideal, but it is not always a reality. The loyalty of each group to its own culture brings about clashes when that group comes in contact with other ways of life. Sometimes, as in "The Wizard," "Indian Business," and "The Oyster," one way of life must be sacrificed to another.

In Isak Dinesen's "Barua a Soldani" two cultures meet with happy results. There is no clash because the individuals involved—the author and the African natives—meet on terms of good will. Samuel Selvon's "Eraser's Dilemma" is also a demonstration of good will on the part of two people—one British and one West Indian. However, "Eraser's Dilemma" is played out against a background of racial misunderstanding in London.

In others of these selections, two cultures come together less fortunately. The young Navaho of "Indian Business" rides off singing happily, but the reader cannot help but feel that the Navaho way of life is living on borrowed time. George Orwell's "Shooting an Elephant" examines the methods by which one people dominate another. The author, representing colonial authority, does his duty, but the hatred of the Burmese masses weighs heavily on his conscience. Yakolev's "The Wizard" is a study in intolerance: the old and the new meet, and one way of life crumples before the machine guns of another. Rumer Godden's "The Oyster" shows cultural conflict between East and West tearing apart the personality of an individual.

Relations between different ways of life have become an important theme in literature because it is an important problem in the modern world. Writers are concerned with this question: Must the world eventually be dominated by one superculture? Or will it be possible for many people, each with its unique culture, to live together in peace and mutual respect?

Barua a Soldani

ISAK DINESEN

Even in the midst of a civilization supposedly devoted to science, we find signs of ancient superstitions. A pair of dice hangs from the rear-view mirror of a sleek, powerful automobile. People carry rabbits' feet, nail horseshoes over their doors, search for four-leafed clovers. Americans often laugh at these rituals, even as they perform them. Africans, on the other hand, accept magic as one of the elemental properties of nature. (See Camara Laye's "The Snake and the Crocodile," page 417.) In this selection from her memoirs of her own years in Africa, Isak Dinesen (the Baroness Blixen) tells how a simple letter from the King of Denmark came to have healing properties. Whether or not the letter actually performed magic, the fact is that symbolically it came to unite two very different traditions.

WHEN I first came out to Africa I could not live without getting a fine specimen of each single kind of African game. In my last ten years out there I did not fire a shot except in order to get meat for my natives. It became to me an unreasonable thing, indeed in itself ugly or vulgar, for the sake of a few hours' excitement to put out a life that belonged in the great landscape and had grown up in it for ten or twenty, or—as in the case of buffaloes and elephants—for fifty or a hundred years. But lion hunting was irresistible to me; I shot my last lion a short time before I left Africa.

As now on this New Year's morning, as noiselessly as possible I got down from the car and, through the long, wet grass that washed my hands, the rifle, and my face, slowly walked closer to the lion, he stirred, rose and stood up immovable, his shoulder towards me, as fine a target for a shot as in the course of a lifetime you would get anywhere in the world. The sun by now was just below the horizon, the morning sky behind the dark silhouette was clear like liquid gold. I was struck by a thought: "I have seen you before, I know you well. But from where?" The answer came at once: "It is a lion out of the royal coat of arms of Denmark, one of our three dark-blue lions on gold ground. *Lion posant or* it is called in the heraldic language—he knows it himself." As I sat on the ground, got Denys' rifle into position on my knee and took aim, I made a resolution: "If I get this lion, the King of Denmark is to have the skin."

341

ISAK DINESEN (1885–1962) *is the
pseudonym of Baroness Karen Blixen.
She grew up near the sea in the
countryside of Denmark. In 1914 she
married Baron Blixen and accompanied
him to British East Africa to manage a
coffee plantation. Life as a farmer
appealed to her. The strangeness of
Africa excited her, and she began to
write. In 1931, she returned to Denmark
where she continued to produce the
books which have won her an
international reputation. Her stories
and novels are eerie and full of
unexpected appearances, strange
characters, and mysterious settings. Her
accounts of life in Africa are sensitive,
penetrating, compassionate studies of a
people whose culture seems strange but
at its roots displays the basic motives
and beliefs of all mankind. Two of
the books that contain her characteristic
stories are* Seven Gothic Tales *and*
Winter's Tales.

As the shot fell, booming loudly in the still
morning landscape and echoing from the hills,
it looked to me as if the lion was carried a
couple of feet straight upwards into the air before he came down and collapsed. He had been
hit in the heart; it was as it should be.

Now it fell out that this lion was an exceptionally fine specimen, what in his own country
they call a black-maned lion, with his thick dark
mane growing all back over his shoulder blades.
Denys' gun bearer, who had seen many hundred
lion skins, declared this one to be the finest he
had ever come across. And as in that same spring
I was going on a visit to Denmark after four
years in Africa, I took the skin with me and on
my way, in London, gave it to the firm of Rowland Ward to be cured and set up.

When in Denmark I told my friends that I
meant to give King Christian X the lion skin,
they laughed at me and said:

"It is the worst piece of snobbery that we
have ever heard of."

"Nay, but you do not understand," I answered them. "You have not lived for a long
time outside your own country."

"But what in the world is the King to do with
the skin?" they asked. "He does not mean to
appear at New Year's levee as Hercules! He
will be in despair about it."

"Well," I said, "if the King will be in despair,
he will have to be in despair. But I do not think
it need come to that, for he will have some attic
at Christiansborg or Amalienborg [1] where he
can put it away."

It so happened that Rowland Ward did not
manage to have the skin ready by autumn when
I was going back to Africa, so that I could not
myself present it to the King, but had to leave
this privilege to an old uncle of mine who was
a chamberlain to the Court. If the King was
really in despair about it, he hid it very nobly.
Some time after my return to the farm I had a
kind letter from him, in which he thanked me
for his lion skin.

A letter from home always means a lot to
people living for a long time out of their country. They will carry it about in their pocket for
several days, to take it out from time to time
and read it again. A letter from a king will mean

[1] *Christiansborg or Amalienborg* The King's resi-
dences.

more than other letters. I got the King's letter about Christmastime, and I pictured to myself how the King had sat at his writing table at Amalienborg, gazing out over a white Amalienborg Square with the snow-clad equestrian statue of his great-great-great grandfather, King Frederic V, in a wig and classic armor, in the midst of it. A short time ago I myself had been part of the Copenhagen world. I stuck the letter into the pocket of my old khaki slacks and rode out on the farm to inspect the clearing of a piece of woodland where we were to plant coffee, a couple of miles from my house. I rode through the forest, which was still fresh after the short rains. Now once more I was part of the world of Africa.

Half an hour before I came out to the wood fellers a sad accident had taken place amongst them. A young Kikuyu,[2] whose name was Kitau, had not managed to get away quick enough when a big tree fell, and had had one leg crushed beneath it. I heard his long moanings while still at a distance. I speeded up Rouge upon the forest path. When I came to the place of disaster Kitau's fellow workers had dragged him out from beneath the fallen tree and laid him on the grass; they were thronging round him there, separating when I came up, but standing close by to watch the effect of the catastrophe on me and to hear what I would say about it.

Kitau was lying in a pool of blood; his leg had been smashed above the knee and was sticking out from his body at a grotesque angle.

I made the wood fellers hold my horse and sent off a runner to the house to have Farah bring out the car, so that I might drive Kitau to the hospital in Nairobi. But my small Ford box-body car was getting on in years; she rarely consented to run on more than two cylinders and indeed it went against her to be started at all. With a sinking heart I realized that it would be some time before she came up. While waiting for her I sat with Kitau. The

other wood fellers had withdrawn some distance. Kitau was in great pain and weeping.

I always had morphia at hand in my house for injured people of the farm carried up there, but here I had neither the medicine nor the syringe. Kitau, when he realized that I was with him, groaned out dolefully: "*Saidea mimi*" (help me) "*Msabu*."[3] And again: "*Saidea mimi*. Give me some of the medicine that helps people," the while groping over my arm and knee. When out riding on the farm I usually had bits of sugar in my pockets to give to the totos[4] herding their goats and sheep on the plain and, at the sight of me, crying out for sugar. I brought out such bits and fed Kitau with them—he would or could not move his badly bruised hands, and let me place the sugar on his tongue. It was as if this medicine did somehow relieve his pains; his moans, while he had it in his mouth, changed into low whimperings. But my stock of sugar came to an end, and then once more he began to wail and writhe, long spasms ran through his body. It is a sad experience to sit by somebody suffering so direly without being able to help; you long to get up and run away or, as with a badly injured animal, to put an end to the anguish; for a moment I believed I looked round for some kind of weapon for the purpose. Again came the clock-regular moaning of Kitau: "Have you got no more, *Msabu?* Have you got nothing more to give me?"

In my distress I once more put my hand into my pocket and felt the King's letter. "Yes, Kitau," I said, "I have got something more. I have got something *mzuri sana*" (very excellent indeed). "I have got a *Barua a Soldani*" (a letter from a King). "And that is a thing which all people know, that a letter from a King, *mokone yake*" (in his own hand) "will do away with all pain, however bad." At that I laid the King's letter on his chest and my hand upon it. I endeavored, I believe—out there in the forest, where Kitau and I were as if all alone—to lay the whole of my strength into it.

---

[2] *Kikuyu* An African tribe.

[3] *Msabu* Term used for addressing a superior.

[4] *toto* Bantu word for boy.

It was a very strange thing that almost at once the words and the gesture seemed to send an effect through him. His terribly distorted face smoothed out, he closed his eyes. After a while he again looked up at me. His eyes were so much like those of a small child that cannot yet speak that I was almost surprised when he spoke to me: "Yes. It is *mzuri*." And again, "Yes, it is *mzuri sana*. Keep it there."

When at last the car arrived and we got Kitau lifted onto it, I meant to take my seat at the steering wheel, but at that he immediately worked himself into a state of the greatest alarm. "No, *Msabu*," he said, "Farah can drive the car. You must tell him to do so. You will sit beside me and hold the *Barua a Soldani* to my stomach as before, or otherwise the bad pain will come back at once." So I sat on the boards beside him, and all the way into Nairobi held the King's letter in position. When we arrived at the hospital Kitau once more closed his eyes and kept them closed, as if refusing to take in any more impressions. But with his left hand on my clothes he kept sure that I was beside him while I parleyed with the doctor and the matron. They did allow me to keep close beside him while he was laid on the stretcher, carried into the building and placed on the operating table; and as long as I saw him he was quiet.

I may tell that in hospital they did manage to set his broken leg. When he got out he could walk, even if he always limped a little.

I may also tell that later on, in Denmark, I learned from the King himself that my lion skin had obtained a highly honorable place in the stateroom of Christiansborg Castle, with the skin of a polar bear on the other side of the throne.

But now the rumor spread amongst the squatters of my farm that I had this *Barua a Soldani*, with its miracle-working power. They began to come up to my house one by one, warily, to find out more about it—the old women first, mincing about like old hens turning their heads affectedly to find a grain for their young

ones. Soon they took to carrying up those of their sick who were in bad pain, so that they might have the letter laid on them and for a while be relieved. Later they wanted more. They demanded to borrow the King's letter, for the day or for the day and night, to take with them to the hut for the relief of an old dying grandmother or a small ailing child.

Amongst my stock of medicine the *Barua a Soldani* from the very first was accurately and strictly placed in a category of its own. This decision was taken by the natives themselves without my giving any thought to the matter. It would do away with pain; in this capacity it was infallible, and no ache or pang could hold out against it. But it must be made use of solely in uttermost need.

It did happen from time to time that a patient with a very bad toothache in his misery cried out to me to let him have *Barua a Soldani*. But his appeal would be met by those surrounding him with grave disapprovement and indignation or with haughty, scornful laughter. "You!" they cried back to him. "There is nothing the matter with you but that you have got a bad tooth! You can go down to old Juma Bemu and have him pull it out for you. How could you have the King's letter? Nay, but here is old Kathegu very ill in his hut with long, hard pains in his stomach, and going to die tonight. His small grandson is up here to get *Barua a Soldani* for him until tomorrow from *Msabu*. To him she will give it." By this time I had had a leather bag with a string to it made for the King's letter. So the small toto, standing up straight on the terrace, would take the remedy carefully from my hands, hang it round his neck and walk away, with his own hands upon it. He would stand up straight on the terrace again next morning. Ay, his grandfather had died at sunrise, but *Barua a Soldani* had helped him well all night.

I have seen this particular attitude, or this particular mentality, in the dark people in other matters as well. They stood in a particular relation to the ways and conditions of life. There are things which can be done and others which cannot, and they fell in with the law, accepting what came with a kind of aloof humility—or pride.

When Fathima, Farah's wife, was to give birth to her first child, she was very ill; for an hour or two her people, and her mother herself, had given up hope about her. Her mother, an imposing figure in my establishment, had arranged for about a dozen Somali ladies of the first families of Nairobi to be present. They arrived in Aly Khan's mule traps, looking very lovely and lively, like old Persian pictures, in their long ample skirts and veils, and filled with sympathy and zeal. The waves of woman's world closed over Farah's house, at some distance from the huts of my houseboys. Farah himself, grave and more subdued than I had ever seen him, together with all other male creatures of my household, had been shooed a hundred yards away. The women then set to heating up the room in which the birth was taking place to an almost unbearable heat, with charcoal in basins. I sat out there for a while, half unconscious, not because I imagined that I could be of any use, but because I felt it was expected of me.

Fathima was a very lovely creature, with big dark eyes like a doe's, supple in all her movements, in daily life of a risible temper. I felt sorry for her now. For the time that I was there I saw them dealing out only one kind of medicine: a matron amongst them brought along an earthenware dish, on the inner side of which a holy man of the town had drawn up, in charcoal, a text from the Koran; the lettering was washed off carefully with water, and the water poured into Fathima's mouth.

This great event on the farm took place at the time when the Prince of Wales—the present Duke of Windsor—was on his first visit to Nairobi. Among the celebrations in his honor was a *concours hippique,*[5] and I had entered my Irish

[5] *concours hippique* Horse race.

pony Poor-Box for the jumping competition; he was at the moment in training at Limuru. In the midst of the bustle round me and in a moment of things looking very dark, I suddenly called to mind that I had promised to bring over a bag of oats for him there, so I would have to leave for a couple of hours. I drove away sadly, taking Kamante with me.

On the way back from Limuru I came past the French Mission and remembered that the Fathers for some time had been promising me seed of a particular kind of lettuce from France. As I pulled up the car, Kamante, who during our drive had not said a word, spoke to me. Fathima was a favorite with Kamante; she was the only human being for whose intelligence I had ever heard him express any kind of respect. "Are you," he asked me, "going into the church to beg the lady in there, who is your friend, to help Fathima?" The lady in the church, who was my friend, was the Virgin Mary, whose statue Kamante had seen when on Christmas night he had accompanied me to midnight mass. I could not very well say no, so I answered yes, and went into the church. It was cool in the church, and in the face of the papier-mâché statue of the Virgin, with a lily in her hand, there was something soothing and hopeful.

When I came back to my house, Fathima's baby was born, and she herself was doing well. I congratulated her mother and Farah in his forest exile. The small boy brought into the world that day was Ahmed, called Saufe, who later became a great figure on the farm. Kamante said to me: "You see, *Msabu,* it was good that I reminded you to ask the lady who is your friend to help Fathima."

Now, one would have imagined that with knowledge of my intimacy with a person of such power, Kamante upon some other occasion would have come back to have me make use of it. But this never happened. There are things which can be done, and other things which cannot. And we who know the laws must fall in with them.

In the course of time, however, my squatters tried to find out more about that King in my own country who had written the letter. They asked me if he was tall, and were here, I believe, still under the impression of the personality of the Prince of Wales, who had dined on the farm, and who had made them wonder at the fact that a person of such great might should be so slim and slight. I was pleased to be able to reply truthfully that there was not a taller man in his kingdom. They then wanted to know whether the horse on which he rode was more *Kali*—fierce—than my own horse, Rouge; then again, if he laughed. This last must have been a matter of importance to the natives in their relations with us. "Your *kabilla*" (tribe) they said to me, "is different to those of the other white people. You do not get angry with us as they do. You laugh at us."

I still have the King's letter. But it is now undecipherable, brown and stiff with blood and matter of long ago.

In a showcase at the Museum of Rosenborg, in Copenhagen, the tourist can see a piece of yellow texture covered with tawny spots. It is the handkerchief of King Christian IV, which the King held to his eye socket when, in the battle of Kolberger Heide three hundred years ago, his eye was smashed by a Swedish shot. A Danish poet has written an enthusiastic ode about these proud, edifying marks.

The blood on my sheet of paper is not proud or edifying. It is the blood of a dumb nation. But then the handwriting on it is that of a King, *mokone yake*. No ode will be written about my letter; still, today it is, I believe, history as much as the relic of Rosenborg. Within it, in paper and blood, a covenant has been signed between the Europeans and the Africans —no similar document of this same relationship is likely to be drawn up again.

Looking at it I have wondered: "Will anything that I myself have written, *mokone yangu* —by my own hand—to anyone, anywhere, be *Barua a Soldani?*"

For Discussion

1. What is the source of the letter's magic powers? Do you feel that Isak Dinesen wanted to preserve her dignity as a member of a superior culture when she introduced the letter as a cure for pain?

2. How has hypnosis been used in modern medicine? Would you say that the letter anesthetized the patient with a kind of hypnosis?

3. How do the natives regulate the use of the letter? How can you explain the elaborate restrictions and rituals that spring into practice after the letter's capacity to heal has been accepted? Why are the natives careful not to abuse the letter's miraculous power?

4. Why does Isak Dinesen make it very clear that Kamante never again asked her to appeal to the powers of the Virgin Mary? What does this sort of restraint reveal about Kamante? How does Isak Dinesen use this incident to show the depth of character possessed by the natives?

5. What does the last sentence of this selection mean? Do you think that Isak Dinesen writes principally to amuse or to help the reader learn more about the world in which he lives? What lesson can be drawn from Isak Dinesen's description of King Christian's blood-stained handkerchief in the Museum of Rosenborg?

Eraser's Dilemma

SAMUEL SELVON

Until quite recently, the British West Indies had few profitable industries other than the tourist trade. West Indian natives with ambition became frustrated, for there was little opportunity for personal fulfillment beyond the monotony of island life. Following the Second World War, thousands of West Indians began to take advantage of their British citizenship and emigrated to England. Eraser, the West Indian hero of this tale, happily drives his bus along the streets of London, pleasing his passengers with his elaborate courtesy and buoyant cheer. Then, one day he finds that an act of informal honesty can, in the terms of a more formal society, appear dishonest.

The author, Samuel Selvon, is himself a West Indian who has lived for many years in London. He has written this story in a style which attempts to suggest the sing-song pattern of West Indian speech. Notice that the verb is often omitted, as in "he such a cheerful conductor" and "he always there to help her on and off." Other features of the West Indian dialect are the omission of the final s for plurals, as in "one or two letter even appear in the newspaper." The dialect also uses the present tense of the verb for the past, as in "he tell Jack, the driver . . ."

IF YOU are one of the hustlers [1] on Route 12 I don't know how you could fail to notice Eraser, he such a cheerful conductor. And if you look good, under the regulation uniform, you might notice him wearing a happy nylon shirt, green, with red stripes.

That shirt is Eraser's pet wear, and if you have a bus fare and want to take a ride—in fact, the beauty is you might be on his bus now even as you reading this—I will give you the ballad [2] about that happy shirt.

To Londoners a bus is a bus. If you queueing for one and another come along, you just hop in, as long as it take you where you want to go.

[1] *hustlers* West Indian slang: travelers, riders.

[2] *ballad* Story.

The red double-deckers come as nothing,[3] a sight you seeing day in and day out.

Eraser had a different feeling about them. Like how a sailor love his ship, so Eraser love his bus, and it hurt him to go off duty and hand over to another conductor who mightn't feel the way he do. Seeing that he couldn't be sure of always working the same bus, Eraser adopt the route and determine to make it the nicest one in London.

And in point of fact, though I wouldn't say that one man able to work a route smoothly or even one bus on the route for that matter, it is true that from the time Eraser begin to work on Route 12, a change for the better take place.

One or two letter even appear in the newspaper complimenting L.T.[4] on the improvement, and once a lady that was helped on and off a bus write to say how wonderful these West Indians were, that she notice they was extremely kind and polite and did their job well. (I only telling you what the lady say.)

Them kind of letter, you don't see them often, but whenever one appear concerning his route Eraser keep the clipping to send home to St Vincent[5] to his grandmother.

Once he send a photo of the bus he working on. He take it out in the garage, with him hugging the bonnet[6] like how you see them jockeys holding on to the horse neck when they come in first, and he send the photo home.

You should hear them in St Vincent, talking about it, wanting to know why the bus so high, and why it have upstairs and downstairs.

Well, when Eraser on duty, it ain't have nothing like woman standing in his bus at all. From the time that begin to happen Eraser saying out loud: "Which gallant Englishman will give this lady his seat?"

I don't have to tell you what happen when Eraser say that. Everybody get quiet as if they in church. A test[7] working in the City, with bowler and brolly, bury his face in the *Financial Times*. Some fellars looking out the window and admiring the London scenery. Other fellars as if they deaf.

"Come now," you should hear Eraser, "surely there are gentlemen on my bus?"

And eventually one or two fellars would get up, glaring at Eraser, and all the women in the bus would look at him and smile among themselves.

Well, it had one of these old ladies what used to catch Eraser bus as regular as clockwork, and he always there to help her on and off. And they would exchange the usual about the weather, and how are you today, and that sort of thing, and if trade not very busy she would tell Eraser to sing a calypso, and he would oblige, because he is that sort of fellar. I mean, all the time he working he whistling or singing, spreading sunshine in the bus. Nothing could dampen the old Eraser.

What happen one day is this. The old lady get on the bus with a parcel, but when she get off she forget to take it. Other passengers see the parcel, but you know how it is in London, everybody lock-up and suspicious, nobody ain't say a word.

Eraser decide to keep the parcel instead of handing it in at the garage, feeling it would be nice to give it to her himself the next day when she catch the bus, and save her the trouble of going quite to Baker Street to the Lost Property Office.

He tell Jack, the driver, who was a steady, unimaginative fellar about it. Jack just shrug and say if he wanted to take the chance it was his business.

Well the next day when the bus get to the stop where the old lady uses to get on, no old lady there. Eraser get uneasy. These English people, they have habits, and Eraser know she would wait for his bus as she always did all the months he on the route.

---

[3] *come as nothing* Come frequently.
[4] *L.T.* London Transport.
[5] *St Vincent* A small West Indian island.
[6] *bonnet* In America, the hood.
[7] *test* West Indian slang: man.

A double-decker bus in London. The Houses of Parliament and Big Ben are in the background.

He went home worried, but thinking he would see she the next day.

Next day come. No old lady.

Eraser went to Jack when they was having a break for tea at the garage.

"You remember that parcel," Eraser say. "Well, the old lady ain't turn up since."

"Do you know her name?" Jack ask.

"No," Eraser say.

"Isn't there any address on the parcel?" Jack ask.

"No," Eraser say.

"You should have handed it in the first day," Jack say.

"I will wait one more day, maybe she is sick," Eraser say.

Jack shrug and went on with his elevenses.[8]

Well the third day come. By the bus stop, no old lady.

Eraser begin to sweat. He even allow a lady to stand up for five minutes before he realise she should be sitting instead of one of the hulky fellars in the bus. Just because he wanted to do

a good turn, it look like trouble catch up with him.

Eraser get off duty at twelve o'clock and didn't even bother about lunch. He went to the bus stop which part the old lady uses to wait. At this stage the parcel like live coal in his hand, and he praying that he would meet somebody who know her.

But three-four people that he stop and ask, none of them know who he mean.

"It can't be far from here," Eraser say to himself, combing the district around the bus-stop.

And this time, he imagining all sorts of things, how L.T. would want to know why he didn't turn in the parcel, if he didn't know the rules and regulations. They might even think he wanted to thief the parcel. What he would say to all that?

And so he in this panic as he searching, because he like his job and things was going all right until this had to happen.

At last, in a small sweet-shop, he strike some luck. Yes, the attendant think she know who he talking about, an old lady called Miss Bellflent, living at No. 5.

[8] *elevenses* II A.M. break for tea.

Eraser take off in this street looking for No. 5, and he ring all the buzzers it had on the door when he get there. He could hardly ask the landlady for Miss Bellflent when she come to the door.

"Miss Bellflent?" the landlady say. "Why, she left a few days ago. She isn't staying here any more."

Eraser see himself in big trouble, out of a job, no bus to conduct.

"Do you know where she lives now?" he ask weakly.

"No."

In his mind Eraser begin taking off his uniform for the last time. Things always hard on the boys, and now he was having his share. He could imagine what everybody would be saying, oh yes they are cheerful and work well, but after all . . .

And the landlady, as if she could see how important it was, and noticing the disappointment on Eraser's face, say: "Wait a minute," and she went inside.

When she come back she give Eraser a address on a piece of paper. "Try there," she said. Eraser was making up the road before he remember to turn round and shout: "Thank you!"

At last it look like there was still hope, and he race to the address, and when he knock and Miss Bellflent open the door, he feel to kiss her.

"Why, it's you!" Miss Bellflent say. "Do come in!"

And when Eraser get inside, she tell him to sit down and she put the tea-kettle on the fire right away.

"You must have a cup of tea," she said kindly.

"I only came about this parcel which you forgot on the bus," Eraser say, throwing the world off his shoulders, and putting down the parcel on the table and wiping his hands, as if he too glad it was finish with.

"But I meant it for you!" Miss Bellflent say in a matter-of-fact way. "I thought I wrote a note on the box. How absent-minded of me."

"For me?" Eraser stand up by the table as if he stun.

"Yes, of course!" Miss Bellflent say, pouring out the tea. "Go on then, aren't you going to open it?"

Eraser touch the parcel as if he frighten. He loosen the string and open a box.

Inside, it had a happy nylon shirt, green, with red stripes.

For Discussion

1. What about Eraser appeals to his London passengers? What does this story reveal about courtesy on a British bus? How does Eraser make the men give their seats to the standing ladies? How does his method indicate that he has an insight into British character?

2. Study the language of this story. Are there grammatical errors in it? What does this reveal about the person who tells the story? What sort of person is he? How can you tell?

3. Why does the forgotten package take on such a great importance to Eraser? Do the consequences of his action suggest that he is not considered an "equal" in British society? What is the meaning of this sentence: "He could imagine what everybody would be saying, oh yes they are cheerful and work well, but after all . . ."? Is there more at stake in "Eraser's Dilemma" than simply Eraser's honor?

4. What does the green nylon shirt with red stripes represent to Eraser? Why doesn't Miss Bellflent choose a more conservative shirt? Does the loud shirt suggest a basic difference between Eraser's tradition and Miss Bellflent's?

Shooting an Elephant

GEORGE ORWELL

Abraham Lincoln wrote, "As I would not be a slave, so I would not be a master." Colonialism often causes as much grief to the men in power as it does to the men they govern. Even a truly benevolent rule cannot eliminate hostility from a colonial situation. Men of one tradition naturally resent having their lives and national progress guided by men from a different culture. No one has expressed the tensions and discords of colonialism more clearly than George Orwell. Orwell, an Englishman, served in the Indian Imperial Police in Burma from 1922 to 1927. He witnessed the bitterness that lay beneath the surface of Britain's domination of India and Burma. In "Shooting an Elephant" he shows dramatically how a simple disturbance of the peace can turn into a major moral issue.

IN MOULMEIN, in lower Burma, I was hated by large numbers of people—the only time in my life that I have been important enough for this to happen to me. I was subdivisional police officer of the town, and in an aimless, petty kind of way an anti-European feeling was very bitter. No one had the guts to raise a riot, but if a European woman went through the bazaars alone somebody would probably spit betel juice over her dress. As a police officer I was an obvious target and was baited whenever it seemed safe to do so. When a nimble Burman tripped me up on the football field and the referee (another Burman) looked the other way, the crowd yelled with hideous laughter. This happened more than once. In the end the sneering yellow faces of young men that met me everywhere, the insults hooted after me when I was at a safe distance, got badly on my nerves. The young Buddhist priests were the worst of all. There were several thousands of them in the town and none of them seemed to have anything to do except stand on street corners and jeer at Europeans.

All this was perplexing and upsetting. For at that time I had already made up my mind that imperialism was an evil thing and the sooner I chucked up my job and got out of it the better. Theoretically—and secretly, of course—I was all for the Burmese and all against their oppressors, the British. As for the job I was doing, I hated it more bitterly than I can perhaps make clear. In a job like that you see the dirty work of Empire at close quarters. The

GEORGE ORWELL (1903–1950) was the
pseudonym of Eric Blair. Born in Bengal
of English parents, he spent much of
his childhood in India. Later, he attended
Eton on a scholarship, and his essay
"Such, Such Were the Joys" brilliantly
portrays the experiences of a frightened,
sensitive child caught up in the severe
discipline of British education. He served
for five years with the Indian Imperial
Police in Burma. His health began to
decline, and this, combined with his
anti-imperialist sympathies, brought
about his resignation. Burmese Days
contains an account of this period of
his life.

Orwell traveled to Paris and London and
became a writer. Among his best
known works are the novel 1984, *a*
vision of the future in which lies are
spoken as truth and the individual
loses his identity in a superstate. His
satire on communism, Animal Farm,
remains one of the most popular fables
of modern times.

---

wretched prisoners huddling in the stinking cages of the lockups, the gray, cowed faces of the long-term convicts, the scarred buttocks of the men who had been flogged with bamboos —all these oppressed me with an intolerable sense of guilt. But I could get nothing into perspective. I was young and ill-educated and I had had to think out my problems in the utter silence that is imposed on every Englishman in the East. I did not even know that the British Empire is dying, still less did I know that it is a great deal better than the younger empires that are going to supplant it. All I knew was that I was stuck between my hatred of the empire I served and my rage against the evil-spirited little beasts who tried to make my job impossible. With one

part of my mind I thought of the British Raj as an unbreakable tyranny, as something clamped down, *in saecula saeculorum,*[1] upon the will of prostrate peoples; with another part I thought that the greatest joy in the world would be to drive a bayonet into a Buddhist priest's guts. Feelings like these are the normal by-product of imperialism; ask any Anglo-Indian official, if you can catch him off duty.

One day something happened which in a roundabout way was enlightening. It was a tiny incident in itself, but it gave me a better glimpse than I had had before of the real nature of imperialism—the real motives for which despotic governments act. Early one morning the sub-inspector at a police station the other end of the town rang me up on the phone and said that an elephant was ravaging the bazaar. Would I please come and do something about it? I did not know what I could do, but I wanted to see what was happening and I got on to a pony and started out. I took my rifle, an old .44 Winchester and much too small to kill an elephant, but I thought the noise might be useful *in terrorem.*[2] Various Burmans stopped me on the way and told me about the elephant's doings. It was not, of course, a wild elephant, but a tame one which had gone "must."[3] It had been chained up, as tame elephants always are when their attack of "must" is due, but on the previous night it had broken its chain and escaped. Its mahout,[4] the only person who could manage it when it was in that state, had set out in pursuit, but had taken the wrong direction and was now twelve hours' journey away, and in the morning the elephant had suddenly reappeared in the town. The Burmese population had no weapons and were quite helpless against it. It had already destroyed somebody's bamboo hut, killed a cow and raided some fruit stalls and devoured the stock; also it had met the municipal rubbish van

---

[1] *in saecula saeculorum* Latin: for ages and ages.
[2] *in terrorem* For causing fear.
[3] *"must"* Wild, mad.
[4] *mahout* Elephant driver.

and, when the driver jumped out and took to his heels, had turned the van over and inflicted violences upon it.

The Burmese subinspector and some Indian constables were waiting for me in the quarter where the elephant had been seen. It was a very poor quarter, a labyrinth of squalid huts, thatched with palm leaf, winding all over a steep hillside. I remember that it was a cloudy, stuffy morning at the beginning of the rains. We began questioning the people as to where the elephant had gone and, as usual, failed to get any definite information. That is invariably the case in the East; a story always sounds clear enough at a distance, but the nearer you get to the scene of events the vaguer it becomes. Some of the people said that the elephant had gone in one direction, some said that he had gone in another, some professed not even to have heard of any elephant. I had almost made up my mind that the whole story was a pack of lies, when we heard yells a little distance away. There was a loud, scandalized cry of "Go away, child! Go away this instant!" and an old woman with a switch in her hand came round the corner of a hut, violently shooing away a crowd of naked children. Some more women followed, clicking their tongues and exclaiming; evidently there was something the children ought not to have seen. I rounded the hut and saw a man's dead body sprawling in the mud. He was an Indian, a black Dravidian [5] coolie, almost naked, and he could not have been dead many minutes. The people said that the elephant had come suddenly upon him round the corner of the hut, caught him with its trunk, put its foot on his back, and ground him into the earth. This was the rainy season and the ground was soft, and his face had scored a trench a foot deep and a couple of yards long. He was lying on his belly with arms crucified and head sharply twisted to one side. His face was coated with mud, the eyes wide open, the teeth bared and grinning with an un-

endurable agony. (Never tell me, by the way, that the dead look peaceful. Most of the corpses I have seen looked devilish.) The friction of the great beast's foot had stripped the skin from his back as neatly as one' skins a rabbit. As soon as I saw the dead man I sent an orderly to a friend's house nearby to borrow an elephant rifle. I had already sent back the pony, not wanting it to go mad with fright and throw me if it smelt the elephant.

The orderly came back in a few minutes with a rifle and five cartridges, and meanwhile some Burmans had arrived and told us that the elephant was in the paddy fields below, only a few hundred yards away. As I started forward, practically the whole population of the quarter flocked out of the houses and followed me. They had seen the rifle and were all shouting excitedly that I was going to shoot the elephant. They had not shown much interest in the elephant when he was merely ravaging their homes, but it was different now that he was going to be shot. It was a bit of fun to them, as it would be to an English crowd; besides they wanted the meat. It made me vaguely uneasy. I had no intention of shooting the elephant—I had merely sent for the rifle to defend myself if necessary —and it is always unnerving to have a crowd following you. I marched down the hill, looking and feeling a fool, with the rifle over my shoulder and an ever-growing army of people jostling at my heels. At the bottom, when you got away from the huts, there was a metaled road and beyond that a miry waste of paddy fields a thousand yards across, not yet plowed but soggy from the first rains and dotted with coarse grass. The elephant was standing eight yards from the road, his left side toward us. He took not the slightest notice of the crowd's approach. He was tearing up bunches of grass, beating them against his knees to clean them, and stuffing them into his mouth.

I had halted on the road. As soon as I saw the elephant I knew with perfect certainty that I ought not to shoot him. It is a serious matter

[5] *Dravidian* An ancient Indian race.

to shoot a working elephant—it is comparable to destroying a huge and costly piece of machinery—and obviously one ought not to do it if it can possibly be avoided. And at that distance, peacefully eating, the elephant looked no more dangerous than a cow. I thought then and I think now that his attack of "must" was already passing off; in which case he would merely wander harmlessly about until the mahout came back and caught him. Moreover, I did not in the least want to shoot him. I decided that I would watch him for a little while to make sure that he did not turn savage again, and then go home.

But at that moment I glanced round at the crowd that had followed me. It was an immense crowd, two thousand at the least and growing every minute. It blocked the road for a long distance on either side. I looked at the sea of yellow faces above the garish clothes—faces all happy and excited over this bit of fun, all certain that the elephant was going to be shot. They were watching me as they would watch a conjurer about to perform a trick. They did not like me, but with the magical rifle in my hands I was momentarily worth watching. And suddenly I realized that I would have to shoot the elephant after all. The people expected it of me and I had got to do it; I could feel their two thousand wills pressing me forward irresistibly. And it was at this moment, as I stood there with the rifle in my hands, that I first grasped the hollowness, the futility of the white man's dominion in the East. Here was I, the white man with his gun, standing in front of the unarmed native crowd—seemingly the leading actor of the piece; but in reality I was only an absurd puppet pushed to and fro by the will of those yellow faces behind. I perceived in this moment that when the white man turns tyrant it is his own freedom that he destroys. He becomes a sort of hollow, posing dummy, the conventionalized figure of a sahib.[6] For it is the condition of his rule that he shall spend his life in

trying to impress the "natives," and so in every crisis he has got to do what the "natives" expect of him. He wears a mask, and his face grows to fit it. I had got to shoot the elephant. I had committed myself to doing it when I sent for the rifle. A sahib has got to act like a sahib; he has got to appear resolute, to know his own mind and do definite things. To come all that way, rifle in hand, with two thousand people marching at my heels, and then to trail feebly away, having done nothing—no, that was impossible. The crowd would laugh at me. And my whole life, every white man's in the East, was one long struggle not to be laughed at.

But I did not want to shoot the elephant. I watched him beating his bunch of grass against his knees, with that preoccupied grandmotherly air that elephants have. It seemed to me that it would be murder to shoot him. At that age I was not squeamish about killing animals, but I had never shot an elephant and never wanted to. (Somehow it always seems worse to kill a *large* animal.) Besides, there was the beast's owner to be considered. Alive, the elephant was worth at least a hundred pounds; dead, he would only be worth the value of his tusks, five pounds, possibly. But I had got to act quickly. I turned to some experienced-looking Burmans who had been there when we arrived, and asked them how the elephant had been behaving. They all said the same thing; he took no notice of you if you left him alone, but he might charge if you went too close to him.

It was perfectly clear to me what I ought to do. I ought to walk up to within, say, twenty-five yards of the elephant and test his behavior. If he charged, I could shoot; if he took no notice of me, it would be safe to leave him until the mahout came back. But also I knew that I was going to do no such thing. I was a poor shot with a rifle and the ground was soft mud into which one would sink at every step. If the elephant charged and I missed him, I should have about as much chance as a toad under a steam roller. But even then I was not thinking particularly of my own skin, only of the watch-

---

[6] *sahib* Native term for a European.

ful yellow faces behind. For at that moment, with the crowd watching me, I was not afraid in the ordinary sense, as I would have been if I had been alone. A white man mustn't be frightened in front of "natives"; and so, in general, he isn't frightened. The sole thought in my mind was that if anything went wrong those two thousand Burmans would see me pursued, caught, trampled on, and reduced to a grinning corpse like that Indian up the hill. And if that happened it was quite probable that some of them would laugh. That would never do. There was only one alternative. I shoved the cartridges into the magazine and lay down on the road to get a better aim.

The crowd grew very still, and a deep, low, happy sigh, as of people who see the theater curtain go up at last, breathed from innumerable throats. They were going to have their bit of fun after all. The rifle was a beautiful German thing with cross-hair sights. I did not then know that in shooting an elephant one would shoot to cut an imaginary bar running from earhole to earhole. I ought, therefore, as the elephant was sideways on, to have aimed straight at his earhole; actually I aimed several inches in front of this, thinking the brain would be further forward.

When I pulled the trigger I did not hear the bang or feel the kick—one never does when a shot goes home—but I heard the devilish roar of glee that went up from the crowd. In that instant, in too short a time, one would have thought, even for the bullet to get there, a mysterious, terrible change had come over the elephant. He neither stirred nor fell, but every line of his body had altered. He looked suddenly stricken, shrunken, immensely old, as though the frightful impact of the bullet had paralyzed him without knocking him down. At last, after what seemed a long time—it might have been five seconds, I dare say—he sagged flabbily to his knees. His mouth slobbered. An enormous senility seemed to have settled upon him. One could have imagined him thousands of years old. I fired again into the same spot. At the second shot

he did not collapse but climbed with desperate slowness to his feet and stood weakly upright, with legs sagging and head drooping. I fired a third time. That was the shot that did for him. You could see the agony of it jolt his whole body and knock the last remnant of strength from his legs. But in falling he seemed for a moment to rise, for as his hind legs collapsed beneath him he seemed to tower upward like a huge rock toppling, his trunk reaching skywards like a tree. He trumpeted for the first and

An elephant being led to work on a Burmese teak plantation

only time. And then down he came, his belly toward me, with a crash that seemed to shake the ground even where I lay.

I got up. The Burmans were already racing past me across the mud. It was obvious that the elephant would never rise again, but he was not dead. He was breathing very rhythmically with long rattling gasps, his great mound of a side painfully rising and falling. His mouth was wide open—I could see far down into caverns of pale pink throat. I waited a long time for him to die, but his breathing did not weaken. Finally I fired my two remaining shots into the spot where I thought his heart must be. The thick blood welled out of him like red velvet, but still he did not die. His body did not even jerk when the shots hit him, the tortured breathing continued without a pause. He was dying, very slowly and in great agony, but in some world remote from me where not even a bullet could damage him further. I felt that I had got to put an end to that dreadful noise. It seemed dreadful to see the great beast lying there, powerless to move and yet powerless to die, and not even to be able to finish him. I sent back for my small rifle and poured shot after shot into his heart and down his throat. They seemed to make no impression. The tortured gasps continued as steadily as the ticking of a clock.

In the end I could not stand it any longer and went away. I heard later that it took him half an hour to die. Burmans were bringing dahs [7] and baskets even before I left, and I was told they had stripped his body almost to the bones by the afternoon.

Afterwards, of course, there were endless discussions about the shooting of the elephant. The owner was furious, but he was only an Indian and could do nothing. Besides, legally I had done the right thing, for a mad elephant has to be killed, like a mad dog, if its owner fails to control it. Among the Europeans, opinion was divided. The older men said I was right, the younger men said it was a shame to shoot an elephant for killing a coolie, because an elephant was worth more than any Coringhee coolie. And afterwards I was very glad that the coolie had been killed; it put me legally in the right and it gave me a sufficient pretext for shooting the elephant. I often wondered whether any of the others grasped that I had done it solely to avoid looking a fool.

For Discussion

1. In this account, does Orwell accept his duties without reservation? Does his attitude indicate a disloyalty to his own government? Does he reveal British cruelty to the Indians? Why? Does he confess where his sympathies lie in the antagonism between the Burmese and the British?

2. In "Shooting an Elephant" does Orwell find no major fault with the Burmese? List the virtues he names. List the failings. What does a comparison of these two lists reveal?

3. In *The Republic*, Plato, the Greek philosopher, says that the tyrant is the most oppressed victim of his own tyranny. His actions tend to create enemies, and as a result he has to spend most of his time guarding his own safety. Can you find a similar pattern in "Shooting an Elephant"? Who is the tyrant? Does this explain why Orwell spends so much time debating whether or not he should shoot the elephant? Of whom is he afraid?

4. In most moral actions, it is difficult to know the right or wrong thing, even after the event. Does this occur in "Shooting an Elephant"? Is Orwell convinced that he has done the right thing? The wrong thing? Neither?

5. Do some of the Burmese values surprise or shock you? Why is an elephant so important in this society? Do we have things of comparable importance in our own society? Why, in our own frontier West, were horse thieves hanged?

---

[7] *dahs* Bowls.

His Mother's People

CHARLES B. NORDHOFF AND JAMES N. HALL

Tahiti and other Polynesian islands have always attracted men who have grown weary of Western civilization's hectic pace. The nineteenth-century Nantucket whaling ships stopped in these ports for fresh water and fruit and brought back the first stories of the flowery charm of a childlike people who lived in a perpetual summertime. The novelists Herman Melville, Robert Louis Stevenson, Joseph Conrad, and James Michener have all found romance and beauty in the South Pacific and have written fine books about it. Paul Gauguin, the French artist, spent the last years of his life on Tahiti, painting the place he felt to be the highest expression of natural beauty on earth. "His Mother's People" is the story of a young man's return to the island of his birth after he has completed his education in England and has distinguished himself in war. In his veins throb the impulses of two separate traditions. Nordhoff and Hall here write a romantic and dramatic tale of the choice the young man is forced to make.

"HIS REAL name was Warner—a big, blue-eyed man, slow-spoken and a little dreamy in manner, with an immense blond mustache and a serenity nothing could disturb. I never knew him to hesitate in making a decision or to speak unless he had something to say. All decent men liked him, and the natives, who were better able than a white man to fathom his simplicity, took to him from the first. He had been miserably out of place in England—squeezed through Cambridge, which he detested, unhappily married, done out of a fortune by the defaulting brother-in-law whose last debt he paid, and divorced just before he came out here.

"It is often observed that when an Englishman's feelings are hurt he travels, and in this respect Varana was not exceptional. One day, a little more than a generation ago, he stepped off the mail boat at Papeete [1]—a rather typical English tourist, I fancy—dressed in tropical costumes from Bond Street and accompanied by an extraordinary quantity of luggage. At the club he ran across Jackson of the Atoll Trading Company—the old man liked him from the first and they used to spend the evenings together, lingering over their glasses,

[1] *Papeete* Main seaport of Tahiti, lying half way between South America and Australia.

357

CHARLES B. NORDHOFF (*1887–1947*) *and*
JAMES N. HALL (*1887–1951*) *formed an*
immensely successful writing team.
They met when they served together as
aviators in the First World War. After
the war, they sought to escape the
pressures of civilization by living in the
South Sea Islands. Later, however, they
returned to the United States. Tahiti
and the islands near it form a background
for many of their books, among which
is the famous Mutiny on the Bounty.

---

talking a little in low tones. A fortnight later
Varana left as quietly as he had come—outbound
in one of Jackson's schooners for a cruise
through the Paumotus.[2]

"It was the year of the hurricane at Motutangi.[3] Varana's boat, commanded by a native
skipper, had drifted through the group in a
desultory way, touching at an island here and
there to pick up a few tons of copra or a bit of
shell. One can imagine the effect on a newcomer of those early days among the atolls—
long sunlit days when gentle breezes filled the
sails of the vessel skirting the shores of the
lagoons—waters of unearthly peace and love-
liness, bordered by leagues of green. And the
nights ashore, when the moon rose at the end
of a path of rippling silver, and the people
gathered before their thatched houses to sing.
. . . It was not long before Varana realized
that he had found his anodyne.

"At home he had been a yachtsman of sorts;
by the time they reached Motutangi the brown
skipper was leaving a good part of the working
of the schooner to his guest. They were diving
in the lagoon that year at the end of a long
rahui on the shell [4]—a sort of closed season,
scrupulously respected by the natives; half a

dozen schooners were anchored off the village,
where every house overflowed with people
from the surrounding islands, and by day their
canoes blackened the water above the patches
of shell.

"The hurricane gave ample warning of its
approach—Varana told me as much as that. He
had spent the night ashore with a trader, whose
old glass [5] rose and fell spasmodically, sinking
always a little lower, until it stood at a figure
which sent the trader off, white and cursing,
to break open a fresh case of gin. None of the
divers went out at daybreak; with the other
people, they stood in little frightened groups before the houses. The older men were already
beginning to hack off the tops of the stout
palms in which they planned to roost. By the
time Varana came off in a canoe the schooners
were double anchored, the wind was shifting
uneasily in sharp gusts, and a tremendous surf
was thundering on the outer beach. The native
skipper, like the people ashore, knew perfectly
well what was coming and, like most of his
kind, his spirit broke in the face of a large
emergency—before the feeling that the forces
of nature were about to overwhelm him. Well,
I've been through one hurricane—I can't say
that I blame him much! Varana found him not
exactly in a funk, but in a state of passive resignation, hoping vaguely that his two anchors
would let him ride it out inside. The crew
was clustered on the after deck, exchanging
scared whispers. Varana, who had the instinct
of a deep-water sailor, took in the situation at
a glance, and next moment he had taken command of the schooner.

"Without a word of protest the men reefed,
got sail on her, heaved up one anchor, and cut
the other cable. Varana had very little to say
about the rest—how he edged out through the
pass and managed to claw off just as the cyclone
struck Motutangi—but afterward the story went
the rounds of every group. All the other schooners in the lagoon, as well as most of the people

---

[2] *Paumotus* Group of neighboring islands.
[3] *Motutangi* One of the Paumotu islands.
[4] *rahui on the shell* A season during which the
gathering of shells for mother-of-pearl is suspended.

[5] *glass* Barometer.

ashore, were lost. How Varana weathered it, without piling up his vessel on any one of half a dozen atolls, is a sort of miracle.

"A week later, when he had sailed his battered schooner—the only survivor of the disaster at Motutangi—into Papeete harbor, he found himself famous by nightfall, for the native captain gave him entire credit for the achievement. Old Jackson's imagination was touched, or perhaps it was the destruction of so many rival schooners in the shell and copra trade—at any rate, he acted on impulse for once in his life, sent for Varana, and offered him a remarkably good berth with a fat screw [6] attached. But the wanderer only smiled and shook his head—he had had a taste of the outer islands. It shakes one's faith in Providence to realize that most men die without finding the place in life for which they were designed.

"It was old Jackson who told him of Rimarutu [7]—probably during one of their almost silent evenings at the club. It was a mistake—Jackson thought—to believe that a man could shut himself off from the world; the mood would pass in time, but if Varana wished seriously to try it, he would find no better place than Rimarutu. There was some copra to be had and a little shell in the lagoon; the people numbered about two hundred, a quiet, pleasant lot, not given to wandering from their island. Varana had salvaged a few thousand pounds from the wreck of his affairs at home; Jackson helped him pick up a schooner at a bargain and load her with what was needed; there was some difficulty about a crew, but his uncanny gift with the natives got him three men content to follow his fortunes. On the morning when he shook hands with the old man, stepped aboard his boat, and sailed out of the harbor, Varana severed the last tie with the world he had known.

"I could tell you a good deal about his life on the island—I worked with him for nearly ten years. He began by renting a bit of land—for his store and copra shed—from the chief and setting himself to learn the language. The Polynesian is a shrewd judge of character; they saw that this man was just, kindly, fearless, and to be trusted. Those who had traveled a little declared Varana a phenomenon—a white trader who respected women and never lay on his veranda in a stupor, surrounded by empty bottles. He seemed to know instinctively the best way to take these people, with whom, from the very first, he found himself on terms of a mutual understanding. They regarded him with a mixture of liking and respect, not accorded us, perhaps, as often as we are apt to think; he worked with them, he played with them, and finally took a daughter of the island as his wife—yet it was characteristic that he never permitted himself to run barefoot and that even after twenty years of friendship the native entering Varana's house took off his hat. I remember Tupuna as a woman of thirty—tall, robust, and grave, with delicate hands and masses of bright, rippling hair; the years were kind to her—even in middle life she did not lose a certain quiet charm. Make no mistake—they were happily mated, this man, turned out by what Englishmen believe the highest civilization in the world, and the daughter of an island chief whose father had been a savage and an eater of men. She was not spoiled like so many traders' wives; when they had been on the reef she walked home behind, carrying the torches and the fish—but he felt for her an affection deep as it was undemonstrative, a strong attachment, proven at the end in his extreme and romantic way.

"During the early years of his life on Rimarutu, Varana had enough to do with his store, his occasional trips for supplies, and his work for the betterment of the island people. He found them living on fish and coconuts, depending for all their luxuries on a dwindling production of copra. He showed them how to thin their palms, how to select nuts for new

[6] *screw* Salary.
[7] *Rimarutu* A small island.

plantings, how to dry their copra with a minimum of effort. The shell in the lagoon was nearly exhausted; he persuaded the chiefs of the two villages to forbid diving for a term of years. After experiments conducted with Tupuna's aid he set the men to catching flying fish, which swarmed in the waters about the island, and taught the women to split them, rub in salt, and dry them on lines in the sun. Rimarutu is high, as atolls go—five or six yards above the sea in spots; he laid out beds of *puraka taro*,[8] and had pits dug on the high portions of the island, lined the bottoms with rock to keep the taproots from salt water, filled them with humus and topsoil—scraped up in handfuls—and planted breadfruit, mango, and lime, brought from the high islands to the north. At long intervals, when in need of something that only civilization could supply—paint, rigging, or a new set of sails—he went north with a cargo of copra and dried fish and took on a brief charter with Jackson. On these trips he visited scores of islands and came to know the people of a thousand miles of ocean.

"It was not until his son was born that Varana began to think seriously of money. His daughters had given him no concern; he explained to me once his peculiar philosophy as to their future. Perhaps he was right. With their happiness in mind, he preferred to bring them up as island girls—without education or knowledge of the outside world and no greater prospects than those of their full-blooded playmates—rather than give them the chances of the usual halfcaste: half-educated and partially Europeanized, whose most brilliant hope is marriage with a white man of the inferior sort. But the birth of Terii set the father to thinking.

"The child was about ten when I saw him first, a fine strong boy, very fair for a half-caste with his father's eyes, a high carriage of the head, and skin touched with a faint bloom of the sun. Tupuna was immensely proud of him.

I was a youngster then and new to the islands, but I had heard of Varana before Jackson introduced me to him. It was at Jackson's place, on the upper veranda, that he told me how he had leased Fatuhina;[9] some one had spoken of my work. I had operated diving machines? He needed a man familiar with them, for he had leased an atoll with some big shell patches in the lagoon, and machines would be necessary to work the deeper portions. I was doing nothing at the time. I liked what I had heard of Varana, and I liked the man better still. In an hour we had come to an understanding. I worked with him, off and on, from that time until the beginning of the war.

"Without caring in the least for wealth, Varana had set out to make himself rich. Long before I knew him he had decided the question of his son: Terii was to have the same chances that his father had had before him—was to see both sides and choose for himself.

"Even Varana's friends spoke of his luck; to my mind his success was inevitable. Regarded with an almost superstitious affection by the people of widely scattered groups, he possessed channels of information closed forever to the ordinary man. It was in this way that he learned of the shell in Fatuhina lagoon; perhaps he did not know that the native who approached him, one evening on a distant atoll, to speak casually of the matter and stroll away, had paddled across twelve miles of sea with no other object than to bring the news to Varana. When the *Gaviota*[10] was beached he was the first to learn of it—that affair alone brought him a neat fortune; and when men had fine pearls to sell they saw him. By the time his son was twelve Varana was a rich man.

"I was on Rimarutu when he left to take the boy to England. Tupuna shed a few tears, but there was no scene—she knew he would return. 'I go to take our son to my own land,' he told her; 'there will be six moons before I come.'

[8] *puraka taro* A tropical plant which produces edible starchy roots.

[9] *Fatuhina* An island atoll.
[10] *Gaviota* Name of a ship.

Five months later I was waiting with the schooner when he stepped off the mail boat. That night, as he lay on a mat on the afterdeck, dressed in a *pareu*[11] and a pair of slippers, he spoke of England briefly in the midst of our talk on island matters. 'Senseless treadmill,' he remarked; 'I can't think how I stood it so many years.' The ordinary man, who had left home under a cloud of misfortune to return twenty years later, after wandering in distant lands, with a fortune and a beautiful child, would have lingered not without a certain relish. But Varana was different; he grudged every moment spent in civilization and lived only for the day when he would again take the wheel of his schooner and watch the ridges of Tahiti sink beneath the horizon.

"The years passed rapidly and tranquilly on Rimarutu. The days of Varana's activity were over; he was no longer young, though he kept his store and took the schooner out at long intervals for supplies. Then came the outbreak of the war.

"I was in Gallipoli when the letter reached me, written in the native language by Varana's old mate. It told a story fantastically unreal—incredible from the viewpoint of everyday life—and yet to me who knew him, as to the people of his island, the end of Varana seemed a natural thing, in keeping with what had gone before. Tupuna had fallen ill (the old man wrote) and had died suddenly and peacefully, as natives do. Varana stood beside her grave with no great display of grief, returned to his house and spent three days putting his affairs in order. On the fourth day he gave the mate a thick envelope of documents, called together the people of the island and bade each one of them farewell. When he turned to leave they did not disperse; the women had begun to sob—they felt already the desolation of a final parting. It was the hour of sunset, when the trade wind dies away and the lagoon lies like a mirror under an opalescent sky. . . . I can see in imagination those

simple and friendly islanders, standing in little groups before the settlement—raising no voice in protest, moving no hand in restraint—while the man they loved walked to the ocean beach, launched a tiny canoe in the surf, and paddled out to the west. The nearest land in that direction is distant six hundred miles. When he had passed the breakers—they say—Varana did not once turn his head; the watchers stood motionless while the sky faded, their eyes fixed on the dot that was his canoe—a dwindling dot, swallowed up at last in the night."

Tari ceased to speak. He was sitting propped on the lounge, arms folded, legs stretched out, eyes staring at the table. Without seeming aware of what he did, he filled his glass, raised it to his lips, and drank. Presently he emerged from his revery to light a pipe.

"In due time," he went on, "I had word from the lawyers, inclosing a copy of the will and informing me that I had been named executor with old Jackson, who seemed to have discovered the secret of eternal life. There was also a letter from Varana, written after Tupuna's death—a friendly and casual note, with a mere line at the end, asking me to do what I could for his boy. The land Tupuna had brought him was to be divided equally among his daughters; all the rest was for Terii, saving his parting gift to me. Only one condition was attached—Terii must visit Rimarutu before inheriting the property of his father; once he had set foot on the island, he would be his own master, free to choose his path in life.

"The boy was nineteen when the war broke out; he joined up at once as a cadet in the Flying Corps. During the second year I began to hear of Lieutenant Warner—he had shot down a German plane near Zeebrugge; he had been wounded; he had received the Military Cross. Once I saw his picture in the *Sphere*[12]—a handsome lad, very smart in the

---

[11] *pareu* Cotton loin cloth.

[12] *Sphere* A local paper.

*"The island was like the memory of a dream—fresh green palms, . . .
cat's-paws ruffling the lagoon in long, blue streaks . . ."*

old uniform of the R.F.C.,[13] with a jaunty cap over one eye and ribbons on his breast. This was the little savage whose shrill cries I used to hear at dawn, when he raced with his half-naked companions on the beach! At the end of the war he was Captain Terry Warner, a celebrity in a small way. . . . I felt a certain pride in him, of course. We had done our best to meet, but something always happened to prevent my getting a glimpse of him.

[13] *R.F.C.* Royal Flying Corps.

"I ran across him as I was homeward bound, leaving San Francisco for the islands. I had already gone aboard and was standing by the rail, watching the last of the luggage swing over the side in nets, when a motor drove up to discharge a party of men and women—fashionables of the city, from their looks. One of them, a lean, tanned boy, with the overcoat of a British officer over his civilian clothes, was saying good-by to the others, shaking hands and smiling very attractively. A little later, when the lines were being cast off, I saw him close beside me at the rail. A girl in blue was standing on the dock, waving up at him. 'Good-by, Terry!' she called. I looked closely; there could be no doubt—it was the son of Varana.

"We had long talks on the voyage south; the lad had not forgotten me. The memory of the old life—of the island, of his mother, of his father—would always be fresh in his mind, but he regarded those days as a distant and beautiful episode, now forever closed. He was going to visit Rimarutu for the last time—to bid farewell to those who remembered him. He had not forgotten the friends of his boyhood; there were many little presents in his boxes, and he told me that the schooner—reported sound as on the day of her launching—would be his gift to Varana's old mate. Afterward he would return to San Francisco, where opportunities had been offered him; he had brought letters to America and had been well received.

"The schooner was in port when we arrived. Varana's mate met us on the dock; there were tears in the old man's eyes as he took the boy's hands in his own and murmured in a trembling voice, '*O Terii iti e.*' [14] The tourists descending the gangplank looked with interest at the spectacle of Captain Warner, almost embracing an old barefoot *kanaka*,[15] dressed in dungarees and a faded shirt, wrinkled brown face working with emotion. As Terii shook hands with the crew—some of them boys with whom he had played in childhood—I noticed that a phrase or two of the native came to his lips—twelve years had not been sufficient to blot all memory of his mother's tongue.

"We had a long passage south, beating against the trade; Varana had installed an engine in the schooner, but time is cheaper than petrol in this part of the world. Terii delighted in handling the boat; there was salt water in his blood; and his father had seen to his training in navigation and the ways of the sea. With each new day I perceived symptoms of a change in the boy. White suits and canvas slippers gave way to pajamas and bare feet; finally the pajamas were replaced by a *pareu*, taken from the trade-room stock. The summers at home had not been wasted; I used to watch him at the wheel, working the schooner to windward, an eye on the canvas aloft, steering with the easy certain movements of a seaman born. He was in love with the schooner before we had been out a week, and he had reason—Frisco-built for the last of the pelagic sealing, Varana's boat was the fastest thing of her tonnage in the South Seas. More than once in our talks Terii seemed to forget the plans he had confided to me. . . . She needed a new foresail; the set of this one did not please him; he was going to have her copper renewed in places; she was getting dingy below; the cabin needed a touch of paint. At times, speaking of these things, he stopped short in the midst of a sentence and changed the talk to other subjects. The language came back to him surprisingly; he was able to understand and make himself understood before we raised the palms of Rimarutu.

"The mate took her in through the pass. It was late afternoon, cool and cloudless, with a gentle sea nuzzling at the reef. The island was like the memory of a dream—fresh green palms, snowy beaches, cat's-paws ruffling the lagoon in long, blue streaks—so beautiful that the sight of it made one's heart ache and the breath catch in one's throat. A dozen canoes put out to meet us from the first settlement; there were greetings from friends and relatives—embraces and tears. Terii lay silent, propped on his elbows and staring ahead, as we slipped across the lagoon; the island people spoke in tones so low that I could hear the crisp sound of the schooner's bows parting the landlocked water. The other village lay beyond the beach ahead of us, Varana's village, where Terii had been born—a place of dreams in the mystery of the evening light. It was not difficult to guess at the boy's

---

[14] '*O Terii iti e*'   'O, Terii, you are home.'
[15] *kanaka*   Native of the South Sea Islands.

thoughts—the moment was one of those which make up the memories of a lifetime. Every man has known them—rapture, pain, the enjoyment of supreme beauty, the flavor of exotic and unrepeatable experience; but not every man is permitted to taste such contrasts as this boy had known in twenty-four years of life. . . . I was a little envious, I think, of the rarity of that poignant home-coming.

"On the first evening, when we had greeted the people of the village, Terii was led away by his old aunt, Tupuna's sister. Just before bedtime I saw them at his mother's grave—a lonely shrine, roofed over in island fashion, where the light of a lamp shone on stunted bushes of frangipani.[16] My eccentricities were not forgotten; they had spread my mat under the palms before Varana's house, and toward midnight Terii came quietly and lay down close by. I was wakeful in a revery, living over the old days with my friend, wondering, with the usual idle and somber doubt, if we were destined to meet again. Low over the palm tops a planet glimmered like a shaded lamp; the Milky Way arched overhead through a sky powdered with fixed stars—remote suns, about which revolve myriads of worlds like ours. . . . I rebelled at the thought that the strong soul of Varana should be snuffed out. Terii said nothing for a long time; I thought he had dropped off to sleep, but suddenly I heard his voice: 'If my father were here I could believe that I had never been away, that everything since I left—England, school, my friends, the war—was no more than a dream. I can't explain to you, but somehow this island seems the most real thing in the world. I've been talking to my aunt—I'd almost forgotten her name, you know—and I managed to understand a good bit of what she had to say. . . . There is no doubt she believes it herself. My father comes to her every now and then, she says, for a talk on family matters; last night he

[16] *frangipani* A tropical shrub.

told her we would come today, and that I would stop here to take his old place among the people. It seems they are good enough to want me to stay—I almost wish I could.' . . .

"The drums were going at daybreak—the feast in Terii's honor was the greatest the island had known since heathen days. The entire population was on hand; the beach black with canoes; dozens of good-humored babies on mats under the trees, with small brothers and sisters stationed to fan the flies away. The people sat in long rows in the shade, strings of shell about their necks, their heads wreathed in hibiscus and sweet fern. Terii was placed between the chief of the other village and Tehina, the chief's daughter, a full-blooded Rimarutu girl of sixteen, barefoot, dressed in a white frock, with gold pendants in her ears and a thick, shining braid of hair. There is an uncommon charm about the women of that island—a stamp of refinement, a delicacy of frame and feature, remarked as long ago as the days of Spanish voyaging in the Pacific. Blood counts for something in Polynesia, and one needed only a glance at Tehina to know that the best blood of the island flowed in her veins; her ancestor—if tradition may be credited—was in the long canoe with Penipeni when the god pulled Rimarutu up from the bottom of the sea. I like those people, and in spite of the night's depression I managed to enjoy the fun—I even danced a bit! Finally I saw that the dancers were taking their seats; voices were lowered, heads were turned.

"Tehina was dancing alone to the rhythm of a hundred clapping hands. In twenty years of the islands I have never seen a girl step more daintily. Little by little she moved toward Terii until she stood directly before him, inviting him to dance, hands fluttering, swaying with an unconscious grace, smiling into his eyes. Every head turned; there were smiles, good-humored chuckles, nudges; they were proud of this girl and anxious that the son of Varana should dance with her. They had not long to wait. Next moment Terii had leaped to his feet and was dancing, with more enthusiasm than skill, to a long burst of cheers and clapping.

"When the canoes put off at nightfall I noticed that Tehina did not leave; she had stopped to visit her uncle, the parson of the village church. I saw Terii with her often during the days that followed—fishing on the lagoon, swimming in the cove, lying on mats in the moonlight where groups of young people were telling their interminable stories of the past. He seemed a little shy of me, and no longer exchanged confidences in the hour which precedes sleep. One evening, smoking and strolling alone after dinner, I passed the parson's house and became aware of the vague figure of Terii walking to and fro impatiently beside the veranda. He stopped—I heard the rattle of a coral pebble on the roof. A moment later Tehina glided like a phantom around the corner of the house, and they went off arm in arm along the path to the sea. I thought to myself that the lad was not doing badly after his twelve years away from the island, but the blood was in him, of course—there was instinct in his manner of tossing the pebble and in the unhesitating way he had led the girl toward the outer beach; the haunt of dreadful presences, a place no ordinary islander would visit after dark. I fancied him sitting there—the rumble of the surf in his ears, watching the lines of breakers rear up under the moon—with Tehina beside him, admiring and afraid. When his eye was not on her she would glance right and left along the beach and back toward the bush, half expecting to see some monstrous thing, crouched and watching with fiery eyes. As for the boy, one could only guess at the troubled flow of his thoughts, stirred by cross-currents of ancestry and experience. In her own environment Tehina was a girl to make any man look twice; for him, with his mother's blood and the memories of his childhood, she must have possessed a powerful appeal—the touch of her hand; her voice, soft and low-pitched, murmuring the words of a half-forgotten tongue; her dark eyes shining in the moonlight; the scent of the strange blossoms in her hair. It was the test, the final conflict Varana had foreseen. I had my own opinion of the result, and yet the other life pulled hard.

"The days passed in pleasant island fashion; the loading of the schooner went on; there was no mention of a change in plans. The chief came to take his daughter home, and when she had gone Terii spoke to me, not too convincingly, of his return to civilization. My trip to Rimarutu was a matter of pleasure alone; I was already planning to take this berth, and was not sorry when Terii announced one morning that we would sail north that afternoon. One seems perpetually saying good-by down here—these islands are havens of a brief call, of sad farewells, of lingering and regretful memory. Our parting from the people of Rimarutu was more than usually painful; they had hoped to the last that Terii would leave some word, some promise; but he remained silent, though I could see that the leave-taking was not without effect.

"Finally the last canoe put off for shore; the anchor came up, the motor started, and Terii steered across the lagoon for the pass. The sails were still furled, for there was a light head wind. I watched his face as he stood in silence at the wheel; there was a look in his eyes which made me sorry for the boy. We crossed the lagoon, glided past green islets, and drew abreast of the other village. The people lined the shore, fluttering handkerchiefs, shouting good wishes and farewells.

"Beyond the settlement the pass led out, blue and deep, between sunken piers of coral, where the surf thundered in patches of white. All at once the old mate sang out and pointed—a dot was on the water ahead of us, a swimmer moving out from land to cut us off. The son of Varana turned the wheel; the schooner swung inshore; I heard a quick command and felt the speed of the engine slacken.

"Terii was staring ahead with a strange intensity—instinct or premonition was at work.

I looked again as we drew near; a cloud of dark hair floated behind the swimmer's head; it was a woman—Tehina! Terii sprang to the rail. A moment later she had been lifted over the side and was standing beside him in the cockpit, dripping, trembling a little with cold and fear, doing her best to smile. The mate was pulling at Terii's arm and pointing back toward the village. A whaleboat had put out from shore and was heading for us at the top speed of the rowers; it was the chief himself, I believe, who stood in the stern and whose shouts were beginning to reach our ears.

"At that moment Terii proved that he was his father's son. He glanced back once, and then, without the smallest interval of hesitation, his arm went about the wet shoulder of Tehina.

"'Full speed ahead,' he ordered in a cool voice."

The schooner was taking it easily with her engine at half speed, riding a gentle swell. The ship's bell rang twice, paused, and rang again—a sharp and mellow sound. It was long past midnight.

"If you ever get down to Rimarutu," said Tari, as he rose to go on deck, "you will find Terii there—he bids fair to leave the island even less than Varana did."

For Discussion

1. Is the elder Warner running away when he first arrives in Papeete? According to civilization's standards, would he be considered a failure? Are the qualities the islanders admire in Warner things that can be taught?

2. Can you explain why the native captain is so terror-stricken at the approach of the hurricane? Why would an islander have a greater fear of a hurricane than a man who has never experienced one? How much of a part does luck play in Warner's weathering the storm?

3. How do you account for the way in which Warner chooses to die? Why does he not continue to live for his son and daughters now that his wife is dead?

4. What change in the life of Warner does the birth of a son bring about? Why does Warner feel it necessary to educate his son in England although he detests civilization? What does this reveal about the character of Warner? What changes does it bring about in the son?

5. What does the change in the name from "Terii Warner" to "Terry Warner" indicate? Can you suggest reasons that made Terii Warner decide to adopt the ways of civilization? The girl on the dock in San Francisco simply waves and calls good-by to Terii. How does this differ from the action taken by Tehina when Terii sets sail from Rimarutu? How does this convince Terii Warner that he belongs on the islands and not on the mainland?

The Oyster

RUMER GODDEN

When the excitement of visiting strange places wears thin, a traveler begins to think of home with affection. He remembers little things with nostalgia and longs to return to the friends and customs he loves best. Those who come to live more permanently in the midst of an alien culture often find themselves with divided loyalties. How much of their past must they surrender? How much of the new may they accept without losing their selves?

"The Oyster" concerns an Indian student, Gopal, who has been raised in the Hindu religion. He has come to live and study in Paris. Here, his mind becomes a battlefield between Eastern and Western culture. To eat or not to eat an oyster or a chicken—it seems a trivial matter. Yet Gopal's choice may determine the direction the rest of his life will take.

"TO TRAVEL is to broaden the mind." Tooni, Gopal's sister-in-law, had told him that but, thought Gopal, the mind can become so broad that it suddenly becomes a wild prairie in which it cannot hope to find its way.

"When in Rome, do as the Romans do."

"To thine own self be true . . ."

Which?

Tooni loved axioms; she had taught Gopal these two as well, she had "instilled them," murmured Gopal. Gopal earnestly intended to believe everything he was told, he knew that Tooni was sensible and wise but now, suddenly, in this restaurant in Paris his mind had become a howling wilderness. "When in Rome . . ."

"To thine own self . . ." Which? He was not old enough to see that by his travels and experiences, he was taking the only possible first step to reconcile these conflicts, by beginning to find out what he was himself.

Gopal was a sweet, naïve, young Indian student, almost breathless with goodwill; yet he was dignified. René Desmoulins, the witty, dark, French, senior-year student, reading English at the University, had seen the dignity and especially marked Gopal out, though he was twenty-three to Gopal's nineteen. Everyone was kind to the young Indian. Gopal was charming to look at; his body was tall and slim and balanced, his teeth and eyes were beautiful and

367

RUMER GODDEN (*1907–*   ) *is an English
novelist, playwright, and poet. Of her
many tales, "The River" and "Black
Narcissus" have been made into films.*

his face was so quick and ingenuous that it
showed every shade of feeling; they teased him
about that but now he suddenly knew he was
not as ingenuous as they, or he, had thought;
he had come across something in himself that
was stronger than his will or his desire to please.
"Aaugh!" shuddered Gopal.

Up to this evening, that should have been the
most delightful of all, everything had been delightful. "Delightful" was Gopal's word. "London is delightful," he wrote home. "The College
is delightful, Professor William Morgan is delightful and so is Mrs. Morgan and the little
Morgans, but perhaps," he added with pain, for
he had to admit that the Morgan children were
rough and spoilt, "perhaps not *as* delightful if
you see them for a very long time. . . . The
Hostel is delightful. . . . I find my work delightful." He had planned to write home that
Paris was delightful. "We went to a famous
French restaurant in the Rue Perpignan"; he
had meant to write, "it is called the *Chez
Perpignan*. It is de——" Now tears made his
dark eyes bright; he could not write that; it
was not delightful at all.

Through his tears he seemed to see far beyond
the white starched tablecloth marked "Perpignan" in a red cotton laundry-mark, beyond
the plates and glasses, the exciting bottle of wine
of which he had asked to inspect the label after
the waiter had shown it to René. He saw beyond the single scarlet carnation in the vase on
the table, beyond everything in the restaurant
that had thrilled him as they came in; the dark-
brown walls with their famous old theatre
posters—"French printed in French" Gopal had

exclaimed as if he had not really believed that
French could be printed—the serving-table
where a flame burnt under a silver dish and a
smell rose into the air mingling with other
strange and, to him, piquant smells, of hot china
plates, starch, coffee, toast, old wine-spills, food
and clothes. He saw, beyond them all, the low
tables spread for dinner at home, one of the
dinners that he had always thought most ordinary, old-fashioned and dull, prepared by his
mother and Tooni. Gopal's family lived in
Bengal; they were Brahmin Hindus and his
mother kept the household to orthodox ways in
spite of all he and his elder brother could do;
now Gopal saw her orthodox food: the flat
brass platters of rice, the pile of *luchis*—flaky,
puffed, pale-gold biscuits—the vegetable fritters
fried crisp, the great bowl of lentil purée and
the small accompanying bowls of relishes,
shredded coconut or fried onion, or spinach or
chillis in tomato sauce or chutney, all to be put
on the rice. He saw fruit piled on banana leaves,
the bowl of fresh curd, the milk or orange or
bael-fruit juice in the silver drinking tumblers;
no meat, nor fish, not even eggs were eaten in
that house, "we shall not take life," said his
mother. Gopal looked down at his plate in
the Perpignan and shuddered.

He had come to Europe with shining intentions, eager, anxious to do as the Romans did,
as the English, the French, as Romans everywhere. "There will be things you will not be
able to stomach," he had been warned; so far
he had stomached everything. His elder brother
Jai had been before him and had come back
utterly accustomed to everything Western;
when Jai and Tooni went out to dinner they had
Western dishes; they ate meat, even beef, but
not in their own home; "Not while I live," said
his mother, and she had told Gopal, "You are
not the same as Jai. You are not as coarse."

"Oh I am, Mother," Gopal had pleaded. "I am
just as coarse," but now another shudder shook
him.

"Are you cold, Gopal-ji?" asked René. Gopal had taught René the endearment, he had thrilled to hear him use it and even now he managed to smile, though in truth even his lips were cold. "I am not at all cold," lied Gopal, "this is . . . delightful."

If it had been the cold that upset him it would have been nothing; all Indians were supposed to feel the cold. Gopal did not mind the lack of sun, the grey rain, though several things were very strange to him; the perpetual wearing of shoes, for instance, made his feet ache but he had liked his feet to ache; he had been proud of them when they ached, he felt they were growing wise. Now he wriggled his toes in his shoes under the table and would have given anything to be sitting with bare sun-warmed feet, and a feeling that he had not had all this time abroad welled up in him; he felt sick, sick for home.

He saw his own family front door, with the family shoes dropped down in a row at the entrance; he saw the hall, empty of everything but a rickety hat-rack that never had a hat hung on it; how could it? They wore no hats. He thought how he would come in, drop off his shoes on the step, and go to the tap to wash and take off his shirt, calling out to his mother and Tooni in a lordly way, 'Isn't there anything to eat in this house?' His mother, who never knew a joke when she heard one, would begin to shoo the maid-servant and Tooni about and hurry them and presently Tooni would bring him a few sweets in a saucer to keep him quiet.

"O Soul, be patient, thou shalt find
a little matter mend all this,"

Tooni would say, and she would add, "That is by Robert Bridges. Bridges was once Poet Laureate of England." Tooni was always anxious to improve her little brother-in-law.

In Europe Gopal had eaten everything. "Roast lamb, kidneysontoast, baconandsausage," murmured Gopal, and when René, who, being a Frenchman, had a proper feeling for food, had talked of the food they would eat in Paris Gopal had not flinched though some of it sounded rather startling to him; "Rather *bare*," he had written to Tooni. "Imagine sucking-pig, Tooni," he had written, "and René says it is laid out *whole* on the dish; *tête de veau*, and that is calf's head with its eyes and its brain all there. He says we shall have steak, rare, I don't know what that means but I shall find out, and oysters, I shall eat oysters. What are oysters? I shall find out. I shall come back more Parisian than Paris!"

René, the dazzling, elderly René, had asked Gopal home with him to Paris for the vacation. "It is a delightful *compliment*," Gopal wrote, "and, let me tell you, there are not many he would ask but he asked me!"

René, with his brilliance, his terse quick wit, his good looks, his ruthlessness and his foreignness, was venerated by the students and a little feared by the masters which made him all the more popular and, when he was kind to Gopal, Gopal was completely dazzled. "You are too good to me," he gasped and, shyly, "You must love me very much." René had the grace not to laugh at him. "You do not know *how* delightful he is!" wrote Gopal to his mother, and to Tooni he wrote, "René is like Hamlet, only humorous; like Byron, only good." He looked at these two comparisons and their qualifications; they seemed to come out null and void and he tried again. "He is like Jesus Christ," he wrote reverently, "only very, very sophisticated." For René, Gopal would have made one of those pilgrimages sometimes made by the devout in India when, at every step, the pilgrim measures his length in the dust.

On that thought Gopal realized how much he missed the dust. What a funny thing to miss, he thought, but he missed the dust. He wriggled his toes uncomfortably in his shoes and thought he could even smell the dust of his own great Bengal town. It seemed to rise in his nostrils as he looked out of the restaurant window; across the Paris twilight and its multitudinous lights, he seemed to see the small oil-flares of the orange-sellers' booths on a certain narrow pavement near his home. He heard the car horns, not Paris horns but the continuous horns of the Sikh taxi-drivers; he heard bicycle-rickshaw bells, the shuffling feet and the pattering noise as a flock of goats was driven by and he wanted to go home, past the white oleander bushes by the gate, past the rows of shoes, up to his own small room where on moonlight nights the shadow of the fig-tree and the bars of his barred window were thrown together on the white-washed wall. How many nights had he lain on his bed and watched the shadow-leaves move, stir gently in the heat, as he had wondered about going away far over the sea to travel in Europe, in England and, yes, in France? And now in France he thought, as he had never thought he could think, of that small room and the tears stung his eyes again.

René saw the tears and was concerned. Under the terseness and the sophistication René was simple and young and kind. "What is it, Gopal-ji?" he asked.

"I . . . swallowed . . . something hot," said Gopal.

"But you are used to hot things."

"Yes, chillis," said Gopal and laughed but it was not safe to think of such homely things as chillis; they made him see a string of them, scarlet, in the kitchen. He saw the kitchen; and his mother's housekeeping, which had often seemed to him old-fashioned and superstitious, now seemed as simple and pure as a prayer; as . . . as uncruel, he thought. His mother rose at five and woke the children so that they could make their morning ritual to the sun; many and many a time had she gently pulled him, Gopal, sleepy and warm and lazy, from his bed. She saw that the house was cleaned, then did the accounts and then, still early, sent Jai, as the eldest son, to market with the list of house-

hold things to buy and the careful allowance of money (few Indian women shopped in the market). When Jai came back, with a coolie boy carrying a basket on his head, the basket had a load of vegetables, pale-green lettuce and lady's-fingers perhaps, or glossy, purple aubergines, beans, the pearly paleness of Indian corn still in its sheaf. The basket held coconut too, ghee-butter and the inevitable pot of curd made fresh that day. The kitchen was very clean; no one was allowed to go there in shoes or in their street clothes. Before Gopal and Jai ate they washed and changed or took off their shirts; the women ate apart, even the go-ahead Tooni. All was modesty, cleanliness, quiet, and it did no hurt, thought Gopal shuddering. All of it had an inner meaning so that it was not . . . not just of earth, he thought. Once a month was household day when the pots and pans and sweeping brushes were consecrated; first they were cleaned, the brass scoured with wood-ash until it shone pale gold, the silver made bright, the brushes and dusting-cloths washed, cupboards turned out, everything washed again in running water and dried in the sun; then prayers were said for the household tools, and marigold flowers and jessamine were put on the shelves. I used to think it was stupid, thought Gopal, I teased my mother and called her ignorant to believe in such things but they made it all different; quite different.

"Gopal, what *is* the matter?" asked René and he laid his hand on Gopal's.

In India it is usual for young men who are friends to hold hands; for René to take Gopal's hand would have filled him with pride half an hour ago; now he flinched, and the intelligent René felt him flinch and took his own hand away and looked at Gopal closely. "Explain what it is," suggested René gently, but Gopal shook his head. He could not explain; how could he tell René that, for the first time, he saw not what the world did to Gopal but what he, Gopal, did to the world.

Last night he had found out what *rare* steak is; he had cut the meat red and eaten it, only thinking of the redness going in to him and wondering if he could get it down, could "stomach" it; now, suddenly, everything was in reverse. René had ordered the famous oysters and Gopal had looked so doubtfully at the plate of grey-brown shells and the strange, glutinous, greenish objects in each, that René had laughed. "Pepper one, squeeze a little lemon on it and let it slide down your throat," said René. He showed Gopal and Gopal had copied him but, when Gopal squeezed the lemon juice on his oyster, he had seen the oyster shrink.

"But . . . but it's alive ! ! !"

"Of course it's alive. It would be dangerous to eat it otherwise. If they served you a dead oyster," René had said gravely, "I should have to take it out and show it to a policeman." Seeing Gopal's face, he said, "Don't worry; it will die as soon as it touches you."

"Auhaugh!" said Gopal.

René had laughed. Now, remembering that, Gopal seethed with rage; his ears were burning, his cheeks and his heart. The plate with the oysters seemed to swim in front of him. Centuries of civilization, of learning, of culture, to culminate in this!

"What *is* the matter?"

"You are a barbarian," said Gopal in a low, burning voice. He trembled to speak like this to René but he spoke. "Your ancestors were running about in blue skins," said Gopal, "when mine had religion, a way of life." For a moment he stopped; René, in a blue skin, would look like Krishna; Krishna, the Hindu God, often had a blue skin, he played the flute and was the God of Love and had many amiable peccadilloes, but Gopal hardened his heart against René, even in his most lovable aspects. It was this learning, this culture, this barbarism, that he had come all this way to share. I want to go home, thought Gopal. I want to go home.

"You all think we Indians should study your customs, why don't you study ours?" he cried to René. "We could teach you a thing or two! Why should we have to Westernize? Why don't you Easternize? It would do you a lot of good, let me tell you that. You are cruel," cried Gopal. "You are not even honest. In England they teach children, 'Little Lamb, who made thee?' and give them the roast lamb for lunch, lamb with mint sauce. Yes! you eat lamb and little pigs and birds. You are cruel. Cruel and barbarous and greedy and . . ." he broke off, trying to think of the word he wanted; it meant "too much," ah yes! a dozen dozen, thought Gopal and hurled the word at René. "You are *gross!*" he cried, and stopped. Though he was sitting down even his legs were trembling. The effort had left him weak. "You are gross," he said in a whisper.

"You are perfectly right," said René. He put another oyster down his throat but there was something so mild, so tempered in his reply that Gopal was checked.

"These are things," said René when he had finished the oyster, "that a man has to arrange for himself."

It was not only a small rebuke, it was a suggestion made as Tooni would have made it, but of course Tooni was not as subtle and delicate as René, the same René who was now preparing to eat the last oyster on his plate; and he had a dozen, thought Gopal, when I had ordered only six! Subtle, delicate René, who was gross and delicate, fastidious and greedy, ruthless and mild. Gopal shook his head in despair.

"Travel broadens the mind." Then if it is broad, thought Gopal, it has to include all sorts of things; he looked at René's hand, putting pepper and squeezing the lemon, that clever, cruel hand. The world, when it was opened out, was not delightful; no, not delightful at all, thought Gopal. It had a bitter taste; he did not like it.

"When in Rome, do as the Romans do." René was a Roman of Romans; now, with grace and elegance, he slid the oyster down his throat and smiled at Gopal. René agreed that he was not delightful; he was content not to be; no, not content, thought Gopal, looking at him; he knows that he cannot hope to be, all of him, delightful. And if René can't, thought Gopal in despair, who can? Excepting . . . Well, it is easy if you stay in one place, like your mother's kitchen, but if you go into Rome?

He thought of that steak, *rare;* he had eaten it and now in his mind there was a vision of the sacred bull that came every day to their house to be fed; he saw its soft, confident nose, its noble face and the eyes lustrous with thick, soft eye lashes; its cream dewlap swung like a fold of heavy velvet and it wore a cap worked in blue and white beads on its hump; Gopal had saved up to buy that cap with his own money.

"To thine own self . . ." Tooni seemed very far away. Gopal turned away his head.

At that moment, René having beckoned, the waiter came and took the plate of oysters away.

"Now what shall we eat?" asked René, and he asked. "Have you ever tasted *vol-au-vent?*"

"How strange! It sounds like hitting balls at tennis," said Gopal, beginning to revive.

"It isn't tennis, it's chicken," said René. "Would you like to try it?"

"Chicken . . . ?" The word semed to hang in the balance, then Gopal asked, "Is it new? Is it exciting?"

"Well." René could not say *vol-au-vent* was exciting. "You may like it."

"Nothing venture, nothing win," said Gopal, and René gave the order to the waiter.

"This is delightful," said Gopal.

For Discussion

1. "When in Rome, do as the Romans do" and "To thine own self be true" are mottos that contradict each other. Yet Gopal attempts to reconcile these two within himself. Can you explain how he accomplishes this? The two mottos reflect in miniature the larger conflict of the story. Explain how Rumer Godden achieves this structural effect.

2. Gilbert Highet, an American critic and scholar, once wrote that Westerners have a difficult time understanding Eastern culture because the Eastern tradition represents a much more mature civilization. Does this story support Highet's remark? How? Do you feel that Gopal is right when he calls René a barbarian and suggests that the West should study the East? Why is the eating of oysters so repulsive to Gopal?

3. What do you learn about everyday Brahmin Indian life in this story? Is it appealing? Reckless? Hurried? Ambitious? What are some of the outstanding characteristics of this way of life? How does it differ from your own?

4. Is Gopal's final choice (eating the *vol-au-vent*) a victory or a defeat? Is it an act of heroism or of cowardice? How would you characterize and evaluate Gopal's actions?

Saudin's Visit to America

AGNES NEWTON KEITH

A British visitor to America once humorously noted that there were no people here; there were just automobiles. These automobiles fed at drive-in restaurants, watched films at drive-in theaters, deposited money at drive-in banks, took baths in drive-in wash stations, and slept in tall automobile hotels in the city. This, of course, is not literally true, but it provides us with a fresh look at something we have taken for granted because its growth has been too gradual to alarm our sense of proportion. In this selection, Saudin, a native of North Borneo, visits America, and his observations open our eyes to the wonders of our own land. He grows excited over things that we take for granted. He experiences fright where we feel only annoyance. But in Saudin's breathless account, the city takes on new perspectives that we have never noticed before, and the place we call home momentarily turns into a setting as strange as The Arabian Nights.

ONE SUNDAY shortly after we had received the broadcast of Martin Johnson's[1] death I was engaged in the struggle with home mail when Arusap interrupted me to say that Saudin had returned from my country with news of its strange doings. We called him in, and Harry and I spent all morning listening to his comments about what he had seen.

Saudin is an aborigine of North Borneo, and a member of the Murut tribe of native hill people, one of the twenty-odd tribes of Borneo natives. He comes from Kampong Ambual, a Murut village in the interior which harbors about thirty of his people. Isolated from coastal contact with civilization, Kampong Ambual is self-supplying and self-sufficing. Saudin has lived most of his life in this small hamlet, where his experience of sophistication has been at worst a mild carousal induced by too much native-made rice beer during the harvest season.

A few years ago Saudin came to Sandakan,[2] and, his reputation being excellent, he was here employed by the Johnsons to take care of the

[1] *Martin Johnson* Jungle explorer who was killed in a plane crash.

[2] *Sandakan* Seaport in British North Borneo.

373

AGNES NEWTON KEITH (*1901–   *), *soon after graduation from college, married a young British official who was stationed in Borneo. She remained there for four years and gave an account of her experiences in* Land Below the Wind, *from which this selection is taken.*

---

wild animals captured or purchased by them for their film. Saudin later accompanied the expedition on its return trip to the United States as a caretaker to the animals on the voyage, and remained in New York for three months in the Johnsons' charge.

When Saudin came up to our bungalow in Sandakan to tell us of his adventures in the outer world he had put away his store clothes and returned again to bare feet and singlet and brief cotton trunks. His manner retained its old native courtesy, and his attitude in presenting his tale of America was that of a Marco Polo who scarcely expects his words to be believed. Saudin told us his story speaking in Malay, which is not the Murut tongue, but is the language most generally used in Borneo. For such words as "elevator" and "Central Park Zoo" we have no local equivalent, but Saudin had gathered the English words into his vocabulary with unconscious erudition.

I tell the story, as nearly as possible in translation, in Saudin's words.

Saudin Speaks

When I came to Sandakan from Kampong Ambual, I thought that Sandakan was a big place. But when I went from Sandakan to Singapore, I thought *that* was a very big place, probably the biggest place there was. At the great size of Singapore I was not surprised, because many Malays come to Borneo from there and tell much about it. Then we went from Singapore to Capetown, and that was even more mighty. So I asked men, was America as great as that? And men answered me that it was even

greater. And now that I return to Borneo from America I think that Sandakan is only as big as the end of my little finger.

We left Singapore on a very big boat. White men did the work of natives on this boat, and spoke a language which was not English. I did not see very much of India because the animals were sick and I was busy taking care of them. So I could not go into India, but I think it is only a small place, probably like Kudat,[3] and that all the natives had come down to meet the boat.

After India we sailed on farther and farther, and the waves became very tall, and the captain said to tell men that a storm was coming. I saw black mountains ahead, and I said, "We are running into mountains!" But men said, "No, that is fog." And it was fog. In that fog we met a very cold climate, and taller and taller waves, and a stronger and stronger storm. The boat threw itself from side to side for many days. I was very sick, and the animals were very sick, and nine small monkeys died, and the orangutan from Kudat died, but I did not. But I was very glad when we arrived at Capetown, which is Africa.

In the distance I could see that Capetown was white and shining, and the only thing that I knew that was like that was the stonewater that white men use and call ice. So I said, "There is ice on everything there!" But men said, "No, that is the houses and the streets shining in the sun." And so it was.

Mr. Johnson took me to land at Capetown, and there the man said I could not land because I was Chinese. I said I was not Chinese, I was Malay. Then I could land. But always it was like this and men would think that I was Chinese. I never told men that I was a man of the Muruts because it seems that nobody knows about Muruts, but all people know about Chinese. So I said I was Malay because some people know about Malays.

[3] *Kudat*   Village near Sandakan.

In Capetown it was a very cold climate, and both the animals and I shivered. I had a shirt and trousers and this is a great deal for a Murut to wear, but it was not enough. Mr. Johnson asked me if I had any more clothes, and when I said no he took me to a store and bought me many clothes. He bought me shirts and trousers, and short coats, and a very long black coat which hung down to my feet and had big shoulders and was very handsome, and a hat and nine neckties. He told me that I must close my shirt and tie up my necktie around my neck when I was in Capetown, as this is the custom there. All my new clothes cost nineteen pounds, nine shillings, and sixpence.[4]

We left Capetown and the ship sailed on until we came to Dakar, which is also Africa, but is very hot. So I said to men, "Why is it so cold in one place and so hot in another place?" And men said, "Well, because it just is that way." So I said, "Yes, probably that is just the way it is."

This time we were on the ship many days, and then we came to America. When we were going to land the customs man said to me, "You are Chinese; you cannot land." So Mr. Johnson said, "No, he is Malay, and I will send him back to Borneo in three months." The customs man said, "Can you speak English and read and write?" I said, "Yes, a little." He said, "Read this," and handed me my passport. I could not read it, but I remembered what was on it, because Mr. Johnson had told me, and so I said what was on it to the man. Then the man said, "O.K. Come into America!"

So we entered into America and went to a very great village with a thousand thousand lights. It was night when we arrived, but when I looked up at the sky above this village it was very bright and red and sparkling and there was light everywhere. And I said, "Is this morning?" And they said, "No, this is New York!"

I was so astonished by New York that I just wanted to look and look and look at it. I forgot all about feeding the animals and my work. Every night men had their names put in the sky with bright lights so that they would not be forgotten, because there are so many people in New York that it would be easy to forget some of them. All the time there was a great noise made by motorcars and buses and trains. There were trains above me on bridges, there were trains below me, and there were more trains that were below the trains that were below. Always the trains were very full of people. I think if the trains all stopped and the people got off them there would be no space in New York for all the people. So the people take turns living in the trains. I used to walk and walk because I was afraid to get on those trains to ride, as I did not know how to get off or where I should be when I did, or if I might have to live on one.

The streets were very clean. They washed and polished them every morning. I thought there could be no sickness there with everything so clean.

The buildings were very tall. Sometimes I had to go up and down in what men call an elevator. This is a little room that you get into, and very suddenly it goes up. And when it stops your stomach does not stop. But when it goes down you feel that everything has gone out of you. It is much worse than an airplane. I was always afraid in it, but said nothing, because I thought men would say, "He is just a jungle man!"

In winter there is a very cold climate in New York. Often I shivered and was cold although I wore many clothes and my handsome black coat. All men wore heavy clothes and coats like mine which hung down to their knees. But truly I was astonished at the women! They did not wear many clothes except around their necks, where they wore the skins of animals. They wore very little under this, because the wind would show me. Their stockings were just like

---

[4] *nineteen pounds, nine shillings, and sixpence* About $95.00 at the time this was written.

nothing. Truly I was astonished that they did not feel cold.

In New York we put Mr. Johnson's animals in Central Park Zoo, and I went there every day to take care of them. At first Mr. Johnson went with me so that I would not be lost, and later I could go alone. But I was always afraid of the motorcars. I walked a great deal, up and down the same street and never far away, as I was afraid of being lost. At night I did not go away at all, because when lights were in the sky all things became different and I was confused.

One day he told me to go to a cinema. When I went in it was daylight, but when I came out it was dark. It was only five o'clock and in my country that is still daytime. But in New York in winter that is night time and the lights are on. When I looked up I could see nothing but very tall buildings and a red glow at the top of the buildings, and no sky. All men were hurrying from here to there, all trains made noises, all lights blinked, and I became confused. I walked and walked, but could not find the place where I lived. Mr. Johnson had written a letter for me telling who I was and where I lived in case I should be lost some day. And, as I was lost then, I looked in my coat, and was much astonished to find that the letter was lost also.

I went to a policeman and asked him how to go to Central Park Zoo, because if I could find that I could find my house, which was near it. The policeman said it was twelve blocks away, so I said, "Thank you very much," and walked on some more. Then I asked another policeman and he said nine blocks farther, and I walked some more. But the next policeman I asked said, "Here is Central Park Zoo!" And there I was at the Zoo, but I did not recognize it with the lights on. So then I found my house, which I think was very good fortune, because I had indeed been lost.

One day newspapermen came to talk to me, and they said, "Do you like New York? What do you like the best?" And I said, "Yes, I like New York, and I like best the red electric light signs that run like streams of fire, and the lights that chase each other around like small animals."

One day I was out walking and I came to a large place with many horses in it. I said to a man with a uniform, "Can I enter?" And he said, "You must buy a ticket." I said, "I will buy a ticket. Now can I enter?" And he said, "Sure!" So I entered and I saw large and wonderful horses, and handsome men with beautiful colored uniforms. They played music and the horses danced to the music. I think the horses in New York are smarter than are the policemen in my country. So I struck my hands together the way people did, with astonishment and joy. When the playing was finished all the people wanted to leave at once in a great hurry, and everybody pushed everybody and I fell down. A man picked me up, and I said, "Thank you very much," and went home.

I went also to see boxing and wrestling. Boxing is all right, but wrestling is too rough. In my country we do not act like that unless we wish to kill men.

One day a man fell down in the streets and lay there wounded. Everybody just looked at him and walked on. So I looked at him and walked on too, because I was afraid if I stayed near him people would think that I had wounded him. Afterwards I told Mr. Johnson and he said, "People get killed here everyday!"

I was out walking one day and met a man who was drunk, the same as a man is in Borneo when he drinks too much rice beer. The man said, "You are a Filipino like me!" I said, "No, I am a Malay." He said, "No, you are a Filipino!" I said, "You are drunk. You had better go home. Don't you know that people get killed here every day?" But he didn't go home, and he wanted to fight me because I wasn't a Filipino. So I ran and stood by an important man in a uniform who stood at the door of a hotel. I stood very close to this important man, and as he wouldn't let the drunken Filipino come to the hotel he couldn't fight me.

" 'I like best the red electric light signs that run like streams of fire . . .' "

A view of 42nd Street, New York, at night

Mr. Johnson took me to eat at a place where you put money in a hole and take out a plate of food. The different holes have names on them to tell you what foods are concealed within. We had vegetable and potato and meat all cooked together in a flour wrapping which they call a pie. I think this place was very cunning indeed, because the hole to receive a ten-cent piece was so small that you could not put in a five-cent piece, and the hole for the five-cent piece did not answer if you put in a one-cent piece.

One time a man gave me some wine to drink.

I drank a little, and then I remembered about the many motorcars and trains outside, the great noise and confusion, and the people who got killed there every day. And I was afraid I might be hit, lost, or killed if I drank any more, so I didn't drink any more.

Mr. Johnson took me to a club where they were going to talk to people about Borneo. When we arrived he told me that I must stand up and talk to them in Malay. I said that it was useless for me to do so, because they did not understand Malay. But he said that I must speak in Malay and then he would tell them in English what I had said. I was afraid and ashamed because there were many people there and I am not practised in speaking to many people. But although I shivered as with cold, I talked, and I told them about my village with only thirty people in it, which was so small that I was astonished that they wished to hear about it. And when I finished they struck their hands together to show that they were pleased, and I sat down and Mr. Johnson talked. He showed them a roll of his film about the bird's-nest caves at Gomantong, and the proboscis monkeys, and the walking fish. Afterwards people came up to me and said, "We liked what you said tonight. What did you say? Was that Chinese you were speaking? Are you Chinese?" So I said, "No, I am Malay. Thank you very much."

Mr. Jim, who used to drive the flying-ship in Borneo, was in New York too, but he did not live there. One day we flew from New York to his home in a very large flying-ship, much larger than Mr. Johnson's, with many people in it. I was not afraid because I was used to flying before, but it was very different from flying over Borneo. In my country I looked down on jungle trees and rivers of which I am not afraid, but here I looked down on buildings and trains which would be difficult to fall upon with comfort. In New York there were snow and ice on the wings of the flying-ship. It was very rough weather, the same as on our boat before

coming to Capetown, and I was sick, but I did not vomit. We went many miles before coming to Mr. Jim's village, but I did not remember the name of this village. We went into his house and his people gave us food and drink. But I was ashamed to eat with them because I did not know how to eat the food cleverly as they did, because all my life in my country I was accustomed to eat with my fingers. It is difficult to carry the food with those small weapons to the mouth. I did not wish to be rude by not eating the food after their custom, so I pretended I was not very hungry, and I went to bed soon. The next day we returned to New York.

One day Mrs. Johnson came to the hotel to take me to talk to some women. I was following after her, but for one minute I looked away and when I looked back I couldn't see her. Then I saw her again and followed her until she turned upon me with anger. Then I saw it wasn't Mrs. Johnson, but a strange woman. So I feared I was lost again, but Mrs. Johnson ran after us and she said to me, "Why do you not follow me?" I said, "I thought I was following you, because this other woman looks just like you." And Mrs. Johnson looked at her and said, "Humph! I don't think so!"

One day Mr. Johnson said to me that in two days he must put me on a ship to return to Borneo. I was very sad to hear this because he was very good to me, and America was so astonishing. First I thought that I would stay in America and work, but the next day I thought, "Well, never mind, if he says I must go, I will go."

This was the day before the New Year and he bought me a watch for a present. I went to Times Square that night to see the New York people make a holiday. There were so many people that I was frightened and wanted to return to my house. I could not return because we were like fish caught in a fish trap. Men blew things in my ears that made the noise of goats. I said to them, "Don't do that!" And they said, "Don't you like that? Don't you do this in your country?" And I said, "No!" I wanted to go home to bed, but I couldn't go home all that night, because it was New Year in New York and you can't go home on New Year in New York.

That was the first day of the month, and I was sad because I had to sail for Borneo that day. Mr. Johnson took my hand and said "*Selamat belayar*" in Malay, and I said "Goodbye" in English, which I think was polite. Mrs. Johnson took me to the Dutch ship *Kota Djandi*, and I felt so sad to leave them that I forgot to take my two blankets, two pillows and my rubber shoes, but I remembered my nine neckties and my big hat and my black coat.

So I sailed for home, and when the ship arrived at Singapore I took a letter to a man there from Mr. Johnson. The man took the letter, and after he read it he said, "Don't you know that this man is already dead? He fell in a flying-ship many days ago, and he is already dead."

And I just looked at him and I could not talk at all because I felt so sad and terrified. I could not believe that it was so. But I asked many men, and all men answered me that this was true. Then I cried like a child for two days and could not eat or sleep. And now I know my heart will always be sad for this man.

Now I will go back to my village and see my people. I will buy more buffaloes and plant more rice. When the harvest season comes I will harvest my rice, and I will drink rice beer and take a wife. But although I will live as all men do here, never will I forget America.

For Discussion

1. Although Saudin's description has a childlike quality, would you say that Saudin himself is childish? Can you find passages that indicate his wisdom? Is he cynical? Trusting?

2. Does Saudin see the difference between America and his native Borneo as a superiority of one over the other? Do you feel that he will live the rest of his life in Borneo in discontent? Explain.

3. Do you feel that Saudin's fear of turbulent city life is natural. What other aspects of ordinary city life would terrify someone born and reared in a jungle? What aspects of ordinary jungle life would terrify someone born and reared in a large American city? Would an American city dweller's fear of getting lost in a jungle be comparable to Saudin's fear of getting lost in a city?

4. A clever writer can sometimes make a story assume a meaning that remains unknown to its fictional narrator. Apply this to the anecdote in which Saudin follows the woman he thinks is Mrs. Johnson. When Mrs. Johnson says, "Humph! I don't think so!" What does her statement tell us that remains a mystery to him? Is the meaning humorous? Why? What does it reveal of Mrs. Johnson? Why can't Saudin see the humor?

5. Does Saudin blame American culture for upsetting him emotionally? Can you find instances where he takes the values of his own culture and applies them to sights and events in America? Pick out some of his descriptions of ordinary things, and explain how his conception adds interest and attractiveness to something we have taken for granted.

Indian Business

ERIC HOWARD

*Emerson, the American philosopher, declared that in modern life,
"Things are in the saddle." And Thoreau, in* Walden, *cried out,
"Simplify! Simplify!" Yet the dominant ideals of modern society
center upon the ownership of money and objects. "Indian Business"
examines a conflict of cultures within the United States. What happens
when the traditional and easy-going ways of the American Indian
come into contact with the white man's ideas about material "progress"?
Seganitso Begay is a spirited young Navajo. As he rides his pony to a
ritual dance where he will see the young lady of his heart, he finds
that he must make a choice between two ways of life.*

SEGANITSO BEGAY whacked his pony and rode
swiftly down the valley of green corn, beside
the wash. In his heart was the rhythm of his
pony's flying feet; on his lips a song. The sun
shone on the silver buttons that ornamented his
green velvet blouse, gleamed on the bracelet en-
circling his wrist, and flashed from his glistening
copper skin.

To be alive was good. To ride far on a day
like this, with the sun shining, the sky cloudless
and the tall buttes of red rock rising into its blue,
was to live. Yet Seganitso Begay, having known
this life since first he could walk, did not consciously think of his well-being. Health and
strength and freedom were normal; he accepted
them as he accepted the swift grace of his pony.
Reflection did not mar the harmony of his
being. Even the song he sang was but an accompaniment to the rhythm of living.

He did not think of yesterday or tomorrow.
He did not dream of the day after. He lived.
Rich blood coursed through his young veins,
as through the veins of his pony. He was a part
of his pony, as his pony was a part of all life.
The sun which warmed them likewise warmed
the cottonwoods in the wash and brought the
corn to its full stature. All this was one. All was
one. So ran the song he alternately hummed
and sang in a high falsetto. So the elders had
said, long ago. The sun's warmth, the growing
corn, the tall trees, the spirited pony—all, and
much more, moved in the eternal rhythm of
life. Seganitso Begay, likewise.

Philosophy was unnecessary. He lived it.

If he thought at all, as he rode, his thoughts
were pleasing pictures. He was going to a "sing,"
where the maidens would be. He saw the smiling, shy, white-toothed girl he had shyly

greeted, at the trader's, in the time of the planting. She would be there. He would take his place in the chorus, with his friends. The water drum would carry the rhythm of the dance far across the land, and the songs of the chanting chorus, as their bodies swayed together, would lift up his heart.

Then he would leave the singers and allow himself to be seen among those who watched the dancing. She would see him, that maiden of the clear eyes and the smiling lips; her mother would see him. They would talk, perhaps, but he would not heed their talk. It was the way of a man to be indifferent, to be sought, not to seek. But his mother owned many sheep, and he himself was well and favorably known among the people of the high mesa. She would seek him out—of that he was sure—and she would lead him into the firelit circle of the dance. He would feign indifference, while his heart pounded in his breast at the touch of her hand on his arm. She would laugh shyly, and he would know that she had chosen him from among all others.

Life went on like a long ride through beautiful scenes. He let his fancy wander—to the clean new *hogan* of cedar where they would dwell, into a future idyllic and delightful, indefinite and sublime.

The vision was more than he could bear. He burst into a wild song of delight, of love, of triumph. He rode the trail of beauty. Beauty was before him, all around him, above him. Beauty was everywhere, in her and in him, in all the world they knew.

His voice rose to an exultant cry. "*Nizhuni! Nizhuni! Nizhuni!*" (Beautiful) he sang.

Then, abruptly, he halted. A car was coming down the road, and he pulled his pony to one side, waiting.

Even at a little distance he recognized the car and its occupants. They were two white men from the Agency, government farmers, sent out to help the Indians with their crops. Seganitso Begay's face clouded, became impassive,

lost its lyrical light. He did not know what happened when he encountered white men, but a mask seemed to veil his countenance. He remembered, long ago, they had come for him, to take him to school; and his mother had hidden him until the officers had departed. Later, she had moved into a deep canyon, where there was feed and water, but where white men did not come. And he had grown up, taught only by his uncles. He had never been to school; his hair had never been cut. There was a wild pride in his bearing, unlike the air of the boys who had been taken away. He was strong and fearless; he had never known the command of a superior, only the directions of his soft-voiced mother and the counsel of his

Indians in camp on a reservation

wise uncles. He was respectful toward the old, gentle with children.

"Where you going?" demanded the man at the wheel of the car, in Navajo that was harsh and unpleasant.

Seganitso Begay gestured vaguely. "Over there," he said.

The driver turned to his companion. "Going to a 'sing,'" he said disgustedly. "I know it! Just when I told them to tend to their crops, the whole flock of them pick up and start for a 'sing.' You can't do a thing with these savages."

Although the words were in English, Seganitso Begay caught their meaning. His face was stern and sullen.

The white man shook his fist at him. "You'd better turn right around and take care of your corn!" he insisted.

The Indian rode close to the car. "Smoke?" he asked, using one of the few English words he knew.

Ungraciously, the white man extended a package of cigarettes. As the Indian lighted one, the farmer proceeded to lecture him about his crop.

"I go over there," said Seganitso Begay, gesturing. "I go on Indian business."

He turned and rode away, leaving the white men cursing.

For some time, as always after such an encounter, the young man's heart was troubled. Always those men came, to interrupt the smooth flow of life. Just when one was most enjoying all that was good and beautiful, they would appear.

But he did not think too long about it. His pony broke into a lope, and again he was riding fleetly and rhythmically on the trail of beauty, in the pathway of the sun.

Soon he began to sing again, and pleasing pictures accompanied him on the way.

When two races meet, one must triumph. "*Nizhuni! Nizhuni! Nizhuni!*" he sang.

For Discussion

1. Would you say that Seganitso Begay is shiftless? Does his indifference to his corn crop promise future unhappiness? Can Seganitso Begay's point of view be defended? How?

2. From what source does Seganitso Begay draw his satisfaction? Suggest a situation that pleases you in which Seganitso Begay would be miserable. Is Seganitso Begay what the white man from the Agency says he is? Does society usually approve of this sort of person?

3. Would a formal education and contact with enlightened people improve Seganitso Begay's values? Might removing him from his culture bring about his moral destruction?

4. When we are young, adult cares and sermons of responsibility seem like shadows that momentarily darken our world. In what way is Seganitso Begay like a child? What represents the adult world? Is either of the two attitudes toward life in this story "right" and the other "wrong"?

The Wizard

ALEXANDER STEPANOVICH YAKOLEV

*Even within the boundaries of a single nation there can be a conflict
between two cultures, and sometimes one is completely wiped out by
the ruthlessness of the other. The Soviet Union is a vast country,
welded together from peoples of varied races. After the assassination
of Czar Nicholas II and during the Revolution of 1917, a civil war
took place. Several revolutionary factions struggled to eliminate each
other and to seize political leadership. Boris Pasternak's novel* Dr.
Zhivago *presents a picture of the savage methods used by the Bolsheviks
to stamp out all rivals during this period. The same conflict is sharply
portrayed in "The Wizard."*

*The forces led by the shrewd divisional commander represent the
"regular" army—the Bolsheviks. The forces led by Batko Gonchar are
irregular guerilla fighters from the Ukraine. The conflict is cultural
as well as political: the divisional commander is a "new" man—he has
no time for the "superstitious" faith of Batko Gonchar's men in their
wizard. Yet he promises them: "Your customs will not be disturbed
in any manner." The simple faith of Batko Gonchar's men is touching,
and the final scene of the story, in which that faith is put to the test,
is one of great power.*

AT NIGHT the three deputies came at last. They
were young muzhiks, [1] with upturned moustaches, as stalwart as stallions, slow-going, with
craftiness in their eyes, calculating, and very
chary of speech. They looked over every man
on the staff inquisitively, yet tried to conceal
their inquisitiveness—their sidelong glances, like
those of thieves, seeming to frisk one, making
one uneasy, and breeding general uneasiness.
They wore, all three of them, short grey over-
coats of Ukrainian cut and towering shakoes
with crowns of raspberry-hued velvet. The
oldest of them had gold braid running around

---

[1] *muzhik*   A Russian peasant.

the crown of his shako. It was he, the oldest one, who began the parley.

"Greetings, once more! Since you have called us, we have come to see you."

As for the other two, they simply took off their shakoes, bowed, and muttered: "Greetings!"

"Sit down, comrades, I beg of you," the divisional commander invited them amiably, and indicated the broad benches running along the walls.

The divisional commander stood up, and with sweeping gestures invited the deputies to sit down. Cheerful, energetic, all on the alert, he opened his silver cigarette-case and offered it to them—opened it with an air as if it were no mere cigarette-case but his own heart, filled to overflowing with love for these sturdy lads with upturned moustaches.

"I'm most happy to welcome here such worthy knights as yourselves, my dear comrades. I have long been seeking ways of forming a liaison with you. It pains me very much that we, fighting for one and the same cause, are scattering our strength. We ought to join forces, comrades."

He spoke somewhat emotionally, with such sincerity that the deputies exchanged glances of suspicion, and because of this exchange the commander grasped that they did not believe him. Then he began to speak plainly, his sincerity no longer assumed. He put the problem baldly:

"Let's join forces, then! State your terms."

The deputies were silent for a while. They exchanged glances again. It was the oldest who began speaking, and this time in Russian, dropping the Ukrainian *mova*: [2]

"Well, our terms are—"

The brave men of Batko [Dad] Gonchar would join the regular Division if they could retain the same command, the same customs

which prevailed among them right now. That was point one. And the second condition was that the Division supply them with machine-guns, rifles and cartridges without delay.

"Comrades!" the commander of the division exclaimed with staggering sincerity. "We find your terms quite satisfactory. Your commanders will retain their posts. Your customs will not be disturbed in any manner. The basic conditions are accepted—"

The deputies exchanged looks, as though they were asking one another: "Should we believe him, or shouldn't we?"

"Let's work out the details," said the commander, and made a sign to his clerk, who had been sitting in a corner of the hut. The clerk hastily placed a sheet of blank paper and some pencils on the table.

Toward morning the terms were worked out, and toward evening the detachment of Batko Gonchar, in full force, was entering the settlement of Peredbrody, where it was solemnly met by the Division. The commander of that division and his full staff—all of them on horseback—were lined up on the square near the church, awaiting their welcome guests. The fighters had ranged themselves in close ranks, stretching far into the broad main street of the settlement, where behind the wattle-fences one could see the white walls of clay-daubed huts and thickets of green trees. The staff officers astride their horses were softly laughing among themselves. They were discussing the ease with which the unification had been consummated.

"I told them: 'We'll give you the stuff,' but they wouldn't believe me," the divisional commander was saying. " 'We'll give you the stuff,' but they wouldn't believe me," he repeated, raising his voice. "But I'm not the sort to let things drop—all that was needed was to get the parley going."

The commander of the regiment twirled his moustache with a devilish gesture of his left hand and said, smiling slyly, flatteringly:

[2] *mova* Language.

"You're a wizard, Comrade Leader!"

The divisional commander winked his left eye and smiled back condescendingly.

A hurdy-gurdy broke out far down the street, followed by thunderous hurrahing, and the detachment of Batko Gonchar came into view on the edge of the square. The staff officers ceased smiling. The division band blared forth *The Welcome*. A field-cart appeared next, harnessed to a white horse, its mane loose and fluffed up and its tail unbound. It was on this cart that the hurdy-gurdy was enthroned, adorned with many bright ribbons. A lanky, gaunt yokel, kneeling before it, was hurriedly turning its curved handle. The hurdy-gurdy, piercingly squealing, was grinding out the *Russian March*. At a distance of ten paces from this hurdy-gurdy a troika was rolling along, all in ribbons and jingle-bells. The magnificent horses —dappled greys—were going at a prancing walk. The driver, walrus-moustached, square-shouldered, in red shirt and sleeveless jacket of corduroy, was standing up as he guided the team. His round velvet cap was adorned with a multitude of peacock feathers. The troika-drawn tarantass [3] was draped with priceless rugs and, squatting like an idol upon them, was a husky man in a thick blue overcoat of Ukrainian cut, with gold braid all over it. Having come up to the staff officers, he condescendingly saluted. The commander of the division gave his mount the merest flick of his whip and rode up to the man, since he had recognized in him the celebrated partisan Batko Gonchar. The troika halted. The music fell silent.

"Greetings to you, dear comrade!" the commander of the division called out.

Batko Gonchar smiled condescendingly.

"And greetings from me to you," he boomed in a bass.

This was followed by general hurrahing. The divisional band again blared forth *The Welcome*.

[3] *tarantass* Russian four-wheeled carriage.

Batko's staff—a score of mounted men, in such bright and motley costumes that they could have joined any masquerade right off— took its place alongside the staff of the division. The field-carts again crawled off in a ribbon; the partisans were seated in these carts in twos and threes, each dressed after his own fashion; they sat with their legs dangling peacefully over the sides, and it was impossible to believe that these were warriors, and only the rifles sticking out on all sides without the least order, and the machine-guns here and there, looking like swine with their snouts turned up to the sky, indicated that the carts were coming not from some fair but from the battle-fields.

The band was playing deafeningly. The field-carts rolled along. The commander of the division was conversing with Gonchar.

Suddenly the field-carts came close together, just as though a long rope had been knotted at the end, and the warriors, as well as the whole staff of the division and all others there, saw a strange sight: behind the two rows of the field-carts, riding a bay, came an old man, all aglitter, like the sun. All of the ancient's apparel, and his conical hat in particular, was studded with tiny mirrors. With his left hand the old man was guiding his horse, while in his outstretched right he was holding a big white cage with a black rooster. Flanking the old man, as well as before and behind him, rode the columns of field-carts. Batko Gonchar was the first to set an example: before any of the others he lifted his cap to the old man. His staff officers immediately bared their heads as well. The commander of the division, just to be on the safe side, saluted the old man, and all his staff did likewise. And only after this, bending toward Gonchar, did the commander ask:

"And what rank does he hold among you?"

Batko Gonchar tugged at the left tip of his moustache with his right hand.

"Why, that's our wizard," said he in a bass.

"How is it he isn't with your staff, then?"

"When you're at your wizardry you've got to be alone—with the fiends," Gonchar answered gravely.

Oho-ho! The commander of the division had, of course, been right in his calculations: the detachment of Batko Gonchar was a wonder-working force, overwhelming all obstacles. These lads, boisterous at their bivouacs, vanishing like water in retreats—they were magnificent in battles. Within three days the settlements and small towns of Smota, Moyachna, and Ozery had been taken. There was a break-through at the front, and the Polacks were hastily retreating northwest. The victory over Ozery was celebrated triumphantly. Batko sent an ukase [4] throughout the district, the beginning of which sounded like a Czar's manifesto and its end like a proclamation:

"And next I command all priests and prelates, as well as all deacons, to say masses for six days in all the churches on the occasion of our victories, and to ring the bells both day and night. All hail to a free Ukraine!"

That's how the ukase-proclamation of Batko Gonchar wound up. And sure enough, in all the churches, near and far, the bells began to boom; for two days and nights they boomed, since Batko's couriers had ridden to each church.

But in the staff of the division (where the celebration had also been a goodly one) Batko Gonchar's ukase had evoked both laughter and indignation.

"Why, he's putting our power to shame, the devil take him!" said the commander of the division to his chief of staff. "I don't know what to do. Should I go and explain things to him? He may take offence, like as not, and mutiny. Suppose I'll have to put up with it."

"Well, as the saying goes, a little evil for a great good," answered the chief of staff. "We'll put up with it for a while."

"Gonchar told me that he always plays things safe—he just follows his wizard's predictions."

[4] *ukase* Order.

"What the devil!" the chief of staff broke into laughter.

"That wizard eyed me rather crossly, somehow, last time I called on Gonchar," said the commander of the division with concern. "Likely enough, he may sense our mood and start stirring up trouble."

"Oh, now, come!" The commander of the division smiled slyly. "For every wizardry of his we will find a counter-measure."

"It's curious, though. Have you noticed—he was riding in the very thick of the ranks when we were approaching Ozery."

"How else? All the partisans are convinced that neither bullet nor sabre can touch a wizard. Behind him one is as if behind a wall of iron."

And, each steaming up the other, they began discussing this weird staff of Batko Gonchar's and the wizard.

"He won't make a step without the wizard. And everything works out as if it were down in black and white. Just what *is* all this?"

"Simple coincidence."

"Occasionally I am overcome by an odd feeling: 'But what if it should suddenly turn out that this wizard does have some sort of inner power?' "

"Now, now, now! That's downright superstition."

"I'm convinced that sooner or later he'll play us some nasty trick."

"We'll find some means against his machinations."

"Yes, but just what means?"

"Oh, we'll see when the time comes. As long as he's acting for our good we can stand it. We'll settle accounts later."

"It'll be a dangerous business. All the partisans are for him, body and soul."

"Well, aren't we used to dangerous situations?"

This conversation took place the day before the detachment was to advance for an attack on Brody—and toward evening a courier from Batko Gonchar came to the commander of the division with a secret note. After reading it the commander furiously ripped out a good round oath.

"What is it?" asked the chief of staff.

"Gonchar refuses to advance to the attack."

"What's his reason?"

"He refuses—and that's all there is to it. And he doesn't explain his reasons. I'll have to go to him immediately."

Gonchar was in the next settlement, carousing with three of his cronies, when the commander arrived to see him.

"Comrade Gonchar, what's the matter with you?" asked the divisional commander, before they were through shaking hands.

Gonchar, who only the moment before had been in peals of laughter over something, suddenly frowned darkly and his face grew stubborn.

"We're not fighting!" said he in a voice low and mysterious.

"Why, what's up?"

"We're not fighting," Gonchar repeated, and shook his head.

The commander of the division became tense, ready to come to grips with this stubborn fellow, but immediately restrained himself and asked in a voice as low as the other's and also a trifle mysterious:

"Tell me—have you received news of any sort, then?"

"No, it's not a matter of any news, but the wizard says we'll be beaten. We've got to wait two weeks."

"Two weeks! What do you mean, two weeks?" the divisional commander cried out, flaring up. "How can one allow such a thing? Have you gone out of your mind or what, you old devil?"

"Sh! Don't say anything!" said Gonchar, still in a low voice, and shook a thick forefinger before the commander's nose. "He'll find out."

"Let him find out. But you, now, Comrade Gonchar—you yourself; is it possible you don't understand that we can't stand still? Why, this will be the death of us!"

"I understand, but the brotherhood wouldn't go, even if I wanted them to. They obey the wizard more than they do me."

"Well, you get the brethren together, and we'll talk both to them and to the wizard."

Five minutes later a trumpet began blaring out on the square, summoning the worthy knights to a conclave. The evening was already far gone, and the whole settlement with its white huts and green gardens was sunk in darkness, except for some small windows glimmering here and there. The sound of voices and the clatter of steps rang out sharply in the quiet street. Two big heaps of straw were lit on the square: the flame rose seven feet high, lighting brightly not only the white enclosure of the church but the dark, stirring throng and the branches of the nearest trees.

Stalwart lads rolled a field-cart out of a nearby yard. Gonchar clambered up on the cart and, while the talk was dying out among the thronged men, cleared his throat and kept twiddling his moustache with both hands.

"Comrades, the commander wants to talk to you," said he, when all talk had died down on the square. "He wants to carry on with the fight——"

"It isn't a matter of my wanting to!" called the commander, clambering up on the cart. "But we *must* go on. The enemy is smashed. The enemy is running away. We must pursue him without a letup, so as not to give him a chance to gather his forces together——"

"We don't want to!" a high tenor piped up out of the crowd.

And at once the whole square, from one side to the other, breathed out as one man:

"We don't want to!"

And there was a universal surge, and a soughing as if of the wind.

"But why don't you?"

"Grandfather orders us not to!" individual voices called out. "Grandfather!"—"There he comes himself!"—"Grandfather!"

Within the heart of the throng, behind the dark ranks, something sparkled. The men parted; fell silent. The flame of the bonfire for a moment sank, then soared still higher—someone had thrown new sheaves upon it. Through the clear space between the two closed rows of the partisans came the wizard. His tall cap and his clothing, adorned with small mirrors, were all aglitter. The light gave a purple tint to everything. In one hand, outstretched before him, the wizard was carrying the black rooster in its white cage, and kept muttering:

"*Grym, glym, telepe. . . .*"

The crowd seemed to have died; no one

A Revolutionary Army unit riding through a Ukrainian town during the 1917 Revolution

spoke, or even coughed; only, somewhere far down the street, a male voice was singing. Muttering gibberish, the wizard approached the field-cart near which were Gonchar, his staff officers, and the commander of the division. He looked point-blank at the commander and asked:

"What are you raising a ruckus for?"

His grey goatee stuck out impetuously, his yellow, somewhat watery eyes were flashing angrily, his cheeks were sunken—it was the first time the commander had seen the wizard so close at hand. He was malevolent and, at the same time, pitiful. His mirrors tinkled faintly.

"What are you raising a ruckus for?" the wizard repeated sternly.

"We must pursue the enemy," the commander answered with an amiable smile.

"We're not fighting, we're not fighting," the wizard answered quietly.

And he shook his head, and rays from his mirror-trimmed hat spattered in all directions.

"But why? Why?" the commander asked.

He understood that the question was useless, and he was becoming irritated, yet wanted to restrain himself.

"We're not fighting," repeated the wizard stubbornly.

"How do you happen to know that we're not fighting, Grandfather?" the commander asked in an irritated voice.

"I know everything," said the wizard, quietly and slowly.

"He knows everything," voices rang out in the ranks. "Even a bullet wouldn't harm him!"

A barely perceptible smile flitted across the commander's face.

"Comrades!" he cried out, once more leaping up on the field-cart. "If matters stand the way they do, then, of course, there's nothing to be done in this instance. But the trouble, comrades, is that my fighters won't believe me. They, the devils, don't believe in wizards of any kind. When I tell them tomorrow that we've got to wait two weeks, as Grandfather bids us, they'll laugh me to scorn. I want Grandfather himself to convince them of his extraordinary power to work miracles."

He paused for a moment, seeking the necessary words.

"Yes—let him do it!" voices cried out in the crowd.

"All of you know, comrades, that neither bullet nor sabre can harm your Grandfather—"

"Right! Neither one nor the other!"

"Very well, then. I ask Grandfather to demonstrate his wonder-working power tomorrow. Let my lads convince themselves that neither bullet nor sabre can harm Grandfather."

And he fell silent. He had the air of a gambler who has tossed out a trump card and is tensely waiting to see whether or not it will be beaten. The crowd was now deathly still. A minute passed in strained silence.

"Well, now, Grandfather, can we have a demonstration?"

His voice could be heard clearly all over the square. The wizard, who had been standing utterly motionless, nodded his hat.

"We can," he answered.

The crowd sighed for joy and began to hum. The commander put out his left hand and uttered solemnly:

"Thanks, Grandfather! You will convince my comrades that fighting is out of the question, as you say."

In the field, beyond the settlement, there was a green knoll, and the road wound over it in a grey ribbon. The wizard in his glittering garments and glittering hat took his stand on this road; Batko Gonchar's men disposed themselves in the field to the right, and those of the regular division to the left. The commander himself indicated the spot where the machine-guns were to be placed. As they were being wheeled up, someone among the partisans called out:

"No need for machine-guns! Make the test with a rifle."

"Isn't it all one what bullets are used?" the commander asked calmly. "What's the difference if they come out of a rifle or a machine-gun?"

"Right! Nothing will harm him anyway!" certain voices responded.

The two machine-guns were placed side by side. The commander chose the best machine-gunners and instructed them in a low voice:

"Aim at the belly—below the mirrors. You, Tarassov, take the right side—and you take the left."

The commander's face was preoccupied. The wizard kept raising aloft the white cage with the black rooster. The partisans and the Army men were tensely silent. Gonchar, three sheets in the wind, who was also hanging around the spot, said in a thick, melancholy bass:

"Nothing will harm him——"

"Well, now, can we begin?" asked the commander.

"Begin!"

The commander himself inspected the sights. The wizard was glittering above the sights of both machine-guns—just right. The commander took two paces back, looked around him. All—both his men and the partisans—were watching him intently.

"Fire!" he commanded.

The machine-guns broke into their choppy laughter in unison. And fell silent. The wizard slowly crumpled to the ground.

"Got him!" came the cries from right and left. "Sawed him right in two!"

The commander looked over his shoulder at Gonchar. Gonchar twirled his right moustache with his left hand and got out in a thick bass:

"You must have a bullet with a spell on it, little brother——"

"Yes—with a spell on it," answered the commander, laughing. "Come, don't you know that I'm a wizard myself?"

For Discussion

1. What is the major difference between Batko Gonchar and the divisional commander? Which of the two seems more concerned with military success? Do these two men seem to have similar cultural backgrounds?

2. What does the presence of the wizard reveal about the men who insist upon his presence and who depend upon his predictions? Can you suggest what the various parts of the wizard's costume represent? What might the black rooster in the white cage symbolize?

3. Many people believe that a rabbit's foot or a four-leaf clover bring good luck and that walking under a ladder or breaking a mirror brings misfortune. These same people pray to God and attend church regularly. Does Batko Gonchar enact

a similar contradiction when he commands priests and prelates to celebrate his victories with masses? Explain how, if he believes in the magic of the wizard, he can still be a Christian.

4. Do you think that the divisional commander's trick of eliminating the wizard will change the beliefs of Batko Gonchar and his men? How many meanings are there in his sly comment, "I'm a wizard myself"?

5. Explain how the divisional commander destroys the wizard with his own magic. Do you feel that the wizard is a fool for submitting to the test? Do you think that he really believes in his own powers? Can you think of a way in which he might have avoided giving visible proof of his invulnerability?

You Say "Tomahto" and We Ask for "Sneakers"

JOAN DASH

The small differences between similar cultures often lead to humorous confusions and misunderstandings. We take our own inconsistencies for granted at the same time that we see eccentricity in foreign variations. In this selection, Joan Dash gives an amusing account of her battle with British terminology. For her the simple process of shopping for food and clothing becomes a contest where logic sometimes misleads and where identical words have entirely different meanings.

BEFORE OUR family left for England it was pointed out to me, by a kindly Englishwoman who makes a hobby of explaining her country to Americans, that in Oxford there is a college named Magdalen and pronounced Maudlin; that in Cambridge there is also a college named Magdalene, pronounced Maudlin, as well as a street named Magdalene, pronounced Maudlin. And in the town of Oxford there is a street named Magdalene, pronounced Magdalene.

No sooner had we set up housekeeping in Cambridge than the full impact of this inconsistency hit me firmly between the ears. I set off on my first shopping expedition with disposable diapers at the head of my list; the British for diaper being "napkin," I entered the nearest chemist's shop with a request for a package of disposable napkins.

The clerk (clark) favoured me with an empty stare.

"Paper ones," I elaborated, "the kind you throw away when they're soiled."

Now a gleam of understanding crossed his face. "You mean serviettes," he told me, placing on the counter a package of paper dinner napkins.

"These are serviettes?" I marvelled.

"Yes, madam, two and sixpence the packet. I believe you Americans call them napkins."

"Aha. Now let's start all over again. I want some disposable diapers to put on a baby. They cover the lower portion of the body. . . ." I described them at length, concluding humbly, "You see, I thought you called them napkins."

He fingered his chin, smiling. "Well we do —but no one ever says anything but nappies. Paper nappies, that's what you want."

Paper nappies they were, and the chemist was out of them.

I took the serviettes anyway, and turned the corner to enter the nearest grocer's, Merton's of Northampton Street. Cornflakes were the next item on my list; now what in the world would be British for cornflakes? Maize flakes, perhaps? Then I spied a familiar package on the shelf. "One of those, please," I pointed, turning the package round to discover its name. Cornflakes. I relaxed a bit. I read off the rest of my list with gathering confidence. My request for oatmeal was immediately met with a box of Scotch porridge; oleomargarine turned out to be oleomargarine, chummily known as "marj." Instant coffee was Nescafé, pronounced ness-cayf. Chocolate pudding? This called for consultation among the clerks, while I rummaged on the shelves for a box with a familiar picture. There it was—chocolate blancmange powder, pronounced blum-mohj.

My last request was for a sponge. I was given a smallish box labelled "Sponge," and displaying a handsome picture of a large golden cake.

"What's this?" I asked.

"Sponge, madam. In a box. You simply add water and bake, and you have a lovely sponge just like the one in the picture."

Oh, nuts, I muttered to myself in American. "I mean the kind of sponge you use to clean up the kitchen."

"That would be a washing-up sponge," the clerk pointed out. "You might try the hardware shop."

At this point madam gathered up her purchases, pocketing her change with a vow to learn all about English coins any day now, and inquired if it were possible to place a grocery order by phone.

"Certainly," said the clerk. "We're listed in the directory, Merton's of Northampton Street." Only she pronounced it Murton's.

"Not Marton's?" I gasped.

"Murton's," she repeated firmly. "M-E-R-T-O-N-S, Murton's." I turned away, baffled. "But you are a clark, aren't you? C-L-E-R-K, clark?"

Smothered laughter from the other side of the counter, and I left the shop wondering what other amazements were lurking, or perhaps larking, in wait for me.

British bathrooms, and attendant paraphernalia, are a complete subject in themselves, but I will diverge for just a moment to point out that washing-up is what one does to the dishes after dinner; before dining, one "has a wash." And in the evening, if one is hardy, one baths. Only Americans bathe. To ask a Britisher the location of the bathroom only leads to confusion; in public places, such as theatres, the cloakroom is what one wants.

When I asked the milkman for skim milk, he told me that the law did not permit it. "All our milk has to be pasteurised, dearie, that's the law," said he, and I left it at that. I discovered that skim milk cannot be bought anywhere. The British frown upon it, and proceed to pour the cream off the top of their unhomogenised milk and into their cornflakes, leaving the skim for the children who don't care for milk anyway unless half of it is tea. Potato chips masquerade as potato crisps, the salt wrapped up separately in a twist of blue paper. Pie is something you find at the butcher's, filled with sausage meat and eaten cold; fruit pies are called tarts. Bacon comes in eight different varieties, and what Americans mean is "lean and streaky."

From grocery shopping I graduated to the purchase of clothing. When our five-year-old came home from school with the announcement that "teacher says I've got to bring some plimsolls to school," she pondered the message for a moment and added, "I guess she really said pencils." We sent the child to school with a good supply of pencils, and she came back with a note requesting a pair of soft shoes for indoor wear.

Soft shoes? Sneakers, perhaps? Yes, said the child, everyone else has sneakers and they leave them in school. By now an experienced shopper, I headed for Marks and Spencer's, the British variant of Sears without catalogues, and asked for sneakers.

This brought an expression of impotence to the salesgirl's face. What sort of object was this "sneaker," she wanted to know.

"A soft shoe for playing tennis."

"Try the sporting goods shop," she suggested, reasonably enough.

"But the school said I could get them here."

"Well, kindly look around and if you see one, point to it." Around I looked, past underpants marked "knickers," and undershirts called "vests," and there they were on the counter, serried rows of child-size sneakers, all black. "Those things," I pronounced triumphantly, "those black sneakers."

"Plimsolls," said the salesgirl.

For Discussion

1. This story takes place in Britain. Are there any sections in the United States where similar confusions might arise? Are there names for things that are familiar to you but that might confuse people from other parts of the country?

2. Characterize the author as she portrays herself. Does she have a contempt for British ways? Does she feel that her ways are superior?

3. Which of the two words, "Plimsoll" (a trade mark) or "sneaker," do you think is the better term for canvas shoes? What are some of the ways in which a person might interpret the word "sneaker"?

4. Using the misunderstandings that occur in this selection as a basis for your reasoning, suggest how a similar lack of communication might lead to serious international complications.

5. This essay makes some basic comments on human communication. A language changes from generation to generation, and we tend to cling to the terminology that prevails during our maturity. List some terms used by older people that seem odd to you. Do you think that this difference in language habits contributes to the misunderstanding that usually exists between generations? Does it sound strange to hear older generations use the same slang that comes naturally to you? Why?

PAUL GAUGUIN

The Young Tahitians

(Collection of Mr. and Mrs. André Meyer)

UNIT 8: PEOPLE AND PLACES

The real has replaced romance.

News of incidents in Bangkok, Madrid, or Hong Kong arrives within minutes of their happening. The *Arabian Nights* quality of far-off places has faded. The speed of modern travel makes neighbors of people formerly thought of as fairytale characters in exotic settings.

Often, we take our own way of life for granted. We assume that our ways are the "best," the most "natural," and we use our own habits of thought to measure other men and nations. The beauty of a Japanese garden, for example, may at first elude us. We expect to find gardens massed with colors and forms: the Japanese arrange their gardens with severe, disciplined economy, and delicate shades of meaning. Our social habits as well are challenged by a look at other cultures. Reading about other people and places, we find that a Moslem may be just as self-sacrificing and devout in his faith as a Christian may be in his. We may see that a man in a thatched hut on a Bolivian mountainside can lead as rich a life as we with our intricate houses, central heating, and electrical comforts. We learn that a Congolese can be as fervently loyal to his cause as the fighters of the American Revolution were for theirs.

The selections in this unit provide a tour for the imaginative reader who enjoys looking beyond the surfaces of other cultures. The romance and excitement of new sights and sounds sometimes blind the tourist to the deeper significances of the country he visits. The authors of the following stories and essays have not attempted to say all that can be said about another culture. Rather, they present the reader with the small, but revealing, incidents. They have tried to set down something of the distinctive quality of another people, another place.

A writer can view a way of life either from the inside or from the outside. That is, he may either belong to a place himself, or he may see that place with the fresh vision of a visitor. This unit contains examples of both kinds of writing.

Travel books are almost as old as literature itself. The Greek historian Herodotus gave readers of his history many descriptions of the customs of other nations—information he had gathered during his own travels in Asia Minor. Much of the fascination of Julius Caesar's *Gallic Wars* is in the great soldier's account of what he saw and heard during his campaigns in the outposts of the Roman Empire. One of the most popular travel books of all time was Marco Polo's account of his visit to Cathay.

A foreign visitor to another land may become deeply involved with the culture he is writing about, or he may be only a casual, curious tourist. Leonard Wibberley, author of "The Language of Oxen," is an example of the casual visitor. Reading his piece about Portugal, we feel that we are in the company of an intelligent and sympathetic traveler, but one who will soon move on to another place. The same is true of Russell Davis and Brent Ashabranner, authors of "The Wonderful Cabbages." On the other hand, Elizabeth Borton de Treviño, in "A Trip to the Post Office," is involved through marriage with the bewildering Mexico she writes of. Even more deeply involved with his subject, though only temporarily, is John D. Rockefeller, 4th. His essay on students in Japan is the result of a prolonged personal experiment in international understanding. Rockefeller lived the life of a Japanese student in order to understand Japan as thoroughly as possible. His writing reflects his earnest, moral concern: it could not have come from the pen of a casual tourist interested only in "local color."

Four of the writers here are members of the societies they are writing about. J. Benibengor Blay gives an account of a curious and ancient custom among the fishermen of his native Ghana. Giovanni Guareschi's story "The Petition" and Jiménez's "Platero and I" could only have been written by men who are intimately connected with the people and places in their stories. Perhaps the most fascinating selection in this unit is Camara Laye's "The Snake and the Crocodile." Here is an account of a boy's growing up in an African tribe, written from the point of view of one who actually underwent such an experience. The reader of Laye's memoir is transported to a private world which no foreign traveler could ever participate in.

Students of Japan

JOHN D. ROCKEFELLER, 4th

History tells of a continual conflict between the past and the present, the traditional and the modern, the conventional and the experimental. Nowhere are these contrasts more marked than in present-day Japan. Since the upheaval of the Second World War, dramatic changes in Japanese life have created a social hostility between the older and younger generations.

John D. Rockefeller, 4th, is the son of one of America's richest and most powerful families. In order to learn the language and customs of Japan, he spent three years in Japanese universities. There he shared the life of his fellow students. The following essay reveals some of his conclusions about the character of Japanese young people and the nature of the problems they confront.

FOR FOUR hours that afternoon Hashimoto and I had discussed a range of problems concerning Japan. Seated on the *tatami* (the straw matting of Japanese houses) in my room, we had sipped the yellow tea that the landlady of the house brought in periodically. Sometimes we sat quietly, thinking, fingering the tea cups or running our hands over furrows of the *tatami*. Hashimoto interrupted one of these silences when he looked up calmly and said, "You and your country will never completely understand the heart and mind of us young Japanese, for you don't know the meaning and significance of the deep personal struggle which is so much of our lives."

Hashimoto's pronouncement may seem errant to many Americans who have had to struggle for what they have in life, but it is nevertheless generally true. The young Japanese person's life is an endless path of conflict and struggle for both mind and body. If we cannot understand the nature of these struggles then we cannot understand the workings of the young Japanese mind, for that mind is formed by the reaction and adjustment to these struggles.

I have spent nearly three years in Japan in an attempt to understand the young Japanese mind. I have learned the language, both in its written and spoken forms. Without the language, any attempt to see into the Japanese mentality must fail, for it is a strange truth that the Japanese are unable to express their thoughts truly in English. The Japanese mind and language are indirect, suggestive and partially abstract. Its ideas cannot be expressed by a language, such as English, which is direct, literal and concrete. Therefore, when the Japanese uses English to converse, he must change his thoughts so as to make them expressible in English. Consequently, a Japanese speaking English is not speaking his true mind.

I have shared the life of the Japanese university student, living as exactly as possible in his manner. For my first two terms, I lived in a small apartment with two graduate students; then for the next term, I lived in a boarding house with six Japanese students and a Chinese-Indonesian student. For the last year and a half at the university I lived in another *gesshuku* (boarding house) with four Japanese students and one Filipino.

The struggle for education is a grim one in Japan. The competition to get into good senior high schools and then into a leading college is far more rigorous than in America. Whereas at leading American colleges perhaps four or five will apply for every one accepted, at the university where I studied near Tokyo, the ratio of applicants to acceptances two years ago was 16 to 1. At the top university, Tokyo University, only 15 to 20 per cent of the freshmen are there on their first try. In Japan, there are "cram schools" which are designed to prepare students for college entrance exams. And there are waiting lines for the cram schools.

The reason for the intensity of the struggle for education is that where one receives one's education means, along with family status, literally everything in job determination. If a student cannot enter a good college, and if he does not have social position (and only a few do), he cannot look forward to a satisfactory job. Consequently, the Japanese student is a more caring and industrious student than the

American (who knows that he can get into any state university). In senior high schools, students will work themselves to a high degree of tension preparing for college exams, studying till 2 or 3 in the morning, week after week. Failure in entrance examinations is a common cause of suicide.

Oda, my roommate for two terms, memorized whole sections of the English dictionary in preparation for his college entrance exam. Perhaps it can be said, however, that such a struggle for education produces high results, for the 98 percent literacy rate in Japan is the highest in the world.

Finding a job is perhaps the greatest hurdle of a young man's life, for in Japan one cannot change jobs, or resign from one job and move to another. And yet a young man has little control over his ability to obtain a job—factors beyond him are decisive. First he applies for a job through his college. Second, colleges do not make overtures to employers but employers to colleges, so that only those companies that offer themselves to the colleges are available to a young man. And third, the feudalism of old Japan remains strong in such matters as jobs; family influence and the proper connections may well determine whether a young man can have the job he seeks.

An example of this arose with one of my closest friends, Nakahara. Nakahara took the examinations for two of Japan's biggest companies, one very traditional and the other a post-war company, supposedly modern in its employment system. In competition with 600 men in both exams, he was one of twenty in each to pass and thus be allowed to take the final interview. I knew the interview would be easy for him, for it lasts only about three minutes and consequently requires only making a good impression. Since Nakahara is truly remarkable in his success with people, I assumed that the job was about to become his.

However, he failed both interviews. There was only one reason for this: he had no connec-

Japanese students taking part in a political demonstration

tions, no influential friend who could write the proper word or make the suitable phone call in his behalf. Without this, even his outstanding qualifications were insufficient. I remember that he did not sleep for three nights after that and I finally had to knock him out with sleeping pills.

One of the companies did appoint him to a small branch in which he had no interest. Yet Nakahara had no alternative; he accepted it. I have never heard him mention his new job, not even when we talked of the future. Nevertheless, he came under the influence of that strange oriental sense of resignation and fate. I watched him gradually adjust himself to the idea and he is now working hard, with every pretense of being well satisfied. He will progress, but slowly.

In today's Japan there is a wide difference in thinking between the pre-war generations and those who have grown up since the war. The older generations are inclined toward traditionalism and feudalism—tight family order based on respect for elders and parents, close control over children, arranged marriages, sober respect for any authority, a sharp regulation of social order and life's habits and actions. The younger generation thinks more like the young people in any industrialized Western country. They want to choose and decide for themselves, blaze their own trails.

This means a profoundly serious conflict for the young Japanese. He has little of the parent-child communication that children the world over take for granted.

Otani, a friend of mine from a Tokyo college,

once said, "There is nothing between my father and me. We live in the same house but we have little to say to each other and I will never go to him for advice. When I do need advice I'll go to my own friends." (Partly because of this and partly because of widespread separation of the sexes in high schools, boys and girls have powerfully close friendships within their sex groups.)

It is common for a college graduate to go monthly to a reunion of his high school class. Young friends need each other in Japan. They use each other for the stability they cannot find in their parents and elders.

It interested me, for example, that the parents of one of my roommates, even though they lived close to our boarding house, never visited or were invited to visit us. As a matter of fact, I never once heard this roommate mention either his father or mother.

Several months ago I visited another roommate's home in the mountains of a remote and poor prefecture. I was the first foreign person ever to enter the village. Here I could clearly see the rigidly traditional, feudal thinking of the town adults as compared to the modern thinking of my friend.

My friend's father, for example, accepted as fact that in the Emperor lay the origin of the whole Japanese race and that he is a divine being, while my friend could only look upon the Emperor system cynically. The difference in their way of thinking amazed me, especially when my friend had to ask me to put a question concerning the Emperor to his father, as he himself was afraid of offending him by the question's lack of reverence for tradition.

One area where this difference in thinking has a disturbing effect on the younger generation is that of boy-girl relationships. The parents generally feel that their children should be given mates through arranged marriages, while the young people want to choose through love. Because of this, I have seen many tragic situations among my friends.

Nahayama was deeply in love with a girl attending the same college as he, and she was

deeply in love with him. They had privately discussed and agreed to marriage. When she asked her doctor father for permission, however, he said no, that she was to marry a young doctor he had selected so that the family tradition of medicine might be carried on. Since the father had a financial leverage on them, the couple realized there was nothing they could do and were forced to stop seeing each other.

This couple survived the blow, but such dilemmas have been the cause of actual suicide pacts for many young couples in modern Japan. And always their burdens must be carried and resolved by the youth themselves, with no help from those from whom we in the Western world receive so much guidance—parents.

There was a sweet and gentle girl at the university I attended who was wildly loved by a graduate student who tried to force her by violent words and sometimes physical punishment to marry him, even though she could not endure him. Yet, consider her reaction. In her lack of wise and calm guidance, she fell back on her training and told me that she would marry him rather than cause worry and trouble to him and to others.

"My life will be buried among black clouds," she said. Yet she felt she had nowhere to turn. It was only because of the intervention of a Japanese friend and myself that she could overcome her problem.

In spite of the recent marriage of the Crown Prince to a commoner, feudalism, with its sense of social position, still dominates the thinking of many older Japanese and prevents marriages of young people of different social groups. The young person will be lucky, therefore, if he can find happiness on his own terms. Two-thirds of marriages in Japan are still arranged (nearly 100 percent in rural areas), and the majority of my friends will have to submit to such procedure. Yet they will make their way in married life, and the chances are that the couples will never divorce, because they expect very little of each other in the first place.

Another reason the young generation of

Japanese must struggle to carry their own burdens is that they have neither religion nor faith. For the young, Shintoism [1] died with the war. Buddhism survives on tourists, and Christianity affects less than one-half of 1 percent of the population.

Furthermore, all pre-war concepts of behavior and attitude have been discredited in the eyes of the young. They fear and distrust their government, convinced that it is trying to centralize control and remilitarize Japan with the help of the Americans (almost to a man, the voting students vote against the Kishi [2] Government).

The young Japanese does not have the instinctive confidence and trust in his country that Americans have in theirs. Indeed, they have little knowledge of or interest in the pre-war culture and nature of Japan, for they feel it bears no relation to them. Consequently, in times of personal trouble, there is no God to turn to, no solace in prayer, no minister to seek help from, no comfort from a national sense of well-being and even, as we have seen, no acceptable parental guidance.

I have often talked with students about this, and they feel that faith in the progress of day-to-day life and the general "continuity of things" is sufficient for them. Very few concern themselves with a concept as vague as God.

Although the young Japanese is deeply affected by the democratic and Christian ethics that have taken root in Japan since the war, he must, essentially, fix his own precedents and standards according to his own wisdom and experience. It can be fairly said that he is spiritually afloat.

The Japanese share one problem that is common to all of Asia's students—poverty. In my three years in Japan, for example, I have met only one student who owned his own car. Most students, in addition to their studies, carry a

heavy load of outside work to earn money. One friend of mine, for example, works five hours a day in the college boiler room for thirteen cents an hour. Three others tutor high school students, and still another works evenings as a servant to an American military family.

The students at my college voted against having any heat in their dormitory during the winter rather than have to pay an annual $1.40 fee. (In fact, no Japanese-style house has a built-in heating system and occupants must endure winter temperatures that are frequently lower indoors than out.) Because Japanese classrooms are not heated, numb feet and legs are an everyday problem.

Japanese students eat only a fraction of what the American student does. During my first year at the university, I ate entirely from the dining hall—and I lost twenty pounds. Although I was hungry most of the day, it is interesting that I was never sick, only thinner. I was accustomed to more than my body really needed.

In pointing out some of the struggles and conflicts of the young person's life in Japan, I have described a gloomy, discouraging situation. And indeed that is what it is, judged from an American viewpoint. But what is significant is that the product of this discouraging situation is far from discouraged. He is definitely a more directed and dedicated person than the average American student, and is also more alert and aware. Why? Because, to survive, he has had to be. Struggle has produced toughness, adaptability and progress. Indeed, one of the greatest lessons I have learned from my three years in Japan is that when people do not have to struggle for what they need in life, they seldom know its value and will not use it wisely.

I spent a week during the winter in a poor farming district of northern Japan as the guest of a friend. It was bitterly cold and I wore two sweaters and heavy ski gloves as we walked around the countryside. Actually it was so cold that I could not take off my gloves to operate my camera.

Yet my friend was wearing only his black

[1] *Shintoism* Ancient native religion of Japan, based in part on ancestor worship and consideration of the Emperor as a divinity.
[2] *Kishi* Premier Kishi headed a moderate pro-American government at the time this essay was written.

student uniform and *geta* (wooden clogs) on bare feet. To me it was significant that, in spite of all my clothing, I was uncomfortable, while he, whether comfortable or uncomfortable, was simply tougher than I.

Japanese young people, because of the lives they lead, have learned to think from a careful and harshly unidealistic viewpoint concerning their country and its future. They are generally agreed that the Emperor system is useless for their nation, and they fear that if it is allowed to remain it will be used again as a tool by militarists, as it was during the last war. Contrary to what is generally accepted, I feel that the young people have little attachment to the Crown Prince and his commoner wife, and I doubt whether they will respond to them in the future. The young Japanese are remarkably materialistic, even more so than we Americans. There has been little in their lives to cause them to be sentimental or spiritual.

In national and international thinking the students distinctly lack the long view, as the short view is what they have brought themselves up on. They wish fervently for their country to be neutral, between the two power blocs. They want Japan to recognize Communist China and to have cordial dealings with it. And they are united in their condemnation of Japan's economic and military reliance on the United States. Their reasoning is realistic. Since China and all its might lies only a short distance away from Japan, is it not unwise to antagonize it by trying to pretend it doesn't exist?

The students are absolutely and unalterably opposed to militarism in any form, and as recent events have shown, they have reacted strongly against the security pact with the United States. For this they have been called Communist-inspired.

Japanese students react more warmly to American people than to any other foreigners, but that is a personal matter. It does not mean that they agree with our policies. My own roommate of two years was an active participant in the wild demonstrations against the security pact with the United States.

I believe completely in the younger generation's desire for peace, because it is realistic, not idealistic. They want peace because they knew war the way no other nation ever has. People still die from the two atomic bombs.

For Discussion

1. Does Rockefeller condemn the older generation for clinging to tradition? Are there reasons to support the old way of life? Do you think that the older generation tries to impose a respect for tradition on their children because they jealously want to preserve the past, or because they feel that it will do the most good for the young people? If you were a Japanese student, which of the two ways would you choose to follow? Explain.

2. What effect do these grim struggles have upon the character of the Japanese student? What are some of Rockefeller's conclusions about these struggles? Do you think you would benefit or lose by having such obstacles placed in the path of your education?

3. What does the author reveal as the goal of the Japanese student? Is the superior student always the one who receives the greatest reward? Is this true of our system of education? Explain.

4. This essay describes various aspects of the Japanese student's life: education, employment, his war with the older generation and tradition, religion, courtship and marriage, and poverty. Select any one of these and compare or contrast it with your own experience. Do you find that the Japanese situation is different from yours? Explain.

Funeral of a Whale

J. BENIBENGOR BLAY

The whale, earth's largest mammal, has always inspired man's curiosity and awe. In the Bible, the Leviathan becomes the earthly symbol of God's power. Herman Melville, in Moby Dick, *used the white whale as a symbol of the forces of nature which man can neither understand nor master.*

The people of Missibi in Ghana are fishermen; they have a religious respect for the mysteries of the sea. Here is an authentic account of a colorful ceremony still practiced in Missibi, which is not far from Accra, the modern capital of Ghana. Natives of that country claim that, after the funeral of the beached whale, the fishing is always rich for the next several days.

THERE IS great excitement in the ancient town of Missibi in Ghana.

The previous night had been wet and stormy and one which the fishermen were not likely to forget. Caught in the storm, their canoes had been dashed to pieces on the rocks and their nets swept away on the swift current. Only the fact that they were all strong swimmers had saved the men from drowning.

The sun is not yet up when they collect again on the shore to watch for their nets. The moon is still shining and little waves dance merrily on the strand, while the sea crabs scuttle among the scattered shells. But these things do not interest the fishermen, and even the search for nets is forgotten as they catch sight of a huge object, surrounded by a shoal of fish, tossing on the rolling sea. Their slow, questing advance is halted as a nauseating stench greets them. Fingers to their noses, they crane and peer. It is a whale —and judging by the smell, it has been dead for some days.

Now, such a sight is no mere spectacle to the people of Missibi. As descendants of a strong and virile race which long ago came by sea in great barge-like ships to settle in these parts, they hold to the tradition that the sea is their home and they worship it to this day. In any crisis—whatever its nature, whether drought or famine or war—they call upon the sea for help. The whale is the king of their sea. And it has been the custom, throughout their long history, to accord a ceremonial funeral to any whale that comes rolling ashore dead.

J. BENIBENGOR BLAY *is a native of Ghana. He is the author of nineteen books and of many radio scripts. He has also served as a member of the Parliament of his country.*

So, bound by tradition, the fishermen must bear the unhappy tidings to the ruler of the town. Their waists girdled with palm leaves and fingers to lips as signs that their news is urgent, and as yet secret, they go on their errand.

The chief's advisers are called together by the court messenger for a palaver.[1] Now the fishermen are permitted to tell their news. Only after the chief's bodyguards have visited the beach to confirm this statement may the towns-folk be told. It is now past eight o'clock in the morning. The state drums boom out the warning of great calamity. The people from the busy market place, the farmers, coconut breakers and rice growers who have risen at cock-crow and gone to the farms, all come trooping to the palace yard, agog with excitement.

The chief comes to the courtyard with his advisers and sits on the landing of the dais.[2] His face betokens sadness. His attendants bow and leave the palace. The drums are still booming. Outside are packed lorries[3] and cars from up country bringing loads of hawkers and buyers to the market while the occupants move in with the still surging crowd.

The court messenger comes into the yard, bows to the chief and courtiers, commands silence and after giving a brief survey of the history of Missibi and her connection with the sea, makes his announcement to the assembled throng.

[1] *palaver* A lengthy discussion. The word usually refers to a conference with or among African natives.

[2] *dais* A raised platform, such as that on which a throne is set.

[3] *lorries* Trucks. The word is used more in Britain than in America; Ghana was formerly a British colony.

"The State is in mourning. A whale is dead and has been washed ashore. The funeral will be held at two o'clock at Aposika where the king of the sea now lies."

There is no whisper nor laughter nor cough as the great crowd moves from distant parts, out of the palace. The market day is postponed. The school bell's tolling stopped. All is sad silence. Yet it is a great day for the hawkers from distant parts, for now they will see something of which so far they have only heard. To the aged of the town it is history repeating itself, and the announcement seems to bring back pictures of half-forgotten times.

By order of a committee appointed by the chief's advisers, funeral preparations are put in hand at once. A body of young men is engaged in the erection of bamboo huts, and the bush around the area is cleared, while musicians polish their instruments in readiness. Word is passed to neighboring places and more people arrive to swell the numbers.

At two o'clock the procession leaves for the scene of the funeral, guns booming, state guns rumbling, ivory horn blaring. The chief and his counselors are dressed in red. The women-folk, besmeared with red clay and wearing pieces of red calico tied around their hair, are in front with the children. The men bring up the rear.

The tail of the column is as yet only at the outskirts of the town when its head reaches the place where, a little off the beach, lies the great shapeless mass of the whale. Gallons of disinfectant have already been sprinkled around to kill the smell.

Now the chief's messenger calls for silence and orders the crowd to be seated. The chief steps forward followed by his advisers. Dropping the red cloth from his shoulder and gathering the folds in his left arm, with a glass of rum held in his right hand, he first raises his eyes to heaven then looks to the ground as he pours out a libation with these words: "Tradition binds us to the sea and the whale is king of the elements there. My people and I pay you homage and lament your death. How it happened we do not know. Whether it was in combat with your fellow kings, or whether it was inflicted by those who delight in making sport of you, or whether it was a natural death, we are afflicted all the same with a great sense of personal loss. We reaffirm our traditional ties with your descendants, will look to them in anxious days for help, and beg of you, who now belong to the ages, to release this land from starvation and sickness; leave in their place health and plenty. Rest in peace."

The funeral ceremony being declared open, the women like minstrels tell the story of the whale in parables; its connection with the state is recounted and the dead one praised. The chief and his advisers are head mourners and make themselves responsible for the fair distribution of drinks, providing food for those who have come from afar and recording donations received.

The young men keep order and play native instruments, while the old correct any departure from the traditional funeral procedure. Boys and girls play. Hunters fire off guns and firecrackers at intervals in honor of the majesty of the dead. Fishermen fish in the waves and cast their nets on the beach; farmers sow their seeds on the strand, fetish priests [4] play tom-toms and perform their feats of walking barefoot on broken bottles and gashing their stomachs with sharp knives. Everybody, in fact, is doing something.

As the celebration continues, weeping becomes the order of the day; there is competition among the womenfolk in pitch, tone and rendering of phrases, and prizes are offered to those who maintain the high standard of wailing set by their ancestors.

Further away from the crowds a great number of seagulls gather. Some are twittering, others are flying around the whale. The tide begins to rise and the waves are swelling high. Deep clouds overshadow the clear blue sky, and for a while the heavens are pouring rain. It seems that nature, too, is paying tribute to the king of the sea.

At six o'clock, as the sun is setting behind the clouds, the celebrations reach their climax—the solemn spreading of a long white sheet over the whale. Now each mourner takes a pebble, a shell, a stick, a coin or anything handy and, whispering a few words, whirls it around his head and throws it in the direction of the whale. Then without a further glance, all return to town.

The funeral of the king of the sea is over.

For Discussion

1. Why should the whale, of all the creatures of the sea, inspire such reverence in the people of Missibi?

2. What does the ritual of the whale's funeral reveal about the people of Missibi? What kind of society is this? Can you guess what sort of religion these people practice? Do the people of Missibi seem warlike or peaceful? Explain.

3. For many years in the nineteenth century, the seafaring men of Nantucket, an island off the coast of Massachusetts, hunted the whale from ocean to ocean. They held a great respect for their powerful prey and wrote glowing accounts of the courage and ferocity of the whale. What is the difference between the attitudes toward the whale of the men from Nantucket and the people of Missibi?

4. How does the funeral of the whale indicate the attitude toward tradition of the people of Missibi? What is the story that seems to give rise to this performance?

---

[4] *fetish priests* Magicians or witch doctors who handle charms and sacred objects.

Language of Oxen

LEONARD WIBBERLEY

It is possible to travel through time as well as through space. In many countries of the modern world, there remain corners—small villages, country districts, the older parts of the capitol city—where life goes on much as it did centuries ago. If you walk through the Iron Market of Port-au-Prince, along the edge of Dublin's River Liffey, or beneath the walls of Toledo in Spain, the sights you see are much the same as you would have seen a century ago—only an occasional truck or Coca-Cola sign obtrudes from the present. In this essay, the writer describes such a journey backward in time. During a visit to Portugal, he suddenly finds himself in a land where men talk to animals and wooden gears still prevail. Here, in the midst of a modern nation, is a quaint past that refuses to surrender itself to the present.

ONE MORNING, while I was still abed, I heard in the thin, clear mountain air a wavering cry which ended with an abrupt staccato note and then was repeated again and again. I had never heard such a cry before and lay for a while listening to it. Plainly it was made by a man. It had a sort of oriental nuance to it, like the cry of the Muezzin [1] summoning the faithful to prayer.

It was a beautiful day. Out of the window I could see huge white clouds, soft and expanding, rolling majestically across a sky of deep blue. The sun appeared and gently disappeared, and I knew that on the mountain opposite the house, in the tiny fields cleared from the forests, there would be a procession of cloud shadow over the ground—a wonderful display of forms, ever changing in shape and density and moving across the ground.

I got up and at breakfast asked Maria who was making the strange sound.

"The men are plowing," she said. "They are talking to their oxen. That is the way one talks to an ox all over the world."

I finished breakfast quickly and, taking Kevin,[2] went out to see this wonder—a man talking to an ox. The man was in a field on the mountainside across the valley. In the clear air he was perfectly outlined against the brownish

---

[1] *Muezzin* In the Mohammedan religion, one who calls the faithful to prayer.

[2] *Kevin* The author's son.

earth on which he stood, as sharp as a figure in an etching. He had a plow and two oxen yoked to it. The oxen had long, graceful horns, which appeared as beautiful curved lines even at that distance. The man wore a stocking cap with a bobble at the end of it. It hung down over one side of his face. I could see him jerk the plow up out of the ground and then we heard, with exquisite clarity, the plaintive cry with the staccato stop on a high note. Slowly the oxen leaned forward on the yoke; slowly they put one big and yet graceful foot in front of the other; slowly the plow moved. And as ox and plow moved laboriously forward, the man repeated his wavering cry, at once a plea, a command, and a complaint that the oxen and himself should be so harnessed to the ground and made to earn their bread in this manner.

I was enchanted, and with Kevin raced down our side of the mountain and across the little road and river at the bottom and up the other flank of the mountain to the field in which the man was plowing. He came slowly along the field toward us, stopping, it seemed, every minute to jerk the plow up out of the furrow, clear off the share some root or clump of tangled grass, and then continue.

When he drew near he looked at us out of a blank mahogany face; like the Spirit of the Ages might look upon mere mortals, with patience and sorrow. Then he took off his stocking cap and bowed with a beautiful gesture and said, "*Bom dia, senhor.*" [3]

"*Bom dia, senhor,*" I replied, for I had now been long enough in Portugal to appreciate the deep politeness of the Portuguese. The meanest beggar you meet in the meanest street is "senhor" which may roughly be translated as "gentleman." To inquire the way you do not say, "Can you tell me the road to Lisbon?" but, "Can the gentleman (or the lady) tell me the road to Lisbon?"

I had by now sufficient Portuguese to ask the plowman what words he spoke to his oxen and whether he guided them only by words. He explained that the oxen did not understand Portuguese, but there was a kind of oxen language in which they were well versed. This language was a language of sound only—a glissando [4] of the voice through a series of quarter notes which the oxen all over Portugal understood. One learned it only by listening to it. He had learned it from his father, who had gotten it from his father, and so on.

"Can the gentleman tell me how long this language of the oxen has been spoken in Portugal?"

The plowman reflected.

It was *muito antiqua* [5]—it has always been so. Then I began to realize that here was one of the most ancient agricultural cries in the world. Perhaps it was a thousand or two thousand years old, this cry. It was a cry which Vasco da Gama, should he return to Portugal, would recognize immediately. No doubt it had been a dear and familiar sound to him and he had thought of it often during his splendid voyage into the unknown.

The plowman had with him a long, slim pole like a fishing pole. This was his other means of communicating with his oxen. When he put it in front of them, they stopped. When he touched them on a horn with it, they turned to the side touched.

Might I examine his plow?

Certainly. He jerked it out of the four-inch furrow which it had made in the ground and again I realized I was in the presence of something incredibly old. For the plow was of the exact same design one sees in drawings of the plows of Saxons [6] of the sixth and seventh centuries. It was little more than a pointed piece of wood, like the nose of a shark, which carved

---

[3] "*Bom dia, senhor*" Portuguese: "Good morning, sir."

[4] *glissando* A musical, sliding tone.

[5] *muito antiqua* Very ancient.

[6] *Saxons* One of the Germanic peoples who migrated to England during the fifth and sixth centuries.

A miller carrying grain to a windmill in Portugal

a furrow in the ground, one single furrow, when pulled by the huge oxen. There was not even a wheel on this plow. There was a screw by which the depth of the furrow could be regulated. This screw was not of metal, but beautifully carved out of a piece of olivewood. It was then a screw such as Archimedes [7] must have whittled centuries before the birth of Christ.

I should have been more respectful in the presence of such an ancient instrument, the prototype of all the plows ever developed by

[7] *Archimedes* Greek mathematician and inventor.

man and one of which some examples are to be seen in the wall paintings in Egyptian tombs. But I was from the New World, and brash.

"Would not the gentleman's work be easier," I inquired, "if he used a metal plow with several shares and had it pulled by a machine?"

He smiled at me patiently. He explained he had heard of such plows though he had never seen one. But they would be of no use to him. His farm was small and all the fields small—the largest no bigger than three acres. If he used such a plow his field would be plowed in less than an hour.

and from the top of the stony knoll on which the windmill was situated looked over the roofs and little crooked back streets of the village of Malveira da Serra. The village, when I first caught sight of it, had seemed oddly familiar, as if I had been there some time before. The little lanes between chest-high stone walls, the red-tiled roofs of the houses—five or six or even eight roofs to a house, all at different angles and few of them more than six feet from the ground—awoke some memory in me.

On these roofs, pumpkins were ripening in the sun and white pigeons waddled and pouted, or wheeled over them in fluttering splashes of light. Attached to each house were stables for donkeys or cattle or oxen, and cats slept in the discarded bracken while one or two hardy flies (for this was December) buzzed sleepily about. Little children, ragged but healthy, played among the cats and the donkeys, and their grandames sat with shawls over their heads, knitting or taking the sun.

Certainly it was all famliar. But where had I seen it before?

The ancient cry of the plowman came to me across the fields and the little whistles on the windmill twittered above my head and a dog dashed after a hen that disappeared in a flurry of squawks and feathers.

And suddenly I knew where I had seen it all before. It was in the paintings of Breughel [9] and Rubens and a dozen other Renaissance painters. I found myself there in The Europe of the Renaissance. It was not a stage setting that surrounded me but the real substance. The lanes with the chest-high walls—those were the places where swords had flashed and the blood of dying men had mingled with the mud while their prayers for the salvation of their souls fell upon the dark night air.

The mean tavern at the corner was the place where the traveler knocked after sunset, and was eyed fearfully through a little wooden shutter that opened in the stout door. And the barnyard strewn with bracken and cats and old women—there are a thousand paintings of such barnyards with cats and women, and pumpkins ripening on the roof, and white pigeons circling in the air, all of them three hundred years old.

I had slipped out of the twentieth century into the fifteenth. It was enchantment, and yet it was true. This was the Portugal that unknowingly, drawn by some deep instinct, I had set out to find.

For Discussion

1. What arguments are there to defend a society's choice to resist change? What arguments attack this sort of attitude? What are some of the problems that might confront young people growing up in this society?

2. What are some of the arguments that the plowman presents against mechanization? Are they convincing? What is the plowman's attitude toward the oxen?

3. What do the whistles on the arms of the windmills reveal about the people who put them there? What kind of education do you feel is most popular among these people? Explain.

4. Is the author critical or sympathetic to this way of life? Can you find passages that support your conclusion? How does his view of this society show us part of his own personality? Would you say that he is romantic or realistic? Explain.

5. Do you feel that leisure plays an important part in the life of this society? Why? From evidence in the selection, how do you think these people spend their spare time?

---

[9] *Breughel* Pieter Breughel the Elder (1520?–1569), and his sons Pieter and Jan were all Flemish painters.

The Wonderful Cabbages of Mutahwie Ben Ali Ben Sassie El Nasee

RUSSELL G. DAVIS AND BRENT K. ASHABRANNER

Mutahwie Ben Ali Ben Sassie El Nasee is a man whose lazy wisdom makes an embarrassing comment on the highly organized agency that has dedicated itself to the task of improving his living conditions. In this selection the aggressive efficiency of the Western world collides with the patient disorder of the East, and the lesson that emerges provides an understanding of each. The Westerner, who sets out to make others conform to his methods, learns that he must make certain important compromises along the way. And the Easterner, who selfishly contrives to reap benefits without expending any energy, becomes a more impressive advertisement for "progress" than he intended.

POINT FOUR [1] work has its disappointments as well as its rewards, but often the disappointments can be traced to the fact that the technician does not know enough about the people he is trying to help. Usually this is not the technician's fault; it takes time to learn the ways of people new to him, and unless he is just lucky, he is likely to make some errors of judgment early in his overseas career. These slips aren't often very serious, and no one gets upset about them but the technician himself. It isn't often, however, that a slip of this type brings about the surprising results reported in the following story. The technician tells his own story.

On my first Point Four assignment, I was sent out to the Middle East as an agricultural extension agent. My main job was to train some young fellows in this kind of work. I wanted it to be training by doing—on-the-job training—so we took to the road right away. Luckily, the

[1] *Point Four* A U.S. Government program of technical assistance to foreign nations, so called because it was the fourth point made by President Truman in his inaugural address of 1949.

country was enough like my part of the Southwest that I got to know it pretty fast. I thought I was getting to know the people, too, but that was before I met Mutahwie Ben Ali Ben Sassie El Nasee.

My crew and I moved around the part of the country I was assigned to, doing a little good, I think, but mostly just getting acquainted with the farmers and their problems and their ways of doing things. The crew was learning that you don't do farm extension work sitting behind a desk in the big city.

About July I noticed that none of the farmers in the area were starting hot beds for planting cabbage seeds, and this puzzled me. From visiting the markets and talking with the food-sellers in the city—which was about a hundred miles from the farming area where I was working—I had learned that cabbage was a popular winter food. I had just automatically assumed that it was grown up here in my area.

But when I started asking around, I found that this wasn't true. It seemed that no one in these parts had ever raised cabbages. Cabbages that went to the city came from another part of the country. I tried to find out why no one in my area grew cabbages, but I couldn't get any reason. They just didn't grow them. And that really was the only reason: no one had ever started. Their fathers and grandfathers had not raised cabbages, so they didn't raise them.

Here, I thought, was a great chance to introduce a good new cash crop in this area and at the same time to help the food supply in the city. That's what I thought. When I tried to sell my idea to the farmers, I came up against a stone wall that I couldn't make a crack in. They all listened politely, smiled, nodded, and agreed that growing cabbages was a wonderful idea—for someone else. For themselves they thought that it was better that they should grow the crops they had always grown. They were sure of these; they were not sure about cabbages. The fact that we were offering free cabbage seeds didn't make any difference. Of

course I could have raised the cabbages myself, but it wouldn't have been the same thing as having one of the local farmers do it.

I thought that we had tried every farmer in the area that we could reach, and I had given up the idea. Then one afternoon when we were bouncing over a dusty back trail in our jeep, we stopped at a ramshackle little mud farmhouse for some water for our radiator. There seemed to be two rooms in the house, but one of the walls was sagging badly; and if the house had ever had a drop of whitewash, it had long since vanished. There was no livestock in sight. The only two living things around, in fact, were a tired-looking acacia tree and an even more tired-looking farmer. He was stretched out in the tree's meager shade and appeared to be sound asleep, but as we approached he sat up and finally stood up. He was as ramshackle as his house, a skinny, sad-eyed little guy with dirty clothes and of course no shoes.

We shook hands all around and introduced ourselves. He told us solemnly that his name was Mutahwie Ben Ali Ben Sassie El Nasee.

One of my men smiled and said, "That means he is Mutahwie, the son of Ali, the son of Sassie the Forgetful."

"That's a lot of name to remember," I said.

When this remark was translated, the little farmer replied generously, "You may call me Mutahwie Ben Ali."

We got our water and while we were doing that, Metahwie Ben Ali brought out a battered blue teapot and a little charcoal burner from his house, and we had to join him for several glasses of tea. These people love nothing so much as making and drinking tea and they take every chance to do so. I have kept count, and on some days of visiting farmers I have drunk as many as thirty glasses. It's sweet, strong stuff—boiled down until it is almost pure tannic acid—but you can't refuse it without being rude. When you consider how little money these people make, their offering you tea and sugar is almost unbelievable generosity.

Anyway, we were sitting around the acacia tree drinking tea, and I decided that I might as well try the cabbage idea one more time. I had one of my men explain the idea to Mutahwie Ben Ali. The farmer sipped his tea noisily, listened, and then spoke at great length. It sounded to me like he was giving a lecture on the whole history of agriculture. But when my interpreter spoke, he simply said:

"This farmer says that he has no cabbage seeds."

"Tell him we will give him the seeds," I said.

This information was passed along, and Mutahwie Ben Ali spoke again. My interpreter said, "He says that he knows nothing about planting cabbages."

"Tell him we will plant them for him," I said.

Mutahwie Ben Ali was informed of this, and again he spoke at considerable length. "This man says that he knows nothing about caring for cabbages," my interpreter said.

"Tell him we will help him raise them," I said.

When Mutahwie Ben Ali heard this, he drank another glass of scalding hot tea, wiped his mouth on his sleeve, and spoke briefly.

My interpreter said, "Mutahwie Ben Ali Ben Sassie El Nasee understands that we will furnish the cabbage seeds, that we will plant the cabbage seeds, and that we will help care for the cabbages as they grow. Very well. He says that he will grow cabbages."

So we were in the cabbage business at last. Now it may seem a bit foolish to you that we would agree to furnish the seeds and do all the work too, but remember that I was interested in just one thing—showing the farmers in the area the value of growing a good new cash crop. I would have wanted to do the work anyway, to make sure that it was done right and to give my young crew experience. The fact that Mutahwie Ben Ali was driving a hard bargain didn't bother me a bit.

We went to work late in July. We prepared the seed bed, planted the seeds, and tended the young shoots regularly throughout August. Mutahwie Ben Ali always watched us with considerable interest, and he never failed to make us tea when we were finished. But he never quite got around to doing any of the work.

When the shoots were ready for transplanting in September, we set them out on his land. I insisted that Mutahwie Ben Ali take a hand in this work and he did, though it was as small a hand as he could possibly make it. He seemed to think that it was foolish for a man of his tea-making talents to waste them in a cabbage patch.

We fertilized the cabbages, kept the worms off of them, and kept the weeds away from them. They grew beautifully, as I had been sure that they would, and by December Mutahwie Ben Ali had as fine a cabbage crop as I had ever seen.

When marketing time came, Mutahwie Ben Ali took over with considerable energy. He hired the neighboring farmers to help with the hauling, and that was fine with me because it would give them a good look at the wonderful cabbage crop. Naturally I was interested in the final results, so I was on hand for the harvesting. All told, Mutahwie Ben Ali took fifty wagonloads of cabbage out of his field and the total weight was around sixty-two tons! At the going price, I figured that that much cabbage would net him around five hundred dollars. It would be a fortune—and not a small one, either—for a poor farmer like him.

I did not go into the city with him; but when we heard that he was back, we went over to his farm to see him. I was now ready to put the second part of my plan into operation. I wanted Mutahwie Ben Ali to put at least two-thirds of his new wealth into improving his farm. I had in mind the adding of some chickens and a milk cow, the building of some good outbuildings, the purchase of good seeds and a new plow and

A farmer leading his sheep to pasture in Iran

mule team, and the repair and whitewash of his house. When they saw Mutahwie Ben Ali's farm blooming like this, I figured that the other farmers in the area would really be sold on the value of farm extension agents' advice.

We found Mutahwie Ben Ali sitting under his acacia tree as usual. He arose and welcomed us and we sat down to drink tea together. Then through my interpreter I explained my great plans for his farm.

Mutahwie Ben Ali spoke briefly and my interpreter said, "This farmer says that what you say is a wonderful idea. He is sorry that he has no money to do these things."

I was stunned. "Why, he made a fortune on those cabbages," I said. "He's got to have money."

When my comment was repeated to Mutahwie Ben Ali, he stood up and went into his house. When he returned, he had a new Winchester automatic rifle in his hands. It was a beautiful gun of the type I had been wanting to buy when I got enough money ahead.

Mutahwie Ben Ali spoke. "He says that he bought this gun with his money," my interpreter said.

"That gun doesn't begin to cost as much money as he made," I said.

Mutahwie Ben Ali then took us around to the shady side of his house. A nice-looking Arab horse was tied there to a small bush.

"This man says that he also bought this race horse to run in the local contests," my interpreter said.

It was a good-looking race horse, all right, but it wouldn't be of much help on a farm. I was getting mad, but I tried not to show it. "Tell him that the gun and the horse still would not take all of the money he made," I said.

The interpreter repeated my words, and Mutahwie Ben Ali nodded his head in agreement. He addressed me earnestly and at length, just as if I understood every word he said.

When he finished, my interpreter said, "Mutahwie Ben Ali says that you are right. The horse and the gun did not take all of his money. But he also bought a fine new wife—it is only his second, he says—and that took every bit of money that was left. He says he is sorry that the customs of his country do not permit him to show her to you."

Mutahwie Ben Ali spoke once more, and the interpreter said, "Although the money is all gone, this man says that he is now very happy. He thanks you very much for helping him."

Well, to say that I was disgusted is putting it very mildly. It looked to me like all of our hard work in helping him with those cabbages had gone for nothing.

But I was wrong, and it showed me again that I hadn't learned much about these people. Mutahwie Ben Ali's riding around on his new horse, carrying his new gun, and talking about his new wife was the best advertisement that the rewards of cabbage-raising could possibly have had. When cabbage time rolled around again, we were swamped with requests for seeds and help.

But the Ministry of Agriculture was smarter than I was. Before they would hand out seeds or agree to our giving help, a farmer had to sign a paper agreeing to put half of his profits into farm improvement. The plan worked beautifully and the farmers worked hard at their new crop. It all made me feel a lot better.

So far as I know, Mutahwie Ben Ali Ben Sassie El Nasee never came around again for seeds. Why should he? He had everything he wanted.

For Discussion

1. Name some of Mutahwie Ben Ali's values that differ from the authors'. Are Mutahwie Ben Ali's values bad because they are different? Can you present arguments in favor of Mutahwie Ben Ali's way of life?

2. Does the initial description of Mutahwie Ben Ali prepare the reader for his later acts? Explain. What makes the reader suspect Mutahwie Ben Ali's sincerity? Do the authors reveal their own suspicions?

3. What do the authors expect in return for helping Mutahwie Ben Ali? Are they justified in accusing Mutahwie Ben Ali of ingratitude? Why?

4. What are the significant characteristics of Mutahwie Ben Ali and the authors that come into conflict in this selection? Are the authors trying to reap any private benefit from their efforts to reform the agricultural practices of these people? Can you suggest how in this instance the misunderstanding of motives could lead to hostility?

The Snake and the Crocodile

CAMARA LAYE

Africa is a land of contradictions. Villages where life remains as it was centuries ago stand only a few minutes' drive from modern industrial centers. The minds of many Africans are divided in loyalty to two modes of thought: the folk wisdom passed down from father to son for generations and the technological methods that attend economic progress.

Camara Laye has lived in both worlds. As he tells in the following selection, he grew up as a member of an African tribe. Later he went to Paris to study engineering. The fascination of his autobiography, The Dark Child, *comes from the fact that it is written by a man with a "modern" mind who looks back upon his own childhood and bears witness to mysterious events that he can neither explain nor deny.*

I

I was a little boy playing around my father's hut. How old would I have been at that time? I cannot remember exactly. I must still have been very young: five, maybe six years old. My mother was in the workshop with my father, and I could just hear their familiar voices above the noise on the anvil and the conversation of the customers.

Suddenly I stopped playing, my whole attention fixed on a snake that was creeping around the hut. After a moment I went over to him. I had taken in my hand a reed that was lying in the yard—there were always some lying around; they used to get broken off the fence of plaited reeds that marked the boundary of our concession [1]—and I thrust it into his mouth. The snake did not try to get away; he was beginning to enjoy our little game; he was slowly swallowing the reed; he was devouring it, I thought, as if it were some delicious prey, his eyes glittering with voluptuous bliss; and inch by inch his head was drawing nearer to my hand. At last the reed was almost entirely swallowed, and the snake's jaws were terribly close to my fingers.

I was laughing. I had not the slightest fear, and I feel sure that the snake would not have

---

[1] *concession* The area within an African village that belongs to one family.

hesitated much longer before burying his fangs in my fingers if, at that moment, Damany, one of the apprentices, had not come out of the workshop. He called my father, and almost at once I felt myself lifted off my feet: I was safe in the arms of one of my father's friends.

Around me there was a great commotion. My mother was shouting hardest of all, and she gave me a few sharp slaps. I wept, more upset by the sudden uproar than by the blows. A little later, when I was somewhat calmer and the shouting had ceased, my mother solemnly warned me never to play that game again. I promised, although the game still didn't seem dangerous to me.

My father's hut was near the workshop, and I often played beneath the veranda that ran around the outside. It was his private hut, and like all our huts built of mud bricks that had been pounded and moulded with water; it was round, and proudly helmeted with thatch. It was entered by a rectangular doorway. Inside, a tiny window let in a thin shaft of daylight. On the right was the bed, made of beaten earth like the bricks, and spread with a simple wicker-work mat on which lay a pillow stuffed with kapok. At the rear, right under the window where the light was strongest, were the tool-boxes. On the left were the *boubous* and the prayer-rugs.[2] At the head of the bed, hanging over the pillow and watching over my father's slumber, stood a row of pots that contained extracts from plants and the bark of trees. These pots all had metal lids and were profusely and curiously garlanded; it did not take long to discover that they were the most important things in the hut; they contained magic charms—those mysterious liquids that keep the evil spirits at bay, and, if smeared on the body, make it invulnerable to every kind of black magic. My father, before going to bed, never failed to

smear his body with a little of each liquid, first one, then another, for each charm had its own particular property: but exactly *what* property I did not know: I had left my father's house too soon.

From the veranda under which I played I could keep an eye on the workshop opposite, and the adults for their part could keep an eye on me. This workshop was the main building in our concession, and my father was generally to be found there, looking after the work, forging the most important items himself, or repairing delicate mechanisms; there he received his friends and his customers, and the place resounded with noise from morning to night. Moreover, everyone who entered or left our concession had to cross the workshop. There was a perpetual coming and going, though no one seemed to be in any particular hurry; each had his bit of gossip; each lingered at the forge to watch. Sometimes I came near the door, but I rarely went in; everyone there frightened me, and I would run away as soon as anyone tried to touch me. It was not until very much later that I got into the habit of crouching in a corner of the workshop to watch the fire blazing in the forge.

My private domain at that time was the veranda that encircled my father's hut, my mother's hut, and the orange tree that grew in the middle of the concession.

As soon as you crossed the workshop and went through the door at the back, you would see the orange tree. Compared with the giants of our native forests, the tree was not very big, but its mass of glossy leaves cast a dense shade that kept the heat at bay. When it was in flower a heady perfume pervaded the entire concession. When the fruit first appeared we were only allowed to look: we had to wait patiently until it was ripe. Then my father, who as head of the family—and a very large family it was—governed the concession, gave the order to pick the fruit. The men who did the picking brought their baskets one by one to my father, who portioned them out among the people who lived

---

[2] *boubous and prayer-rugs* Like many West Africans, Laye's family were Moslems. The *boubou* is the characteristic long, loose garment worn by Moslem men during prayers. Each Moslem has his own prayer-rug upon which he kneels.

in the concession and among his neighbors and customers. After that we were permitted to help ourselves from the baskets and we were allowed as much as we liked! My father was open-handed; in fact, a lavish giver. Any visitor, no matter who he was, shared our meals; since I could never keep up with the speed at which such guests ate I might have remained forever hungry if my mother had not taken the precaution of putting my share aside.

"Sit here," she would say, "and eat, for your father's mad."

She did not look upon such guests with a kindly eye. There were too many for her liking, all bent on filling their bellies at her expense. My father, for his part, ate very little; he was an extremely temperate man.

We lived beside a railroad. The trains skirted the reed fence of the concession so closely that sparks thrown off from the locomotive set fire to it every now and then which had to be quickly extinguished so that the whole concession would not go up in smoke. These alarms, frightening yet exciting, made me aware of the passing trains. And even where there were no trains—for in those days the railroad was dependent on a most irregular water traffic—much of my time was spent watching the iron rails. They glistened cruelly in a light which nothing in that place could relieve. Baking since dawn, the roadbed was so hot that oil which dropped from the locomotives evaporated immediately, leaving no trace. Was it the oven-like heat or the smell of oil—for the smell remained in spite of everything—which attracted the snakes? I do not know. But often I came upon them crawling in that hot roadbed. It would have been fatal if they had gotten into the concession.

Ever since the day when I had been forbidden by my mother to play with snakes I ran to her as soon as I saw one.

"There's a snake!" I would cry.

"What? Another?"

And she would come running to see what sort of snake it was. If it was just a snake like any other snake—actually they were all quite different—she would immediately beat it to death; and, like all the women of our country, she would work herself into a frenzy, beating the snake to a pulp. The men contented themselves with a single hard blow, neatly struck.

One day, however, I noticed a little black snake with a strikingly marked body. He was proceeding slowly in the direction of the workshop. I ran to warn my mother, as usual. But as soon as she saw the black snake she said to me gravely:

"My son, this one must not be killed: he is not like other snakes, and he will not harm you; you must never interfere with him."

Everyone in our concession knew that this snake must not be killed—everyone except myself, and, I suppose, my little playmates, who were still ignorant children.

"This snake," my mother added, "is your father's guiding spirit."

I gazed dumbfounded at the little snake. He was proceeding calmly toward the workshop, gracefully, very sure of himself, and almost as if conscious of his immunity; his body, black and brilliant, glittered in the harsh light of the sun. When he reached the workshop, I noticed for the first time a small hole in the wall, cut out level with the ground. The snake disappeared through this hole.

"Look," said my mother, "the snake is going to pay your father a visit."

Although I was familiar with the supernatural, this sight filled me with such astonishment that I was struck dumb. What business would a snake have with my father? And why this particular snake? No one was to kill him because he was my father's guiding spirit! At any rate, that was the explanation my mother had given me. But what exactly *was* a "guiding spirit"? What were these guiding spirits that I encountered almost everywhere, forbidding one thing, commanding another to be done? I could not understand it at all, though their presences surrounded me as I grew to manhood. There were good spirits, and there were evil ones; and more evil than good ones, it seemed. And how was I to know that this snake was harmless? He was a snake like the others: black, to be sure, with extraordinary markings—but for all that a snake. I was completely perplexed, but I did not question my mother: I had decided that I must ask my father about it, as if this were a mystery to be discussed only between men, a mystery in which women had no part. I decided to wait until evening to speak to him.

Immediately after the evening meal, when the palavers were over, my father bade his friends farewell and sat under the veranda of his hut; I seated myself near him. I began questioning him in a dilatory manner, as all children do, regarding every subject under the sun. Actually I was no more talkative than on other evenings. Only this evening I withheld what troubled me, waiting for the opportunity when—my face betraying nothing—I might ask the question which had worried me so deeply from the moment when I first saw the black snake going toward the workshop. Finally, unable to restrain myself any longer, I asked:

"My father, what is that little snake that comes to visit you?"

"What snake do you mean?"

"Why, the little black snake that my mother forbids us to kill."

"Ah!" he said.

He gazed at me for a long while. He seemed to be considering whether to answer or not. Perhaps he was thinking about how old I was, perhaps he was wondering if it was not a little too soon to confide such a secret to a twelve-year-old boy. Then suddenly he made up his mind.

"That snake," he said, "is the guiding spirit of our race. Can you understand that?"

"Yes," I answered, although I did not understand very well.

"That snake," he went on, "has always been with us; he has always made himself known to one of us. In our time, it is to me that he has made himself known."

"Yes," I said.

And I said it with all my heart, for it seemed obvious to me that the snake could have made himself known to no one but my father. Was not my father the head man in our concession? Was it not my father who had authority over all the blacksmiths in our district? Was he not the most skilled? Was he not, after all, my father?

"How did he make himself known?" I asked.

"First of all, he made himself known in the semblance of a dream. He appeared to me several times in sleep and told me the day on which he would appear to me in reality: he gave me the precise time and place. But when I really saw him for the first time, I was filled with fear. I took him for a snake like any other snake, and I had to keep myself under control or I would have tried to kill him. When he saw that I did not receive him kindly, he turned away and departed the way he had come. And there I stood, watching him depart, wondering all the time if I should not simply have killed him there and then; but a power greater than I stayed my hand and prevented me from pursuing him. I stood watching him disappear. And even then, at that very moment, I could easily have overtaken him; a few swift strides would have been enough; but I was struck motionless by a kind of paralysis. Such was my first encounter with the little black snake."

He was silent a moment, then went on:

"The following night, I saw the snake again in my dream. 'I came as I foretold,' he said, 'but thou didst not receive me kindly; nay, rather I did perceive that thou didst intend to receive me unkindly: I did read it thus in thine eyes. Wherefore dost thou reject me? Lo, I am the guiding spirit of thy race, and it is even as the guiding spirit of thy race that I make myself known to thee, as to the most worthy. Therefore forbear to look with fear upon me, and beware that thou dost not reject me, for behold, I bring thee good fortune.' After that, I received the snake kindly when he made himself known to me a second time; I received him without fear, I received him with loving kindness, and he brought me nothing but good."

My father again was silent for a moment, then he said:

"You can see for yourself that I am not more gifted than other men, that I have nothing which other men have not also, and even that I have less than others, since I give everything away, and would even give away the last thing I had, the shirt on my back. Nevertheless I am better known. My name is on everyone's tongue, and it is I who have authority over all the blacksmiths in the five cantons. If these things are so, it is by virtue of this snake alone, who is the guiding spirit of our race. It is to this snake I owe everything; it is he who gives me warning of all that is to happen. Thus I am never surprised, when I awake, to see this or that person waiting for me outside my workshop: I already know that he will be there. No more am I surprised when this or that motorcycle or bicycle breaks down, or when an accident happens to a clock: because I have had foreknowledge of what would come to pass. Everything is transmitted to me in the course of the night, together with an account of all the work I shall have to perform, so that from the start, without having to cast about in my mind, I know how to repair whatever is brought to me. These things have established my renown as a craftsman. But all this—let it never be forgotten —I owe to the snake, I owe it to the guiding spirit of our race."

He was silent; and then I understood why, when my father came back from a walk he would enter the workshop and say to the apprentices: "During my absence, this or that person has been here, he was dressed in such and such a way, he came from such and such a place and he brought with him such and such a piece of work to be done." And all marveled at this curious knowledge. When I raised my eyes, I saw that my father was watching me.

"I have told you all these things, little one, because you are my son, the eldest of my sons,

and because I have nothing to hide from you. There is a certain form of behavior to observe, and certain ways of acting in order that the guiding spirit of our race may approach you also. I, your father, was observing that form of behavior which persuades our guiding spirit to visit us. Oh, perhaps not consciously: but nevertheless it is true that if you desire the guiding spirit of our race to visit you one day, if you desire to inherit it in your turn, you will have to conduct yourself in the selfsame manner; from now on, it will be necessary for you to be more and more in my company."

He gazed at me with burning eyes, then suddenly he heaved a sigh.

"I fear, I very much fear, little one, that you are not often enough in my company. You are all day at school, and one day you will depart from that school for a greater one. You will leave me, little one. . . ."

And again he heaved a sigh. I saw that his heart was heavy within him. The hurricane-lamp hanging on the veranda cast a harsh glare on his face. He suddenly seemed to me an old man.

"Father!" I cried.

"Son . . ." he whispered.

And I was no longer sure whether I ought to continue to attend school or whether I ought to remain in the workshop: I felt unutterably confused.

"Go now," said my father.

I went to my mother's hut. The night was full of sparkling stars; an owl was hooting nearby. Ah! what was the right path for me? Did I know yet where that path lay? My perplexity was boundless as the sky, and mine was a sky, alas, without any stars. . . . I entered my mother's hut, which at that time was mine also, and went to bed at once. But sleep did not come and I tossed restlessly on my bed.

"What's the matter with you?" asked my mother.

"Nothing."

No. I couldn't find anything to say.

"Why don't you go to sleep?" my mother continued.

"I don't know."

"Go to sleep!" she said.

"Yes," I said.

"Sleep . . . Nothing can resist sleep," she said sadly.

Why did she, too, appear so sad? Had she divined my distress? Anything that concerned me she sensed very deeply. I was trying to sleep, but I shut my eyes and lay still in vain: the image of my father under the hurricane-lamp would not leave me: my father who had suddenly seemed so old and who was so young, so lively —younger and livelier than the rest of us, a man no one could outrun, who was swifter of limb than any of us. . . . "Father! . . . Father! . . . !" I kept repeating. "What must I do if I am to do the right thing?" And I wept silently and fell asleep still weeping.

After that we never mentioned the little black snake again: my father had spoken to me about him for the first and last time. But from that time on, as soon as I saw the little snake, I would run and sit in the workshop. I would watch him glide through the little hole in the wall. As if informed of his presence, my father at that very instant would turn his eyes to the hole and smile. The snake would go straight to him, opening his jaws. When he was within reach my father would stroke him and the snake would accept the caress with a quivering of his whole body. I never saw the little snake attempt to do the slightest harm to my father. That caress and the answering tremor—but I ought to say: that appealing caress and that answering tremor—threw me each time into an inexpressible confusion. I imagined I know not what mysterious conversations: the hand inquired and the tremor replied. . . .

Yes. It was like a conversation. Would I too converse that way some day? No. I would continue to attend school. Yet I should have liked so much to place my hand, my own hand, on that snake, and to understand and listen to

that tremor too; but I did not know whether the snake would have accepted my hand, and I felt now that he would have nothing to tell me. I was afraid that he would never have anything to tell me.

When my father felt that he had stroked the snake enough he left him alone. Then the snake coiled himself under the edge of one of the sheepskins on which my father, facing his anvil, was seated.

II

Of all the different kinds of work my father engaged in, none fascinated me so much as his skill with gold. No other occupation was so noble, no other needed such a delicate touch. And then, every time he worked in gold it was like a festival—indeed it *was* a festival—that broke the monotony of ordinary working days.

So, if a woman, accompanied by a go-between, crossed the threshold of the workshop, I followed her in at once. I knew what she wanted: she had brought some gold, and had come to ask my father to transform it into a trinket. She had collected it in the placers of Siguiri[3] where, crouching over the river for months on end, she had patiently extracted grains of gold from the mud.

These women never came alone. They knew my father had other things to do than make trinkets. And even when he had the time, they knew they were not the first to ask a favor of him, and that, consequently, they would not be served before others.

Generally they required the trinket for a certain date, for the festival of Ramadan or the Tabaski[4] or some other family ceremony or dance.

[3] *placers of Siguiri* Places where gold is washed from the river at Siguiri, a town in what is now the Republic of Guinea.

[4] *Ramadan, Tabaski* The Ramadan is the ninth month of the Mohammedan calendar, a period of fasting. The Tabaski is also a Moslem religious holiday.

Therefore, to enhance their chances of being served quickly and to more easily persuade my father to interrupt the work before him, they used to request the services of an official praise-singer, a go-between, arranging in advance the fee they were to pay him for his good offices.

The go-between installed himself in the workshop, tuned up his *cora*, which is our harp, and began to sing my father's praises. This was always a great event for me. I heard recalled the lofty deeds of my father's ancestors and their names from the earliest times. As the couplets were reeled off it was like watching the growth of a great genealogical tree that spread its branches far and wide and flourished its boughs and twigs before my mind's eye. The harp played an accompaniment to this vast utterance of names, expanding it with notes that were now soft, now shrill.

I could sense my father's vanity being inflamed, and I already knew that after having sipped this milk-and-honey he would lend a favorable ear to the woman's request. But I was not alone in my knowledge. The woman also had seen my father's eyes gleaming with contented pride. She held out her grains of gold as if the whole matter were settled. My father took up his scales and weighed the gold.

"What sort of trinket do you want?" he would ask.

"I want . . ."

And then the woman would not know any longer exactly what she wanted because desire kept making her change her mind, and because she would have liked all the trinkets at once. But it would have taken a pile of gold much larger than she had brought to satisfy her whim, and from then on her chief purpose in life was to get hold of it as soon as she could.

"When do you want it?"

Always the answer was that the trinket was needed for an occasion in the near future.

"So! You are in that much of a hurry? Where do you think I shall find the time?"

"I am in a great hurry, I assure you."

"I have never seen a woman eager to deck herself out who wasn't in a great hurry! Good! I shall arrange my time to suit you. Are you satisfied?"

He would take the clay pot that was kept specially for smelting gold, and would pour the grains into it. He would then cover the gold with powdered charcoal, a charcoal he prepared by using plant juices of exceptional purity. Finally, he would place a large lump of the same kind of charcoal over the pot.

As soon as she saw that the work had been duly undertaken, the woman, now quite satisfied, would return to her household tasks, leaving her go-between to carry on with the praise-singing which had already proved so advantageous.

At a sign from my father the apprentices began working two sheepskin bellows. The skins were on the floor, on opposite sides of the forge, connected to it by earthen pipes. While the work was in progress the apprentices sat in front of the bellows with crossed legs. That is, the younger of the two sat, for the elder was sometimes allowed to assist. But the younger—this time it was Sidafa—was only permitted to work the bellows and watch while waiting his turn for promotion to less rudimentary tasks. First one and then the other worked hard at the bellows: the flame in the forge rose higher and became a living thing, a genie implacable and full of life.

Then my father lifted the clay pot with his long tongs and placed it on the flame.

Immediately all activity in the workshop almost came to a halt. During the whole time that the gold was being smelted, neither copper nor aluminum could be worked nearby, lest some particle of these base metals fall into the container which held the gold. Only steel could be worked on such occasions, but the men, whose task that was, hurried to finish what they were doing, or left it abruptly to join the apprentices gathered around the forge. There were so many, and they crowded so around my father, that I, the smallest person present, had to come near the forge in order not to lose track of what was going on.

If he felt he had inadequate working space, my father had the apprentices stand well away from him. He merely raised his hand in a simple gesture: at that particular moment he never uttered a word, and no one else would: no one was allowed to utter a word. Even the go-between's voice was no longer raised in song. The silence was broken only by the panting of the bellows and the faint hissing of the gold. But if my father never actually spoke, I know that he was forming words in his mind. I could tell from his lips, which kept moving, while, bending over the pot, he stirred the gold and char-

coal with a bit of wood that kept bursting into flame and had constantly to be replaced by a fresh one.

What words did my father utter? I do not know. At least I am not certain what they were. No one ever told me. But could they have been anything but incantations? On these occasions was he not invoking the genies of fire and gold, of fire and wind, of wind blown by the blast-pipes of the forge, of fire born of wind, of gold married to fire? Was it not their assistance, their friendship, their espousal that he besought? Yes. Almost certainly he was invoking these genies, all of whom are equally indispensable for smelting gold.

The operation going on before my eyes was

An African village of mud houses with thatched roofs

certainly the smelting of gold, yet something more than that: a magical operation that the guiding spirits could regard with favor or disfavor. That is why, all around my father, there was absolute silence and anxious expectancy. Though only a child, I knew there could be no craft greater than the goldsmith's. I expected a ceremony; I had come to be present at a ceremony; and it actually was one, though very protracted. I was still too young to understand why, but I had an inkling as I watched the almost religious concentration of those who followed the mixing process in the clay pot.

When finally the gold began to melt I could have shouted aloud—and perhaps we all would have if we had not been forbidden to make a sound. I trembled, and so did everyone else watching my father stir the mixture—it was still a heavy paste—in which the charcoal was gradually consumed. The next stage followed swiftly. The gold now had the fluidity of water. The genies had smiled on the operation!

"Bring me the brick!" my father would order, thus lifting the ban that until then had silenced us.

The brick, which an apprentice would place beside the fire, was hollowed out, generously greased with Galam butter. My father would take the pot off the fire and tilt it carefully, while I would watch the gold flow into the brick, flow like liquid fire. True, it was only a very sparse trickle of fire, but how vivid, how brilliant! As the gold flowed into the brick, the grease sputtered and flamed and emitted a thick smoke that caught in the throat and stung the eyes, leaving us all weeping and coughing.

But there were times when it seemed to me that my father ought to turn this task over to one of his assistants. They were experienced, had assisted him hundreds of times, and could certainly have performed the work well. But my father's lips moved and those inaudible, secret words, those incantations he addressed to one we could not see or hear, was the essential part. Calling on the genies of fire, of wind, of

gold and exorcising the evil spirits—this was a knowledge he alone possessed.

By now the gold had been cooled in the hollow of the brick, and my father began to hammer and stretch it. This was the moment when his work as a goldsmith really began. I noticed that before embarking on it he never failed to stroke the little snake stealthily as it lay coiled up under the sheepskin. I can only assume that this was his way of gathering strength for what remained to be done, the most trying part of his task.

But was it not extraordinary and miraculous that on these occasions the little black snake was always coiled under the sheepskin? He was not always there. He did not visit my father every day. But he was always present whenever there was gold to be worked. His presence was no surprise to *me*. After that evening when my father had spoken of the guiding spirit of his race I was no longer astonished. The snake was there intentionally. He knew what the future held. Did he tell my father? I think that he most certainly did. Did he tell him everything? I have another reason for believing firmly that he did.

The craftsman who works in gold must first of all purify himself. Great respecter of ceremony as he was, it would have been impossible for my father to ignore these rules. Now, I never saw him make these preparations. I saw him address himself to his work without any apparent preliminaries. From that moment it was obvious that, forewarned in a dream by his black guiding spirit of the task which awaited him in the morning, my father must have prepared for it as soon as he arose, entering his workshop in a state of purity, his body smeared with the secret potions hidden in his numerous pots of magical substances; or perhaps he always came into his workshop in a state of ritual purity. I am not trying to make him out a better man than he was—he was a man and had his share of human frailties—but he was always uncompromising in his respect for ritual observance.

The woman for whom the trinket was being made, and who had come often to see how the work was progressing, would arrive for the final time, not wanting to miss a moment of this spectacle—as marvelous to her as to us—when the gold wire, which my father had succeeded in drawing out from the mass of molten gold and charcoal, was transformed into a trinket.

There she would be. Her eyes would devour the fragile gold wire, following it in its tranquil and regular spiral around the little slab of metal which supported it. My father would catch a glimpse of her and I would see him slowly beginning to smile. Her avid attention delighted him.

"Are you trembling?" he would ask.

"Am I trembling?"

And we would all burst out laughing at her. For she would be trembling! She would be trembling with covetousness for the spiral pyramid in which my father would be inserting, among the convolutions, tiny grains of gold. When he had finally finished by crowning the pyramid with a heavier grain, she would dance in delight.

No one—no one at all—would be more enchanted than she as my father slowly turned the trinket back and forth between his fingers to display its perfection. Not even the praise-singer whose business it was to register excitement would be more excited than she. Throughout this metamorphosis he did not stop speaking faster and ever faster, increasing his tempo, accelerating his praises and flatteries as the trinket took shape, shouting to the skies my father's skill.

For the praise-singer took a curious part—I should say rather that it was direct and effective—in the work. He was drunk with the joy of creation. He shouted aloud in joy. He plucked his *cora* like a man inspired. He sweated as if he were the trinket-maker, as if he were my father, as if the trinket were his creation. He was no longer a hired censer-bearer,[5] a man whose services anyone could rent. He was a man who created his song out of some deep inner necessity. And when my father, after having soldered the large grain of gold that crowned the summit, held out his work to be admired, the praise-singer would no longer be able to contain himself. He would begin to intone the *douga*, the great chant which is sung only for celebrated men and which is danced for them alone.

But the *douga* is a formidable chant, a provocative chant, a chant which the praise-singer dared not sing, and which the man for whom it is sung dared not dance before certain precautions had been taken. My father had taken them as soon as he woke, since he had been warned in a dream. The praise-singer had taken them when he concluded his arrangements with the woman. Like my father he had smeared his body with magic substances and had made himself invulnerable to the evil genies whom the *douga* inevitably set free; these potions made him invulnerable also to rival praise-singers, perhaps jealous of him, who awaited only this song and the exaltation and loss of control which attended it, in order to begin casting their spells.

At the first notes of the *douga* my father would arise and emit a cry in which happiness and triumph were equally mingled; and brandishing in his right hand the hammer that was the symbol of his profession and in his left a ram's horn filled with magic substances, he would dance the glorious dance.

No sooner had he finished, than workmen and apprentices, friends and customers in their turn, not forgetting the woman for whom the trinket had been created, would flock around him, congratulating him, showering praises on him and complimenting the praise-singer at the same time. The latter found himself laden with

[5] *censer-bearer* A censer is a receptacle in which incense is burned during religious ceremonies. A "censer-bearer" would be anyone assisting at a ceremony.

gifts—almost his only means of support, for the praise-singer leads a wandering life after the fashion of the troubadours of old. Aglow with dancing and the praises he had received, my father would offer everyone cola nuts, that small change of Guinean courtesy.

Now all that remained to be done was to redden the trinket in a little water to which chlorine and sea salt had been added. I was at liberty to leave. The festival was over! But often as I came out of the workshop my mother would be in the court, pounding millet or rice, and she would call to me:

"Where have you been?" although she knew perfectly well where I had been.

"In the workshop."

"Of course. Your father was smelting gold. Gold! Always gold!"

And she would beat the millet or rice furiously with her pestle.

"Your father is ruining his health!"

"He danced the *douga*."

"The *douga!* The *douga* won't keep him from ruining his eyes. As for you, you would be better off playing in the courtyard instead of breathing dust and smoke in the workshop."

My mother did not like my father to work in gold. She knew how dangerous it was: a trinket-maker empties his lungs blowing on the blow-pipe and his eyes suffer from the fire. Perhaps they suffer even more from the microscopic precision which the work requires. And even if there had been no such objections involved, my mother would scarcely have relished this work. She was suspicious of it, for gold cannot be smelted without the use of other metals, and my mother thought it was not entirely honest to put aside for one's own use the gold which the alloy had displaced. However, this was a custom generally known, and one which she herself had accepted when she took cotton to be woven and received back only a piece of cotton cloth half the weight of the original bundle.

III

I realize that my mother's authoritarian attitudes may appear surprising; generally the role of the African woman is thought to be a ridiculously humble one, and indeed there are parts of the continent where it is insignificant; but Africa is vast, with a diversity equal to its vastness. The woman's role in our country is one of fundamental independence, of great inner pride. We despise only those who allow themselves to be despised; and our women very seldom give cause for that. My father would never have dreamed of despising anyone, least of all my mother. He had the greatest respect for her too, and so did our friends and neighbors. That was due, I am sure, to my mother's character, which was impressive; it was due also to the strange powers she possessed.

I hesitate to say what these powers were, and I do not wish to describe them all. I know that what I say will be greeted with skeptical smiles. And today, now that I come to remember them, even I hardly know how I should regard them. They seem to be unbelievable; they *are* unbelievable. Nevertheless I can only tell you what I saw with my own eyes. How can I disown the testimony of my own eyes? Those unbelievable things. I saw them. I see them again as I saw them then. Are there not things around us, everywhere, which are inexplicable? In our country there were mysteries without number, and my mother was familiar with them all.

One day—it was toward evening—I saw some men request her to use her powers to get a horse on his feet after he had resisted all attempts to make him rise. He was out at pasture, but he was lying down, and his owner wanted to bring him back to the stable before nightfall. The horse obstinately refused to move, although there was no apparent reason why he should disobey. But his inclination was otherwise, though it might have been a magic spell that immobilized him. I heard the men telling my mother about it, and asking her help.

"Well, then, let's go and have a look at this horse," said my mother.

She called the eldest of my sisters and told her to look after the cooking of the evening meal, and then went off with the men. I followed her. When we arrived at the pasture, we saw the horse: he was lying in the grass, gazing at us unconcernedly. His owner tried again to make him get up and spoke to him in honeyed tones, but the horse remained deaf to all entreaty. His master raised a hand to strike him.

"Do not strike him," said my mother. "It won't do any good."

She went up to the horse and, lifting her own hand, declaimed in a solemn tone: "I command you, horse, rise up!"

And we all saw the horse get up at once and follow his master quietly away. I have told in very simple words, and very exact words, what I saw then, with my own eyes, and to my mind it is unbelievable; but the event was just as I have described it: the horse got up without any further delay and followed his master: if he had refused to follow him, my mother's intervention would once more have had its effect.

Where did these powers come from? Well, my mother was the next child born after my twin uncles in Tindican. Now, they say that twin brothers are wiser than other children, and are practically magicians. As for the child that follows them, and who receives the name *sayon*, that is, the younger brother of twins, he too is endowed with the gift of magic, and he is even considered to be more powerful and more mysterious than the twins in whose lives he plays a very important role.

I have given one example of my mother's supernatural powers; I could give many others, equally strange, equally mysterious. How many times I have seen her, at daybreak, walk a few steps into the yard and turn her head in one direction or another to shout at the top of her voice:

"If this business goes any further, I shall not hesitate to expose you. That's my final word!"

In the early morning her voice traveled far: it was intended to reach the ears of the witch-doctor, for whom the warning had been uttered. He understood that if he did not stop his nocturnal activities, my mother would denounce him in public; and this threat always worked: from then on, the witch-doctor kept quiet. My mother used to receive warning of these activities while she was asleep. We never wakened her, for fear of interrupting the course of the revelations that flowed through her dreams. This power was well known by our neighbors and by the whole community: no one ever doubted it.

Though my mother could see what evil was being hatched and could denounce the author of it, her power went no further. Even if she had wished, her power to cast spells did not allow her to do any evil on her own account. She was never suspect. If people made themselves pleasant to her, it was not at all out of fear. They were pleasant because they thought she deserved it, and because they respected her power to cast spells from which nothing was to be feared. On the contrary, much was to be hoped from them.

As well as this gift, or rather part-gift, of magic, my mother had other powers that she had inherited in the same way. At Tindican her father had been a skillful blacksmith and my mother possessed the usual powers of that caste from which the majority of soothsayers are drawn. It was in my mother that the spirit of her caste was most visibly—I was going to say ostensibly—manifested. I don't pretend that she was more faithful to it than my uncles were, but she alone demonstrated her fidelity. Finally, she had inherited, as a matter of course, my grandfather's totem which is the crocodile. This totem allowed all Damans to draw water from the Niger without running any danger of harm.

Normally, everyone draws water from the river. The Niger flows slowly and abundantly; it can be forded; and the crocodiles, which keep to the deep water upstream or downstream from where the water is drawn, are not to be feared. You can bathe quite freely on the banks of pale sand and do your washing there.

But when the water rises, the volume of the river is increased three-fold. The water is deep, and the crocodiles are dangerous. One can see their triangular heads breaking the surface. Everyone, therefore, keeps away from the river and instead draws water from the little streams.

My mother used to continue to draw water from the river. I watched her draw it from the place where the crocodiles were. Naturally I watched her from a distance, for my totem is not my mother's. And I had every reason to fear those voracious beasts; but my mother could draw water without fear, and no one warned her of the danger, because everyone knew that the danger did not exist for her. Whoever else had ventured to do what my mother used to do would inevitably have been knocked down by a blow from a powerful tail, seized in the terrible jaws and dragged into deep water. But the crocodiles could do no harm to my mother; and this privilege is quite understandable: the totem is identified with its possessor: this identification is absolute, and of such a nature that its possessor has the power to take on the form of the totem itself; it follows quite obviously that the totem cannot devour itself. My uncles at Tindican enjoyed the same prerogative.

I do not wish to say more, and I have told you only what I saw with my own eyes. These miracles—they were miracles indeed—I think about now as if they were the fabulous events of a far-off past. That past is, however, still quite near: it was only yesterday. But the world rolls on, the world changes, my own world perhaps more rapidly than anyone else's; so that it appears as if we are ceasing to be what we were, and that truly we are no longer what we were, and that we were not exactly ourselves even at the time when these miracles took place before our eyes. Yes, the world rolls on, the world changes; it rolls on and changes, and the proof of it is that my own totem—I too have my totem—is still unknown to me.

For Discussion

1. How would modern science and psychology explain the relationship between Camara Laye's father and the small black snake? Can you explain the father's knowledge of things and events he has not seen? Can you explain the snake's presence whenever Laye's father forged gold trinkets? Do you believe that all this is true?

2. Apart from his mystical friendship with the snake, what kind of man was Camara Laye's father? Does he have weaknesses and virtues that seem strange? Does he possess the characteristics of people you know?

3. Shakespeare's Hamlet says to his student friend, "There are more things in heaven and earth, Horatio, than are dreamt of in your philosophy." Does this apply to "The Snake and the Crocodile"? Do you feel that there are some areas of reality that science cannot explain? Give examples.

4. What is the significance of the railroad line that runs beside the concession where Camara Laye's father practices his blacksmith trade? Do you feel that this detail is the author's way of expressing the side-by-side existence of the old world and the new? Explain.

5. What are the differences between Laye's mother and father and the guiding spirits of each—the crocodile and the snake? Is the mother's protection against the crocodiles more easily explained? Can you give reasons for her other powers? What does the author mean when he states that his totem is still unknown to him? Can you offer any reasons why?

African Encounter

ERNEST HEMINGWAY

*Occasionally you find yourself in a situation where the mere fact of
living suddenly becomes an unexplainable joy. It may occur at the
seashore, at a party, on a hunting trip, even in a sun-flooded kitchen
eating breakfast with your family, or raking and burning leaves in the
fall. The world, for one harmonious moment, seems bright, kind, and
full of peace. The friends around us seem perfect friends. But time in-
trudes, and the routine reality of life returns. The interlude fades into a
warm memory. It is just such a moment in his own life which Ernest
Hemingway writes about in this selection from* Green Hills of Africa.
*Riding across Africa in an open car on a hunting expedition, he meets
a group of natives who perhaps have never seen a car or a white man
before. For a moment, Hemingway sees the untamed African landscape
as a Garden of Eden, where brotherhood and peace and love and
happiness prevail.*

BY NOW there was no more road, only a cattle
track, but we were coming to the edge of the
plain. Then the plain was behind us and ahead
there were big trees and we were entering a
country the loveliest that I had seen in Africa.
The grass was green and smooth, short as a
meadow that had been mown and is newly
grown, and the trees were big, high-trunked,
and old with no undergrowth but only the
smooth green of the turf like a deer park and
we drove on through shade and patches of sunlight following a faint trail the Wanderobo
pointed out. I could not believe we had suddenly
come to any such wonderful country. It was a

country to wake from, happy to have had the
dream and, seeing if it would clown away, I
reached up and touched the Wanderobo's ear.
He jumped and Kamau snickered. M'Cola
nudged me from the back seat and pointed and
there, standing in an open space between the
trees, his head up, staring at us, the bristles on
his back erect, long, thick, white tusks up-curv-
ing, his eyes showing bright, was a very large
wart-hog boar watching us from less than
twenty yards. I motioned to Kamau to stop and
we sat looking at him and he at us. I put the
rifle up and sighted on his chest. He watched
and did not move. Then I motioned to Kamau

to throw in the clutch and we went on and made a curve to the right and left the warthog, who had never moved, nor showed any fright at seeing us.

I could see that Kamau was excited and, looking back, M'Cola nodded his head up and down in agreement. None of us had ever seen a warthog that would not bolt off, fast-trotting, tail in air. This was a virgin country, an unhunted pocket in the million miles of bloody Africa. I was ready to stop and make camp anywhere.

This was the finest country I had seen but we went on, winding along through the big trees over the softly rolling grass. Then ahead and to the right we saw the high stockade of a Masai village. It was a very large village and out of it came running long-legged, brown, smooth-moving men who all seemed to be of the same age and who wore their hair in a heavy club-like queue that swung against their shoulders as they ran. They came up to the car and surrounded it, all laughing and smiling and talk-

"It was a country to wake from, happy to have had the dream . . ."

An African landscape, with Mount Kilimanjaro in the background

ERNEST HEMINGWAY (1898–1961) was a Nobel Prize–winning American novelist and short-story writer. Born in Oak Park, Illinois, he spent much of his life in Europe, Africa, and Cuba. His passion for fishing, boxing, hunting, and bullfighting are reflected in many of his stories. His own experience and interests provided the backgrounds for his major writings: service as a lieutenant in the Italian Army during World War I (A Farewell to Arms) *and as a newspaper correspondent in the Spanish Civil War* (For Whom the Bell Tolls); *hunting* (The Snows of Kilimanjaro, The Short, Happy Life of Francis MacComber); *and fishing* (The Old Man and the Sea).

The selection reprinted in this book is from Green Hills of Africa, *an account of a big-game hunting trip which Hemingway made as a young man. In a prefatory note, the author stated the purpose of the book: "The writer has attempted to write an absolutely true book to see whether the shape of a country and the pattern of a month's action can, if truly presented, compete with a work of the imagination." The phrase "if truly presented" sums up the central passion of his life—to write honestly and well.*

---

ing. They all were tall, their teeth were white and good, and their hair was stained a red brown and arranged in a looped fringe on their foreheads. They carried spears and they were very handsome and extremely jolly, not sullen, nor contemptuous like the northern Masai, and they wanted to know what we were going to do. The Wanderobo evidently said we were hunting kudu and were in a hurry. They had the car surrounded so we could not move. One said something and three or four others joined in and Kamau explained to me that they had seen two kudu bulls go along the trail in the afternoon.

"It can't be true," I said to myself. "It can't be."

I told Kamau to start and slowly we pushed through them, they all laughing and trying to stop the car, making it all but run over them. They were the tallest, best-built, handsomest people I had ever seen and the first truly light-hearted happy people I had seen in Africa. Finally, when we were moving, they started to run beside the car smiling and laughing and showing how easily they could run and then, as the going was better, up the smooth valley of a stream, it became a contest and one after another dropped out of the running, waving and smiling as they left until there were only two still running with us, the finest runners of the lot, who kept pace easily with the car as they moved long-legged, smoothly, loosely, and with pride. They were running too, at the pace of a fast miler, and carrying their spears as well. Then we had to turn to the right and climb out of the putting-green smoothness of the valley into a rolling meadow and, as we slowed, climbing in first gear, the whole pack came up again, laughing and trying not to seem winded. We went through a little knot of brush and a small rabbit started out, zig-zagging wildly and all the Masai behind now in a mad sprint. They caught the rabbit and the tallest runner came up with him to the car and handed him to me. I held him and could feel the thumping of his heart through the soft, warm, furry body, and as I stroked him the Masai patted my arm. Holding him by the ears I handed him back. No, no, he was mine. He was a present. I handed him to M'Cola. 'Cola did not take him seriously and handed him to one of the Masai. We were moving and they were running again now. The Masai stooped and put the rabbit on the ground and as he ran free they all laughed. M'Cola shook his head. We were all very impressed by these Masai.

"Good Masai," M'Cola said, very moved. "Masai many cattle. Masai no kill to eat. Masai kill man."

The Wanderobo patted himself on the chest.

"Wanderobo—Masai," he said, very proudly, claiming kin. His ears were curled in the same way theirs were. Seeing them running and so damned handsome and so happy made us all happy. I had never seen such quick disinterested friendliness, nor such fine looking people.

"*Good* Masai," M'Cola repeated, nodding his head emphatically. "*Good, good* Masai." Only Garrick seemed impressed in a different way. For all his khaki clothes and his letter from B'wana Simba, I believe these Masai frightened him in a very old place. They were our friends, not his. They certainly were our friends though. They had that attitude that makes brothers, that unexpressed but instant and complete acceptance that you must be Masai wherever it is you come from. That attitude you only get from the best of the English, the best of the Hungarians and the very best Spaniards; the thing that used to be the most clear distinction of nobility when there was nobility. It is an ignorant attitude and the people who have it do not survive, but very few pleasanter things ever happen to you than the encountering of it.

So now there were only the two of them left again, running, and it was hard going and the machine was beating them. They were still running well and still loose and long but the machine was a cruel pacemaker. So I told Kamau to speed it up and get it over with because a sudden burst of speed was not the humiliation of a steady using. They sprinted, were beaten, laughed, and then we were leaning out, waving, and they stood leaning on their spears and waved. We were still great friends but now we were alone again and there was no track, only the general direction to follow around clumps of trees and along the run of this green valley.

For Discussion

1. Why does the author take the trouble to describe aiming his rifle at the wart-hog and then not bother to explain why he decides against shooting? Why is this incident—his refusal to kill the wart-hog—well placed early in this selection?

2. The author never tells us directly that the Masai are fast runners. How is this information conveyed to the reader? Does the author himself completely understand the mystery of his brotherly relationship with the Masai?

3. What does Hemingway mean when he says that the Masai had a noble attitude that he has found in the "best" of the English, Hungarians, and Spaniards? What do you think he means here by "best"?

4. Why do the speedy Masai love the race? Does their competition with the car have any larger significance? Between man and machine, which does the author give the greater dignity? What does the author mean when he says he prefers to "speed it up and get it over with" in the last paragraph? What are the opposites that momentarily come together in this paragraph?

5. Hemingway's style is famous for the absolute clarity with which he presents action and feelings in simple language. Judging from this selection, would you agree with this statement? In reading this passage, is there any point at which you do not clearly see and feel what is happening?

The Savage My Kinsman

ELISABETH ELLIOT

In 1954 the primitive Auca Indians of Ecuador killed a group of American missionaries, among them the Reverend James Elliot. Two years later, his widow, Elisabeth Elliot, together with her four-year-old daughter Valerie and another American woman, went to live among the Aucas in order to resume the work that had been left unfinished. Here is her account of the everyday life of the Aucas, and of the problems that beset a civilized woman living in a primitive society. Behind the physical discomforts, the language barrier, and social differences, lies the dramatic sincerity of a woman who has chosen to "love her enemies" —the very people who martyred her husband. Elisabeth Elliot's bravery, humility, and compassion make her a living symbol of the doctrine which she seeks to bring to the Aucas.

I

OUR NEW home was a clearing about 75 yards in diameter, bordered on one side by tall forest trees and on the other by the Tiwaenu River. When we arrived, there were half a dozen very small huts in the clearing and two "houses"— mere roofs of woven palm, supported by six palm poles. Rachel was invited to share one of these houses with Gikita, his wife Mankamu and her children, and I was given a smaller house adjoining theirs. The absence of walls seemed to bother no one but me. Valerie did not notice the lack of walls, floors or furniture. She had her "bed"—two or three bamboo poles, split and flattened and laid across three logs on the bare ground. On this she soon spread out her doll's blanket, a little scrap of cloth, and was immediately at home.

Man always adapts himself to his environment but to see the way another man has done it, in an environment which seems anything but hospitable to human habitation, is impressive. At first one might ask of the Auca way of life, "Is this the best they can do?" But one soon finds that they do very well indeed.

The Aucas keep a fire burning continuously —in the daytime for cooking and some slight protection from insects, at night for protection from animals and for warmth. Not all jungles are hot and steaming. This area, close to the foothills of the Andes, has an elevation of about 1,500 feet, a mean temperature of 72° and cool nights. The Auca, though naked, is comfortable as long as his feet are warm. His fire is right beside his hammock, and he sleeps with his feet in the smoke. When the fire dies down enough to cool them off, he wakes and simply reaches down and pushes the logs closer together. Occasionally he sits up and rubs his hands over the flame to warm them. In the morning a woman need only reach for a pot of food, usually cooked the night before, and set it on the fire. Breakfast is ready before she gets up!

The only furnishing in an Auca house besides the fire is the hammock, the most versatile piece of furniture ever devised. Woven of a light-weight palm fiber, it is portable and takes no floor space. It is, I discovered, very comfortable for sleeping, eating or studying—once you learn to lie in it diagonally as the Aucas do. I learned to keep my fire going too. I found it very cheering to wake on a windy, rainy night and see it glowing warm beside me. Valerie sleeps on her bamboo slab next to my hammock in a blanket which has been folded and sewed up on two sides, forming a bag like a pillowcase. It is impossible to keep her covered if she sleeps in a hammock, so I devised this method. I contemplated other arrangements one night after finding a snake coiled near Valerie's head as she slept, but any change would have introduced new problems.

There have been some very long days in the jungle when all the Aucas have been off fishing or planting. There have been peaceful nights when they fell asleep early and I lay in my hammock by the embers and read by candle-light. Suddenly a night breeze or a moth would put the candle out and I would be jerked back to this moonlit jungle clearing, the quiet people asleep with their feet over the fires, the little girl who was a part of both worlds rolled in her blanket beside me. When the candle went out and the shrill cacophony of the jungle night arose again to my consciousness and I saw those feet in the fireglow, I asked God for the answers and tried to learn what He wanted to teach me through this insulation: insulation from my own world by distance, insulation from the Auca world by lack of communication.

The difference between these worlds is great. Speaking together in the subdued tones used among Indians, laughing childishly over small things, interested in the tiniest events about them, the Aucas sometimes offer a refreshing contrast to our civilization, with its elaborate dress, loud voices, sophisticated humor and world-consciousness. But at other times I am terribly depressed by their crudeness, pitilessness, limited interests, incomprehensible language, everlasting meddling with my possessions and my affairs, and abject poverty of soul.

Other Indians with whom I have worked had to some degree bowed to the white man's "superiority." The Aucas has no such idea. He has not a reason in the world for thinking us his betters, and he probably has some very valid reasons for thinking us his inferiors.

The Aucas have no use for money. At first they shared their food with us, but I had nothing to offer in return. At times, also, they had no food to share. I could see that their supply was gone, and although they were accustomed to go without and make up for it with a huge meal later, we were hungry. At last it became evident that we must have a separate source of supply, so we arranged with the Missionary Aviation Fellowship to make food drops every Friday. I usually give one of the Auca men the job of cutting up the hunks of frozen beef.

"It burns!" they say of the coldness. Each family is given a piece, however small it may have to be. We want to share with them whatever we have that they like.

Only occasionally do they seem to adopt a practice of the outside world, and then it usually involves some simple tool. They formerly cut their bangs with sharp shells from the river but are now glad to use our scissors.

II

From all appearances, the Aucas accepted us at the beginning as equals. This was what I had thought I wanted. Something happened one day which showed me the falsity of my own position. I was sitting in my leaf house with a clay pot near at hand. Two old women were in the house a few yards away. "Bring that pot here," one of them called, in the urgent half-whisper which is their way of shouting. It was my pot but I took it to her. "Well, don't bring it *empty*. Go get some water in it."

I had to go down to the river by means of a log which lay at a steep angle, fill the pot and carry it (it had no handles and was very heavy) back up the slippery log. The old woman took it without a word. I pondered what I had meant by a desire to be "accepted." I decided that I had wanted to enjoy all the benefits of being a member of their society without its obligations.

This helped me to understand my situation. My reason for being a missionary is one of the few things I have never doubted. I know one thing: I must obey God, and I believe this is the thing He meant me to do, just as He meant others to be fishermen, tax collectors, draftsmen, housewives. The role seems incidental. The goal is all-important.

There remains the message which I have to communicate. In a sense, everything that we do while living with the Aucas is an attempt at communication, even to accepting their name for me, Gikari or "Woodpecker" (I have never discovered their reason for naming me this). To eat what they eat, to live in the same kind of house, to swim and fish with them, to learn to spin cotton thread or weave a hammock as they do, to listen hour after hour to their stories and try to write down what they say—all this is communication.

Gikita, one of the Aucas who killed my husband Jim and the other four men, takes a special interest in seeing that I understand the language. Often he imitates my mistaken pronunciation of an Auca word and then repeats it correctly time after time. "Do you hear?" he says. "Gikari, do you hear? Do you hear?"

Valerie is another help in learning the language. It took her almost no time to learn the phrases she needed to get along with the children and she was soon mimicking the expressions of disdain which are so common. An Indian woman was spinning cotton thread on a very primitive spindle. "Here," she said, handing it to me, "you try it." I clumsily tried. Val walked in at that moment and shouted out the Auca phrase meaning, "Everybody get a load of *this!*"

Several times she came to me and said, "Mama, why do you say so-and-so [using my pronunciation of an Auca word]?" "What do the Aucas say?" I asked. She then gave me the correct form. She is very particular about pronunciation of nasals, and when I carelessly omitted them in the use of an Auca name when I was speaking English, she mimicked the slip in a loud, sneering tone, exactly as the Aucas do, finishing with their expression roughly equivalent to "Listen to her!" It is not that she is disrespectful to me in English. It is simply that she not only speaks Auca but thinks in Auca.

In every phase of life with the Aucas I am painfully conscious of my ignorance. I have been asked if the Auca intelligence is below average. My answer is no. If an Auca were asked that about me, I feel sure he would answer yes. I am ignorant of the Aucas' crafts, of their foods (what is edible, what is not; how to obtain, plant or prepare the foods), of their customs and legends, of the flora and fauna of their forests, of their history and the long, detailed stories they know so well. I cannot even follow a jungle trail without help. The trails of the forest look hopelessly alike when I can see them at all. I go rushing off on what I take to be the trail, only to be called back with, "Where in the world do you think *you're* going?"

On fishing expeditions the men sharpen up their long, supple fish spears. They know which way the fish will dart and start running in this direction. A lunge—"*Baru!*"—the spear is whipped high out of the water, the fish slides down the shaft, spins brightly as the man cracks its head with the knife he holds in his left hand.

Valerie loves fishing trips. She has learned to slide along the river bed on her hands, watching closely for the tiny armored catfish and cupping her hands quickly to seize them. River fish are not especially tasty and Valerie prefers them smoked. She has learned to do it the Auca way, placing the fish over a fire of green sticks and covering them with green leaves to concentrate the smoke.

When a meal is ready, each mother serves her own family group—her husband and her children plus any orphans for whom she is responsible. The quantities of manioc (a starchy tuber [1] that thrives in the area) and meat which an Auca can eat at a sitting are amazing, but then he has the ability to go for long periods without anything to eat at all. Rarely does an adult get a noon meal. The hunter leaves at dawn and takes nothing with him but his weapons, and the woman takes no food with her to the manioc patch when she goes out to work.

They know how to get all the good out of a food, too. Monkeys are singed whole and cooked with the skin on so that the thin layer of fat under the skin is not lost. The tail is smoked and eaten and heads are eaten with brains, eyes, ears and all. Sometimes even the teeth are carefully pulled and thoroughly sucked before being thrown away. Meat and fish are not the only protein foods. Aucas relish the great pale grubs

[1] *tuber* Family of starchy vegetables which usually grow underground. The potato and sweet potato are the most familiar in the United States.

which are the larvae of a giant beetle, bringing them home squirming in a leaf package to be eaten raw or roasted.

Our cooking arrangements are the same as the Aucas'—a fire on the ground. The getting of firewood is a problem for several reasons. I want to be one with the people wherever possible and there are enough things I cannot do. Collecting wood is one thing I felt I could do, though I am no woodsman. I can cut wood all right, but when it comes to splitting I provide the Aucas with a hilarious comedy.

When the meal is cooked and eaten, we have to wash dishes. The Aucas consider this absurd. All the paraphernalia—soap and sponge, pot, spoon, bowls and cup, the plastic container in which I shake up Valerie's powdered milk—must be carried down the muddy bank to the river. And *three* times a day. "There she goes again," they say. "She's going down to wash her pots and her plates and her clothes and her daughter."

I am hopelessly a foreigner and feel pretty sheepish about it. If my pot falls off the three logs which support it, dumping the contents into the fire, the community rocks with laughter. "Gikari's pot fell!" is shouted from one house to another. "Gikari's pot fell!"

"All of it?"

"All of it. Ha-ha!"

Everyone enjoys teasing animals or children. Valerie takes her share of this. She came shrieking to me one day, having been told that Dabu was going to chop her up with an ax. The same man who told her this could be seen at another moment patiently showing Valerie how to roast a green banana in the coals of the fire. Dabu is fascinated by the children's picture books Valerie has, especially those with animals. He and Valerie look at them together by the hour. In this and other ways they have a bond of communication I sometimes envy.

I seldom have to think of ways to amuse my daughter. Occasionally she does not even come home for lunch because she is so occupied with the joys of the jungle and her Auca playmates.

The children know how to snare large bumble-bees with a thin strand of palm fiber without getting stung. They "fly" these the way Ameri-can boys fly toy airplanes, and the bumblebee has a real buzzing motor which never needs re-winding. When they get tired of this, they tie a tiny wad of cotton or kapok on the other end of the string and watch the bee sail off into the forest, trailing the white speck in the sunlight.

The Aucas are curious about everything. There is scarcely a moment of the day when at least one of them is not watching us, asking questions, sorting through our belongings. Pull-ing out a package of dried soup mix or a foun-tain pen, they ask, "What is this?" Usually I know no Auca word to describe it. Then, "Who made this?" (To an Auca, it makes no sense if you do not know who made a thing you own. Among his own possessions he can always tell, by individual touches in the workmanship, who wove a given basket or who made a given spear.) I tell my interrogators I have never seen the one who made it. Incredulous stares. "Then why did he give it to you?"

There is no way to explain.

Turning to something else they ask, "Do you know how to make these?"

"No." Then they turn to something simpler which anyone should know how to make, per-haps a clay cooking pot.

"Do you know how to make these?"

"No."

"Do you weave hammocks?"

"No."

"Do you make fishnets?"

"No."

"What *do* you do?"

"Well"—I try desperately to think of some-thing—"we write. We make marks on this paper." The Aucas are silent but their expres-sions say clearly: "What a useless way to spend one's time."

The Aucas have no formal social organiza-tion, no government, no central authority of any kind. The only social unit is the family.

For the most part Auca men are faithful to the wife or wives they have chosen. But even the head of the house is hardly recognized as such. I watched Dabu, when he had been bitten by a snake and was still very weak, tell his three wives to help him get roof leaf because the rain was beating in on him as he lay in his hammock. The wives said "*Bah!*" ("No") and that was **that**. Dabu got it himself.

Discipline is not very highly developed in the family. When they disobey, children are some-times slapped with nettles or flogged with jungle vines. But parents tend to wink at dis-obedience unless the issue affects the adults' comfort.

Public criticism seems to be the rule. Only rarely have I heard an Auca criticize another behind his back. In fact, many of our civilized sins are conspicuous by their absence. I notice almost no vanity or personal pride, no covetous-ness, avarice or stinginess. The men are not lazy or selfish: when a man brings back an animal, it is divided among his own family, his sisters if they have no other man to look after them, any widows who need meat, and Rachel and me. The Apostle Paul had to rebuke the Corinthians for not caring properly for their widows. The Auca does it without knowing any law but his own conscience.

Tales of the endless killings which have taken place are told with the greatest animation. The narrator remembers who speared whom and in what part of the body. Often revenge is taken in exactly the same way, the killer specifying the reason for each blow as he plunges the spear: "*Ba-ah!* You speared my father's hands. Take that and that. *Ba-ah! Ba-ah!* You speared his chest on the right side and on the left. Take that, and that, and that!" This is the code. It is not a new one: an eye for an eye.

What do we mean when we speak of a peo-ple as being "savage?" I realized that I had un-consciously equated the level of the Auca's culture with the level of his morals. But I found "raw" savagery no more awesome than the fami-liar variety.

The Auca knows nothing of drunkenness or wife beating. He may kill his neighbor for what seems to him a good reason but he does not squabble with him. He does not greet a friend or bid him goodby, but he entertains without charge any guest who happens in, even if he is a Quichua Indian whom he has never seen.

In short, I was soon faced with the fact that socially I had nothing to offer the Aucas. Any comparison between myself and them, from this standpoint, was to my disadvantage. Why was I here?

There was no answer but the simplest, most elemental: Jesus Christ. To obey Him, to present Him.

III

Nowhere did I sense the gulf between us more than in my ignorance of the language. The Auca tongue is extremely rich in onomatopoeia, filled with words that sound like the things they represent. I find it quite impossible to translate fully an Auca's description of the hunt. His narrative is punctuated with imitative words that describe the leaping of a chattering monkey from bough to bough, the sound of the dart as it strikes him, the plunge to the ground, the impact of the body, the whack of the machete as it finishes him off.

But in expressing abstract ideas the Auca language is highly inadequate. So far as I know, there are no words meaning "to be able" or "to know." Often the Aucas come around while I am speaking on the short-wave radio to the missionary aviation base. They always ask, "What do they say?" More often than not, if the base says anything more than "O.K.," I am unable to translate it into Auca.

And if communication is so difficult in the material realm, how are we to convey anything of the spiritual? I can now hold up my end of a simple conversation in the Auca language, but explaining Christianity in it is still beyond my powers.

The Auca has, so far as I know, no form of religion. He knows nothing of prayer, sacrifice, worship, placating evil spirits (though he believes in their existence) or adoring the good. He is not consciously seeking after anything. But obviously, failing to recognize a need does not mean that the need does not exist.

It is true that the Aucas have a word for God. They think of Him as the one who made men. The name is the same as for a species of fish. The word for son is the same as the word for child, of whatever age or sex. So in speaking of God's Son to the Aucas we use exactly the same words that they use in speaking of the offspring of the fish. What possibility is there that the Aucas will grasp any significance in words spoken by "the offspring of the fish"? But we try.

Dayuma is an Auca woman who was away from the tribe for a long time and worked for years with Rachel. She has learned a great deal which she can teach her people, and she faithfully does so.

"Tomorrow," Dayuma says to the Aucas on Saturday, "is the day I am going to speak about God." They have no idea of weeks, nor any names for days, so first she had to explain to them the seven-day cycle we call a week. At dawn Sunday she calls out, "Everyone come." She then tells stories from the Bible in the Auca language with appropriate sound effects, gestures, and explanatory footnotes—often punctuated with admonitions to "shut up," since it is a new idea to the Aucas to have to be still while one person speaks.

As Dayuma talks, the others sit as they do at any other time, quite innocent of any idea of reverence. Dawa searches her ribs for chiggers,[2] Mankamu picks her son Dika's teeth, Uba inspects the foot fungus of her daughter and exhibits it to her neighbor. A row of little naked boys, clad in their Sunday-go-to-meeting skein of string, are spellbound by the story of Jesus stilling the storm at sea, but some of the old women find it hard to concentrate. They have

---

[2] *chigger* A kind of flea.

their own stories—stories of their own people, their husbands, their fathers, how they were killed, how they used to live. Why listen to this story of a man who lived so far away and so very long ago? He was a foreigner. What has this to do with them? And surely, even if He has something to say to them, it does not involve obedience?

If Dayuma tells them that He said they must not kill, the Aucas conclude that this is merely one more strange foreign custom. The Auca, too, believes that it is wrong to kill—*except* under certain conditions. He has a conscience about killing. Some of the men who killed the five missionaries say now that they did not do well to kill them. But it was only a mistake. The Auca was trying to preserve his own way of life, his own liberty. He believed the foreigners were a threat to that liberty, so he feels he had every right to kill them. In America we decorate a man for defending his country. If death blows are dealt, what does it matter if it is with wooden spears or ballistic missiles?

We have come to those who have been called one of the most savage tribes on earth. We are in their homes. We must live with them, love them, try to understand them and, above all, demonstrate to them what we mean by eternal life: a new *kind* of life, not simply a longer one.

We have come to offer something which, apparently, the Auca was not even looking for: a Hope, an anchor for the soul, the person of Jesus Christ. The lucid recognition of the Auca as my kinsman is at the same time a new acknowledgment of Jesus Christ, of our common need of Him.

When it comes time to pray at our Sunday meetings, Dayuma instructs those present to close their eyes, and other Aucas who have done this before supplement her instructions with, "Now we will all sleep. Everyone sleep!" And they obediently close their eyes, though checking now and then to make sure the others are doing so. Seeing that Dayuma puts her hand over her face, some copy this. All are silent through the long, long prayer, with Dayuma's earnest petitions that her own people will think about God, live in a new way and learn to love their enemies. Sometimes Dayuma asks them to repeat what she said in prayer. Some are happy to oblige. This may be a sign of the new birth, but I have to remind myself not to regard as a "spiritual awakening" what may be the sociable desire to please—nor, on the other hand, to regard lightly the hunger that is in every man, recognized or not. I must be patient. God knows the heart, and He knows which man loves what he has seen of Him.

For Discussion

1. Does Mrs. Elliot sympathize with the Aucas' tendency to resist civilization? Does she feel they are wrong? Does she present both sides of the argument and refrain from making a judgment? Do her feelings toward the Aucas reveal anything about her own character? Explain.

2. Why does Valerie have an easier time adapting to the ways of the Aucas? Do you think that she provides a good argument for a return to a simpler form of life? What advantage do children have over adults in adjusting to a violent social change? Why? What are some of the dangers that confront

Valerie in her jungle life? What are some of the dangers that would confront her in a modern American city or suburb? What conclusions can you draw from a comparison between these two?

3. What are the parts of Auca life that Mrs. Elliot enjoys? What are the parts she dislikes? Does she try to reform these people in any way? Explain.

4. Do you feel that Elisabeth Elliot is an intruder? Can you judge exactly how the Aucas feel about her from the information in this account? Do you need to know more? Do you think that you could involve yourself in a similar society and survive?

A Trip to the Post Office

ELIZABETH BORTON DE TREVIÑO

Bureaucracy accompanies civilization the whole world over. Official checks and balances, designed to produce efficiency and security, often produce only frustration and delay. Here, Elizabeth Borton de Treviño gives a light-hearted account of her encounters with the postal officials of her adopted country, Mexico.

I HAVE a dear friend named Rose who lives in Boston, who has never forgotten my birthday, no matter where in the wide world I have been wandering. Always some package arrives with her loving remembrance.

On my birthday in Monterrey, I received a notice that a package was waiting for me in the post office. I thought of course it must be from Rose. So I happily put on my hat and walked over to the Independencia Square, where the post office sits on a slight incline, looking down over the city.

I marched up to a window and presented my notice that a package had been sent me.

"Your identification?" asked the clerk.

I hadn't brought any identification, so I turned around and walked home again.

At lunchtime I showed the notice to Luis [1] who studied it carefully. "Wait for me," he said. "We will go together to find out about this package."

But next day he had forgotten my package, and I having nothing to do, so I thought to myself, I will take my driving license as identi-

fication, and go and ask for my package by myself.

I went up to the same window and showed my driving license.

"This is a foreign document," said the clerk sternly. "I cannot admit it as evidence."

I slunk away.

At lunchtime I confessed to Luis that I had again gone to the post office and what had happened there.

"You haven't got any identification, I suppose," he said thoughtfully. "That is, no Mexican identification. I will have to go and take you with me, and swear before a notary that you are my wife."

"But good heavens," I protested wildly. "All this row over what is probably a little handmade cotton apron?"

"We are dealing with the most ruthless and complicated system in the whole complicated Mexican Government," said Luis. "People have gone to get packages from the post office, carrying their identification and when their starved corpse is found, years later, the document helps their families to identify them, so they can take them away to be buried. Why . . ."

---

[1] *Luis*   The author's husband.

"It can't possibly be as bad as that!"

"I've heard that it is a little worse in Central China," admitted Luis.

So we went back with Luis's identification, and a copy of our marriage lines.

"This was a foreign marriage," commented the clerk. "Not legal in Mexico. You must show a certificate of Mexican civil marriage."

This was before Luis and I had got married again in front of the Civil Registrar; we had no idea at the time, that this was so crucial.

"We will go and get you a Mexican driving license," said resourceful Luis. "That ought to do it."

So I went to the Palace of Government, made an appointment for my medical examination next day and an appointment with the examiner who was to find out that I really knew how to drive. In about a week's time, I had the license, with my picture and thumb print on it, the proper stamps, certificate of payment of fee, etc., etc., etc.

With this firmly clutched I went back and faced the post-office clerk again.

He ruefully admitted that I was to all intents and purposes to be identified as Elizabeth Borton de Treviño and that I apparently had the right to receive the package addressed to a person of that name. Or at least to take the next step. It seemed they didn't just hand over the package. Too simple.

I was given a bit of paper with a number on it and sent to another window. When my turn came, the clerk looked at me severely and asked, "Who sent you this package?"

"Why it says on the notice that the point of origin is Boston, so I thought perhaps my friend Rose . . ." I babbled.

He drew out his papers and consulted them.

"No," he said, looking at me over the tops of his glasses. "Not Rose."

"Well, I have no idea. I have lots of friends. Various people send me presents . . ."

"What is in this package?"

"How do I know?" I shouted. "It was sent to me, wasn't it? But I haven't been allowed to get near it! How should I know what's in it?"

I glared, and he looked pained. I had yet to learn that when you lose your temper in dealing with the bureaucracy in Mexico you merely set yourself back. He calmly beckoned to the person behind me in line, and there was nothing for me to do but go home and take a little *boldo* tea to calm my liver (that was boiling like an angry sea) and wait for Luis.

Again we took up the matter of my war with the post office and worked out a fresh strategy.

Luis said, "It is now a little difficult. Of course you could just let the notice lapse and then the package would either be confiscated or go back to the person who sent it. If it goes back to the person who sent it, you will probably get a letter asking what to do with it."

"I'm not going to give up yet," I gritted through my teeth.

"Well, when you go back to the post office, be a little bit more feminine about the whole thing. Say you can't imagine what the package can be. Act helpless and they may give you a tiny hint. Cry a little bit."

I went back to the post office, wearing a ruffled blouse, and a picture hat. I took my place in the line. I presented my notice.

"Your identification?"

I presented it.

"What is in this package?"

"A surprise to me! You see, we were just married, that is, not so long ago, and it must be a gift!" I leaned over close and shone my eyes on the granite-faced gentleman in the window. "I hope it is a box of wedding silver!"

He thawed a little, and said sadly,

"I'm afraid it is not silver."

"Oh, what a disappointment!" I allowed my chin to quiver. He became agitated and said, "Now, now!"

I braced up a little, and seemed to get a grip on myself.

"Do you smoke?" he asked me.

"Why, why, sometimes! That is, I used to! My husband doesn't like me to, in Mexico."

"Different customs."

"That's right. My husband is Mexican and I try to adopt his ways."

"Please your husband. That's a good rule." Here he leaned over confidentially and whispered, as the line grew longer and people shuffled their feet behind me. "Well, *señora,* this package contains *a carton of American cigarettes!*"

"Oh, lovely!" I clapped my hands. "Luis will be so glad!"

"But there is—a difficulty."

"Another difficulty?"

"You are not allowed to import cigarettes."

"Import? But I haven't imported anything. I had no idea anybody was sending me cigarettes."

"Well, I am going to let you make out this special solicitude, this special request, to the postmaster, asking that you be allowed to receive the package. It's irregular. But I will make an exception in your case." And he handed me a sheaf of papers, four or five sheets of carbon paper, and a stubby pencil.

"Go over there and sit down and make out the forms," he directed me. "Take your time and answer all the questions carefully. This will have to go to the head of the Customs Department. That is, if the postmaster approves it."

I took my papers and sat down. It took me about an hour to read it through, for it was all fine print, and I had been brought up by a lawyer father to read all the fine print. Then I adjusted all the carbons and painstakingly answered all the questions, writing down my age, where I was born, name of father and mother, their professions, their religion, their nationality, my husband's profession, his religion, his nationality. And so on. Rather cross eyed from my toil among the fine print I went

back, got in line again, and smilingly handed the man in the window my papers.

He handed them right back to me.

"Go upstairs, down the hall and turn to the right. You will come to an ante-room. There you may ask for an appointment with the postmaster. When you see him, you must give him your solicitude."

I followed directions carefully. In the waiting room were several other shell-shocked citizens who had received some kind of package from abroad and whose lives would never be the same again.

A secretary sat there taking down names and addresses and dispensing little appointment cards with numbers on them. My number was 23. After a while a door opened and a woman in widow's weeds emerged from the inner office. The next number was called. It was 14. My heart sank. But I settled down to wait. If I did not turn up at home, Luis at least knew where to send the search parties.

A square in a typical Mexican town

When at last my number was called, I arose to my now numb feet and staggered in.

A calm gray-haired gentleman received my papers, read them through, and shook his head gravely over some points. Then he said, "You will receive an official acknowledgment of these documents in a few days." He got up and bowed, and I was released into the world again.

When I recounted to Luis everything that had happened, he said, "Now my advice is to relax and forget the whole matter. If some day you receive an official paper of some kind, we will then see what is to be done."

I followed my husband's counsel and life went on as before. I daily wrote to my parents, urging them to come and visit me. And I again tried to learn to make *tortillas*, patting the dough between my palms, but again I was a total failure.

About three weeks later I got an official envelope. I laid this on the lunch table at Luis's place and asked him as my attorney, to open and read it. I said, "I think the GPU [2] is after us."

He read the letter inside and told me that it said that my solicitude to receive a certain package had been received and would be acted upon in good time.

"I will lock this up in my strong box," said Luis, "for they admit that they have your package and that they received your solicitude to receive your package. Now we've got something on them. We've almost got a case."

"But don't I *do* anything?" I wailed

"Not a thing but sit tight. Before we get through, we may be asked to leave the country as undesirables. We must act cautiously and be very careful what we say from now on."

Finally one day I got another notice from the post office, this time ordering me to appear before the postmaster.

I went, showed my identification, got in several lines, was handed an appointment card,

and finally was received. The postmaster handed me back my original solicitude, now decorated with many seals and countersigns, and informed me that I would now be allowed to pay the duties, affix the stamps, and see my package.

I was told to present myself at window 10 with a carbon copy of my solicitude, which he then pressed into my eager hand. He kept the originals with the ribbons and seals.

At window 10 I again filled out a special form, under the coaching of the clerk and then I was told to go to window 21, get in line, and buy a certain number of stamps, of a specified value. By this time I was beginning to understand why Mexico has no unemployment.

This operation of buying the stamps took some time. After I had them, I was placed in charge of a gentleman who wore an enormous key suspended on a cord from his belt. He led me up to a strange sort of cell, a kind of cage of stout wire, with a tiny opening in it at eye height. Into this cage I was locked with my stamps, and the man with the key went away.

"This is what I get for mixing myself up with the post office department," I muttered to myself, and I wondered whether I would be exposed to public censure inside my cage or put on a train and deported in it.

But behold, the man with the keys returned, and through the small window he pushed some documents and a pen. These papers said that I swore a mighty oath that I had received my package and that it was in good order.

I should not have signed this, for I had not received my package, but I was in a cage, and I was too weak to fight any more. I signed.

Then through the little window, at last, came my battered package.

"Open it," I was ordered.

With trembling fingers I undid the strings and knots. Inside was a carton of Chesterfields, and a card which said, "Love from Marian." I had to show the card to the guard, but he decided, after due thought, to let me keep it. He

---

[2] *GPU*   The Russian secret police.

then told me how to stick each stamp on each package of cigarettes in such a way that when the package was opened, the stamps would be torn. I did this all very carefully, conscious of the guard's suspicious eye on me. He then took all the cigarettes away from me, turned a key in the lock, and let me out.

"Window 17," he said.

I went to window 17. I again showed my notice, my identification, my solicitude, and copy of the paper which said I had received my package in good order. The man with the key whispered in the ear of the man in window

17, and I was given more papers to sign and told to pay one peso and seventeen cents storage charges.

Then they gave me my package.

I stumbled home and threw myself on my bed, and called for an ice cap. While I lay there promising to be a good girl for years and years if I would only be spared any more trials like this one, the doorbell rang and Blanca went to answer it. She came back with a little pink card. A notice from the post office that a package was waiting for me, origin Los Angeles.

I tore the little card into very small pieces.

For Discussion

1. Hyperbole is an exaggeration used for literary effect. Can you find examples of hyperbole in this selection? What is the effect the author tries to achieve through its use?

2. Have you ever experienced the frustrations of red tape? Compare your reactions with the reactions of the author. Does the author seem to take the process seriously? What kind of person is she?

3. How does the author portray the civil servants with whom she has to deal? Does she seem to make fun of them? In what way? Do they take themselves too seriously? Give examples.

4. Does this episode reveal more of the Mexican national character than just the behavior of postal clerks and authorities? Explain. Can you suggest any reason (climate, wealth of the country, education, social structure) why this sort of procedure is characteristic?

5. Does the author express any malice toward the Mexican ways that caused her so much inconvenience? Does she express any affection? Is it possible to criticize an institution and still retain a warm affection for that which you disapprove? Explain. Can you find evidence of this in "A Trip to the Post Office"?

The Petition

GIOVANNI GUARESCHI

Giovanni Guareschi's novels, The Little World of Don Camillo *and*
Don Camillo and His Flock, *are about a village priest in the Po River
valley who struggles against the communist mayor, Peppone, for the
allegiance of the villagers. Don Camillo, a large, strong man, has a
flaring temper and frequently finds himself apologizing to God for the
physical violence he uses to convince his more rebellious parishioners
of the error of their ways. The citizens of his village derive their living
from the land. Their habits are simple; their attitude toward life is
realistic. Don Camillo attends to their spiritual needs, meddles in their
private lives, defends their dignity, and berates their ignorance in a
series of comic incidents that warmly illuminate life in an Italian
country town. In "The Petition," Don Camillo and Peppone compete
for signatures of men and women who are not fully aware of the
significance of the documents they sign.*

DON CAMILLO was walking quietly along the
Low Road toward the village, smoking his usual
cigar, when, just around a curve, he came upon
Peppone's gang. There were five of them, and
Smilzo was in charge. Don Camillo looked at
them with frank curiosity.

"Are you planning to bump me off?" he asked
them. "Or have you some better place in mind?"

"Don't you dare incite us to violence!" said
Smilzo, taking a sheet of paper out of an envelope and unfolding it before him.

"Is this for the last wishes of the condemned
man?"

"It's for everyone that wants peace to sign,"
said Smilzo. "If you don't sign, then you don't
want peace. From now on, honest men and
warmongers are going to be clearly divided."

Don Camillo examined the dove printed at the
top of the paper.

"I'm an honest man," he said, "but I'm not
signing. A man that wants peace doesn't have
to testify to it with his signature."

Smilzo turned to Gigo, who was standing beside him.

"He thinks this is a political move," he said. "According to him, everything we do is tied up with politics."

"Look, there's no politics in this," put in Gigo. "It's just a question of preserving peace. Peace is good for all political parties. It will take a lot of signatures to get us out of the Atlantic Pact,[1] and if we don't get out, it's going to get us into a war, as sure as shooting."

Don Camillo shook the ashes off the end of his cigar.

"You'd better get going," he said. "If I'm not mistaken, you haven't even started."

"Of course not. We wanted you to have the honor of being the first name on the list. That's only natural. When peace is at stake, the clergy ought to take the lead."

Don Camillo threw out his arms. "It can be taken for granted that the clergy's in favor of peace, so it's just as if my signature were there."

"Then you are not going to sign?"

Don Camillo shook his head and walked away.

"If we're saddled with a clergy of this kind, then we'll have to fight not one war but two," Smilzo said bitterly, putting the paper back in the envelope.

A little later Peppone arrived at the rectory door.

"No politics involved," he declared. "I'm here in the capacities of mayor, citizen, father of a family, Christian, and honest man."

"Too many people!" exclaimed Don Camillo. "Too big a crowd! Come in just as Peppone, and leave the rest outside."

Peppone came in and sat down.

"We've come to the ragged edge," he began. "If honest men don't stick together, the world's headed for a smashup."

[1] *Atlantic Pact* An anticommunist alliance among Italy, the United States, Britain, and other Western nations.

"Sorry to hear it," Don Camillo answered seriously. "Is there anything new?"

"Only that if we don't safeguard peace, everything's going to pieces. Let's leave politics and parties out of it and all get together."

Don Camillo nodded. "That's the way I like to hear you talk," he said. "It's about time you cut loose from that brood of Satan."

"I said we'd leave politics out of it," retorted Peppone. "This is a time for thinking in worldwide terms."

Don Camillo looked at him with astonishment, for he had never heard him mouth such big words.

"Do you want peace or don't you?" asked Peppone. "Are you with Jesus Christ or against Him?"

"You know the answer."

Out of his pocket Peppone took the envelope and paper Don Camillo had seen earlier in the day.

"When it comes to fighting for peace, the clergy must be in the front line," he asserted.

Don Camillo shook his head. "You're changing the rules of the game. Didn't you say politics wasn't in it?"

"I'm here as a plain citizen," Peppone insisted.

"Very well, then, as one citizen to another, I tell you I'm not biting." And as Peppone started to rise excitedly to his feet, he added: "You know very well that if I sign your paper, a lot of other signatures will follow. Without me, you can only hope for those of your own people, and a lot of them can't write their own names. Since you see that I'm not to be taken in, put that pigeon back in your pocket and hand me two glasses from the sideboard. Otherwise, you and your pigeon and your cause of peace may as well go back where you came from."

Peppone tucked the paper away.

"Since you're giving yourself such airs," he said proudly, "I'll show you that I can get all the signatures I want without yours as an attraction."

Don Camillo and Peppone in a scene from the movie based on Guareschi's novels

Smilzo and the rest of the "peace gang" were waiting outside.

"Start making the rounds," said Peppone. "But go to our people last. Everyone's got to sign. Peace must be defended with blows if necessary."

"Chief, if I go to jail, what will happen?" Smilzo asked him.

"Nothing will happen. A man can serve the cause perfectly well in jail."

These words were not exactly comforting. But Smilzo set out, with the gang at his heels, strengthened by some reinforcements from the People's Palace.[2]

Now, when people have haystacks and vineyards and fields, it's almost impossible for them to say no to a fellow who asks them to sign up for peace and swears politics doesn't enter into it. And in a village the first five or six signatures are what count. It took several evenings

to cover the whole area. But there were no arguments, except from Tonini, who shook his head when they showed him the paper.

"Don't you want peace?"

"No," said Tonini, who was a fellow with hands as big as shovels. "I happen to like war. It kills off a lot of rascals and clears the air."

Here Smilzo made a very sensible observation.

"But you know, of course, that more honest men are killed off than rascals?"

"But I care even less for honest men."

"And what if you get killed yourself?"

"I'd rather be killed than sign a paper. At least, when you die, you know where you're going."

The gang started to come forward, but Tonini picked up his shotgun, and Smilzo said he needn't bother.

Everything else went smoothly, and when Peppone saw the sheets full of signatures, he was so happy that he brought his fist down on the table hard enough to make the People's

[2] *People's Palace*   The local Communist headquarters.

Palace tremble. He compared the peace list with the village census and found that they tallied. The mayors of the neighboring villages complained that they couldn't get people to sign because the reactionaries obstructed them. There had been shooting at Castellina and fisticuffs at Fossa for a whole day. And to think that Smilzo, after taking an hour to persuade each of the first five or six signatures, had won over the rest without a murmur.

"It's the prestige I enjoy as mayor," said Peppone, and he gathered together the papers and went to savor his triumph.

Don Camillo was reading a book when Peppone appeared before him.

"The power of the clergy is on the decline!" Peppone announced to him. "I thank you in the name of world's democracies for not having signed. Your signature wouldn't have brought in half as many others. It's too bad for the Pope, that's all." And he added, spreading his papers out on the table, "America's done for! The Atlantic Pact is no good, because we have a totality of votes against it. And everywhere else it's going to be the same way."

Don Camillo scrutinized the lists carefully. Then he threw out his arms. "I'm sorry to tell you, but one signature is missing. Tonini's. So you can't claim a 'totality.'"

Peppone laughed.

"I have all the rest," he said. "What is one against eight hundred?"

Don Camillo opened the drawer, took out some papers, and scattered them in front of Peppone.

"You have signatures against the Pact and I have signatures in its favor."

Peppone opened his eyes wide.

"Russia's done for," said Don Camillo. "Because I have Tonini's signature along with the rest."

Peppone scratched his head.

"There's nothing so remarkable about it," Don Camillo pointed out. "I worked by day, and your men went around by night, when people were already softened up. As a matter of fact, they were glad to sign for you, because that canceled their signing for me. The only one who didn't like it was Tonini, because I had to knock his head against a wall. But I advise you not to go after him, because he says that before he'll sign another petition he'll shoot to kill."

Peppone took his papers away. And so it was that in Don Camillo's village, America triumphed by one to zero, all on account of Tonini.

[*translated by* FRANCES FRENAYE]

For Discussion

1. What does the first meeting between Don Camillo and Smilzo reveal about the relationship of the two? Is Don Camillo afraid of the gang? What later event proves that he is capable of handling any threat that Smilzo might make?

2. What kind of relationship exists between Don Camillo and Peppone? Do they hate each other? Would you say that behind the surface of anger and annoyance each man enjoys the rivalry? Explain. What is the significance of Don Camillo's statement, "You're changing the rules of the game"?

3. What is the difference between Peppone's attitude toward the villagers and Don Camillo's? Which of the two do you feel is the more realistic? Explain.

4. Would you say that this is a happy story? Is it possible that Don Camillo and Peppone use their disagreement as a means to break the boredom of peaceful village life? Can you compare their difference of opinion to a family argument? Do you think that they would unite to fight against a common enemy? Explain.

Platero and I

JUAN RAMÓN JIMÉNEZ

The most widely read modern book in Spanish—together with García Lorca's plays and poems—is Juan Ramón Jiménez's Platero and I. *This collection of short prose impressions reflects life in the small village in Andalusia where the Nobel Prize–winning poet was born. The framework of the book is slight: the poet rides about the town and countryside on his beloved donkey, Platero. He writes accounts of the sights and sounds about him as if he were speaking to Platero. The effect of this literary device is to suggest the poet's loneliness and isolation from his own townspeople. When at last Platero dies, the reader feels that Juan Ramón has lost his best and only intimate friend. The complete version of* Platero and I *contains more than a hundred chapters or sections, of which seven are reprinted here.*

PLATERO

PLATERO is small, downy, smooth—so soft to the touch that one would think he were all cotton, that he had no bones. Only the jet mirrors of his eyes are hard as two beetles of dark crystal.

I let him run loose and he goes off to the meadow; softly, scarcely touching them, he brushes his nose against the tiny flowers of pink, sky-blue and golden yellow. I call him gently: "Platero?" and he comes to me at a gay little trot as though he were laughing, lost in a clatter of fancy.

He eats everything I give him. He likes tangerines, muscatel grapes, all amber-colored, and purple figs with their crystal point of honey.

He is tender and loving as a little boy, as a little girl; but strong and firm as a stone. When I ride him on Sunday through the lanes at the edge of the town, the men from the country, clean-dressed and slow-moving, stand still to watch him.

"He is made of steel."

He is made of steel. Both steel and quicksilver.

CORPUS CHRISTI

As we enter the Calle de la Fuente [1] on our return from the orchard, the bells, which we had already heard three times from the path by the streams, are making a stir in the white town with their crying crown of bronze. Their pealing weaves and winds in echo among the noisy sparkling bursts of fireworks and the shrill metallic ring of the music.

The street, newly limed [2] and trimmed with red ochre, is quite green from its decking of popular and cypress. The windows display hangings of garnet damask, [3] yellow silk, sky-blue satin and, in the houses where there is mourning, snow-white wool with black ribbons.

Between the farthermost houses at the corner by the church gallery, the cross of mirrors makes its slow appearance and, among the beams of the setting sun, already catches the light from the red candles. Slowly the procession passes. The carmine banner and San Roque, the patron of the bakers, laden with fresh twists of bread; the light-green banner and San Telmo, patron of the sailors, with his ship of silver in his hands; the yellow banner and San Isidro, patron of farm workers, with his little yoke of oxen, and more colored banners and more saints, and then Santa Anna instructing the Virgin, and San José in brown, and the Immaculate Virgin in blue. . . . Finally, between the Civil Guards, the Monstrance, [4] its fretted silver twined with ripe sheaves of grain and clusters of green grapes, moving slowly in its blue cloud of incense.

The Andalusian Latin [5] of the Psalms rises clearly through the fading afternoon. The sun, now rose, casts its low rays up the Calle del Río [6] to sparkle over the heavy gold of the old copes. [7] Above and around the scarlet tower, over the smooth opal of the calm June hour, the doves weave their high garlands of glowing snow.

Platero brays. And his gentleness, together with the church bell, the fireworks, the Latin and the music, becomes associated with the clear mystery of the day; his braying is softened as it soars and, as it floats low, seems divine.

THE BULLFIGHT

I'll bet you don't know, Platero, why those children came? To see if I would let them take you with them to ask for the key of the bull pen this afternoon. But don't you worry. I have already told them they need not even think of such a thing.

They came mad with excitement, Platero. The whole town is agitated because of the bullfight. The band which has been playing since dawn sounds ragged and out of tune now in front of the taverns; coaches and horses come and go, up Calle Nueva [8] and down again. Back there in the side street they are preparing the Canario, the yellow coach the children love so much, for the bullfighters. The patios have been stripped of all their flowers, for the presiding ladies. It makes me sad to see the boys walking sluggishly through the streets with their wide hats, their blouses and their cigars, smelling of the stable and of brandy.

At about two o'clock, Platero, at that moment of solitude and sun, that bright interval in the day, while matadors and ladies are dressing, you and I will go out through the back door and down the lane to the country, as we did last year.

---

[1] *Calle de la Fuente* The Street of the Fountain, therefore one of the principal streets of the town.

[2] *limed* Paved with white cement.

[3] *garnet damask* A deep red cloth.

[4] *Monstrance* A sacred vessel used in Catholic ceremonies. The consecrated Host is carried in it so that it may be seen and venerated by the faithful.

[5] *Andalusian Latin* The people are reciting the Latin words with the accent of their own Andalusian Spanish.

[6] *Calle del Río* The Street of the River.

[7] *cope* A kind of embroidered cape worn by the priests during certain ceremonies.

[8] *Calle Nueva* The New Street.

CARNIVAL

How handsome Platero looks today! It is Carnival Monday, and the children who have dressed in costume have put Moorish trappings on him, all heavily worked in arabesques of red, blue, white and yellow.

Rain, sun and cold. The twisting colored papers are blown in parallel lines along the sidewalk by the bitter wind of the afternoon, and the shivering maskers turn anything into pockets for their blue-cold hands.

When we reach the square, a group of women dressed as lunatics, with long white shirts and garlands of green leaves in their flowing black hair, pull Platero into the center of their riotous circle and whirl gaily about him.

Confused, Platero pricks up his ears, raises his head, and, like a scorpion surrounded by fire, tries nervously to escape in any direction. But he is so small that the lunatics are not afraid of him and continue whirling and singing and laughing around him. The children, seeing him captive, bray to make him bray. The whole square is now an insolent concert of brass, braying, laughter, songs, tambourines and mortars.[9]

At last, making up his mind like a man, Platero breaks through the circle and comes trotting and crying to me, his rich trappings [10] in disarray. Like me he wants to have nothing to do with Carnival. We were not made for this sort of thing.

[9] *mortars* Cannons.
[10] *trappings* His ornamented harness and other decorations.

How beautiful the countryside is these festival days, when everyone abandons it. In the vineyards and the vegetable gardens one sees scarcely a single old man bending over the brittle vine or the pure stream. In the distance there rises over the town, like a jester's crown, the full clamor of the crowd, the clapping, and the music from the bull ring, all of which we lose as we go serenely toward the sea. And the soul, Platero, feels truly queen of all it surveys by virtue of its own feelings and of the great sound body of Nature, who when respected gives submissively to those who are worthy the spectacle of her splendid and eternal beauty.

THE DONKEYS OF THE SAND VENDOR

Look, Platero, at the donkeys of Quemado; sluggish, dowtrodden, bearing their red heaping loads of wet sand in which are stuck, as if in their hearts, the rods of wild olive used to beat them.

DEATH

I found Platero stretched out on his bed of straw, his eyes soft and sad. I went to him, patted him, talked to him and tried to help him up.

The poor animal gave a sudden jerk and got one leg kneeling. He could not do it. Then I stretched his foreleg out on the floor, patted him again tenderly and sent for his doctor. As soon as he saw him, old Darbón drew in his great toothless mouth to the nape of his neck and rocked his congested head back and forth, pendulumlike, on his chest.

"Not good, is it?"

I do not know what he answered. . . . That the poor animal was sinking . . . Nothing could be done . . . That a pain . . . Some poisonous root . . . The dirt in the grass . . .

By noon Platero was dead. His little cotton belly had swollen up like a globe, and his discolored legs stuck stiffly skyward. His curly coat looked like the moth-eaten flax of old doll's hair which falls at the touch in dusty sadness.

Flying about the silent stall was a beautiful butterfly, its three colors shining each time it passed through the ray of sunlight from the little window.

NOSTALGIA

Platero, you do see us, don't you?

You do see how the clear cold water in the orchard well is laughing in peace; how the painstaking bees fly around the green and mauve rosemary turned gold and rose in the sunlight lingering over the hill?

Platero, you do see us, don't you?

You do see the sad, lame, tired little donkeys of the washerwomen climbing the red slope to the old fountain, in the vast purity uniting heaven and earth in a single crystal splendor?

Platero, you do see us, don't you?

You really do see the children dashing among the rockroses whose own flowers are posed on their branches like a light swarm of tremulous white butterflies, speckled crimson?

Platero, you do see us, don't you?

You really do see us? Yes, you see me. And I hear in the cloudless sunset, softening the whole valley filled with vineyards, your gentle, doleful bray. . . .

[*translated by* WILLIAM H. *and* MARY M. ROBERTS]

For Discussion

1. What does the festival of Corpus Christi reveal about the personality of the people? How does the poet's description suggest his feelings toward the life he observes? Would you say that he looks at things through childlike eyes? Explain.

2. Why does the poet choose a donkey for his companion instead of another human being?

3. Why does the poet mention the butterfly that flutters through the stall where Platero has just died? What effect does the arrival of the butterfly have on the poet?

4. Explain the section entitled "Nostalgia." What effect does the death of Platero have on the poet's understanding of life and the world?

UNIT 9: NO MAN IS AN ISLAND

"No man is an island, entire

of it self," wrote John Donne more than three hundred years ago. "Any mans death diminishes me, because I am involved in Mankind."

Each man on this earth is involved with all of humanity. This fact provides one of the constant themes of world literature. What is meant by these words "mankind" and "humanity"? They refer not only to those in our own town and in our own nation, but to every other man on the face of the earth.

This concept of humanity implies a responsibility both to the past and to the future, that is, to those who have gone before us and to those who will follow us. Mankind moves forward toward a destiny that only time will reveal. The success or failure of that destiny depends upon man's acceptance of his responsibility.

Most of us will agree that there exists a "brotherhood of man." But in what kinds of emotions and actions does this brotherhood show itself? How is it neglected? How is it violated? The selections that follow examine these questions.

Men differ greatly in language, clothing, stature, arts, and customs. Yet there remains a human nature which all men share. The loyalty of one man resembles the loyalty of all men: he may be a member of an African tribe or of Napoleon's army or of an Australian soccer team. A mother's love for her child is the same in Chile or in China or in the Egypt of the Pharaohs.

Some of the selections that follow demonstrate ways in which men have been able to achieve an ideal of brotherhood. The keynote for the unit is the Biblical tale of the Good Samaritan. The point of this parable lies in the fact that the Good Samaritan gives his aid to a total stranger, to a man with whom he has no ties of kinship, loyalty, or affection. The single thing those two have in common is the fact that they are men. To the Samaritan, this fact alone justifies his generous action. A modern parallel to the Biblical tale is found in a true story set in a small Mexican town, "Stopover in Querétaro." In this case the traveler is an American tourist and the Good Samaritans who come to his aid are a group of Mexican villagers. In Pearl Buck's "The Enemy" aid is also given to a suffering stranger. But it is complicated by the fact that the helpers and the helped are divided by the lines of a great war.

Some of the selections in this unit discuss the obstacles that arise to prevent men from coming together in brotherhood and cooperation. Three of these obstacles are social distinctions, war, and money. The ancient Persian writer Saadi looks at the first of these in his "Legend of the King and the Peasant." Here, two men from different stations in life find that their common humanity can unite them across the boundaries of class. Thomas Hardy's poem "The Man He Killed" protests against the way in which war forces men into acts of inhumanity. Leo Tolstoy's ironic story "A Conversation Among Wealthy People" demonstrates the power that money and position wield over man's ideals.

Goethe, the great German playwright and poet, once wrote in a letter, "If you enquire what the people are like here, I must answer, 'The same as everywhere.'" But a darker view is presented by the great Russian writer Dostoyevsky: "Until you have become really, in actual fact, a brother to everyone, brotherhood will not come to pass. No sort of scientific teaching, no kind of common interest, will ever teach men to share property and privileges with equal consideration for all."

The theme of the literature that completes this book is the sense many writers have shared of the unity of humanity. These stories, essays, and poems examine the kinds of responsibility we bear toward our neighbor.

The Parable of the Good Samaritan

ST. LUKE

Few, if any, deny that they bear responsibilities to their neighbor. The question in most men's minds is that put to Jesus by "a certain lawyer": "Who is my neighbor?"

Is my neighbor my friend only? My countryman? Or the unkown peasant suffering from famine on the other side of the globe? The parable with which Jesus replied to the lawyer (Luke 10:30–37) remains a classic answer to the ever-recurring question.

AND, BEHOLD, *a certain lawyer stood up, and tempted him, saying, Master, what shall I do to inherit eternal life?*

He said unto him, What is written in the law? How readest thou?

And he answering said, Thou shalt love the Lord thy God with all thy heart, and with all thy soul, and with all thy strength, and with all thy mind; and thy neighbor as thyself.

And he said unto him, Thou hast answered right: this do, and thou shalt live.

But he, willing to justify himself, said unto Jesus, And who is my neighbor?

And Jesus answering said:

A certain man went down from Jerusalem to Jericho, and fell among thieves, who stripped him of his raiment, and wounded him, and departed, leaving him half dead.

And by chance there came down a certain priest that way: and when he saw him, he passed by on the other side.

And likewise a Levite, when he was at the place, came and looked on him, and passed by on the other side.

But a certain Samaritan, as he journeyed, came where he was: and when he saw him, he had compassion on him; and went to him, and bound up his wounds, pouring in oil and wine, and set him on his own beast, and brought him to an inn, and took care of him.

And on the morrow when he departed, he took out two pence, and gave them to the host, and said unto him, Take care of him; and whatsoever thou spendest more, when I come again, I will repay thee.

Which now of these three, thinkest thou, was neighbor unto him that fell among the thieves?

And he said, He that showed mercy on him.

Then Jesus said unto him, Go and do thou likewise.

The Tolling Bell

JOHN DONNE

John Donne, one of the major poets of the English language, was a contemporary of Shakespeare's. At the age of forty-two he took orders in the Church of England, and thereafter most of his writing was in prose and was devoted to religious subjects. Donne himself was seriously ill at the time of writing the meditation from which this passage is taken. He lies in bed and hears the bell tolling for the dead. For whom? His neighbor? Himself? The tolling bell reminds him that no earthly life is permanent, and this thought in turn leads him to reflect upon the oneness of humanity.

PERCHANCE HE for whom this *Bell* tolls, may be so ill, as that he knows not it tolls for him; And perchance I may think my self so much better than I am, as that they who are about me, and see my state, may have caused it to toll for me, and I know not that. The *Church* is *Catholic, universal,* so are all her *Actions; All* that she does, belongs to *all.* When she *baptizes* a *child,* that action concerns me; for that child is thereby connected to that *Head* which is my *Head* too, and engrafed into that *body,* whereof I am a *member.* And when she *buries a Man,* that action concerns me: All *mankind* is of one *Author,* and is one *volume;* when one Man dies, one *Chapter* is not *torn* out of the *book,* but *translated* into a better *language;* and every *Chapter* must be so *translated; God* employs several *translators;* some pieces are translated by *age,* some by *sickness,* some by *war,* some by *justice;* but *God's* hand is in every *translation;* and his hand shall bind up all our scattered leaves again, for that *Library* where every book shall lie open to one another. As therefore the *Bell* that rings to a *Sermon,* calls not upon the *Preacher* only, but upon the *Congregation* to come; so this *Bell* calls us all: but how much more me, who am brought so near the *door* by this *sickness.* The *Bell* doth toll for him that *thinks* it doth; and though it *intermit* again, yet from that *minute,* that that occasion wrought upon him, he is united to *God.* Who casts not up his *Eye* to the *Sun* when it rises? But who takes off his *Eye* from a *Comet* when that breaks out? Who bends not his *ear* to any *bell,* which upon any occasion rings? But who can remove it from that *bell,* which is passing a *piece* of *himself* out of this world? No man is an *island,* entire of it self; every man is a piece of the *Continent,* a part of the *main,* if a *Clod* be washed away by the *Sea, Europe* is the less,

"And therefore never send to know for whom the bell *tolls; It tolls for* thee."

as well as if a *Promontory* were, as well as if a *Manor* of thy *friend's* or of *thine own* were; any mans *death* diminishes *me*, because I am involved in *Mankind*; And therefore never send to know for whom the *bell* tolls; It tolls for *thee*. Another man may be sick too, and sick to *death*, and this *affliction* may lie in his *bowels*, as *gold* in a *Mine*, and be of no use to him; but this *bell*, that tells me of his *affliction*, digs out, and applies that *gold* to *me*: if by this consideration of anothers danger, I take mine own into contemplation, and so secure my self, by making my recourse to my *God*, who is our only security.

For Discussion

1. What indication is there that Donne himself is ill?

2. Explain the meaning of the word "Catholic" in the second sentence.

3. Donne uses three major metaphors to express the unity of humankind. What are they?

4. In what way does Donne compare the bell to the sun?

Stopover in Querétaro

JERROLD BEIM

In this true story, the parable of the Good Samaritan finds a parallel in modern Mexico. When personal tragedy struck the writer's family, as he tells in this simple, restrained narrative, he found that he was not alone, in spite of the fact that he was thousands of miles from home, among an alien people.

TWO YEARS ago my family and I were driving to Mexico City on the Juarez highway. We had a blowout and the car turned over. My wife, who was driving, and my daughter were killed instantly. One of my twin sons, Andy, suffered a severe concussion and had to be hospitalized in a town called Querétaro, about ninety kilometers from Mexico City. My other son, Seth, was uninjured but stunned by what had happened; and I had minor injuries and was in a state of shock.

Many people have said to me since: "Wasn't it awful that it had to happen in a strange country?" And I'll confess that at the time, staying at the hospital in Querétaro, I felt that I was at the end of the world, far from family or friends who could have been of help or comfort to me. But let me tell it as it happened.

Immediately after the accident we were surrounded by Mexicans, mostly country people in sombreros and *rebozos*,[1] and all, naturally, total strangers. But one man, in a business suit, was leading Seth and me to his car. In excellent English he explained that he had been behind us and had seen our car turn over. It was he who had summoned the police and ambulance from Querétaro, and now he was driving Seth and me to the hospital. The ambulance had sped ahead with Andy. The man told me his name was Juan Martinez. He asked if I knew any Spanish, and when I told him I spoke only a little he assured me that he would stay with me until he saw we were getting proper care.

[1] *sombreros and rebozos* Sombreros are the broad-brimmed hats of Mexican men; *rebozos* are the shawls worn by women over their heads and shoulders.

460

Querétaro was a sizable town, but it seemed primitive, and I doubted that we could get adequate medical attention. The sight of the hospital did not ease my anxiety. It was run by a Dr. Francisco Alcozer Pozo, and did not even look like a hospital. The nurse who greeted us explained that the doctor lived on one side of the patio,[2] and his mother lived on the opposite side. To the rear was the hospital itself, a row of little rooms opening off the patio. Seth and I were taken into one of these rooms. The nurse explained too rapidly for me to understand (Juan Martinez interpreted) that the doctor was busy with Andy.

Juan took Seth out to the patio while the nurse cleaned and bandaged the cut on my head. I glanced about the room and noticed that the paint on the walls was scaling, the furnishings were antiquated. I was overwhelmed by what had happened to my wife and daughter, and certain that in this God-forsaken place Andy would not receive the medical care he would need to survive.

Soon Juan returned with Seth and a man in a white coat.

"This is the doctor," Juan said. "Doctor Pozo."

My spirit rallied slightly when I saw the doctor. He was tall and thin, and he had an intelligent face. In slow and not very good English he expressed his deep sympathy for all that had happened. He said he doubted that any of Andy's bones were broken—he'd have to wait for the X rays—but he was sure Andy had a severe concussion. The boy was still unconscious.

I wanted to send to Mexico City for a specialist at once. Doctor Pozo said he would do whatever I desired but he thought we should see the X rays first. He looked at the cut on my head, my finger, and then he examined Seth, who was sitting on the foot of the bed.

[2] *patio* The inner courtyard of the house.

Suddenly from outside I heard voices that made my heart leap. They were definitely American!

"It must be *Señor* and *Señora* MacKenzie," Doctor Pozo explained. "They are Americans who live here."

Americans here! They came in, an attractive man and woman, who apparently knew the doctor well. Doctor Pozo left me alone with them.

The MacKenzies had heard of the accident and had come at once to offer help. They said they were the only Americans in Querétaro, Mr. MacKenzie being the manager of a local gabardine factory. They assured me that Doctor Pozo was a very competent physician; but I felt that they would have to say that, under the circumstances.

Seth, apparently still stunned, sat silent on the bed.

"Let us take Seth home for the time being," Mrs. MacKenzie suggested. "We have a five-year-old boy who would love his company. At least, you won't have to worry about him."

Even though these people were complete strangers, Seth readily went with them. I think he was glad to get away from all the horrors of the past few hours.

There were scores of things I had to do. My family and my wife's family had to be notified, and the MacKenzies helped to get them on the telephone which was just outside the room. . . . When they finally left they promised to bring Seth back for a visit the next day.

It wasn't until they were gone that I realized Juan Martinez had disappeared. I rang for the nurse and made her understand that I was looking for the man who had brought me here. She said he had left the hospital. And I hadn't even had a chance to thank him for all he had done.

Later Doctor Pozo returned. Andy was still unconscious, and it was clearly evident that he had a severe concussion. I repeated that I wanted to call in a brain specialist from Mexico City, and Doctor Pozo put in the call. The specialist said that Andy could not be moved for weeks, and he didn't feel there was any point in his coming to Querétaro. It was obvious to him that Andy's progress depended on time and he said that Doctor Pozo could handle the situation as well as he. He suggested, however, that we keep him informed by telephone. I still wasn't satisfied. If Andy pulled through, I felt it would be only a matter of luck.

Doctor Pozo now turned to setting my dislocated finger. I remember fading from consciousness while it was being done and dreaming we were in the car again, on our way to Mexico City. Then I would come to and realize what had happened. Only heavy sedatives put me to sleep that night.

Another nurse was on duty in the morning. This one spoke a bit of English, and told me there was no change in Andy, but that a man was waiting to see me.

It was Juan Martinez. I greeted him like an old friend. Where had he disappeared to yesterday?

He had seen me with the Americans, and knew they would take care of me. But he had stayed overnight in Querétaro wanting to be of further help and hoping that maybe the little boy would be better. Now he had to get on to Mexico City.

I didn't know how to express my gratitude for all he had done. We exchanged addresses. I would look him up in Nogales. We would be sure to see each other again.

I was lonelier than ever after Juan Martinez left. Only the telephone kept me bolstered through the day. Family and friends called, offering all kinds of help. It was decided that I should send Seth to his grandmother's while I remained with Andy.

Mrs. MacKenzie visited me during the day, too, bringing Seth, along with her own boy. The children had had a wonderful time together. Arrangements were made for Seth to be driven to Mexico City, then to go on to the United States by plane.

While Mrs. MacKenzie was there, Doctor Pozo summoned me. Andy had regained consciousness. He stared at me with recognition, though not a sound came from his lips. Doctor Pozo said it might be weeks before he spoke.

Late in the afternoon an unexpected call came through from my brother. He lived in San Francisco, but he had flown to Mexico City and was leaving for Querétaro in a few minutes.

His first words as he came in were, "We must have you removed to Mexico City at once!"

I explained why that couldn't be done. But it was wonderful having him with me. He spent the night in the hospital, and we sat up talking for hours.

For the next few days Andy's condition scarcely changed. Doctor Pozo drained fluid from the boy's spine and hinted that an operation might be necessary if he didn't begin to talk soon.

Doctor Pozo had suggested to my brother that I should leave Andy's bedside for a while, and explore the town. So one sunny morning we ventured outdoors. The hospital was located on a narrow, cobble-stoned street and at the very next corner was a small-town Mexican market place, swarming with flies and filled with unappetizing food. My brother had come through this market on his arrival in Querétaro —that was why he had been so shocked. We walked until we reached the plaza, with its inevitable bandstand, and we sat on one of the benches under large shade trees. I felt myself being eyed by everyone who walked past.

"This town is off the usual tourist beat," I told my brother. "They're not accustomed to seeing Americans."

An old woman in a dark-blue shawl approached us.

"I guess she wants money," my brother said, digging into his pocket. But her hand wasn't out, and she was speaking to me. After she had repeated her words, I understood, and I fought to keep back the tears.

"She knows that I am the American who was in the accident," I told my brother, "and that my little boy is very sick. She is praying—for the souls of my wife and daughter—and for the recovery of my boy."

One afternoon just before my brother had to leave, I was sunning in the patio while he sat with Andy. Suddenly he came running toward me.

"I showed him a book and asked if he'd like me to read it to him—and he spoke. Just one word—'*Yes*'—but he spoke!"

We found the doctor and went to Andy's bedside. Yes—he spoke—just a word at a time, slowly, with effort, and only when asked something—but he spoke!

As I returned to the hospital after seeing my brother off, a cluster of ragged urchins was around the door. They looked at me and grinned.

"*El niño está hablando!*"[3] one of them said. They had heard the good news already. And one of the children held out a toy, a little horse carved of balsa wood and painted colorfully. "*Por el niño!*"[4]

One afternoon I ventured into a local hotel for lunch; I had waited until Andy had fallen asleep, and had left word where I would be. Soon after I was seated the waiter told me I was wanted on the telephone. I became alarmed, and as I lifted the phone it was a vast relief to hear the voice of an American—a man:

"You don't know me, sir, but I'm here with a group of American doctors visiting hospitals and clinics all over Mexico. I met Doctor Pozo this morning and he told me about your accident. I saw him perform an operation this morning, and I thought you would be interested in knowing that I consider him a very fine doctor and an excellent surgeon. Your son is in very good hands."

I apologized to Doctor Pozo for my lack of confidence. He said that it was only natural for a father to be anxious, especially one who had gone through all I had.

As the days went by Andy got constantly better. He was talking more and soon he was able to sit up in the sunny patio.

One afternoon Doctor Pozo said Andy could travel at the end of the week, if we would like to move to Mexico City. Andy would have to be hospitalized for a while longer, but Doctor Pozo thought we would be more comfortable there.

I had a job to do before I left, one that I had put off for days. I had to decide what to do with my wife's and daughter's clothes. I spoke to Doctor Pozo and he suggested that I give the adult clothes to the clinic where they would be distributed to needy people, and the child's things to the orphanage. Doctor Pozo would take the things for the clinic, but he thought it would be nice if I went to the orphanage myself. It was in a building that once had been a private residence, and Doctor Pozo said it was an example of pure colonial architecture that I ought to see.

It wasn't an easy mission, sorting my little girl's clothes and then carrying them to the orphanage. All the buildings along the street looked very much alike, with crumbling pink, blue or white walls; but the convent was easily distinguishable by its sturdy architecture and by the cross over the doorway. I rang the bell and managed to say to the old man who let me in, "Clothes for the children."

He led me into the most beautiful patio I have ever seen. A fountain played in an expanse of green lawn and arches curved on the three walls of the house that enclosed it. The Mother Superior in her long black robes came toward me. We conversed for a few moments, and then I started to leave.

"The children wish to thank you," she said, and motioned me into one of the interior rooms.

It was an immense, beautiful room, with shiny

---

[3] "*El niño está hablando*" Spanish: "The boy is talking."

[4] "*Por el niño*" Spanish: "For the boy."

tile floors and a high, carved ceiling. It was sparsely furnished, but what there was looked like precious Spanish antiques. The Mother Superior disappeared for a moment, then returned leading a line of small girls in neat blue pinafores.

My daughter had been blue-eyed and flaxen-haired. These little girls were black-haired, with dark, shining eyes. I had been deprived of my daughter and these were children without fathers or mothers. I wanted to take every one in my arms. They thanked me for the clothes, in clear, piping voices, and then I left.

I remember being unable to go right back to the hospital. I sat in the plaza, getting control of myself, so that I could return to Andy. Then I noticed a tall, nice-looking man about my age, walking hesitantly toward me.

He sat down beside me. Was I the gentleman staying at the hospital with the little boy who had been hurt?

Yes, I was.

He owned that dry-goods store on the corner, he told me, nodding proudly toward it. I tried to convey that I thought it a fine-looking store. I couldn't bring myself to say that I wanted to be alone.

And then he explained why he had ventured to intrude on my privacy. He had seen me sitting here in the plaza and had wanted to talk to me many times. Because he felt a deep sympathy for me. A few years ago he and his family had started for Mexico City. His wife's parents lived there, and he used to take his wife and their three children to visit them once or twice a year. On that last trip, his car had been in an accident, too—a speeder had crashed into it. His wife and two of his children had been killed. And since then life for him had been an agony.

"Only now it is a little better. It is such an old proverb and it must sound foolish to you now, but time does help things. And time will help you, even though you still have much pain to live through."

I couldn't answer him. But suddenly I wasn't alone and I knew that really I had never been a stranger in Querétaro, nor was this such a foreign land. I was sitting beside someone who had been through the same ordeal. There were benches like this and people like us in every country of the world.

It was about two days later that I left by hired car for Mexico City. Andy was settled comfortably in the back seat and I was beside the driver.

Doctor Pozo, the MacKenzies, the nurses, the servants—all had said good-by to us from the hospital door. Word had got around that we were leaving, and people of the town—men in sombreros, women in shawls, a man in the doorway of a dry-goods store—waved to us as we left Querétaro.

For Discussion

1. Characterize the "tone of voice" the writer uses for his story. What message does he try to communicate to the reader through this choice of style?

2. The opening paragraph of the selection provides an example of literary understatement. Why has Beim chosen not to dramatize the automobile accident or to linger over its details?

3. At first, what is the author's attitude toward the Querétaro hospital? How does he convey this attitude? How does it change during his stay?

4. What is shown by the remark made by the author's brother: "I guess she wants money"?

5. Comment on this quotation: "There were benches like this and people like us in every country in the world."

The Legend of the King and the Peasant

SAADI

The following legend is drawn from the Gulistan *("Garden of Roses"), one of the masterpieces of Persian literature. It is a long work in both poetry and prose, mixing tales, lyrics, religious verse, and pithy sayings.*

A KING, attended by his courtiers, was out on a hunting expedition in the midst of winter. They had got far from the hunting lodge, and the night was falling fast when they saw a peasant's house in the distance.

The king said, "Let us go there, where we may shelter ourselves for the night from this freezing wind."

One of the courtiers replied, "It would not become the dignity of a king to enter the cottage of a low peasant. Rather, let us pitch a tent here and light a fire."

The peasant saw what was happening. He came forth with all the refreshments he had on hand and laid them at the king's feet. He kissed the ground and said, "Nothing can destroy the lofty dignity of Your Majesty, not even enter-ing my poor house. These gentlemen must be unwilling to see the condition of a poor peasant exalted."

The king was pleased with this speech, and, in spite of the objections of his courtiers, he passed into the peasant's cottage, where he spent the night. In the morning he bestowed a hand-some cloak and many fine gifts upon his host.

I have heard that the peasant accompanied the king for some distance along the road, walking by the side of his horse and touching the king's stirrups. The peasant said:

"The state and pomp of the king suffered no degradation by being a guest in the house of a peasant. But the brim of the peasant's cap rose to a level with the sun when the shadow of such a monarch fell upon it."

For Discussion

1. From this story, how much can the reader de-duce about Persia in the Middle Ages?

2. What is implied by the statement that the peasant walked by the side of the king's horse, "touching the king's stirrups"?

3. How are the king and the peasant contrasted with the courtiers?

4. How does this legend exemplify the theme of this unit, "No Man Is an Island"?

Five Poems

Here five poets reflect on the brotherhood of man: Emily Dickinson dramatizes the theme in terms of nature; Hardy and Whitman against a background of war; Muñoz, the governor of Puerto Rico, from a political viewpoint; and the German poet Rilke through four universals that bind him to the rest of humanity.

PAMPHLET

I have broken the rainbow
against my heart
as you break a useless sword across your knee.
I have sent the rose-and-blood-colored clouds
blowing beyond the farthest horizon.
I have drowned my dreams
to feed the dreams that sleep in the veins
of men who sweated, wept, and raged
to sweeten my coffee . . .

A dream that sleeps in lungs stifled
  by tuberculosis
  (A little air, a little sunshine!)
a dream in stomachs strangled by hunger
  (A piece of bread, a piece of white bread!)
a dream in bare feet
  (Fewer stones on the road, Lord, fewer
    broken bottles!)
a dream in calloused hands
  (Moss . . . clean linen . . . smooth, soft,
    soothing!)
a dream in trampled hearts
  (Love . . . Life . . . Life! . . .)

I am God's pamphleteer,
I am God's agitator,
I march with a mob of stars and hungry men
towards the great dawn . . .

              LUIS MUÑOZ MARIN

POEM

If I can stop one heart from breaking,
I shall not live in vain;
If I can ease one life the aching,
Or cool one pain,
Or help one fainting robin
Unto his nest again,
I shall not live in vain.

              EMILY DICKINSON

THE SOLEMN HOUR

Whoever weeps now somewhere in the world,
weeps for no reason in the world,
weeps for me.

Whoever laughs now somewhere in the night,
laughs for no reason in the night,
laughs at me.

Whoever wanders somewhere in the world,
wanders for no reason in the world,
comes towards me.

Whoever dies now somewhere in the world,
dies for no reason in the world,
looks at me.

              RAINER MARIA RILKE

THE MAN HE KILLED

"Had he and I but met
　By some old ancient inn,
We should have sat us down to wet
　Right many a nipperkin!

"But ranged as infantry,
　And staring face to face,
I shot at him as he at me,
　And killed him in his place.

"I shot him dead because—
　Because he was my foe,
Just so—my foe of course he was;
　That's clear enough; although

"He thought he'd 'list perhaps,
　Off-hand like—just as I—
Was out of work—had sold his traps—
　No other reason why.

"Yes; quaint and curious war is!
　You shoot a fellow down
You'd treat if met where any bar is,
　Or help to half-a-crown."

　　　　　　　　　　THOMAS HARDY

AS TOILSOME I WANDER'D VIRGINIA'S WOODS

As toilsome I wander'd Virginia's woods,
To the music of rustling leaves kick'd by my
　　feet (for 'twas autumn),
I mark'd at the foot of a tree the grave of a
　　soldier;
Mortally wounded he and buried on the retreat
　　(easily all could I understand),
The halt of a mid-day hour, when up! no time
　　to lose—yet this sign left,
On a tablet scrawl'd and nail'd on the tree by
　　the grave,
Bold, cautious, true, and my loving comrade.

Long, long I muse, then on my way go wander-
　　ing,
Many a changeful season to follow, and many a
　　scene of life,
Yet at times through changeful season and scene,
　　abrupt, alone, or in the crowded street,
Comes before me the unknown soldier's grave,
　　comes the inscription rude in Virginia's
　　woods,
Bold, cautious, true, and my loving comrade.

　　　　　　　　　　WALT WHITMAN

For Discussion

1. Examine each of these five poems in the light of the theme of this unit, "No Man Is an Island." Show how each poem exemplifies the theme. What universal symbols do the poets use? What particular or clearly personal symbols do they use?

2. Of the five poems, which in your opinion is the simplest? Which is the most complicated? Which is the most philosophical? The most dramatic? The most personal? Which is most concerned with man as a social being?

THE MAN HE KILLED: *wet . . . a nipperkin* = have a drink together; *'list* = enlist in the army; *sold*

his traps = the hunting traps with which he may have made his living; *half-a-crown* = British coin.

The Enemy

PEARL BUCK

One of the most universally popular novels of this century has been Pearl Buck's The Good Earth. *For it, she was awarded the Nobel Prize for literature. Mrs. Buck lived for many years in China, and the Orient has provided the material for her best tales. She has a unique ability to interpret the East to the West. Her books abound with information on the sights, sounds, and social customs of Asia. But more important is her ability to convey to her readers something of the workings of the Oriental mind.*

The theme of common humanity asserted against a background of war is an ancient one. In Western literature it reaches back as far as Homer's The Iliad. *In this collection it forms the basis of the stories by Hebel and Camus, the memoirs of del Castillo and Udet, and poems by Hardy, Whitman, and others.*

DR. SADAO HOKI'S house was built on a spot of the Japanese coast where as a little boy he had often played. The low square stone house was set upon rocks well above a narrow beach that was outlined with bent pines. As a boy Sadao had climbed the pines, supporting himself on his bare feet, as he had seen men do in the South Seas when they climbed for coconuts. His father had taken him often to the islands of those seas, and never had he failed to say to the little grave boy at his side, "Those islands yonder, they are the stepping stones to the future for Japan."

"Where shall we step from them?" Sadao had asked seriously.

"Who knows?" his father had answered. "Who can limit our future? It depends on what we make it."

Sadao had taken this into his mind as he did everything his father said, his father who never joked or played with him but who spent infinite pains upon him who was his only son. Sadao knew that his education was his father's chief concern. For this reason he had been sent at twenty-two to America to learn all that could be learned of surgery and medicine. He had come back at thirty and before his father died he had seen Sadao become famous not only as a surgeon but as a scientist. Because he was now perfecting a discovery which would render wounds entirely clean, he had not been sent abroad with the troops. Also, he knew, there was some slight danger that the old General might need an operation for a condition for which he was now being treated medically, and for this possibility Sadao was being kept in Japan.

Clouds were rising from the ocean now. The unexpected warmth of the past few days had at night drawn heavy fog from the cold waves. Sadao watched mists hide outlines of a little island near the shore and then come creeping up the beach below the house, wreathing around the pines. In a few minutes fog would be wrapped about the house too. Then he would go into the room where Hana, his wife, would be waiting for him with the two children.

But at this moment the door opened and she looked out, a dark-blue woolen *haori*[1] over her kimono. She came to him affectionately and put her arm through his as he stood, smiled and said nothing. He had met Hana in America, but he had waited to fall in love with her until he was sure she was Japanese. His father would never have received her unless she had been pure in her race. He wondered often whom he would have married if he had not met Hana, and by what luck he had found her in the most casual way, by chance literally, at an American professor's house. The professor and his wife had been kind people, anxious to do something for their few foreign students, and the students, though bored, had accepted this kindness. Sadao had often told Hana how nearly he had not gone to Professor Harley's house that night—the rooms were so small, the food so bad, the professor's wife so voluble. But he had gone and there he had found Hana, a new student, and had felt he would love her if it were at all possible.

Now he felt her hand on his arm and was aware of the pleasure it gave him, even though

they had been married years enough to have the two children. For they had not married heedlessly in America. They had finished their work at school and had come home to Japan, and when his father had seen her the marriage had been arranged in the old Japanese way, although Sadao and Hana had talked everything over beforehand. They were perfectly happy. She laid her cheek against his arm.

It was at this moment that both of them saw something black come out of the mists. It was a man. He was flung up out of the ocean—flung, it seemed, to his feet by a breaker. He staggered a few steps, his body outlined against the mist, his arms above his head. Then the curled mists hid him again.

"Who is that?" Hana cried. She dropped Sadao's arm and they both leaned over the railing of the veranda. Now they saw him again. The man was on his hands and knees crawling. Then they saw him fall on his face and lie there.

"A fisherman perhaps," Sadao said, "washed from his boat." He ran quickly down the steps and behind him Hana came, her wide sleeves flying. A mile or two away on either side there were fishing villages, but here was only the bare and lonely coast, dangerous with rocks. The surf beyond the beach was spiked with rocks. Somehow the man had managed to come through them—he must be badly torn.

They saw when they came toward him that indeed it was so. The sand on one side of him had already a stain of red soaking through.

"He is wounded," Sadao exclaimed. He made haste to the man, who lay motionless, his face in the sand. An old cap stuck to his head soaked with sea water. He was in wet rags of garments. Sadao stooped, Hana at his side, and turned the man's head. They saw the face.

"A white man!" Hana whispered.

Yes, it was a white man. The wet cap fell away and there was his wet yellow hair, long, as though for many weeks it had not been cut, and upon his young and tortured face was a

[1] *haori* A loose outer garment.

rough yellow beard. He was unconscious and knew nothing that they did to him.

Now Sadao remembered the wound, and with his expert fingers he began to search for it. Blood flowed freshly at his touch. On the right side of his lower back Sadao saw that a gun wound had been reopened. The flesh was blackened with powder. Sometime, not many days ago, the man had been shot and had not been tended. It was bad chance that the rock had struck the wound.

"Oh, how he is bleeding!" Hana whispered again in a solemn voice. The mists screened them now completely, and at this time of day no one came by. The fishermen had gone home and even the chance beachcombers would have considered the day at an end.

"What shall we do with this man?" Sadao muttered. But his trained hands seemed of their own will to be doing what they could to stanch the fearful bleeding. He packed the wound with the sea moss that strewed the beach. The man moaned with pain in his stupor but he did not awaken.

"The best thing that we could do would be to put him back in the sea," Sadao said, answering himself.

Now that the bleeding was stopped for the moment, he stood up and dusted the sand from his hands.

"Yes, undoubtedly that would be best," Hana said steadily. But she continued to stare down at the motionless man.

"If we sheltered a white man in our house we should be arrested and if we turned him over as a prisoner, he would certainly die," Sadao said.

"The kindest thing would be to put him back into the sea," Hana said. But neither of them moved. They were staring with a curious repulsion upon the inert figure.

"What is he?" Hana whispered.

"There is something about him that looks American," Sadao said. He took up the battered cap. Yes, there, almost gone was the faint letter-ing. "A sailor," he said, "from an American warship." He spelled it out: "U.S. Navy. The man was a prisoner of war!"

"He has escaped," Hana cried softly, "and that is why he is wounded."

"In the back," Sadao agreed.

They hesitated, looking at each other. Then Hana said with resolution:

"Come, are we able to put him back into the sea?"

"If I am able, are you?" Sadao asked.

"No," Hana said. "But if you can do it alone . . ."

Sadao hesitated again. "The strange thing is," he said, "that if the man were whole I could turn him over to the police without difficulty. I care nothing for him. He is my enemy. All Americans are my enemy. And he is only a common fellow. You see how foolish his face is. But since he is wounded . . ."

"You also cannot throw him back to the sea," Hana said. "Then there is only one thing to do. We must carry him into the house."

"But the servants?" Sadao inquired.

"We must simply tell them that we intend to give him to the police—as indeed we must, Sadao. We must think of the children and your position. It would endanger all of us if we did not give this man over as a prisoner of war."

"Certainly," Sadao agreed. "I would not think of doing anything else."

Thus agreed, together they lifted the man. He was very light, like a fowl that has been half-starved for a long time until it is only feathers and skeleton. So, his arms hanging, they carried him up the steps and into the side door of the house. This door opened into a passage and down the passage they carried the man toward an empty bedroom. It had been the bedroom of Sadao's father and since his death it had not been used. They laid the man on the deeply matted floor. Everything here had been Japanese to please the old man, who would never in his own home sit on a chair or sleep in a foreign bed. Hana went to the wall cupboards and slid back a door and took out a soft quilt. She hesitated. The quilt was covered with flowered silk and the lining was pure white silk.

"He is so dirty," she murmured in distress.

"Yes, he had better be washed," Sadao agreed. "If you will fetch hot water I will wash him."

"I cannot bear for you to touch him," she said. "We shall have to tell the servants he is here. I will tell Yumi now. She can leave the children for a few minutes and she can wash him."

Sadao considered a moment. "Let it be so," he agreed. "You tell Yumi and I will tell the others."

But the utter pallor of the man's unconscious face moved him first to stoop and feel his pulse. It was faint but it was there. He put his hand against the man's cold breast. The heart too was yet alive.

"He will die unless he is operated on," Sadao said, considering. "The question is whether he will not die anyway."

Hana cried out in fear. "Don't try to save him! What if he should live?"

"What if he should die?" Sadao replied. He stood gazing down on the motionless man. This man must have extraordinary vitality or he would have been dead by now. But then he was very young—perhaps not yet twenty-five.

"You mean die from the operation?" Hana asked.

"Yes," Sadao said.

Hana considered this doubtfully, and when she did not answer Sadao turned away. "At any rate something must be done with him," he said, "and first he must be washed." He went quickly out of the room and Hana came behind him. She did not wish to be left alone with the white man. He was the first she had seen since she left America and now he seemed to have nothing to do with those whom she had known there. Here he was her enemy, a menace, living or dead.

She turned to the nursery and called, "Yumi!"

But the children heard her voice and she had to go in for a moment and smile at them and play with the baby boy, now nearly three months old.

Over the baby's soft black hair she motioned with her mouth, "Yumi—come with me."

"I will put the baby to bed," Yumi replied. "He is ready."

She went with Yumi into the bedroom next to the nursery and stood with the boy in her arms while Yumi spread the sleeping quilts on the floor and laid the baby between them.

Then Hana led the way quickly and softly to the kitchen. The two servants were frightened at what their master had just told them. The old gardener who was also a house servant pulled the few hairs on his upper lip.

"The master ought not to heal the wound of this white man," he said bluntly to Hana. "The white man ought to die. First he was shot. Then the sea caught him and wounded him with her rocks. If the master heals what the gun did and what the sea did they will take revenge on us."

"I will tell him what you say," Hana replied courteously. But she herself was also frightened, although she was not superstitious as the old man was. Could it ever be well to help an enemy? Nevertheless she told Yumi to fetch the hot water and bring it to the room where the white man was.

She went ahead and slid back the partitions. Sadao was not yet there. Yumi, following, put down her wooden bucket. Then she went over to the white man. When she saw him her thick lips folded themselves into stubbornness. "I have never washed a white man," she said, "and I will not wash so dirty a one now."

Hana cried at her severely, "You will do what your master commands you!"

"My master ought not to command me to wash the enemy," Yumi said stubbornly.

There was so fierce a look of resistance upon Yumi's round dull face that Hana felt unreasonably afraid. After all, if the servants

should report something that was not as it happened?

"Very well," she said with dignity. "You
understand we only want to bring him to his
senses so that we can turn him over as a
prisoner?"

"I will have nothing to do with it," Yumi
said. "I am a poor person and it is not my
business."

"Then please," Hana said gently, "return to
your own work."

At once Yumi left the room. But this left
Hana with the white man alone. She might
have been too afraid to stay had not her anger
at Yumi's stubbornness now sustained her.

"Stupid Yumi," she muttered fiercely. "Is this
anything but a man? And a wounded helpless man!"

In the conviction of her own superiority she
bent impulsively and untied the knotted rags
that kept the white man covered. When she
had his breast bare she dipped the small clean
towel that Yumi had brought into the steaming hot water and washed his face carefully.
The man's skin, though rough with exposure,
was of a fine texture and must have been very
blond when he was a child.

While she was thinking these thoughts,
though not really liking the man better now
that he was no longer a child, she kept on washing him until his upper body was quite clean.
But she dared not turn him over. Where was
Sadao? Now her anger was ebbing and she was
anxious again and she rose, wiping her hands on
the wrung towel. Then lest the man be chilled
she put the quilt over him.

"Sadao!" she called softly.

He had been about to come in when she
called. His hand had been on the door and now
he opened it. She saw that he had brought his
surgeon's emergency bag and that he wore his
surgeon's coat.

"You have decided to operate!" she cried.

"Yes," he said shortly. He turned his back
to her and unfolded a sterilized towel upon

the floor of the *takonoma* alcove, and put his
instruments out upon it.

"Fetch towels," he said.

She went obediently, but how anxious now,
to the linen shelves and took out the towels.
There ought also to be old pieces of matting
so that the blood would not ruin the fine floor
covering. She went out to the back veranda
where the gardener kept strips of matting with
which to protect delicate shrubs on cold nights
and took an armful of them.

But when she went back into the room, she
saw this was useless. The blood had already
soaked through the packing in the man's wound
and had ruined the mat under him.

"Oh, the mat!" she cried.

"Yes, it is ruined," Sadao replied, as though
he did not care. "Help me to turn him," he
commanded her.

She obeyed him without a word, and he began to wash the man's back carefully.

"Yumi would not wash him," she said.

"Did you wash him then?" Sadao asked, not
stopping for a moment his swift concise movements.

"Yes," she said.

He did not seem to hear her. But she was used
to his absorption when he was at work. She
wondered for a moment if it mattered to him
what was the body upon which he worked so
long as it was for the work he did so excellently.

"You will have to give the anesthetic if he
needs it," he said.

"I?" she repeated blankly. "But never have I!"

"It is easy enough," he said impatiently.

He was taking out the packing now and the
blood began to flow more quickly. He peered
into the wound with the bright surgeon's light
fastened on his forehead. "The bullet is still
there," he said with cool interest. "Now I
wonder how deep this rock wound is. If it is not
too deep it may be that I can get the bullet. But
the bleeding is not superficial. He has lost much
blood."

At this moment Hana choked. He looked up
and saw her face the color of sulphur.

"Don't faint," he said sharply. He did not put down his exploring instrument. "If I stop now the man will surely die." She clapped her hands to her mouth and leaped up and ran out of the room. Outside in the garden he heard her retching. But he went on with his work.

"It will be better for her to empty her stomach," he thought. He had forgotten that of course she had never seen an operation. But her distress and his inablity to go to her at once made him impatient and irritable with this man who lay like dead under his knife.

"This man," he thought, "there is no reason under heaven why he should live."

Unconsciously this thought made him ruthless and he proceeded swiftly. In his dream the man moaned but Sadao paid no heed except to mutter at him.

"Groan," he muttered, "groan if you like. I am not doing this for my own pleasure. In fact, I do not know why I am doing it."

The door opened and there was Hana again. She had not stopped even to smooth back her hair.

"Where is the anesthetic?" she asked in a clear voice.

Sadao motioned with his chin. "It is as well that you came back," he said. "This fellow is beginning to stir."

She had the bottle and some cotton in her hand.

"But how shall I do it?" she asked.

"Simply saturate the cotton and hold it near his nostrils," Sadao replied without delaying for one moment the intricate detail of his work. "When he breathes badly move it away a little."

She crouched close to the sleeping face of the young American. It was a piteously thin face, she thought, and the lips were twisted. The man was suffering whether he knew it or not. Watching him, she wondered if the stories they heard sometimes of the sufferings of prisoners were true. They came like flickers of rumor, told by word of mouth and always contradicted. In the newspapers the reports were always that wherever the Japanese armies went the people received them gladly, with cries of joy at their liberation. But sometimes she remembered such men as General Takima, who at home beat his wife cruelly, though no one mentioned it now that he had fought so victorious a battle in Manchuria. If a man like that could be so cruel to a woman in his power, would he not be cruel to one like this for instance?

She hoped anxiously that this young man had not been tortured. It was at this moment that she observed deep red scars on his neck, just under the ear. "Those scars," she murmured, lifting her eyes to Sadao.

But he did not answer. At this moment he felt the tip of his instrument strike against something hard, dangerously near the kidney. All thought left him. He felt only the purest pleasure. He probed with his fingers, delicately, familiar with every atom of this human body. His old American professor of anatomy had seen to that knowledge. "Ignorance of the human body is the surgeon's cardinal sin, sirs!" he had thundered at his classes year after year. "To operate without as complete knowledge of the body as if you had made it—anything less than that is murder."

"It is not quite at the kidney, my friend," Sadao murmured. It was his habit to murmur to the patient when he forgot himself in an operation. "My friend," he always called his patients and so now he did, forgetting that this was his enemy.

Then quickly, with the cleanest and most precise of incisions, the bullet was out. The man quivered but he was still unconscious. Nevertheless he muttered a few English words.

"Guts," he muttered, choking. "They got . . . my guts. . . ."

"Sadao!" Hana cried sharply.

"Hush," Sadao said.

The man sank again into silence so profound that Sadao took up his wrist, hating the touch of it. Yes, there was still a pulse so faint, so feeble, but enough, if he wanted the man to live, to give hope.

"But certainly I do not want this man to live," he thought.

"No more anesthetic," he told Hana.

He turned as swiftly as though he had never paused and from his medicines he chose a small vial and from it filled a hypodermic and thrust it into the patient's left arm. Then, putting down the needle, he took the man's wrist again. The pulse under his fingers fluttered once or twice and then grew stronger.

"This man will live in spite of all," he said to Hana and sighed.

The young man woke, so weak, his blue eyes so terrified when he perceived where he was, that Hana felt compelled to apology. She served him herself, for none of the servants would enter the room.

When she came in the first time she saw him summon his strength to be prepared for some fearful thing.

"Don't be afraid," she begged him softly.

"How come . . . you speak English . . ." he gasped.

"I was a long time in America," she replied.

She saw that he wanted to reply to that but he could not, and so she knelt and fed him gently from the porcelain spoon. He ate unwillingly, but still he ate.

"Now you will soon be strong," she said, not liking him and yet moved to comfort him.

He did not answer.

When Sadao came in the third day after the operation he found the young man sitting up, his face bloodless with the effort.

"Lie down," Sadao cried. "Do you want to die?"

He forced the man down gently and strongly and examined the wound. "You may kill yourself if you do this sort of thing," he scolded.

"What are you going to do with me?" the boy muttered. He looked just now barely seventeen. "Are you going to hand me over?"

For a moment Sadao did not answer. He finished his examination and then pulled the silk quilt over the man.

"I do not know myself what I shall do with you," he said. "I ought of course to give you to the police. You are a prisoner of war—no, do not tell me anything." He put up his hand as he saw the young man about to speak. "Do not even tell me your name unless I ask it."

They looked at each other for a moment, and then the young man closed his eyes and turned his face to the wall.

"Okay," he whispered, his mouth a bitter line.

Outside the door Hana was waiting for Sadao. He saw at once that she was in trouble.

"Sadao, Yumi tells me the servants feel they cannot stay if we hide this man here any more," she said. "She tells me that they are saying that you and I were so long in America that we have forgotten to think of our own country first. They think we like Americans."

"It is not true," Sadao said harshly, "Americans are our enemies. But I have been trained not to let a man die if I can help it."

"The servants cannot understand that," she said anxiously.

"No," he agreed.

Neither seemed able to say more, and somehow the household dragged on. The servants grew daily more watchful. Their courtesy was as careful as ever, but their eyes were cold upon the pair to whom they were hired.

"It is clear what our master ought to do," the old gardener said one morning. He had worked with flowers all his life and had been a specialist in moss. For Sadao's father he had made one of the finest moss gardens in Japan, sweeping the bright green carpet constantly so that not a leaf or a pine needle marred the velvet of its surface. "My old master's son knows very well what he ought to do," he now said, pinching a bud from a bush as he spoke. "When the man was so near death why did he not let him bleed?"

"That young master is so proud of his skill to save life that he saves any life," the cook said contemptuously. She split a fowl's neck skillfully and held the fluttering bird and let its blood flow into the roots of a wistaria vine.

Blood is the best of fertilizers, and the old gardener would not let her waste a drop of it.

"It is the children of whom we must think," Yumi said sadly. "What will be their fate if their father is condemned as a traitor?"

They did not try to hide what they said from the ears of Hana as she stood arranging the day's flowers in the veranda near by, and she knew they spoke on purpose that she might hear. That they were right she knew too in most of her being. But there was another part of her which she herself could not understand. It was not sentimental liking of the prisoner. She had come to think of him as a prisoner. She had not liked him even yesterday when he had said in his impulsive way, "Anyway, let me tell you that my name is Tom." She had only bowed her little distant bow. She saw hurt in his eyes but she did not wish to assuage it. Indeed, he was a great trouble in this house.

As for Sadao, every day he examined the wound carefully. The last stitches had been pulled out this morning, and the young man would in a fortnight be nearly as well as ever. Sadao went back to his office and carefully typed a letter to the chief of police reporting the whole matter. "On the twenty-first day of February an escaped prisoner was washed up on the shore in front of my house." So far he typed and then he opened a secret drawer of his desk and put the unfinished report into it.

On the seventh day after that two things happened. In the morning the servants left together, their belongings tied in large square cotton kerchiefs. When Hana got up in the morning nothing was done, the house not cleaned and the food not prepared, and she knew what it meant. She was dismayed and even terrified, but her pride as a mistress would not allow her to show it. Instead, she inclined her head gracefully when they appeared before her in the kitchen, and she paid them off and thanked them for all that they had done for her. They were crying, but she did not cry. The cook and the gardener had served Sadao

since he was a little boy in his father's house, and Yumi cried because of the children. She was so grieving that after she had gone she ran back to Hana.

"If the baby misses me too much tonight, send for me. I am going to my own house and you know where it is."

"Thank you," Hana said smiling. But she told herself she would not send for Yumi however the baby cried.

She made the breakfast and Sadao helped with the children. Neither of them spoke of the servants beyond the fact that they were gone. But after Hana had taken morning food to the prisoner she came back to Sadao.

"Why is it we cannot see clearly what we ought to do?" she asked him. "Even the servants see more clearly than we do. Why are we different from other Japanese?"

Sadao did not answer. But a little later he went into the room where the prisoner was and said brusquely, "Today you may get up on your feet. I want you to stay up only five minutes at a time. Tomorrow you may try it twice as long. It would be well that you get back your strength as quickly as possible."

He saw the flicker of terror on the young face that was still very pale.

"Okay," the boy murmured. Evidently he was determined to say more. "I feel I ought to thank you, doctor, for having saved my life."

"Don't thank me too early," Sadao said coldly. He saw the flicker of terror again in the boy's eyes—terror as unmistakable as an animal's. The scars on his neck were crimson for a moment. Those scars! What were they? Sadao did not ask.

In the afternoon the second thing happened. Hana, working hard on unaccustomed labor, saw a messenger come to the door in official uniform. Her hands went weak and she could not draw her breath. The servants must have told already. She ran to Sadao, gasping, unable to utter a word. But by then the messenger had simply followed her through the garden and there he stood. She pointed at him helplessly.

Sadao looked up from his book. He was in his office, the outer partition of which was thrown open to the garden for the southern sunshine.

"What is it?" he asked the messenger and then he rose, seeing the man's uniform.

"You are to come to the palace," the man said. "The old General is in pain again."

"Oh," Hana breathed, "is that all?"

"All?" the messenger exclaimed. "Is it not enough?"

"Indeed it is," she replied. "I am very sorry."

When Sadao came to say good-by she was in the kitchen, but doing nothing. The children were asleep and she sat merely resting for a moment, more exhausted from her fright than from work.

"I thought they had come to arrest you," she said.

He gazed down into her anxious eyes. "I must get rid of this man for your sake," he said in distress. "Somehow I must get rid of him."

"Of course," the General said weakly, "I understand fully. But that is because I once took a degree in Princeton. So few Japanese have."

"I care nothing for the man, Excellency," Sadao said, "but having operated on him with such success . . ."

"Yes, yes," the General said. "It only makes me feel you more indispensable to me. Evidently you can save anyone—you are so skilled. You say you think I can stand one more such attack as I have had today?"

"Not more than one," Sadao said.

"Then certainly I can allow nothing to happen to you," the General said with anxiety. His long pale Japanese face became expressionless, which meant that he was in deep thought. "You cannot be arrested," the General said, closing his eyes. "Suppose you were condemned to death and the next day I had to have my operation?"

"There are other surgeons, Excellency," Sadao suggested.

"None I trust," the General replied. "The best ones have been trained by Germans and would consider the operation successful even if I died. I do not care for their point of view." He sighed. "It seems a pity that we cannot better combine the German ruthlessness with the American sentimentality. Then you could turn your prisoner over to execution and yet I could be sure you would not murder me while I was unconscious." The General laughed. He had an unusual sense of humor. "As a Japanese, could you not combine these two foreign elements?" he asked.

Sadao smiled. "I am not quite sure," he said, "but for your sake I would be willing to try, Excellency."

The General shook his head. "I had rather not be the test case," he said. He felt suddenly weak and overwhelmed with the cares of his life as an official in times such as these when repeated victory brought great responsibilities all over the south Pacific. "It is very unfortunate that this man should have washed up on your doorstep," he said irritably.

"I feel it so myself," Sadao said gently.

"It would be best if he could be quietly killed," the General said. "Not by you, but by someone who does not know him. I have my own private assassins. Suppose I send two of them to your house tonight—or better, any night. You need know nothing about it. It is now warm—what would be more natural than that you should leave the outer partition of the white man's room open to the garden while he sleeps?"

"Certainly it would be very natural," Sadao agreed. "In fact, it is so left open every night."

"Good," the General said, yawning. "They are very capable assassins—they make no noise and they know the trick of inward bleeding. If you like I can even have them remove the body."

Sadao considered. "That perhaps would be best, Excellency," he agreed, thinking of Hana.

He left the General's presence then and went home, thinking over the plan. In this way the whole thing would be taken out of his hands. He would tell Hana nothing, since she would be timid at the idea of assassins in the house, and yet certainly such persons were essential in an absolute state such as Japan was. How else could rulers deal with those who opposed them?

He refused to allow anything but reason to be the atmosphere of his mind as he went into the room where the American was in bed. But as he opened the door, to his surprise he found the young man out of bed, and preparing to go into the garden.

"What is this!" he exclaimed. "Who gave you permission to leave your room?"

"I'm not used to waiting for permission," Tom said gaily. "Gosh, I feel pretty good again! But will the muscles on this side always feel stiff?"

"Is it so?" Sadao inquired surprised. He forgot all else. "Now I thought I had provided against that," he murmured. He lifted the edge of the man's shirt and gazed at the healing scar. "Massage may do it," he said, "if exercise does not."

"It won't bother me much," the young man said. His young face was gaunt under the stubbly blond beard. "Say, doctor, I've got something I want to say to you. If I hadn't met a Jap like you—well, I wouldn't be alive today. I know that."

Sadao bowed but he could not speak.

"Sure, I know that," Tom went on warmly. His big thin hands gripping a chair were white at the knuckles. "I guess if all the Japs were like you there wouldn't have been a war."

"Perhaps," Sadao said with difficulty. "And now I think you had better go back to bed."

He helped the boy back into bed and then bowed. "Good night," he said.

Sadao slept badly that night. Time and time again he woke, thinking he heard the rustling of footsteps, the sound of a twig broken or a stone displaced in the garden—a noise such as men might make who carried a burden.

The next morning he made the excuse to go first into the guest room. If the American were gone he then could simply tell Hana that so the General directed. But when he opened the door he saw at once that it was not last night. There on the pillow was the shaggy blond head. He could hear the peaceful breathing of sleep and he closed the door again quietly.

"He is asleep," he told Hana. "He is almost well to sleep like that."

"What shall we do with him?" Hana whispered her old refrain.

Sadao shook his head. "I must decide in a day or two," he promised.

But certainly, he thought, the second night must be the night. There rose a wind that night, and he listened to the sounds of bending boughs and whistling partitions.

Hana woke too. "Ought we not to go and close the sick man's partition?" she asked.

"No," Sadao said. "He is able now to do it for himself."

But the next morning the American was still there.

Then the third night of course must be the night. The wind changed to quiet rain and the garden was full of the sound of dripping eaves and running springs. Sadao slept a little better, but he woke at the sound of a crash and leaped to his feet.

"What was that?" Hana cried. The baby woke at her voice and began to wail. "I must go and see."

But he held her and would not let her move.

"Sadao," she cried, "what is the matter with you?"

"Don't go," he muttered, "don't go!"

His terror infected her and she stood breathless, waiting. There was only silence. Together they crept back into the bed, the baby between them.

Yet when he opened the door of the guest room in the morning there was the young man. He was very gay and had already washed and was now on his feet. He had asked for a razor yesterday and had shaved himself and today there was a faint color in his cheeks.

"I am well," he said joyously.

Sadao drew his kimono round his weary body. He could not, he decided suddenly, go through another night. It was not that he cared for this young man's life. No, simply it was not worth the strain.

"You are well," Sadao agreed. He lowered his voice. "You are so well that I think if I put my boat on the shore tonight, with food and extra clothing in it, you might be able to row to that little island not far from the coast. It is so near the coast that it has not been worth fortifying. Nobody lives on it because in storm it is submerged. But this is not the season of storm. You could live there until you saw a Korean fishing boat pass by. They pass quite near the island because the water is many fathoms deep there."

The young man stared at him, slowly comprehending. "Do I have to?" he asked.

"I think so," Sadao said gently. "You understand—it is not hidden that you are here."

The young man nodded in perfect comprehension. "Okay," he said simply.

Sadao did not see him again until evening. As soon as it was dark, he had dragged the stout boat down to the shore and in it he put food and bottled water that he had bought secretly during the day, as well as two quilts he had bought at a pawnshop. The boat he tied to a post in the water, for the tide was high. There was no moon and he worked without a flashlight.

When he came to the house he entered as though he were just back from his work, and so Hana knew nothing. "Yumi was here today," she said as she served his supper. Though she was so modern, still she did not eat with him. "Yumi cried over the baby," she went on with a sigh. "She misses him so."

"The servants will come back as soon as the foreigner is gone," Sadao said.

He went into the guest room that night before he went to bed and himself checked carefully the American's temperature, the state of the wound, and his heart and pulse. The pulse

was irregular but that was perhaps because of excitement. The young man's pale lips were pressed together and his eyes burned. Only the scars on his neck were red.

"I realize you are saving my life again," he told Sadao.

"Not at all," Sadao said. "It is only inconvenient to have you here any longer."

He had hesitated a good deal about giving the man a flashlight. But he had decided to give it to him after all. It was a small one, his own, which he used at night when he was called.

"If your food runs out before you catch a boat," he said, "signal me two flashes at the same instant the sun drops over the horizon. Do not signal in darkness, for it will be seen. If you are all right but still there, signal me once. You will find fish easy to catch but you must eat them raw. A fire would be seen."

"Okay," the young man breathed.

He was dressed now in the Japanese clothes which Sadao had given him, and at the last moment Sadao wrapped a black cloth about his blond head.

"Now," Sadao said.

The young American without a word shook Sadao's hand warmly, and then walked quite well across the floor and down the step into the darkness of the garden. Once—twice—Sadao saw his light flash to find his way. But that would not be suspected. He waited until from the shore there was one more flash. Then he closed the partition. That night he slept.

"You say the man escaped?" the General asked faintly. He had been operated upon a week before, an emergency operation to which Sadao had been called in the night. For twelve hours Sadao had not been sure the General would live. The gall bladder was much involved. Then the old man had begun to breathe deeply again and to demand food. Sadao had not been able to ask about the assassins. So far as he knew they had never come. The servants had returned and Yumi had cleaned the guest room thoroughly and had burned sulphur in it to get the white man's smell out of it. Nobody said anything. Only the gardener was cross because he had got behind with his chrysanthemums.

But after a week Sadao felt the General was well enough to be spoken to about the prisoner.

"Yes, Excellency, he escaped," Sadao now said. He coughed, signifying that he had not said all he might have said, but was unwilling to disturb the General farther. But the old man opened his eyes suddenly.

"That prisoner," he said with some energy, "did I not promise you I would kill him for you?"

"You did, Excellency," Sadao said.

"Well, well!" the old man said in a tone of amazement, "so I did! But, you see, I was suffering a good deal. The truth is, I thought of nothing but myself. In short, I forgot my promise to you."

"I wondered, Your Excellency," Sadao murmured.

"It was certainly very careless of me," the General, said. "But you understand it was not lack of patriotism or dereliction of duty." He looked anxiously at his doctor. "If the matter should come out you would understand that, wouldn't you?"

"Certainly, Your Excellency," Sadao said. He suddenly comprehended that the General was in the palm of his hand and that as a consequence he himself was perfectly safe. "I can swear to your loyalty, Excellency," he said to the old General, "and to your zeal against the enemy."

"You are a good man," the General murmured and closed his eyes. "You will be rewarded."

But Sadao, searching the spot of black in the twilighted sea that night, had his reward. There was no prick of light in the dusk. No one was on the island. His prisoner was gone—safe, doubtless, for he had warned him to wait only for a Korean fishing boat.

He stood for a moment on the veranda, gazing out to the sea from whence the young man had come that other night. And into his mind, although without reason, there came other white faces he had known—the professor at whose house he had met Hana, a dull man, and his wife had been a silly talkative woman, in spite of her wish to be kind. He remembered his old teacher of anatomy, who had been so insistent on mercy with the knife, and then he remembered the face of his fat and slatternly landlady. He had had great difficulty in finding a place to live in America because he was a Japanese. The Americans were full of prejudice and it had been bitter to live in it, knowing himself their superior. How he had despised the ignorant and dirty old woman who had at last consented to house him in her miserable home! He had once tried to be grateful to her because she had in his last year nursed him through influenza, but it was difficult, for she was no less repulsive to him in her kindness. But then, white people were repulsive of course. It was a relief to be openly at war with them at last. Now he remembered the youthful, haggard face of his prisoner—white and repulsive.

"Strange," he thought, "I wonder why I could not kill him?"

For Discussion

1. " 'The kindest thing would be to put him back into the sea,' Hana said." Why do Hana and Sadao decide differently? Define their motive for bringing the American into their house. Is their action completely rational? Or is it emotional?

2. What kind of a relation exists between Sadao and Hana? How does the author establish it?

3. " 'This man,' [Sadao] thought, 'There is no reason under heaven why he should live.' " Does Sadao believe this? If so, how are his actions a comment on the statement? If there is a "reason" why the American should live, what is it?

4. Write a brief essay answering the question Sadao asks himself at the end of the story.

A Conversation Among Wealthy People

LEO TOLSTOY

"A Conversation Among Wealthy People" appears to be no more than what its title declares. But, in fact, it is a very personal statement. Leo Tolstoy, the great novelist, was born into the wealthy, leisured aristocracy of Czarist Russia. After a wild youth, he underwent a religious experience which convinced him that only in love of his fellow man could he find happiness. He tried to practice Christ's admonition to "sell what you have, and give to the poor." His wife, family, and friends set upon him with exactly the kind of arguments given to the idealistic youth in the story below. Tolstoy was never able completely to put into practice his humanitarian beliefs.

None of the wealthy people in the story is particularly cruel or selfish. Their conversation is Tolstoy's ironic comment on the distance between the ideals to which we all pay lip service and those habits by which we really live.

SOME GUESTS assembled at a wealthy house one day happened to start a serious conversation about life.

They spoke of people present and absent, but failed to find anyone who was satisfied with his life.

Not only could no one boast of happiness, but not a single person considered that he was living as a Christian should do. All confessed that they were living worldly lives concerned only for themselves and their families, none of them thinking of their neighbors, still less of God.

"Then why do we live so?" exclaimed a

youth. "Why do we do what we ourselves disapprove of? Have we no power to change our way of life? We ourselves admit that we are ruined by our luxury, our effeminacy, our riches, and above all by our pride—our separation from our fellow-men. To be noble and rich we have to deprive ourselves of all that gives man joy.

"Why do we live so? Why do we spoil our lives and all the good that God gives us? I don't want to live in that old way! I will abandon the studies I have begun—they would only bring me to the same tormenting life of which we are all now complaining. I will renounce my property and go to the country and live among the poor. I will work with them, will learn to labour with my hands, and if my education is of any use to the poor I will share it with them, not through institutions and books but directly by living with them in a brotherly way.

"Yes, I have made up my mind," he added, looking inquiringly at his father, who was also present.

"Your wish is a worthy one," said his father, "but thoughtless and ill-considered. It seems so easy to you only because you do not know life. There are many things that seem to us good, but the execution of what is good is complicated and difficult. New paths are made only by men who are thoroughly mature and have mastered all that is attainable by man. It seems to you easy to make new paths of life only because you do not yet understand life. It is an outcome of thoughtlessness and youthful pride. Your active life lies before you. You are now growing up and developing. Finish your education, make yourself thoroughly conversant with things, get on to your own feet, have firm convictions of your own, and then start a new life if you feel you have strength to do so. But for the present you should obey those who are guiding you for your own good, and not try to open up new paths of life."

The youth was silent and the older guests agreed with what the father had said.

"You are right," said a middle-aged married man, turning to the youth's father. "It is true that the lad, lacking experience of life, may blunder when seeking new paths of life and his decision cannot be a firm one. But you know we all agreed that our life is contrary to our conscience and does not give us happiness. So we cannot but recognize the justice of wishing to escape from it.

"The lad may mistake his fancy for a reasonable deduction, but I, who am no longer young, tell you for myself that as I listened to the talk this evening the same thought occurred to me. It is plain to me that the life I now live cannot give me peace of mind or happiness. Experience and reason alike show me that. Then what am I waiting for? We struggle from morning to night for our families, but it turns out that we and our families live ungodly lives and get more and more sunk in sins. We work for our families, but our families are no better off, because we are not doing the right thing for them. And so I often think that it would be better if I changed my whole way of life and did just what that young man proposed to do; ceased to bother about my wife and children and began to think about my soul. Not for nothing did Paul say: 'He that is married careth how he may please his wife, but he that is unmarried careth how he may please the Lord.' "

But before he had finished speaking his wife and all the women present began to attack him.

"You ought to have thought of that before," said an elderly woman. "You have put on the yoke, so you must draw your load. Like that, everyone will say he wishes to go off and save his soul when it seems hard to him to support and feed his family. That is false and cowardly. Of course it would be easy enough to save your own soul all by yourself. But to behave like that would be to run contrary to Christ's teaching. God bade us love others; but in that way you would in his name offend others. No. A married man has his definite obligations and he must not shirk them. It's different when your family

Leo Tolstoy in the latter part of his life. He is wearing peasant's clothing.

are already on their own feet. Then you may do as you please for yourself, but no one has a right to force his family."

But the man who had spoken did not agree. "I don't want to abandon my family," he said. "All I say is that my family should not be brought up in a worldly fashion, nor brought up to live for their own pleasure, as we have just been saying, but should be brought up from their early days to become accustomed to privation, to labour, to the service of others, and above all to live a brotherly life with all men. And for that we must relinquish our riches and distinctions."

"There is no need to upset others while you yourself do not live a godly life," exclaimed his wife irritably. "You yourself lived for your own pleasure when you were young, then why do you want to torment your children and your family? Let them grow up quietly, and later on let them do as they please without coercion from you!"

Her husband was silent, but an elderly man who was there spoke up for him.

"Let us admit," said he, "that a married man, having accustomed his family to a certain comfort, cannot suddenly deprive them of it. It is true that if you have begun to educate your children it is better to finish it than to break up everything—especially as the children when grown up will choose the path they consider best for themselves. I agree that for a family man it is difficult and even impossible to change his way of life without sinning. But for us old men it is what God commands. Let me say for myself: I am now living without any obligations, and to tell the truth, simply for my belly. I eat, drink, rest, and am disgusting and revolting even to myself. So it is time for me to give up such a life, to give away my property, and at least before I die to live for a while as God bids a Christian live."

But the others did not agree with the old man. His niece and godchild was present, to all of whose children he had stood sponsor and gave presents on holidays. His son was also there. They both protested.

"No," said the son. "You worked in your time, and it is time for you to rest and not trouble yourself. You have lived for sixty years with certain habits and must not change them now. You would only torment yourself in vain."

"Yes, yes," confirmed his niece. "You would be in want and out of sorts, and would grumble and sin more than ever. God is merciful and will forgive all sinners—to say nothing of such a kind old uncle as you!"

"Yes, and why should you?" added another old man of the same age. "You and I have perhaps only a couple of days to live, so why should we start new ways?"

"What a strange thing!" exclaimed one of the visitors who had until now been silent. "What a strange thing! We all say that it would be good to live as God bids us and that we are living badly and suffer in body and soul, but as soon as it comes to practice it turns out that the children must not be upset and must be brought up not in godly fashion but in the old way. Young folk must not run counter to their parents' will and must live not in a godly fashion but in the old way. A married man must not upset his wife and children and must live not in a godly way but as of old. And there is no need for old men to begin anything: they are not accustomed to it and have only a couple of days left to live. So it seems that none of us may live rightly: we may only talk about it."

[*translated by* AYLMER MAUDE]

For Discussion

1. Evaluate the youth's proposals to renounce his property and live among the poor. Are they practical? Impractical? Does the question of practicality have anything to do with it?

2. The whole structure of this tale builds toward the simple statement of the paradox in the last sentence. Is this final comment a just one?

3. Evaluate the arguments put forth by the following: the youth's father, the elderly woman, the son and niece of the old man.

4. Write a continuation of the conversation of these wealthy people. Introduce yourself as one of the characters. What position would you take in the discussion?

Glossary of Pronunciation

Key

<table>
<tr><td colspan="11">vowels</td><td colspan="6">consonants</td></tr>
<tr>
<td>ā</td><td>tāle</td><td>ē</td><td>ēve</td><td>ō</td><td>cōld</td><td>ŭ</td><td>cŭp</td><td>b</td><td>bat</td><td>h</td><td>house</td><td>n</td><td>noon</td><td>t</td><td>tool</td>
</tr>
<tr>
<td>à</td><td>àsk</td><td>ĕ</td><td>sĕnd</td><td>ŏ</td><td>rŏd</td><td>ü</td><td>German</td><td>ch</td><td>chip</td><td>j</td><td>jet</td><td>N</td><td>French</td><td>v</td><td>heavy</td>
</tr>
<tr>
<td>ä</td><td>färm</td><td>ê</td><td>êvent</td><td>ô</td><td>ôbey</td><td></td><td>grün</td><td>d</td><td>dull</td><td>k</td><td>king</td><td></td><td>bon</td><td>w</td><td>winter</td>
</tr>
<tr>
<td>â</td><td>bâre</td><td>ē</td><td>farmēr</td><td>ōō</td><td>fōōd</td><td>û</td><td>bûrn</td><td>f</td><td>fast</td><td>l</td><td>loop</td><td>p</td><td>part</td><td>y</td><td>yet</td>
</tr>
<tr>
<td>ă</td><td>infănt</td><td></td><td></td><td>o͝o</td><td>fo͝ot</td><td>û</td><td>ûnite</td><td>g</td><td>gone</td><td>m</td><td>mask</td><td>r</td><td>roll</td><td>z</td><td>zone</td>
</tr>
<tr>
<td></td><td></td><td>ī</td><td>rīce</td><td>ô</td><td>absôrb</td><td></td><td></td><td></td><td></td><td></td><td></td><td>s</td><td>set</td><td></td><td></td>
</tr>
<tr>
<td></td><td></td><td>ĭ</td><td>bĭt</td><td>ou</td><td>out</td><td></td><td></td><td></td><td></td><td></td><td></td><td></td><td></td><td></td><td></td>
</tr>
</table>

Adrienne àd·rē·ĕn'

Agamemnon àg·ä·mĕm'nŏn

Ahmed ä'mĕd

Alcazar äl·kä·sär' *or* äl·kä·thär'

Amalienborg à·màl'ĭ·ĕn·bôrg

Amundsen, Roald ä'mo͝on·sĕn rō'äl

Andalusia än·dä·lo͞o·sē'ä

Antilia à·tĭl'ē·ä

Anukul ä·no͞o'ko͞ol

a priori ä prī·ō'rī *or* ä prī·ô'ê

Aragon ä·rä·gôn'

Archimedes är·kĭ·mē'dēs

Atreus àt'rē·ŭs

Aucas ou'käz

Auvergne ō·vârn'

Badoglio bä·dō'lyō

Balaev bà·là'yĕv

Balducci bäl·do͞o'chē

Baraset bä·rä'sĕt

Bargello bär·jĕ'lō

Barua a Soldani bä·ro͞o'ä ä sōl·dä'nē

Basho bä'shō'

Batko Gonchar bät'kō gôn'chär

Baudelaire, Charles bō·dlâr', shärl

Bechalla bä·chä'yä

Bémont bä·moN'

Bercovici, Conrad bâr·kō·vē'sē, kôn'ràd

Bertoni bâr·tō'nē

Bidoin bē·dwàN'

Björnson, Björnsterne byûrn'sōn, byûrn'stĕrn·ä

Blay, Benibengor blä, bĕn·ĭ·bĕn'·gôr

Bluntschli blŭnt'shlē

Boavista bō·ä·vēs'tä

Bobadilla, Doña Beatriz de bō·bä·dē'yä, dōn'yä bä·ä·trēs' dä

Bom dia, Senhor bôm dē'ä, sän·yôr'

Bordeaux bôr·dō'

boubou bo͞o'bo͞o

Breughel, Pieter (Jan) broy'gĕl, pē'tĕr (yàn)

Brian Boru brī·àn bôr·o͞o'

Briareus brē·är'ä·ŭs

Bronya brôn'yä

Bunno bo͞o'nō

Buson bo͞o·sōn'

Cadiz kä'dēs *or* kä'dēth

Calderón de la Barca käl·dâr·ōn' dä lä bär'kä

Callao kä·lou'

Calle de la Fuente kä'yä dē là fwĕn'tä

Calle Nueva kä'yä nwä'vä

Calle del Rio kä'yä dĕl rē'ō

Callimachus kä·lĭm'ä·kŭs

Camus, Albert kä·mü', àl·bâr'

Canario kä·nä'ryō

Cão, Diego kou, dē·ā'gō

Carcharodon carcharias kär·chär·ō'dōn kär·chär·ē'ás

Carian kà·rĭ'ăn

Castellina kàs·tĕl·ē'nä

Catullus kä·tŭl'ŭs

Caughnawaga kôg·nä·wä'gä

ça va bien sä vä byàN

Ceraso sâr·ä'sō

Cervantes, Miguel de sâr·vän'täz *or* thâr·vän'täz, mē·gĕl' dä

Chaillot shī·yō'

Champagne shàm·pän'

chateau shà·tō'

Chavaniac shà·vän·yàk'

Cheche shĕsh

Chekhov, Anton chĕ'kôf, àn'tôn

Cheng Chiu chĕng chû

Chez Perpignan shä pâr·pēn·yäN'

Chiao-chi chĭ·ou'chē

Chin chĭn

Chomolungma chō·mō·lo͞ong'mä

Christianborg krĭst'yàn·bôrg

cina-cina sē'nä sē'nä

Collège du Plessis kōl·ĕzh' dü plä·sē'

Colom, Christovão kô·lōm', krēs·tō·vou'

colon kô·lôN'

concours hippique côN·cōōr'
ē·pēk'
cora kô'rä
Córdoba kôr'dō·bä
Coringhee kôr·in'gē
Corsica kôr'sĭ·kǎ
Cosa, Juan de la kō'sä, hwän dā lä
cosas de España kō'säs dā ĕs·pän'-
yä
couloir kōō'lwär
coup de grâce kōō dē gräs
Cousteau, Jacques-Yves kōōs·tō'
zhäk ēv
curaçao kōō'rä·sou'
Curie, Pierre kŭ'rē', pē·âr'
Cyclops sī'klŏps
Cypango sē·päng'ō

Dakar dä·kär'
Dalecarlia däl·ĕ·kär'lyä
Damany dä·män'ē
Dante Alighieri dän'tä ä·lē·gyä'rē
Darbón där·bōn'
d'Artois, Comte de där·twä',
kônt dē
Daru dä·rŭ'
D'Ayen, Duc de dī·äN', dŭk dē
Dayuma dà·yoo'mä
Debierne, André dĕ·bērn', än'drä
del Castillo, Michel dĕl käs·tē'yō,
mē·shĕl'
Della Rovere dĕ'lä rō·vâr'ä
Desmoulins, René dā·mōō·láN'
rā·nā'
Didi dē'dē
Die Meistersinger dē mī'stâr·
sēng·âr
Diego dē·ā'gō
Dinesen, Isak dĭn'ĕ·sǎn, ī'zàk
Dion (of) Tarsus dī'ŏn tär'sŭs
Djerba jâr'bä
Dluski, Casimir dlōōs'kē, kä'sē·
mēr
Don Camillo dōn kà·mĭl'ō
Don Quixote dōn kē·hō'tä
Donatello dō·nä·tĕ'lō
douga dōō'gä
Du bist ein Schwein, Bertoni dōō
bĭst' īn shvīn', bâr·tō'nē
Dulcinea del Toboso dŭl·sē·nā'ä
dĕl tō·bō'sō
Dumas, Alexandre dü'mä, à·lĕk·
säN'dr

Eau de canal ō dē kä·näl'
El Ameur ĕl ä·mûr'
El niño está hablando! ĕl nē'nyō
ĕ·stä' ä·blän'dō
Elie Monnier ā'lē mō·nyä'
envoi ĕn'voi (English) *or* äN'vwä
(French)
Et nunc et in perpetua ĕt nŭnk ĕt
ĭn pâr·pĕt'tōō·ä

Farah fä'rä
fata morgana fä'tä môr·gä'nä
Fathima fä·tĕ'mä
Fatuhina fä·tōō·hē'nä
Felipa, Doña fä·lē'pä, dō'nyä
Feng Chih fĕng chē
Fernandez fâr·nän'dēs
Ferro fâr'ō
Fossa fō'sǎ
Fossoli fō·sō'lē
Fouguier-Tinville fōōg·yä' tàN·
vēl'
Frauenburg frŏw'ĕn·bûrg
Frestón frĕs·tōn'
Friedel frē'dĕl
Fukien fōō'kyĕn

Galicia gä·lē'syä
Galileo gä·lĭ·lā'ō
Gallipoli gà·lĭp'ō·lē
Garcia Lorca, Federico gär·sē'ä
(*or* gär·thē'ä) lôr'kä, fä·dā·
rē'kō
Gaviota gä·vē·ō'tä
gendarme zhàN·därm'
Gentilly zhän·tē·yē'
gesshuku gĕ·shōō'kōō
geta gē'tä
Ghana gä'nä
Ghiberti gē·bâr'tē
Gigo zhē'gō
Gikari gē·kär'ē
Gikita gĭ·kē'tä
Gloria in excelsis Deo glō'ryä ĭn
ĕx·sĕl'sēs dā'ō
Goethe, Johann Wolfgang von
gû'tĕ, yō'hän vôlf'gäng fôn
Gopal gō·päl'
Granada grä·nä'dä
Guareschi, Giovanni gwär·ĕs'kē,
jyō·vän'nē
Guinea gĭn'ē
Gulla gōōl'ä
Gunther gŏōn'târ

Gustaf gōō'stäf
Gut, gut, wie Sie wollen gōōt'
gōōt' vē sē vôl'ĕn
Guynemer, Charles gē·nĕ·mâr',
shärl

Habsheim häb'shīm
haiku hī'kōō
Hana hä'nä
hand auf herz händ ouf hârts
Hanslick, Eduard häns'lĭk,
ĕd'wärd
haori hä'ôr'ē
Hashimoto hä·shē·mō'tō
Hashin hä'shēn
Haugland, Knut houg'länd,
k'nōōt
Hebel, Johann Peter hä'bĕl,
yō'hän pä'tĕr
Heine, Heinrich hī'nĕ, hīn'rĭk
Heraclitus hâr·ä·clī'tŭs
Heyerdahl, Thor hī'âr·däl, tôr
Hierro ē·âr'ō
Hispaniola his·pàn·yō'lä
Hoogvliet ōg'vlēt
Hotel du Louvre ō'tĕl dü lōōv'r
Huelva wäl'vä
Hugo, Victor ü·gō', vēk'tôr

Iam lucis orto sidere yäm lōō'sēs
ôr'tō sē'dĕ·rä
in terrorem ĭn târ·ôr'ĕm
Infante Dom Henrique ēn·fän'tä
dōm ĕn·rē'kä
Irène ē·rĕn'
Issa ĭs'ä

Jagdstaffel yägd'stä·fĕl
Jai jī
Jami jä'mē
jellaba jĕl·ä'bä
Jerez de la Frontera hâr·ĕs (*or*
hâr·ĕth') dā lä frōn·târ'ä
Jiménez, Juan Ramón hē·mä'nĕz
hwän rä·mōn'
Juarez hwär'ĕz
Juma Bemu jōō'mä bē'mōō
junta jŭn'tä (English) hōōn'tä
(Spanish)

kabilla kī·bĭl'ä
kadamba kä·däm'bä
Kali kä'lē
Kamante kä·män'tē

Kamau kä·mou′

Kampong Ambual käm′pông äm·bŏō′ăl

Kanaka kä·nä′kä

Kangchenjunga kŭn·chĕn·jŭng′ä

Kataev, Valentine kä·tä′yĕv, vȧ·lĕn·tēn

Kathegu kȧ·thē′gŏō

Ken-nin kĕn·nēn′

Kesselring kĕs′ĕl·ring

Kikaku kē·kä′kŏō

Kikuyu kĭ·kŏō′yŏō

Kilimanjaro kĭl·ĭ·män·jȧr′ō

Kiltartan kĭl·tär′tăn

kimono kĭ·mō′nō

Kishi kē′shē

Kitau kĭt′ou

Khodasevich, Vladislav hō·dä·sä′vĭch, vläd′ĭ·släv

Koestler, Arthur kûst′lĕr, är′tŏōr *or* är′thŭr

Kokushkin kō·kŏōsh′kĭn

Kolberger Heide kōl′bâr·gĕr hī′dĕ

Kota Djandi kō′tä jän′dē

Krishna krĕsh′nä

Krupskaya kroop·skī′yä

Kyoshi kĭ·ō′shē

La Fontaine lä fôn·tĕn′

La Gallega lä gä·yä′gä

Lafayette, Gilbert, Marquis de lä·fī·yet′, zhēl·bâr, mär·kē dē

La Rábida lä rä′bē·dä

La Ravière, Comte de lä rē·vyâr′, kônt dē

Lagerlöf, Selma lä′gēr·lûf, sĕl′mä

Lagos lä′gos

Lassus läs′ŭs

Lavoisier lä·vwä·syā′

Laye, Camara lā, kä′mä·rä

Leeuwenhoek, Antony lā′vĕn·hŏōk, än′tō·nē

Lhotse lōt′zē

Li Fu Yen lē foo yĕn

Li I lē ē

Lierval lēr′väl

lion posant or lē·ôN′ pō·säN′ tôr

Lom Palanka lôm pä·län′kä

Lope de Vega lō′pä dä vä′gä

luchis lŏō′chēs

Ludmilla lŏōd·mēl′ä

Ludmillotchka lŏōd·mĭl·ôch′kä

Lushkoff lŏōsh′kôf

Luxemburg, Rosa lŏōks′ĕm·bŏōrg, rō′sä

Lynch, Benito lĭnch, bĕn·ē′tō

Maeterlinck, Maurice mä′târ·lĭnk, mō·rēs′

Maio mä·ē′ō

Makalu mä′kä·lŏō

Malveira da Serra mäl·vâ′rä dä sâ′rä

Mankamu män·kä′moo

maravedis mä·rä·vä·dēs′

Marchena, Antonio de mär·chä′nä, än·tō′nyō dä

Marie Antoinette mȧr·ē′ än·twän·ĕt′

Mario mä′ryō

Maro mä′rō

Marseilles mär·sā′

Martial märsh′l

Martinez, Juan mär·tē′nĕz, hwän

Masai mä·sī′

Maupassant, Guy de mō·pä·säN′, gē de

M'Cola m′kō′lä

Medici mä′dē·chē

Medina Celi mä·dē′nä sä·lē

métier mā′tyä

Missibi mĭs·ĭ′bē

Moki, Sadao mō′kē, sä·dä′ō

Montanelli, Indro môn·tä·nĕl′ē, ēn′drō

Motutangi mō·tŏō·täng′ē

Moulmein mŏōl·mān′

Moustiérs mŏō·styä′

mova mō′vä

Moyachna moi·äch′nä

muito antiqua mŏō·ē′tō än·tē·kwä

Müller mü′lâr

Murut mŏō′rŏōt

Mutahwie Ben Ali Ben Sassie El Nasee mŏō·tä′wē bĕn ä′lē bĕn säs′ē ĕl näs′ē

muzhik mŏō′zhĭk

Nahayama nä·hä·yä′mä

Naidu, Sarojini nī′dŏō, sä·rō·jē′nē

Nairobi nī·rō′bē

Nakahara nä·kä·hä′rä

Neisse nī′sē

Nevers nĕ·vâr′

Nicean nī·sē′än

Nicola nĭ′kō·lä

Niebla nē′blä

Niger nī′gĕr

Niña nēn′yä

nizhuni nē·zŏō′nē

Noailles nō·ī′

Nogales nō·gä′läs

Nōh nō

Norgay, Tenzing nôr′gä, tĕn′zĭng

novio de la muerte nō′vyō dē lä mŭ·âr′tä

Nuptse nŏōp′tsē

Obata, Shigeyoshi ō·bä′tä, shĭ·gä·yō′shē

O'Faolain, Sean ō·fä·lôn′, shôn

Oman ō′măn

Onitsura ō·nĭt·sŏō′rä

Otani ō·tä′nē

Overaas, Thord ō′vĕr·ôs, tôrd

Palos pä′lōs

Panza, Sancho pän′zä *or* pän′thä, sän′chō

Papeete pä·pē′tē

pareu pä′rä·ŏō

Pashka päsh′kä

Pasternak, Boris pȧs′târ·nȧk, bôr′ĭs

patio pä′tyō

Paumotus pou·mō′tûs

Peppone pĕ·pō′nä

Peredbrody pâr·ĕd′brŏd·ē

Pérez, Juan pâr′es *or* pâr′eth, hwän

Perrin, Jean pâr·àN′, jäN

Persson, Israel Per pâr′sŏn ĭs′rä·ĕl pâr

Pfeiffer, Robert fī′fâr, rō′bâr

Phailna fāl′nä

Philippopolis fĭ·lĭ·pä′pō·lĭs

Pinta pēn′tä

Pinzón, Martin Alonso pēn·zōn′, mär·tēn′ ä·lōn′sō

Platero plä·tä′rō

Pokrovski pŏ·krôv′skē

Polyphemus pŏ·lē·fē′mŭs

Por el niño! pôr ĕl nē′nyō

Portofino pôr′tō·fē′nō

Poseidon pō·sī′dŏn

Pozo, Francisco Alcozer pō′sō, frän·sēs′kō äl·kō·sâr′

Prosvirin prŏs·vē′rēn

Provence prō·väNs′

Psyche sī'kē
purako taro pōōr·ä'kō tä'rō

*Que era plazer grande el gusto de
las mañanas* kā ā'rä plä·sâr'
grän'dä ĕl gōōs'tō dä läs män·
yä'näs
Quemado kā·mä'dō
Querétaro kâ·rē'tär·ō
Quixote, Don kē·hō'tä, dōn

Raaby, Torstein rä'bē, tôr'stīn
Rafu ra'fōō
rahui rä·hōō'ē
Raicharan rī·chär'än
Raina rä·ē'nä
Ramadan rä·mä·dän
Raroia rär·oy'ä
Raudin rō·däN'
rebozos rē·bō'sōs
Regnier de Graaf rän'yä dē gräf
Rihaku rē·hä'kōō
Rilke, Rainer Maria rĭl'kē, rī'nĕr
mä·rē'ä
Rimaratu rē·mä·rä'tōō
Rimbaud, Arthur räm·bō', är'tōōr
Rio Saltés rē'ō säl·tĕs'
Rio Tinto rē'ō tēn'tō
Rochambeau rō·shäm·bō
Rocinante rō·sē·nän'tā *or* rō·
thē·nän'tä
Rosenborg rō'sĕn·bôrg
Rouen rōō·äN'
Rue Lhomond rü lō·môN'
Rue Perpignan rü pâr·pēn·yäN'

Saadi sä'dē
Sacco sà'kō
Sadovaya sä·dō·vī'yä
Saecula saeculorum sā'kōō·lä sä·
kōō·lôr'ĕm
Sagnac, Georges sän·yäk', zhôrzh
sahib sä'hēb
Salvemini, Gaetano säl·vä·mē'nē,
gī·tä'nō
Salve Regina säl'vä rä·jē'nä
San Fernando sän fär·nän'dō
San Isidro sän ē·sē'drō
San José sän hō·sā'
San Roque sän rō'kā
San Rosario sän rō·sär'yō̆
San Salvador sän säl'vä·dôr
San Sebastian sän sä·bäs·tyän'
San Telmo sän tĕl'mō

San Vittore sän vē·tô'rä
Sandakan sän·dä'kän
Santa Clara sän'tä clär'ä
Santa Fe sän'tä fä
Santa Maria sän'tä mä·rē'ä
Santagel, Luis de sän·tä·gĕl',
lwēs dä
Saranoff sär'än·ôf
Saudin sou'dĕn
Saufe sōf
sayon sä·yôN'
Schultze shōōlts
Schutzenberger shōōtz'ĕn·bâr·
gär
Seami Motokiyo sä·ä'mē mō·tō·
kē'ō
Seganitso Begay sĕ·gä·nĭt'sō
bĕ·gā'
Selamat belayar sĕ·lä'mät bĕ·lī'är
señor sā·nyôr
Sergius sĕr'jyŭs
Seville sĕ'vĭl *or* sĕ·vĭl'
Shiki shē'kē'
Siguiri sē·gē'rē
Sigurd sē'gûrd
Sikh sēk
Silesia si·lä'syä *or* sĭ·lē'syä
Simonides sī·mŏn'ĭ·dēz
Siva sē'vä
Sklodovska, Marya sklôd·ôv'skä,
mär'yä
Skvortsoff skvôrt'sôf
Slivnitza slĭv·nēt'zä
Smilzo smĕl'sō
Smota smō'tä
sombrero sôm·brä'rō
Sorbonne sôr·bôn'
Stille Nacht, heilige Nacht stēl'ē
näkt hī'lĭ·gē näkt
Storliden, Karen stôr'lĭ·dĕn,
kär'ĕn
Svärd svôrd
Sucharev sōō'chär·ĕv
Suess swäs

Tabaski tä·bäs'kē
Tadjid tä·jēd'
Tagore, Rabindranath tä·gôr',
rä·bĭn'drä·nàth
Tailliez tī·yä'
Takima tä·kē'mä
takonoma tä·kō·nō'mä
Talavera, Hernando de tä·lä·
vē'rä, âr·nän'dō dä

Tanguy tän·gē'
Tannhaüser tän'hoy·zēr
Tarassov tä·rä'sôf
tatami tä·tä'mē
Tehina tä·hē'nä
Tenerife tä·nä·rē'fä
Terii târ'ĭē
tête de veau tĕt dē vō
Thermopylae thĕr·mŏp'ĭ·lē
Thucydides thōō·sĭ'dĭ·dēs
Tien-shan tĭ·ĕn'shän
tierra tē·ä'rä
Tindican tĭn'dē·kän
Tinguit tĭn·gwē'
Titicaca tĭt·ĭ·kä'kä'
Tiwaenu tē·wä·ä'noo
Tonini tō·nē'nē
Tooni tōō'nē
tortillas tôr·tē'yäs
Treviño, Luis trä·vēn'yō, lwēs
Triana, Roderigo de trē·ä'nä,
rō·dĕr·ē'gō dä
Tristan und Isolde trēs'tän ŏont
ē·sōl'dē
Tsuneyo tsōō·nä'ō
Tuamotu tōō·ä·mō'tōō
Tupuna tōō·pōō'nä

Udet, Ernst ōō'dĕt, ârnst
Upsala ŭp'sä·lä

Vanzetti vàn·zĕ'tē
Varana vär·ä'nä
Vauthier vō·tē·ä
Versailles vâr·sī'
Victoire vēk·twär'
Vieux Charles vĭ·û' shärl
Villon, François vē·yôN', fräN·
swä'
vol-au-vent vôl ō văN

Wagner, Richard väg'nâr, rē'kärd
Wanderobo wän·dâr·ō'bō

Yakamochi yä·kä·mō'chē
Yakolev, Alexander Stepanovich
yä'kō·lĕf, ä·lĕx·än'dâr stĕ·pän'·
ō·vĭch
yayay yä·yä'ē
Yeats yāts
Yumi yoo'mē

Zambezi zàm·bē'zē
Zeebrugge zä'brŭg·ĕ
Zeus zōōs

Index